ATOMIC NUMBERS AND ATOMIC WEIGHTS OF THE ELEMENTS[a]

Element	Symbol	Atomic Number	Atomic Weight	Rounded Value	Element	Symbol	Atomic Number	Atomic Weight	Rounded Value
Actinium	Ac	89	(227)	—	Mendelevium	Md	101	(256)	—
Aluminum	Al	13	26.98154	27.0	Mercury	Hg	80	200.59	200.6
Americium	Am	95	(243)	—	Molybdenum	Mo	42	95.94	95.9
Antimony	Sb	51	121.75	121.8	Neodymium	Nd	60	144.24	144.2
Argon	Ar	18	39.948	39.9	Neon	Ne	10	20.179	20.2
Arsenic	As	33	74.9216	74.9	Neptunium	Np	93	237.0482	237.0
Astatine	At	85	(210)	—	Nickel	Ni	28	58.70	58.7
Barium	Ba	56	137.33	137.3	Niobium	Nb	41	92.9064	92.9
Berkelium	Bk	97	(249)	—	Nitrogen	N	7	14.0067	14.0
Beryllium	Be	4	9.01218	9.01	Nobelium	No	102	(254)	—
Bismuth	Bi	83	208.9804	209.0	Osmium	Os	76	190.2	190.2
Boron	B	5	10.81	10.8	Oxygen	O	8	15.9994	16.0
Bromine	Br	35	79.904	79.9	Palladium	Pd	46	106.4	106.4
Cadmium	Cd	48	112.41	112.4	Phosphorus	P	15	30.97376	31.0
Calcium	Ca	20	40.08	40.1	Platinum	Pt	78	195.09	195.1
Californium	Cf	98	(251)	—	Plutonium	Pu	94	(242)	—
Carbon	C	6	12.011	12.0	Polonium	Po	84	(210)	—
Cerium	Ce	58	140.12	140.1	Potassium	K	19	39.0983	39.1
Cesium	Cs	55	132.9054	132.9	Praseodymium	Pr	59	140.9077	140.9
Chlorine	Cl	17	35.453	35.5	Promethium	Pm	61	(145)	—
Chromium	Cr	24	51.996	52.0	Protactinium	Pa	91	231.0359	231.0
Cobalt	Co	27	58.9332	58.9	Radium	Ra	88	226.0254	226.0
Copper	Cu	29	63.546	63.5	Radon	Rn	86	(222)	—
Curium	Cm	96	(247)	—	Rhenium	Re	75	186.207	186.2
Dysprosium	Dy	66	162.50	162.5	Rhodium	Rh	45	102.9055	102.9
Einsteinium	Es	99	(254)	—	Rubidium	Rb	37	85.4678	85.5
Erbium	Er	68	167.26	167.3	Ruthenium	Ru	44	101.07	101.1
Europium	Eu	63	151.96	152.0	Samarium	Sm	62	150.4	150.4
Fermium	Fm	100	(253)	—	Scandium	Sc	21	44.9559	45.0
Fluorine	F	9	18.998403	19.0	Selenium	Se	34	78.96	79.0
Francium	Fr	87	(223)	—	Silicon	Si	14	28.0855	28.1
Gadolinium	Gd	64	157.25	157.3	Silver	Ag	47	107.868	107.9
Gallium	Ga	31	69.72	69.7	Sodium	Na	11	22.98977	23.0
Germanium	Ge	32	72.59	72.6	Strontium	Sr	38	87.62	87.6
Gold	Au	79	196.9665	197.0	Sulfur	S	16	32.06	32.1
Hafnium	Hf	72	178.49	178.5	Tantalum	Ta	73	180.9479	180.9
Hahnium	Ha	105	(260)	—	Technetium	Tc	43	98.9062	98.9
Helium	He	2	4.00260	4.00	Tellurium	Te	52	127.60	127.6
Holmium	Ho	67	164.9304	164.9	Terbium	Tb	65	158.9254	158.9
Hydrogen	H	1	1.0079	1.01	Thallium	Tl	81	204.37	204.4
Indium	In	49	114.82	114.8	Thorium	Th	90	232.0381	232.0
Iodine	I	53	126.9045	126.9	Thulium	Tm	69	168.9342	168.9
Iridium	Ir	77	192.22	192.2	Tin	Sn	50	118.69	118.7
Iron	Fe	26	55.847	55.8	Titanium	Ti	22	47.90	47.9
Krypton	Kr	36	83.80	83.8	Tungsten	W	74	183.85	183.9
Kurchatovium	Ku	104	(247)	—	Uranium	U	92	238.029	238.0
Lanthanum	La	57	138.9055	138.9	Vanadium	V	23	50.9444	50.9
Lawrencium	Lr	103	(257)	—	Xenon	Xe	54	131.30	131.3
Lead	Pb	82	207.2	207.2	Ytterbium	Yb	70	173.04	173.0
Lithium	Li	3	6.941	6.94	Yttrium	Y	39	88.9059	88.9
Lutetium	Lu	71	174.97	175.0	Zinc	Zn	30	65.38	65.4
Magnesium	Mg	12	24.305	24.3	Zirconium	Zr	40	91.22	91.2
Manganese	Mn	25	54.9380	54.9	Name to be determined		106	(263)	

[a]Based on carbon-12. Numbers in parentheses are the mass numbers of the most stable or best-known isotopes.

CHEMISTRY
An Introduction

Little, Brown and Company
BOSTON   TORONTO

Chemistry
An Introduction

SYDNEY B. NEWELL

Library of Congress Catalog Card No. 76–29282

First Printing

Published simultaneously in Canada
by Little, Brown & Company (Canada) Limited

Printed in the United States of America

Book design: Clint Anglin
Art editor: Tonia Noell-Roberts
Art: Vantage Art
Cover design: Richard Emery

TO THE INSTRUCTOR

I enjoy chemistry. I enjoy teaching it, and I enjoy seeing students learn it. Like most chemists, I find chemistry vital and exciting—a fascinating window on the world. Communicating even a small part of this excitement to students is one of my great pleasures as a chemistry teacher. Teaching chemistry majors has been rewarding and fun, but for me the real delight has been in conveying chemical concepts to nonchemists.

Like most chemistry teachers, I've found that some students don't come with a built-in interest in chemistry. These students have stimulated my creativity and ingenuity over many years of teaching. They have taught me to see chemistry from many perspectives. In return, I have taught them that chemistry is one of many interesting ways of looking at life.

I have written this book for students who need to know chemistry, those who want to know chemistry, and those who may yet become chemistry majors. The book's content and coverage is flexible enough to allow selectivity in topics, whether for a course to satisfy a science or chemistry requirement or as preparation for a more rigorous course in chemistry.

In this book, it is my aim to make chemistry accessible to more students by lowering the learning barrier. Traditional treatments of chemistry often assume a prior interest of their audience. Without this interest, a historical approach can raise the learning barrier through boredom; an approach that builds from basics can raise it through anxiety. To provide interest and motivation, I've used an approach that parallels but does not formalize the scientific method and the history of chemistry—a history that reflects a continual progression from the macroscopic to the microscopic. Elements and compounds were discovered before atoms, which were discovered before electrons. Electrons were discovered before anyone knew how they were arranged in atoms or even that they were part of atoms. In the same way, this book frequently begins with the macroscopic and proceeds toward the microscopic. The macroscopic can take the form of a familiar situation where chemistry is at work, such as blood and its ability to carry oxygen. This leads inward to an explanation of pH and finally to buffers and how they work.

Instead of telling the whole story about every concept as soon as it's introduced, it often makes sense to treat a topic more than once, in increasing levels of detail. This philosophy is in keeping with the "outside-in," macro-to-micro approach described above. For example, the Periodic Table is initially introduced as a convenient means of keeping track of the elements and their properties, then as a tool for predicting formulas, then to explain bonding, and finally in relation to atomic structure. Likewise, some terms and concepts, such as energy or chemical reaction, receive at first a simple definition that is expanded on later as students acquire more sophistication.

The subject matter in the second half of the book (from changes in states of matter through biochemistry) lends itself well to interesting applications that motivate the learning of the material. But it's in the organization of the first half of the book, where the basics are established, that I've used the "what-before-why" approach on a larger scale. Here, the macroscopic is the reality (the "what") of chemistry—the elements and their behavior, names, formulas, the Periodic Table, equations, calculations; these are covered in Chapters 1–6. Then, after having seen that ionic and covalent compounds behave differently, we find out "why" in the discussion of bonding. Moving still further inward, we see that even bonding is a "what" compared with the "why" of atomic structure. An added bonus of this organization is that it provides necessary background for laboratory work early in the course. However, instructors who prefer to begin with atomic structure and bonding may do so, by using Chapter 9 at an earlier time.

To most chemists, chemistry without quantity is incomplete. But to many students, mathematics is a stumbling block. I have tried to give students an appreciation for the answers mathematics can provide by first presenting specific applications and then expanding on those applications in step-by-step example problems. The mathematics of problem solving is supported by a math review in Appendixes A and B, which deal with numbers and units. The motivational approach used in the text extends also to the Appendixes, where I have drawn on day-to-day experiences—including the use of the now-familiar hand-held calculator—to support the explanations. The Appendixes and their exercises can be used as introductory chapters or just as places where students can go for help. For maximum clarity and simplicity, I use the factor-unit and mole-ratio methods to solve problems with conversion factors.

My own experience, coupled with the constructive criticism of many colleagues and reviewers, has led me to use a number of other teaching and learning aids. A set of review questions at the end of each chapter emphasizes the important points of the chapter section-by-section, while the exercises serve to test skills learned in the chapter. Appendix C lets students check and correct their own work by providing answers and numerical solutions to the odd-numbered exercises. Defined terms are printed in italics in the text and in boldface type in the margin opposite the text where they first appear. In the index, page references to these terms appear in boldface type so that they can be located in the text where they are defined, rather than in an out-of-context glossary.

A complementary instructor's manual accompanies the text. It contains various supplementary materials and suggestions for lectures and demonstrations.

Acknowledgments

As always in a project of this nature, many people contributed to the final product. My own students at Lowell Technological Institute (now the University of Lowell) and at Carnegie-Mellon University inspired me to write this book and helped me to improve it. Students at Santa Barbara Community College, Schoolcraft College, and Catonsville Community College also provided valuable input. Detailed advice that contributed to the structure and direction of the work came from Margaret E. Goodrich, Seattle Central Community College; E. Park Guymon, Weber State College; George Kewish, De Anza College; Miriam Malm, University of New Mexico; Stanley Manahan, University of Missouri; Raymond F. O'Connor, Santa Barbara City College; Lee Pederson, University of North Carolina, Chapel Hill; Grace S. Petrie, Nassau Community College; Robert O. Reynard, Catonsville Community College; Eugene Roberts, City College of San Francisco; George H. Schenk, Wayne State University; John Searle, College of San Mateo; Judith K. Tilden, University of Lowell; Martin A. Volkar, Community College of Allegheny County; William J. Wasserman, Seattle Central Community College; Andrew C. Watson, Schoolcraft College; and Leverett J. Zompa, University of Massachusetts, Boston. To all these, my thanks.

The staff of Little, Brown and Company has my appreciation for the completion of the project. Cynthia Chapin capably supervised the whole production process. Key to the project's success was Jane Aaron, who performed the herculean task of seeing the book through from start to finish, and who had primary responsibility for it. Not only did she provide excellent and thorough suggestions for reworking, reorganization, and rendering my prose less convoluted, but in the course of the work she became an excellent chemical critic as well. In many instances her questions and suggestions prompted major changes for the better.

Finally, I am indebted to Dr. Ronald Rohrer, whose constant surveillance from a technical but nonchemical point of view provided essential feedback on clarity, relevance, and readability.

The preface comes last for the author, but first for the reader. This book has required the best of many people, including myself. I hope that reading and using it will be an enjoyable experience for students and instructors alike.

S.B.N.

TO THE STUDENT:
INTRODUCING MAXWELL'S DEMON

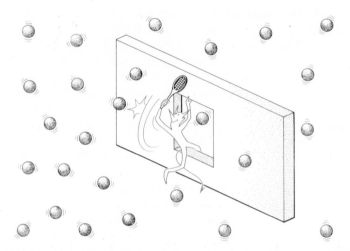

Much of chemistry involves changes—many dramatic, most very fast—from one condition to another. We could see better how chemical processes work if we could slow them down or take them apart and look at them piece by piece. But we mortals can't do that, so in this book I use the services of a cartoon character, Maxwell's Demon.

I didn't invent the demon. He was invented in 1871 by James Clerk Maxwell, a scientist who made contributions in the fields of mathematics, physics, and chemistry. Maxwell conjured up a tiny creature who could reverse natural processes in a way impossible for human beings to do. Many of us would like to undo things that have been done, such as un-breaking a glass, un-burning a forest, or collecting smoke that has spread through the air and stuffing it back into a factory smokestack. We'd also like to make things happen the way we want them to, like having the right horse win the race or making a chemical process happen in a certain way. These are the kinds of things Maxwell's Demon can do.

Maxwell's Demon allows me to be present in this book. Through him, I can talk more conversationally than I feel would be appropriate in the text's running narrative. He'll help us to share the experience of observing chemical principles as he illustrates them in a way that only a demon can.

S.B.N.

CONTENTS

1   WHAT IS CHEMISTRY?   1

2   ATOMS AND ELEMENTS   7

3   MEASURING ATOMS   31

9 ATOMIC STRUCTURE   181

10 CHANGES IN STATES OF MATTER   205

14 ELECTROCHEMISTRY   323

15 RATES AND EQUILIBRIA OF CHEMICAL REACTIONS   355

16   NUCLEAR REACTIONS   377

17   INTRODUCTION TO ORGANIC CHEMISTRY   399

REFERENCE LIST
OF SELECTED TABLES AND FIGURES

1

What Is Chemistry?

It is part of human nature to try to understand ourselves and our environment. Wondering what we are, what we're made of, and what else there is occupies a lot of our energy.

There are two kinds of space, outer and inner. Outside our bodies, there's the earth we live on. Beyond the earth, there's the moon. Beyond the moon, our solar system. Beyond our solar system, our galaxy. Beyond our galaxy, the universe. Beyond the universe—who knows? The sky is not the limit. There's no indication that our outer space stops with the universe. This outward approach is used by astronomy and related sciences to explore our outer space.

We can explore our inner space too. Within our bodies, there are tissues. Within the tissues, there are cells. Within the cells, there are molecules. Within the molecules, there are atoms. Within the atoms, there are smaller particles. The inward exploration doesn't stop at the smaller particles, but this book will. Biology, chemistry, and nuclear physics all take this inward approach. Biology usually deals with tissues and cells, and sometimes with molecules. Chemistry deals mostly with molecules and atoms, looking occasionally at the smaller particles. Nuclear physics goes within the atom to the smaller particles and even probes below that level.

This chemistry book is about atoms and molecules—what they are, how they behave, and how chemists study them and manipulate them. We'll see some of our surroundings from the chemical viewpoint, and we'll see how chemistry touches our lives.

1.1 A CHEMICAL VIEW OF THE WORLD

Chemistry is really a language, a special way of describing things that we see and use every day. Just about anything we can think of can be "translated" into chemistry. Figure 1.1 shows some familiar things and their chemical "translations." If someone wrote a paragraph in a language we didn't understand, the words and sentences wouldn't mean any more to us than the chemical "translations" in Figure 1.1. If we studied the language, though, and learned the vocabulary and grammar, then we'd understand the meaning. In this book, we'll learn about these and other chemical "translations." The chemical "translations" in Figure 1.1 are called *formulas*. We'll learn how to read and write formulas and how to work with them.

formula

matter

All things are made of matter. *Matter* is anything that takes up space and requires energy to make it move. As far as we know, all matter is made of small particles called atoms. A collection of a single kind of atom is called an *element*. Each of the letters in the formulas of Figure 1.1 stands for a kind of element: C stands for carbon, O for oxygen, N for nitrogen, H for hydrogen, K for potassium, S for sulfur. We already see an advantage to chemical formulas: we can describe these thirteen familiar substances in terms of only six elements.

element

FIGURE 1.1
Familiar things in chemical terms

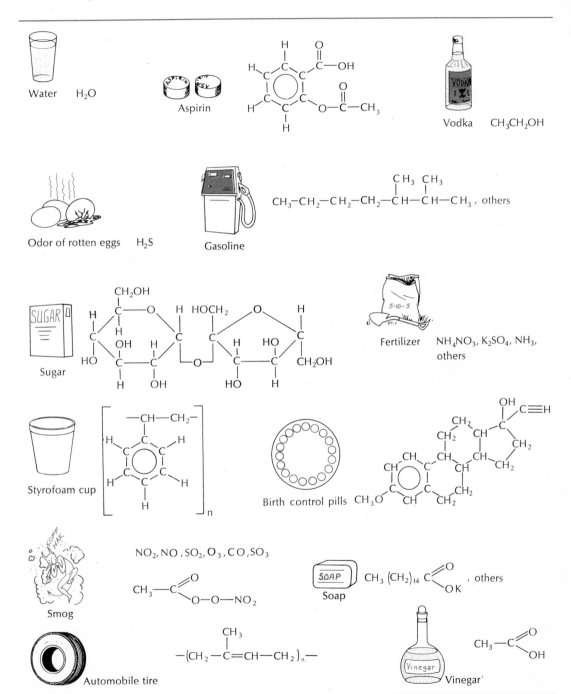

Water H_2O

Aspirin

Vodka CH_3CH_2OH

Odor of rotten eggs H_2S

Gasoline $CH_3-CH_2-CH_2-CH_2-\underset{\underset{CH_3}{|}}{CH}-\underset{\underset{CH_3}{|}}{CH}-CH_3$, others

Sugar

Fertilizer NH_4NO_3, K_2SO_4, NH_3, others

Styrofoam cup

Birth control pills CH_3O

Smog $NO_2, NO, SO_2, O_3, CO, SO_3$

Soap $CH_3(CH_2)_{14}C\overset{O}{\underset{OK}{\diagdown}}$, others

Automobile tire

Vinegar $CH_3-C\overset{O}{\underset{OH}{\diagdown}}$

Elements are the building blocks of chemistry, just as they are the building blocks for the substances shown in Figure 1.1. So far chemists have discovered 106 different elements. Our study of chemistry will be simpler than that, though, because only about forty out of the 106 elements are abundant enough to deal with at any length in this book. Still, millions of substances can be formed from these forty.

We can see from Figure 1.2A that only ten elements make up over 99 percent of the earth's crust, water, and atmosphere. Oxygen is the most abundant element. It's an important part of the atmosphere and is also found in the earth in combination with other elements. Rocks and sand are mostly made of silicon and oxygen, which is why silicon is the next most abundant element.

When we talk about the earth's crust, water, and atmosphere, we're not including the plants and animals that inhabit it. Of the elements that make up living things or their by-products, oxygen is still the most abundant. Carbon takes second place. The ten most abundant elements in the human body are shown in Figure 1.2B. The human body and other organisms also contain small amounts of other elements as well.

FIGURE 1.2
Relative abundance of elements in the earth's crust, waters, and atmosphere, and in the human body

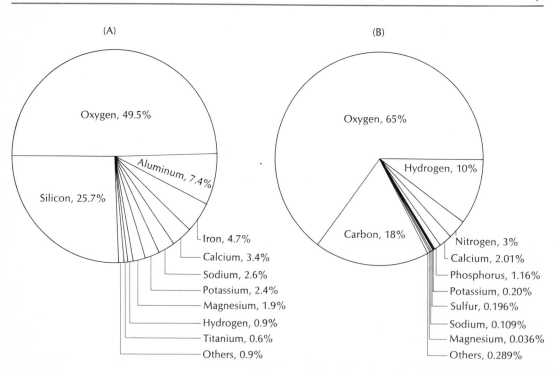

(A)

Oxygen, 49.5%

Silicon, 25.7%

Aluminum, 7.4%

Iron, 4.7%
Calcium, 3.4%
Sodium, 2.6%
Potassium, 2.4%
Magnesium, 1.9%
Hydrogen, 0.9%
Titanium, 0.6%
Others, 0.9%

(B)

Oxygen, 65%

Hydrogen, 10%

Carbon, 18%

Nitrogen, 3%
Calcium, 2.01%
Phosphorus, 1.16%
Potassium, 0.20%
Sulfur, 0.196%
Sodium, 0.109%
Magnesium, 0.036%
Others, 0.289%

From the chemical viewpoint, chemistry runs our lives. We're made of chemicals and so are our surroundings. It's important for us to get to know these substances on which our existence is based, and to know how and why they behave the way they do. That's what chemistry is all about.

1.2 HOW CHEMISTS DISCOVER THINGS

Chemistry is an experimental science, which means that chemical discoveries are made as a result of experiment. This is true of most other sciences as well as chemistry. Many scientific discoveries were made by accident, or as the result of trying to investigate something else. Radioactivity was discovered because someone accidentally left a piece of ore on top of a sealed photographic plate, and then it was found that the film had been exposed through its wrapping. Penicillin was discovered when someone's bacteria became accidentally contaminated with mold. However, when these accidents did lead to discoveries, it was because the discoverers' minds were receptive and alert enough to seize upon these lucky clues and explore them.

However, scientists do usually set out to discover something, or to test a hypothesis. A *hypothesis* is a guess about why some physical event happens. The *scientific method* is an approach that involves suggesting hypotheses and then putting them to the test of experiment. To do this, "if . . . then" reasoning is used. "*If* my hypothesis is correct, *then* such and such should happen."

hypothesis

scientific method

It's much easier to disprove a hypothesis than it is to prove it. A positive result of an experiment doesn't prove the hypothesis. It just supports the hypothesis. But a negative result does disprove the hypothesis.

This scientific approach can be illustrated by referring to the early controversy over whether the sun orbits the earth or vice versa. The favored hypothesis was that the sun orbits the earth. We can then make a prediction based on this hypothesis:

If the sun orbits the earth, *then* the sun should rise on one horizon, cross the sky, and set on the other horizon.

This prediction, of course, is true. Here is an example of a false hypothesis leading to a true prediction.

For many years, the earth-centered hypothesis was believed in. But finally, mathematical proof showed it to be false, through the same kind of reasoning.

If the sun orbits the earth, *then* the positions of the other planets relative to the earth should agree with the theoretical positions calculated on the basis of the sun orbiting the earth.

This prediction did not come true, and the hypothesis was proven to be false. It was revised to the hypothesis that the earth orbits the sun. This hypothesis has stood the test of many experiments. The more positive the results of experiments that support a hypothesis, the more strongly we believe in the hypothesis. But there's always the chance that someone else will come along and do the disproving experiment we never thought of.

To use the scientific method, the hypothesis has to be testable by experiment. The sun-orbiting-the-earth hypothesis couldn't be disproved until the necessary scientific instruments existed to perform the proper experiments.

Amazingly enough, the ancient Greeks didn't use this method to test their hypotheses. They tried to prove them just by logic and argument. The philosopher Aristotle was especially guilty of impeding scientific progress by upholding his beliefs on religious grounds and refusing to put them to the test of experiment. Many of his hypotheses held up and were believed in for two thousand years before anyone tried to test them. For instance, Aristotle had a hypothesis that heavy objects fall faster than light objects. He never tried to test it, though, and neither did anyone else at the time.

This would seem to be an easy hypothesis to test, but no one did for two thousand years. Then Galileo did test it. He used this logic:

If heavy objects fall faster than light objects, *then* if I drop a heavy object and a light object from a tower at the same time, the heavy object should reach the ground first.

This prediction didn't come true. Both objects arrived at the ground at the same time. Even so, Aristotle's reputation was so great that those who believed in Galileo's experiment (and Galileo himself) were considered crazy. Aristotle's hypothesis came into disfavor only very slowly.

Now scientists try to accept the results of experiments that disprove hypotheses, even though it's sometimes difficult to let go of a pet theory. We'll see some instances later in the book of how the scientific method was used to make discoveries.

2

Atoms and Elements

In the last chapter, we talked a little bit about atoms and elements without really saying what they are or what they are like. In this chapter, we'll treat them in more detail. We'll see what they're made of and look at some of the different kinds.

Since an element is a collection of many atoms of the same kind, first we'll look at the atoms themselves. Then we'll go on to discuss them in groups, as elements.

2.1 WHAT ATOMS ARE MADE OF

atom

subatomic particle

proton

neutron

electron

mass

Atoms are small basic particles of matter. At the start of the last chapter, we hinted about particles even smaller than atoms. These are called *subatomic particles,* and there are three main kinds: *protons, neutrons,* and *electrons.* Scientists describe these particles with two important quantities, mass and charge, and we have to know what these are before we discuss the particles themselves.

MASS. We already know that everything is made of matter, which takes up space and requires energy to move. If we want to know how much matter something has, we must first know how much mass it has. *Mass* is the un-

AN EARLY VIEW OF MATTER

A long time ago, people started wondering what matter was all about. Around 470 B.C., the Greek philosopher Democritus had some ideas about matter. Here's a summary of what he proposed. (1) Everything is made of atoms. (2) Atoms have space between them. (3) Atoms are too small to be seen. (4) Atoms can't be divided. (5) Atoms are the same all the way through. (6) Atoms can't be compressed. (7) Atoms differ from each other only in form, size, and geometry. (8) How matter behaves depends on the arrangement of atoms.

A lot of what Democritus said we still believe to be true. In almost twenty-five centuries, only his ideas that atoms can't be divided and that they are the same throughout have been disproved. Not bad, considering that the ancient Greeks didn't know about the scientific method, didn't do any experiments at all, and didn't have any advanced scientific instruments. They just watched what went on around them, thought about things, and argued with each other about their hypotheses.

varying amount of matter that any object has. Mass is the measure of matter, just as length is the measure of distance. The basic unit of length is arbitrary (it can be inches, feet, meters, miles, and so forth) and so is that of mass. Now that we're talking about subatomic particles, our unit of mass will be the *atomic mass unit (amu)*, and it's approximately the mass of a proton or a neutron. An electron has very little mass by comparison with a proton or neutron. The mass of an electron is about 1/1840 amu, whereas a proton or neutron is about 1 amu. When we add the masses of neutrons, protons, and electrons, we usually neglect the electron's mass altogether.

**atomic mass
unit (amu)**

We compare the masses of two different objects by using a balance, which is like a seesaw. We know that a heavy person must sit closer to the middle of a seesaw when trying to balance with a lighter person. Figure 2.1 shows this kind of relationship in comparing the masses of the subatomic particles.

To measure how much mass something has, we compare it with another object whose mass we know absolutely. In chemistry laboratories, we use a balance that operates on the same principle as a seesaw, although it doesn't look exactly like one.

CHARGE.

Electricity is all around us. We see it in lightning. We receive electric shocks when we walk on a nylon rug on a dry day and then touch something (or someone). We can see sparks fly from a cat's fur when we pet it in the dark. We can rub a balloon on a sweater and make the balloon stick to the wall or the ceiling. Our clothes cling together when we take them from the dryer.

These are all examples of *static electricity*. They happen because there is a buildup of one of the two kinds of electrical charge, either positive or negative. Rubbing a rubber rod with a piece of fur gives the rod one kind of charge. Rubbing a glass rod with a piece of silk gives the glass rod the other kind of charge. The two rods will have *unlike* charges and will *attract* each other. Two charged rods with *like* charges will *repel* each other.

**static
electricity**

We define the kind of charge the rubber rod has as a *negative charge*, and the kind of charge the glass rod has as a *positive charge*. Electrons and protons have unlike charges. We define the kind of charge the electron has as a negative charge, and the proton, a positive charge. A neutron has no charge. We say that a neutron is electrically neutral, and that's where its name comes from.

**negative charge
positive charge**

An object has a negative charge because it has more electrons than it has protons. Electrons are more easily moved than protons. When we rub the rubber rod with the fur, electrons are transferred from the fur to the rod, and they give the rod a negative charge. An object with fewer electrons than protons has a positive charge, like the glass rod. When we rub the glass rod with silk, electrons are removed from the rod by the silk. Figure 2.2 summarizes the discussion above.

We use an *atomic charge unit* to say what amount and what kind of charge a subatomic particle has. An atomic charge unit is defined as −1 for an electron. The proton has the same amount of charge as the electron, but is

**atomic charge
unit**

opposite in sign, so its charge is +1 atomic charge unit. The neutron has 0 atomic charge units.

Table 2.1 summarizes the masses and charges of the subatomic particles.

2.2 INTRODUCING THE WHOLE ATOM

The smaller particles that atoms are made of—protons, neutrons, and electrons—are only part of the atom's story. The way these particles are

FIGURE 2.1   Relative masses of subatomic particles

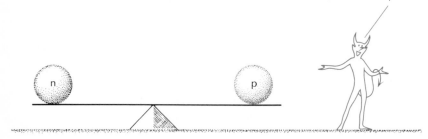

Here in my lab, I've got a special seesaw that can hold subatomic particles. This proton and neutron balance each other, because they have about the same mass.

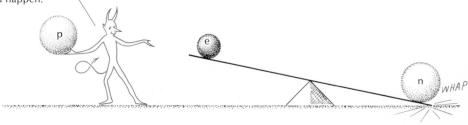

A neutron has much more mass than an electron. This is what happens if we try to balance these two with the same length of board on the seesaw. Of course, if I had put this proton on in place of the neutron, the same thing would happen.

WHAP

To get the electron to balance with the proton (or neutron), I had to make the electron's end of this seesaw *1840 times* as long as the proton's end! That's because the proton's mass is 1840 times the electron's mass.

FIGURE 2.2
**Like charges
repel,
unlike charges
attract**

11

Here's a positively
charged glass rod that
I've hung on a string.

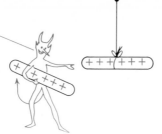

See what happens when I hold
another positively charged rod next to
it? *Like* charges *repel* each other.

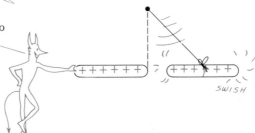

SWISH

But now if I bring this negatively
charged rubber rod close to it, it'll
go toward it. *Unlike* charges *attract*
each other.

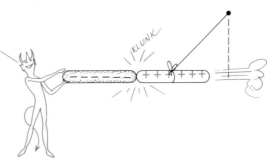

KLUNK

The positively charged rod had more
protons on it, and the negatively
charged rod had more electrons on it—
so it shouldn't surprise us that this
single proton is attracted to this single
electron! They have unlike charges.

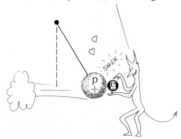

No electrical attraction between a proton
and a neutron. A neutron has no charge. It
wouldn't feel one way or the other about an
electron, either.

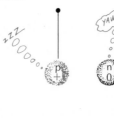

**TABLE 2.1
Summary of
charge and mass
of subatomic
particles**

	Atomic Charge Units	Atomic Mass Units (amu)
Electron	−1	1/1840 (usually neglected)
Proton	+1	1
Neutron	0	1

arranged in the atom is important too, because the arrangement helps explain why and how matter takes the many different forms it does. For now, we'll look only briefly at the most modern ideas about atomic structure. Later, in Chapter 9, we'll examine this topic in more detail.

nucleus

At the center of every atom is the *nucleus,* which contains the protons and neutrons. The particles in the nucleus give it two characteristics: (1) it contains most of the mass of the atom, since protons and neutrons have much greater masses than electrons; and (2) it is positively charged, since it contains protons with positive charges and neutrons with no charge. The total charge of the nucleus is the sum of the proton charges.

electron cloud

The nucleus is only a small fraction (1/100,000, to be precise) of the total size of an atom. Most of an atom's size is due to its *electron cloud*, which is mostly empty space with electrons rapidly moving about the nucleus. To get some idea of the space occupied by the electron cloud, imagine the outer limits of the cloud to be the fence around a baseball stadium. Compared to that, the atom's nucleus would be the size of a fly on the pitcher's cap! (Of course, atoms are much, much smaller than baseball stadiums. The average atom is not quite 1/250,000,000 of an inch in diameter.)

Since electrons are negatively charged, the electron cloud is also negatively charged. The total charge of an electron cloud is the sum of the electron charges. Whole atoms, however, are neither positively charged (like their nuclei) nor negatively charged (like their electron clouds). They are neutral, which means that there must be the same number of electrons as protons. Equal amounts of opposite charges cancel each other.

Figure 2.3 shows an artist's conception of the simple atomic model we've been describing.

To describe an atom, we assign two numbers to it. One is the number of its protons (its atomic number). The other is the total number of protons and neutrons it has (its mass number). We'll look at these two quantities one at a time.

ATOMIC NUMBER. We saw in Chapter 1 that there are 106 different kinds of atoms, and that groups of the same kind of atom are called elements. The characteristic of atoms that determines what kind they are is the

**atomic
number (Z)**

atomic number, symbolized by Z. The atomic number is the number of protons an atom has. It's also the number of electrons an atom has, since an atom has the same number of electrons as protons. Later in this chapter, we'll see that each element behaves the way it does because of how many

FIGURE 2.3
Pictorial
representation
of an atom

13

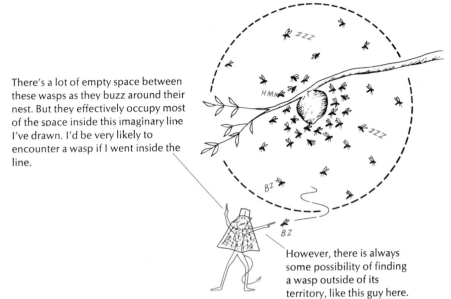

There's a lot of empty space between these wasps as they buzz around their nest. But they effectively occupy most of the space inside this imaginary line I've drawn. I'd be very likely to encounter a wasp if I went inside the line.

However, there is always some possibility of finding a wasp outside of its territory, like this guy here.

This fuzzy cloud represents the space that's effectively occupied by the electrons in an atom. It's fuzzy because there's always some possibility of finding an electron outside of it, just as with the wasps. However, we'd be much more likely to encounter an electron inside it.

I've sliced the atom in half, so that we can see what's inside: the nucleus. The nucleus contains the neutrons and protons. In Chapter 9, we'll get a much more detailed picture of the atom.

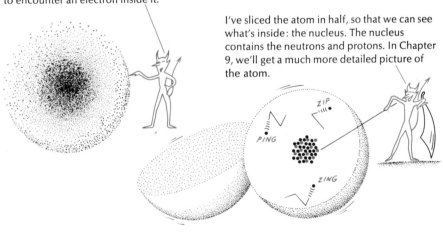

electrons it has. The atom's atomic number is the sole factor that causes an element to be the element it is.

We also saw in Chapter 1 that elements have names and letters (*symbols*) representing them: H is the symbol for hydrogen; O is the symbol for oxygen, and so forth. Some symbols contain two letters instead of one: Si for silicon, Co for cobalt, Cl for chlorine. These and other symbols come from the

symbol

English names, but many symbols come from older Latin or German names that were used before the names were changed to English. Each element has its own atomic number, name, and symbol. Table 2.2 gives a list of the elements, with their names, symbols, and atomic numbers.

MASS NUMBER.

mass number (A)

The sum of the number of neutrons and protons in an atom is the *mass number*, symbolized by A. These particles are always together in the atom's nucleus, and it's their combined mass that gives the nucleus its large mass. Notice that protons not only give an element its identity (its atomic number), they also contribute to its mass. Neutrons, however, contribute only to the mass of an atom. The number of neutrons can vary, even among atoms of the same element. (As we'll soon see, it's even possible for a hydrogen nucleus to have *no* neutrons.) Electrons, being so much lighter than either protons or neutrons, contribute virtually nothing

TABLE 2.2
Names, symbols, and atomic numbers of the elements

Atomic Number, Z	Name	Symbol	Atomic Number, Z	Name	Symbol
1	Hydrogen	H	27	Cobalt	Co
2	Helium	He	28	Nickel	Ni
3	Lithium	Li	29	Copper (Latin: Cuprum)	Cu
4	Beryllium	Be	30	Zinc	Zn
5	Boron	B	31	Gallium	Ga
6	Carbon	C	32	Germanium	Ge
7	Nitrogen	N	33	Arsenic	As
8	Oxygen	O	34	Selenium	Se
9	Fluorine	F	35	Bromine	Br
10	Neon	Ne	36	Krypton	Kr
11	Sodium (Latin: Natrium)	Na	37	Rubidium	Rb
12	Magnesium	Mg	38	Strontium	Sr
13	Aluminum	Al	39	Yttrium	Y
14	Silicon	Si	40	Zirconium	Zr
15	Phosphorus	P	41	Niobium	Nb
16	Sulfur	S	42	Molybdenum	Mo
17	Chlorine	Cl	43	Technetium	Tc
18	Argon	Ar	44	Ruthenium	Ru
19	Potassium (Latin: Kalium)	K	45	Rhodium	Rh
20	Calcium	Ca	46	Palladium	Pd
21	Scandium	Sc	47	Silver (Latin: Argentum)	Ag
22	Titanium	Ti	48	Cadmium	Cd
23	Vanadium	V	49	Indium	In
24	Chromium	Cr	50	Tin (Latin: Stannum)	Sn
25	Manganese	Mn	51	Antimony (Latin: Stibium)	Sb
26	Iron (Latin: Ferrum)	Fe	52	Tellurium	Te

to the mass of an atom. As we've seen, though, the electrons determine the atom's atomic number, just as the protons do.

Let's look at hydrogen, which has an atomic number of 1. Its atomic number tells us that it's hydrogen, and that it has one proton and one electron. However, there are three different varieties of hydrogen atoms, each with a different number of neutrons, and thus a different mass number. They're all hydrogen, though, because each has one proton and one electron. Atoms or nuclei having the same atomic number but different mass numbers are called *isotopes*.

isotopes

To tell which isotope of something we're talking about, we call it by its name or symbol and then its mass number. Here are the three isotopes of hydrogen:

hydrogen-1 (H-1): one proton, no neutrons; $Z = 1$, $A = 1$.
hydrogen-2 (H-2): one proton, one neutron; $Z = 1$, $A = 2$ (deuterium).
hydrogen-3 (H-3): one proton, two neutrons; $Z = 1$, $A = 3$ (tritium).

Atomic Number, Z	Name	Symbol	Atomic Number, Z	Name	Symbol
53	Iodine	I	80	Mercury (Latin: Hydrargyrum)	Hg
54	Xenon	Xe	81	Thallium	Tl
55	Cesium	Cs	82	Lead (Latin: Plumbum)	Pb
56	Barium	Ba	83	Bismuth	Bi
57	Lanthanum	La	84	Polonium	Po
58	Cerium	Ce	85	Astatine	At
59	Praseodymium	Pr	86	Radon	Rn
60	Neodymium	Nd	87	Francium	Fr
61	Promethium	Pm	88	Radium	Ra
62	Samarium	Sm	89	Actinium	Ac
63	Europium	Eu	90	Thorium	Th
64	Gadolinium	Gd	91	Protactinium	Pa
65	Terbium	Tb	92	Uranium	U
66	Dysprosium	Dy	93	Neptunium	Np
67	Holmium	Ho	94	Plutonium	Pu
68	Erbium	Er	95	Americium	Am
69	Thulium	Tm	96	Curium	Cm
70	Ytterbium	Yb	97	Berkelium	Bk
71	Lutetium	Lu	98	Californium	Cf
72	Hafnium	Hf	99	Einsteinium	Es
73	Tantalum	Ta	100	Fermium	Fm
74	Tungsten (German: Wolfram)	W	101	Mendelevium	Md
75	Rhenium	Re	102	Nobelium	No
76	Osmium	Os	103	Lawrencium	Lr
77	Iridium	Ir	104	Kurchatovium (tentative)	Ku
78	Platinum	Pt	105	Hahnium (tentative)	Ha
79	Gold (Latin: Aurum)	Au	106	(Name to be determined)	

For the ultimate in lists of elements, sing to the tune of "I am the very model of a modern major-general" by Sir Arthur Sullivan, or listen to a recording of this song.

THE ELEMENTS[1]

There's antimony, arsenic, aluminum, selenium
And hydrogen, and oxygen, and nitrogen, and rhenium
And nickel, neodymium, neptunium, germanium
And iron, americium, ruthenium, uranium

Europium, zirconium, lutetium, vanadium
And lanthanum, and osmium, and astatine, and radium
And gold, and protactinium, and indium, and gallium
And iodine, and thorium, and thulium, and thallium

There's yttrium, ytterbium, actinium, rubidium
And boron, gadolinium, niobium, iridium
And strontium, and silicon, and silver, and samarium
And bismuth, bromine, lithium, beryllium and barium

There's holmium and helium and hafnium and erbium
And phosphorus and francium and fluorine and terbium
And manganese and mercury, molybdenum, magnesium
Dysprosium and scandium and cerium and cesium

And lead, praseodymium, and platinum, plutonium
Palladium, promethium, potassium, polonium
And tantalum, technetium, titanium, tellurium
And cadmium and calcium and chromium and curium

There's sulfur, californium, and fermium, berkelium
And also mendelevium, einsteinium, nobelium
And argon, krypton, neon, radon, xenon, zinc, and rhodium
And chlorine, carbon, cobalt, copper, tungsten, tin, and sodium!

These are the only ones[2] of which the news has come to Ha'vard—
And there may be many others, but they haven't been discavard.

1. "The Elements," from *An Evening Wasted With Tom Lehrer*, Reprise Records, RS6199. Copyright © 1959 by Tom Lehrer. Used by permission.
2. These lyrics list 102 elements. Lawrencium, 103, was discovered in 1961. Element 104 was said to have been discovered in 1964 by Russian scientists and in 1969 by American scientists. Element 105 was discovered in 1970. In 1974 element 106 was discovered.

Usually there are, at most, two ways that we can tell the difference between isotopes. The first is obvious: the mass. For instance, we said in Chapter 1 that water is H_2O—that means that water has two hydrogen atoms for every oxygen atom. Water can also be made from hydrogen-2. The kind of water made of hydrogen-2 has more mass and is called "heavy water." Hydrogen-2 itself is called "heavy hydrogen." The second way uses the fact that some isotopes are radioactive. We'll learn more about this in Chapter 16, but it means that the nucleus can come apart by itself.

Hydrogen isn't the only element that has different isotopes. In fact, all the elements can have more than one isotope. Some of them don't occur in nature and have to be made by humans. One example is the uranium isotope U-233, which plays a big role in nuclear power, as we'll see in Chapter 16. One of the most common natural isotopes is carbon-12 (C-12). Since we know from Table 2.2 that carbon's atomic number is 6, we also know that C-12 contains 6 protons and 6 neutrons. Two other carbon isotopes, C-13 and C-14, contain 7 neutrons and 8 neutrons, respectively.

2.3 DESCRIBING THE ELEMENTS

Atoms are very small. They are so small that a 1-carat diamond contains about 10,000,000,000,000,000,000,000 carbon atoms. In chemistry, we work with large quantities of atoms just to be able to see or measure them. Because of this, we usually describe an element instead of an individual atom.

We can describe a person in a lot of ways. If we know the person well enough, we can describe his or her temperament as, say, tranquil, fiery, cold, or irrational. We can mention physical characteristics like body shape, or color of hair, eyes, and skin. We can use numbers to describe height, weight, age, and social security number.

We can describe the elements in ways similar to these. In this chapter, we'll talk about the elements' chemical and physical characteristics, and we'll save the numbers for the next chapter.

CHEMICAL PROPERTIES. The *chemical properties* of elements are like the personalities of people. They describe the way an element behaves in its interaction with other elements or substances, or the way it participates in a chemical reaction. A *chemical reaction* is an interaction involving different atoms, in which chemical bonds are formed, or broken, or both. A *chemical bond* is a strong attractive force that holds two or more atoms together. Both chemical reactions and chemical bonds will be dealt with in great depth in later chapters, and we'll expand our definitions of them when we have more specific information to build on.

When two elements react with each other, a chemical reaction occurs, and a compound is formed. A *compound* is a substance composed of two or more different elements joined by chemical bonds. For example, the element hydrogen reacts with the element oxygen to form the compound water, which contains hydrogen and oxygen joined by chemical bonds.

Elements exist either as compounds with other elements, or as free elements. Some free elements occur as single atoms, and they are called *monatomic*. (*Mono-*, or sometimes just *mon-*, means "one.") The mon-

chemical property

chemical reaction

chemical bond

compound

monatomic element

atomic elements are helium, neon, argon, xenon, krypton, and radon. In other elements, atoms bond to atoms of the same element to form **molecule** *molecules,* particles made of two or more atoms joined together by chemical bonds. Some elements form molecules that contain two atoms **diatomic** each, called *diatomic molecules.* (*Di-* means "two.") The elements that do **molecule** this are fluorine, chlorine, bromine, iodine, oxygen, hydrogen, and nitrogen. Many other elements have much more complex structures, as we'll see later.

chemical *Chemical reactivity* is the tendency of an element to participate in **reactivity** chemical reactions. The more reactive an element is, the greater its tendency to combine with other elements. If an element is very reactive, it's more likely to occur in nature combined with other elements—that is, in compounds—than it is to occur as the free element. Elements that are relatively unreactive don't tend to combine with other elements much, and so they are often found in nature as free elements. For example, sodium is very reactive and never occurs as the free element. On the other hand, gold is very unreactive and does occur as the free element. When gold is mined, it's in the form of pure, elemental gold.

Chemical reactivity is such an important concept that we find it convenient to break it down into a number of subtopics. The following chemical properties all involve chemical reactions and are all just special cases of chemical reactivity.

1. *Reacting with water.* When iron reacts with water, it rusts. Some elements—for example, sodium and potassium—react violently with water. Others, such as silver, don't react with water at all.

2. *Reacting with air.* Some elements, such as aluminum or copper, tarnish just from sitting around in the air. They react slowly with the oxygen in the air. Others, such as gold or mercury, don't react with air at all.

burning 3. *Burning.* This is reacting with air, too, but at a much higher temperature. When something burns, it combines with the oxygen in the air. For instance, charcoal, which consists largely of the element carbon, burns in the presence of oxygen or air. The elements iodine and neon are examples of elements that don't burn.

exploding 4. *Exploding.* Sometimes an element reacts so violently with air, water, or other substances that an explosion results.

supporting 5. *Supporting combustion.* This means that something else can burn *in* **combustion** the substance. Things will burn in air; this is because the oxygen in the air supports combustion. Nitrogen supports the combustion of some things, but not many. Helium, neon, argon, and krypton are examples of elements that don't support combustion at all. If we put a lighted match into one of these, the match would go out.

toxicity 6. *Toxicity.* Some elements are poisonous. They react chemically with parts of our body and prevent the body from functioning properly. Chlorine gas is very poisonous to breathe. Beryllium metal is poisonous to touch or to swallow. We'll see, though, that many elements that are toxic as elements are not toxic at all in their compounds. Table salt, for example, is a compound of chlorine and sodium, both toxic as elements.

PHYSICAL PROPERTIES.

Anything about an element that we can detect with our senses is a *physical property* of that element. The following are some physical properties of the elements.

physical property

1. *Color.* The element copper has a reddish brown color.
2. *Odor.* We can smell the sharp odor of the element chlorine when we open a bottle of chlorine bleach.
3. *Physical state.* The condition of being a solid, a liquid, or a gas is known as the *physical state*. We'll be meeting it several other times in this book, but for now we'll see briefly what it means by using the familiar example of water.

    physical state

    Ice is solid water; it is water in its *solid state*. The water molecules are fastened firmly together, and they don't move very much. A solid has its own shape and volume, no matter what container you put it in. If we heat ice, it changes to liquid water at its melting point.

    solid state

    Water in its *liquid state* conforms to the shape, but not the volume, of its container. Its molecules are moving around and aren't firmly fastened together. If we heat liquid water, it changes to steam at its boiling point.

    liquid state

    Water in its *gas state* is steam. A gas will always occupy all of any container we put it in, so it takes both the shape and the volume of its container. Gas molecules are fast moving and far apart from each other. The three states of matter are illustrated in Figure 2.4.

    gas state

4. *Metallic properties.* These are thermal (heat) and electrical conductivity; luster (shininess); ductility (can be pulled into a wire without breaking); and malleability (can be pounded out flat without shattering). These properties are illustrated in Figure 2.5. Elements that have all these metallic properties are *metals*. For instance, copper is used for electrical

    metallic properties

    metal

FIGURE 2.4
States of matter

Solid	Liquid	Gas
Atoms or molecules are fastened rigidly together in a fixed order with almost no motion. Solids pay no attention to the shape or volume of the container.	Atoms or molecules are further apart than in the solid state, and move randomly. A liquid takes the shape but not the volume of its container.	Atoms or molecules are far apart and move rapidly and randomly. A gas takes up all the room there is.

**FIGURE 2.5
Metallic
properties**

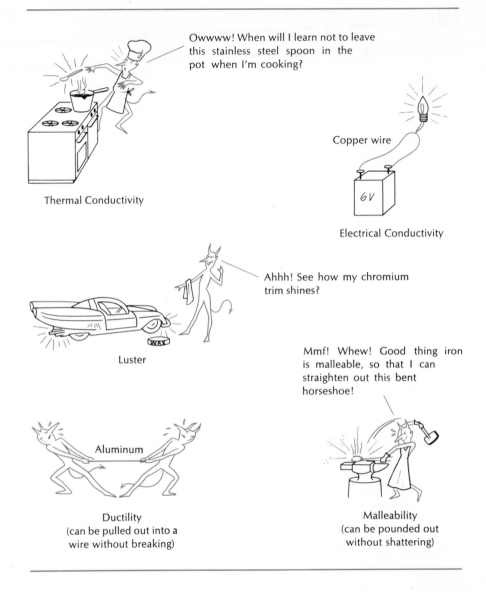

Owwww! When will I learn not to leave this stainless steel spoon in the pot when I'm cooking?

Thermal Conductivity

Copper wire

6V

Electrical Conductivity

Ahhh! See how my chromium trim shines?

Luster

Mmf! Whew! Good thing iron is malleable, so that I can straighten out this bent horseshoe!

Aluminum

Ductility
(can be pulled out into a
wire without breaking)

Malleability
(can be pounded out
without shattering)

nonmetal

metalloid

wires, so that tells us that copper conducts electricity well and is ductile. We know that it's used for the bottom of cooking pots, so it must have good thermal conductivity. Copper is frequently pounded into jewelry, so it must be malleable. When it's clean, it's shiny. It's a metal. Sulfur, on the other hand, isn't shiny at all, doesn't conduct electricity or heat, and isn't malleable or ductile. Substances like sulfur that have none of the metallic properties are *nonmetals*. There's a borderline class of elements, called *metalloids*, that have some, but not all, of the metallic properties. For example, silicon is shiny like a metal. It's a semiconductor, which means that it does conduct electricity, but not nearly as well as a metal. Silicon is not malleable or ductile. Silicon is a metalloid.

GENERAL PROPERTIES. Each element is unique, but there are general statements we can make about all of them.

1. Most elements are solids at room temperature. Mercury and bromine are the only liquids. Hydrogen, nitrogen, oxygen, fluorine, chlorine, helium, neon, argon, krypton, xenon, and radon are the only gases.
2. Most elements are metals, having all the metallic properties. Besides the above gases, the nonmetals are carbon, phosphorus, sulfur, selenium, bromine, and iodine, all with none of the metallic properties. Metalloids, having some but not all of the metallic properties, include boron, silicon, germanium, arsenic, antimony, tellurium, polonium, and astatine.

2.4 INTRODUCING THE PERIODIC TABLE

Up to now, we've simply listed elements. In chemistry, we keep track of the elements in a more orderly way by using the *periodic table of the elements.* The periodic table is the backbone of chemistry, and we'll be using it again and again throughout this book.

    Figure 2.6 shows a simplified periodic table (some of the elements, called the "rare earths" because they *are* rare, have been left out). The elements are arranged in the table so that the ones having similar properties are near each other (we'll see in Chapter 9 why this works). The vertical columns are called *groups* or sometimes *families.* Elements in the same group often have similar properties, especially the elements toward the extreme left or extreme right of the table. The horizontal rows are called *periods,* but we won't need to use them in our discussions here. Nonmetallic elements are to the right of the heavy staircase-shaped line.

    In what follows, we'll discuss briefly the elements in each group, concentrating on the more usual elements. If an element in any group isn't discussed, that's because the element is rather uncommon.

**periodic table
of the elements**

group (family)

period

GROUP IA: THE ALKALI METALS. The elements of group IA are the *alkali metals.* Lithium, sodium, potassium, rubidium, and cesium are shiny metals, and they're so soft that they can be cut with a knife. They all react easily with air, so much so that they have to be stored under oil to avoid contact with the air. If a piece of one is cut, the freshly cut surface will be very shiny for an instant but then will tarnish because of the metal's fast reaction with air. These metals also react violently with water. A small piece placed in a container of water will sputter and burst into flame. None of these metals occurs in nature as elements, because they're too reactive. When sodium combines chemically with the element chlorine, the result is table salt.

    The first member of this group, hydrogen, is unique among elements and really defies classification. Its properties are unlike those of the other members of Group IA, but we put it in the group anyway, for reasons we'll see

alkali metals

FIGURE 2.6
Simplified periodic table of the elements

Alkali Metals | IA

Alkaline Earth Metals | IIA

Transition Elements

Boron Family — IIIA
Carbon Family — IVA
Nitrogen Family — VA
Oxygen Family — VIA
Halogen Family — VIIA
Noble Gases — VIIIA

IA	IIA	IIIB	IVB	VB	VIB	VIIB	— VIIIB —			IB	IIB	IIIA	IVA	VA	VIA	VIIA	VIIIA
1 H (g)																	2 He (g)
3 Li (s)	4 Be (s)											5 B (s)	6 C (s)	7 N (g)	8 O (g)	9 F (g)	10 Ne (g)
11 Na (s)	12 Mg (s)											13 Al (s)	14 Si (s)	15 P (s)	16 S (s)	17 Cl (g)	18 Ar (g)
19 K (s)	20 Ca (s)	21 Sc (s)	22 Ti (s)	23 V (s)	24 Cr (s)	25 Mn (s)	26 Fe (s)	27 Co (s)	28 Ni (s)	29 Cu (s)	30 Zn (s)	31 Ga (s)	32 Ge (s)	33 As (s)	34 Se (s)	35 Br (l)	36 Kr (g)
37 Rb (s)	38 Sr (s)	39 Y (s)	40 Zr (s)	41 Nb (s)	42 Mo (s)	43 Tc (s)	44 Ru (s)	45 Rh (s)	46 Pd (s)	47 Ag (s)	48 Cd (s)	49 In (s)	50 Sn (s)	51 Sb (s)	52 Te (s)	53 I (s)	54 Xe (g)
55 Cs (s)	56 Ba (s)	57 La (s)	72 Hf (s)	73 Ta (s)	74 W (s)	75 Re (s)	76 Os (s)	77 Ir (s)	78 Pt (s)	79 Au (s)	80 Hg (l)	81 Tl (s)	82 Pb (s)	83 Bi (s)	84 Po (s)	85 At (s)	86 Rn (g)
87 Fr	88 Ra	89 Ac	104 Ku	105 Ha	106												

(g) Gas
(l) Liquid
(s) Solid

☐ Metals
▨ Nonmetals
▨ Metalloids

Numbers in boxes are atomic numbers

later. Hydrogen is a colorless, odorless, diatomic gas. When hydrogen is burned in air, it combines with the oxygen in the air to form water. If we confine hydrogen in a container and light a match to it, it will explode. Hydrogen was once used in gas balloons, because it's the lightest element and a gas balloon has to be filled with something lighter than air. In 1939, a huge, hydrogen-filled dirigible named the *Hindenburg* exploded, killing many people. Since then, balloonists have switched instead to helium, which is very unreactive. Hydrogen is an important element in biological molecules. Like the other elements in its group, hydrogen doesn't occur on earth as a free element because it is too reactive.

GROUP IIA: THE ALKALINE EARTH METALS.   The ele-
ments of group IIA are the *alkaline earth metals*. All except magnesium are like toned-down versions of the alkali metals. They react with air and water and other elements, but not quite so violently. They're soft, but not quite so soft. Calcium we know as an important part of bones and teeth. Magnesium is much harder and less reactive than the other members of its group. It is light and shiny and behaves a lot like aluminum (in Group IIIA). It doesn't have to be stored under oil, but it does burn with a bright flame, and so it comes in handy as the filament in flashbulbs. It's also used in alloys to make light-weight structures, such as bicycles.

alkaline earth metal

GROUPS IIIB TO IIB: THE TRANSITION ELEMENTS.
After Groups IA and IIA, distinctions among groups become less clear. The elements in the groups labeled IIIB to IIB are called *transition elements*. They're all metals, and most of them are good conductors of heat and electricity. Silver is the best conductor, followed closely by copper.

transition element

Many of the structural metals are found among the transition elements. By "structural metal" we mean a metal that we can make a structure out of, such as an automobile or a bridge or a building. Steel, for instance, is mostly iron, with various other metals added, such as chromium, nickel, vanadium, manganese, molybdenum, or zirconium, depending on what the steel is to be used for.

These groups also include the metals gold, silver, and platinum, which are called "precious" because they're scarce, unreactive, and soft. They can be shaped easily (into money or jewelry or fillings), and they aren't very reactive so there's little danger of their being destroyed by fire or chemicals. People once called these metals "royal" because of their disdain for other elements. A mixture of acids called "aqua regia," or "royal water," will dissolve the precious metals.

One of the most interesting transition elements is mercury. It's the only metal that's a liquid at room temperature, and it's so heavy that a rock will float on it. Mercury is a very useful element. We see it often in thermometers, where its property of expanding and contracting in a regular way with slight temperature changes makes it ideal. It's also used in switches and thermo-

ALCHEMY AND CHEMISTRY

Some of the earliest chemical discoveries were made through greed for gold. During the Middle Ages in Europe, it was the common belief that so-called baser metals like lead could be turned into gold if the right steps were taken. People whose profession it was to attempt this change were called "alchemists." The alchemists were part charlatan, part magician, and part chemist. Kings, hoping to increase their stores of gold, actively bought, sold, and traded their alchemists with other kings—as baseball team owners do today with their players. With so much at stake, it behooved the alchemists to get results—or at least to fake them, which many did. Discovery of their fraud often meant death or, at the very least, lifetime disgrace.

The theory held by most alchemists was that metals grew and matured like plants, until they became "ripe" as gold—considered the "perfect" metal. The other metals were just "unripe" gold, although silver was considered by them to be nearly ripe. One had only to wait until a metal ripened, or to find some way of hastening the process. Alchemists' vain attempts to hasten this ripening ultimately advanced chemical experimentation and knowledge. Some of their laboratory tools are still used today in more sophisticated form: distilling flasks, crucibles, water baths, and balances. They discovered the elements antimony, arsenic, bismuth, phosphorus, and zinc, as well as the substances alum, borax, cream of tartar, ether, plaster of Paris, red lead, and aqua regia. The scientific treatment of disease with chemicals rather than with magic charms was begun by an early alchemist. If we stretch it a little, and equate scientific knowledge with gold, we could say that the alchemists actually succeeded.

stats. The main industrial use of mercury in the United States is in processing seawater to make sodium, lye, and chlorine.

Mercury can also be dangerous. Although it's fairly unreactive—it would probably pass right through your body if you happened to swallow some (DON'T!)—some of its compounds can help it accumulate in the body and cause poisoning. In its early stages, mercury poisoning causes impaired vision and weakened muscles. In its later stages, the poisoning can cause blindness, paralysis, insanity, and death. Years ago, a mercury compound was used to process the felt in hats. People who worked in hat factories ("hatters") nearly always got mercury poisoning. That's where we get the expression "mad as a hatter."

We still see the ill effects of the industrial use of mercury. In Japan, it has been used in the manufacture of plastics. No one thought that the mercury compounds left over as waste and dumped into the waters would find their way into the systems of plants and animals, but they did. Since 1953, in the fishing village of Minamata, mercury poisoning has killed fifty-two people, crippled about one hundred, and otherwise harmed almost nine hundred. This tragedy has made the world aware of the dangers of mercury pollution.

Introducing the   **25**
Periodic Table

GROUP IIIA: THE BORON FAMILY.

The elements of Group IIIA—the boron family—don't follow a regular pattern of properties. Boron is a metalloid, whereas all the rest are metals. Boron and the next element, aluminum, aren't a bit alike: boron is a black solid and is not very reactive; aluminum is shiny and quite reactive. Aluminum reacts with air to form a protective coating which prevents it from corroding further. That's why aluminum can be used to make pots and pans, and exterior sidings for houses. The Group IIIA elements below aluminum are rather like aluminum, but they're not very common.

GROUP IVA: THE CARBON FAMILY.

In Group IVA, carbon is a nonmetal, silicon and germanium are metalloids, and tin and lead are metals. Diamonds are made of carbon. So are graphite and charcoal (or coke). These are three *allotropic forms* of carbon, which means that the element's atoms are joined together in different ways. When we look at a single, perfect diamond, we are looking at a single molecule. A diamond is made of millions and millions of carbon atoms, each joined to four others by chemical bonds to make a continuous structure. (See Figure 2.7.) A diamond is very hard to cut, because strong chemical bonds have to be broken. Although it's possible to burn a diamond, no one has ever been able to make one melt.

allotropic form

Graphite, on the other hand, is made of a lot of carbon layers stacked one on top of the other, like sheets of paper (see Figure 2.8). Each layer is a molecule. The layers slide over each other, which makes graphite a good lubricant and a good material for pencils. Charcoal is like graphite, except that the layers are broken up into little chunks. Since its particles are much more finely divided than graphite's, charcoal burns much better than graphite. The primary use of charcoal is as a fuel, particularly in making steel.

Carbon is most important to us because it is a basic element in all plant and animal structures. (Recall from Chapter 1 that carbon takes second place in the "top ten" elements important to living organisms.) The last two chapters in this book are given over solely to carbon compounds.

The next member of Group IVA, silicon, is a shiny, gray solid. Silicon is the second most abundant element in the earth's outer layer. Sand and most rocks consist of a compound of silicon and oxygen, called silicon dioxide or silica. Other forms of silicon dioxide are glass and asbestos. People who work around and continuously breathe silicon dioxide are subject to a serious disease called "silicosis." Once silicon dioxide gets into the lungs, it stays, and the lungs eventually get so full of sand that they give up. Miners and installers of asbestos insulation or siding usually wear masks these days. Elemental silicon has several allotropic forms, as does carbon. One of these

**Figure 2.7
Inside view
of diamond
structure**

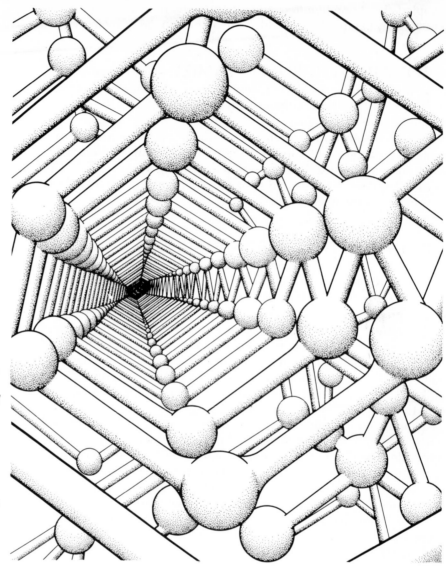

Diamond's carbon atoms
are attached by chemical
bonds in a structure that
goes on and on. If I should
fall through a 1-karat
diamond at the rate of one
carbon atom per minute,
it would take me twenty-
seven years to get to the
other side.

From *The Architecture of Molecules* by Linus Pauling and Roger Hayward.
W. H. Freeman and Company. Copyright © 1964.

is a diamond-type structure, not as hard as diamond, used in making tran-
sistors and circuits for televisions, stereo systems, computers, and the like.

The last two Group IVA metals are tin and lead, both of which we're
familiar with. Tin is used primarily as a coating for steel, as in tin cans, which
are really tin-coated steel cans. The tin coating prevents the steel from reacting with the food in the can. A tin can whose tin layer is broken corrodes

FIGURE 2.8
Layered structure of graphite

27

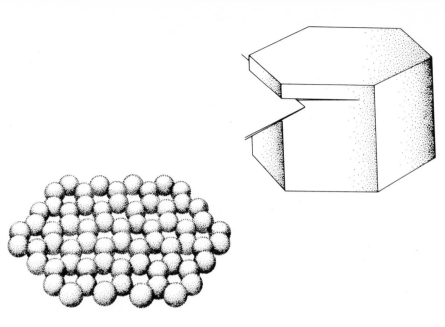

I could slide the top layer of graphite over the others, because the layers are held together by attractions weaker than chemical bonds.

Within a layer, though, the carbon atoms are attached by chemical bonds. The basic structure is a hexagon, like this one I have in my hand.

From *The Architecture of Molecules* by Linus Pauling and Roger Hayward. W. H. Freeman and Company. Copyright © 1964.

rapidly, whereas if the layer is intact, the can will not corrode for many years. Lead's primary use is in storage batteries and in leaded gasoline.

GROUP VA: THE NITROGEN FAMILY.

The first two members of Group VA, nitrogen and phosphorus, are both nonmetals, but they aren't similar in any other ways. Nitrogen occurs naturally as a diatomic, colorless, odorless, unreactive gas. Air is about 79 percent nitrogen, which "dilutes" the oxygen that makes up about 20 percent of the air. All animals and plants contain nitrogen as part of their chemical makeup. Phosphorus— also an important biological element—is a white or red solid. One of its compounds is used in match heads.

Arsenic is an ingredient in mysteries where poisoning is the crime. It behaves somewhat like phosphorus chemically, and it can take the place of phosphorus in important bodily functions, blocking the normal metabolic reactions. Bismuth is an ingredient in such medicines as Pepto-Bismol.

GROUP VIA: THE OXYGEN FAMILY.

All the Group VIA elements are nonmetals except tellurium and polonium, which are metalloids.

Oxygen, the first element, occurs most commonly as a diatomic, odorless, colorless gas. Oxygen supports combustion, and it also supports life. It's the element in air that we must breathe in order to live. We use it to burn up the energy sources that we eat, in order to make energy to run our bodies. Oxygen is the one element that's very reactive but still occurs in nature as the free element. This is because oxygen is constantly being formed by green plants, which "exhale" oxygen as part of their life processes. As long as we have enough green plants, the oxygen that we use up will be continually replaced, and we won't run out of oxygen.

triatomic molecule

Besides the diatomic form, oxygen has another allotropic form, called "ozone." Ozone is a blue, acrid-smelling gas, consisting of *triatomic molecules* (*tri-* means "three"). Passing an electric spark through oxygen will produce ozone, which is the odor we smell whenever we're around heavy electric machinery. Ozone is also a part of smog, and it can corrode automobile tires and cause serious respiratory damage. It performs a useful function, though, in the stratosphere, which is about twenty miles above the earth. There, it screens out a lot of harmful radiation from the sun.

Sulfur is a yellow, solid nonmetal that has several allotropic forms. It burns, is moderately reactive, but doesn't react with water. It occurs in nature both as the free element and in compounds. It's used mostly for manufacturing other chemicals. Selenium and tellurium have properties similar to those of sulfur. Tellurium is the only element in this group that is toxic.

halogen

GROUP VIIA: THE HALOGENS.

At Group VIIA, the elements again have regular properties. These elements are called the *halogens*. They all exist as diatomic molecules, although they're so reactive that none occurs in nature as the free element. Their color becomes more intense going down the group. Fluorine is a pale, yellow-green gas. Chlorine is a greener gas. Bromine is a heavy, reddish brown liquid that causes severe burns if spilled on the skin. Iodine is a brownish solid. All these elements are toxic. Fluorine and chlorine support combustion.

Fluorine has become a familiar element in our lives. One of its compounds is used in drinking water "fluoridation" and in "fluoride" toothpaste, because it helps prevent tooth decay by combining with the calcium in teeth.

We know chlorine from its use in household bleach and in swimming pools, where it disinfects the water. In both cases, chlorine is added to water, sometimes with a stabilizer that keeps the chlorine gas from escaping.

Bromine is used as a disinfectant, and it is also used to make anti-knock gasoline. Iodine is necessary to humans' body chemistry. We need it to make thyroxine, a hormone that regulates our metabolism.

noble gas

rare gas

inert gas

GROUP VIIIA: THE NOBLE GASES.

The group VIIIA is a nice, quiet collection of elements with a lot of names. They're called the *noble gases*, the *rare gases*, or the *inert gases*. All these names describe either their scarcity or their lack of reactivity. "Inert" means not reacting with anything at all. Recently some compounds of xenon and krypton have been prepared, so the name "inert gases" isn't used so much anymore. This group is easy to classify. All the elements in it are colorless, odorless, monatomic gases which neither burn nor support combustion. Their lack of reactivity kept them from being discovered for a long time. Helium was first discovered on the sun in 1868 (*helios* is Greek for "sun"). However, the element wasn't discovered on earth until 1895. At that time, scientists noticed that all the air's nitrogen, oxygen, water vapor, and carbon dioxide added up to only about 99 percent of air. The remaining gas was completely unreactive, and the scientists named it "argon" (*argos* is Greek for "lazy"). Later, this remaining 1 percent of air was also proved to contain small amounts of the other noble gases—helium, neon, krypton, xenon, and sometimes radon. Argon makes up 0.93 percent of the air. Neon is next highest, at 0.0018 percent, and xenon occupies a tiny 0.000008 percent.

Helium, the second lightest element, has been used in gas balloons since hydrogen proved too reactive. We know neon best as an ingredient in neon lights. The neon is contained in a glass tube. The tube also contains an electron "gun" that shoots electrons through the gas, knocking other electrons off the neon atoms. The neon's electrons soon return to their atoms, though, and when they do, the atoms give off the light we see. The other noble gases are used in incandescent and fluorescent lights, or wherever an inert atmosphere is needed. None are toxic. Some are used in oxygen mixtures in place of nitrogen (for example, to prevent divers from getting the bends).

REVIEW QUESTIONS

What Atoms Are Made of

1. What is an *element?*
2. What are *subatomic particles?* What are the main kinds?
3. What is *mass?* What do we use it for?
4. What are the masses of the subatomic particles?
5. Give some examples of *static electricity.*
6. Explain the difference between *positive charge* and *negative charge.*
7. What are the *atomic charge units* of the subatomic particles?

Introducing the Whole Atom

8. What is the *nucleus?* What does it contain?
9. Where are the electrons in an atom?
10. Why is an atom electrically neutral?
11. What is an element's *atomic number? Mass number?*
12. What is an element's *symbol?* Why do some symbols seem to have no relation to the element's English name?
13. What are *isotopes?* What are the three isotopes of hydrogen? What other elements can have isotopes?

14. How can we deduce the number of neutrons an atom has, if we know its mass number and its atomic number?

Describing the Elements

15. Why do we describe elements instead of individual atoms?
16. What do we mean by *chemical properties* of elements? What is a *chemical reaction?*
17. What holds the atoms in a compound together?
18. What is a *molecule?* A *diatomic molecule?* What elements exist as diatomic molecules? What elements are *monatomic?*
19. What is *chemical reactivity?* How does it often determine whether elements occur in nature as free elements or in compounds?
20. What are some chemical properties of the elements?
21. If an element is poisonous, does this mean that all of its compounds are poisonous too?
22. What do we mean by *physical properties* of the elements? List them.
23. What are the *physical states?* In what ways do they differ?

24. How can we change a liquid to a gas? A solid to a liquid? A liquid to a solid? A solid to a gas?
25. What are the *metallic properties*? What does each one mean?
26. What is a *metalloid*? What elements are metalloids?
27. What two elements are liquids? Which elements are gases?

Introducing the Periodic Table

28. What are the vertical columns of the periodic table called? The horizontal rows?
29. How can we tell from the periodic table whether an element is a metal, a nonmetal, or a metalloid?
30. What are the Group IA metals called? List some of their properties.
31. Name some properties of hydrogen.
32. What are the Group IIA metals called? List some of their properties.
33. What are the *transition elements*? Give some important transition elements, with their properties.
34. What familiar metal is found in Group IIIA?
35. What are the similarities and differences between diamond and graphite? What do we call such different forms?
36. What are sand, rocks, and glass made of?
37. What important metals are found in Group IVA? What are some uses of these metals?
38. What part of the air do we need to breathe? Why doesn't it get used up?
39. What are the *halogens*? List some of their properties.
40. What are the *noble gases*? What are some other names for them? List some of their properties.

EXERCISES

1. It has been suggested that a neutron is a combination of a proton and an electron. Does this idea make sense, when you take into account the particles' masses and charges? Explain.
2. Suppose we were building atoms according to the following incomplete table. Fill in the blanks.

No. Protons	No. Electrons	No. Neutrons	Atomic Mass Units (amu)
2	___	2	___
___	3	___	6
3	___	4	___
4	___	___	7

3. With the help of Table 2.2, give the number of protons, neutrons, and electrons in each of the following atoms.
   a. Al-27   c. Cu-64   e. Ni-59
   b. Ar-40   d. Au-197   f. Co-60
4. Give names and symbols for these atoms.
   a. mass no. 107, 60 neutrons
   b. mass no. 204, 123 neutrons
   c. mass no. 232, 142 neutrons
   d. mass no. 238, 146 neutrons
   e. mass no. 91, 51 neutrons
5. Match up the isotopes of the same elements. Give the name of each element.
   a. $Z = 1, A = 3$ e. $Z = 3, A = 7$
   b. $Z = 3, A = 6$ f. $Z = 4, A = 7$
   c. $Z = 4, A = 6$ g. $Z = 3, A = 5$
   d. $Z = 2, A = 5$ h. $Z = 4, A = 8$

6. Three isotopes of helium have mass numbers of 3, 4, and 5. How many neutrons, protons, and electrons does each contain?
7. With the help of the periodic table (Figure 2.6), classify each of the following as a metal, nonmetal, or metalloid: arsenic, oxygen, barium, zirconium, astatine, sulfur, antimony, aluminum.
8. Find the element that doesn't belong in each of the following sets, and state why it doesn't belong.
   a. Na, K, Li, Mg   d. Ar, He, O, I
   b. K, Ca, Cr, Br   e. N, P, Br, Hg
   c. Ne, N, O, F   f. Ag, Au, Cu, Ba
9. If we had samples of each, how could we tell the difference between each of the following pairs?
   a. Na and Mg f. Br and Cl k. Br and I
   b. H and Li   g. N and P   l. Ca and Pb
   c. Hg and Br h. S and Ar m. Au and Hg
   d. Mg and Ca i. O and H n. Fe and Mg
   e. Al and Si   j. Cu and I
10. Sodium is a very soft, malleable metal. Why, then, isn't it used to make jewelry?
11. Which would make the best electrical wire, Ca, Fe, or Se? Why?
12. Which can you see: N, Ar, Cl?
13. The study of chemistry is made easier if one is able to recognize the names and symbols of the most common elements on sight. Try to supply either the name or the symbol, whichever is missing, consulting the list of elements only when necessary.
    a. sodium   d. Li   g. Sn   j. lead
    b. manganese e. K   h. Cu   k. iron
    c. mercury   f. P   i. Ag   l. Br

3

Measuring Atoms

In the last chapter, we described some physical and chemical properties of elements. In this chapter, we'll look at some more physical properties, but ones that we usually measure with numbers. (For a review of working with numbers, see Appendix A.) Every element has numbers that go with these things: atomic number, atomic weight, boiling point, melting point, specific heat, and density. We already know what atomic number is. We'll explore the others in the pages that follow.

3.1 WEIGHING AS A MEANS OF COUNTING

Suppose you're engaged in a building project: laying a floor. You're going to put down 25 boards with 10 nails apiece: that's at least 250 nails you'll need. When you go to the hardware store and say how many nails you want, the clerk doesn't count out 250 nails for you. Nails are sold by the pound. You need eight-penny nails, and there are about 130 of them in a pound. The clerk sells you 2 pounds, so you'll be sure to have enough. When we need a large number of a small item, it doesn't make sense to count them out; weighing is more efficient. We probably won't get exactly the number we want, but if we're dealing in large numbers it won't make much difference if there are a few more or less.

In chemistry, we're stuck with using just this method to count atoms and molecules, because it's the only way we *can* do it. Atoms are too small to count out one-by-one, and yet we do need to know how many we have in a bunch so we can study their behavior, which is what chemistry is all about.

Weighing atoms to count atoms is no more mistake-proof than weighing nails to count nails. But there are so many atoms in any sample of an element that even a million atoms more or less will hardly make any difference. (For a discussion of the significance of very small numbers compared with very large numbers, see Appendix A.2, p. 467.)

mole

To count atoms, scientists use a number called the *mole,* which is 602,000,000,000,000,000,000,000 things. Just as with a number called the "dozen," which is twelve things, we can use the mole to count any kind of thing: atoms, molecules, doughnuts, eggs, billiard balls. We usually write the number for the mole in exponential notation, as 6.02×10^{23}. Using exponential notation, we can easily express and work with very large numbers and very small numbers, without having to write out all the zeros involved. (Appendix A.4, pp. 472–476, contains a review of writing exponents and using them in problems.)

Even though a mole is like a dozen, the actual number is much larger because atoms are much smaller than the eggs or oranges we usually measure by the dozen. Thus, to weigh—and count—the much smaller atoms and molecules, we have to know the mass of a mole of them. We could also weigh oranges in dozens—if we knew that all oranges weighed the same.

Suppose we knew that a dozen oranges weighed 4 pounds and we had a
paper bag of oranges that weighed 2 pounds. We'd know, without counting,
that we had half a dozen, or 0.5 dozen, or 6 oranges in the bag.

Scientists count atoms the same way, only they don't use the pound.
The pound is a unit of weight in the English system of weights and measurements, which is still being used in the United States at the time of this
writing. Scientists the world over (including American scientists) use the
International System of Units (SI), which is a metric system. A few basic SI
units are shown in Table 3.1. (A more complete discussion of SI and other
units is contained in Appendixes B.1 and B.2, pp. 480–483.)

Scientists find it convenient to use grams and kilograms to measure mass,
instead of using pounds to measure weight. The *weight* of an object is a   **weight**
measure of the amount of gravitational attraction on that object. An object's
weight can vary, because the gravitational attraction on it can vary from one
location to another. Mass doesn't vary, because it doesn't depend on gravitational attraction. However, we do determine the mass of an object by weighing, because weight is proportional to mass. When we weigh an object, we
compare the weight of its mass with the weight of a known mass. "Weighing," then, really means "determining the mass." As yet, there's no verb "to
mass" in the scientific vocabulary, although perhaps there should be. Unfortunately, weight and mass are often used interchangeably. We might
hear "such and such weighs 3.2 kilograms," but this is incorrect. Kilograms,
grams, and metric tons are all units of mass and not of weight.

We know the mass of a mole of carbon-12 atoms is 12.0 grams. If we had
6.00 grams of carbon, we'd know that we had half a mole, or 0.500 moles.
And just as we'd know we had 6 oranges if we had half a dozen oranges, so
we'd also know we had 3.01×10^{23} carbon-12 atoms, because that's half a
mole. (See Figure 3.1.) But how do we know that the mass of a mole of
carbon-12 atoms is 12.0 grams?

Quantity	SI Unit	English Equivalent
Mass	**Basic Unit: Kilogram (kg)**	2.20 pounds (lb)
	Gram (g) = 10^{-3} kg	1/454 pounds (lb)
Length	**Basic Unit: Meter (m)**	3.28 feet (ft)
	Centimeter (cm)[a] = 10^{-2}m	0.394 inches (in)
	Kilometer (km) = 10^3m	0.621 miles (mi)
Volume	**Basic Unit: Cubic Meter (m³)[b]**	35.3 cubic feet (ft³)
	Liter (l) = 10^{-3} cubic meters (m³)	1.06 quarts (qt)
	Milliliter (ml) = 10^{-3} liters (l)	0.0340 liquid ounces (oz)
	1 ml = 1 cubic centimeter (cm³)	

**TABLE 3.1
Some commonly
used SI units
and their English
equivalents**

[a]The centimeter is not an officially approved SI unit, but it is used by chemists because of its
convenient size.
[b]Although the cubic meter is the basic SI unit, it is too large to be practical for chemists, who use the
smaller units of volume instead.

**FIGURE 3.1
Counting
oranges
or atoms
by weighing**

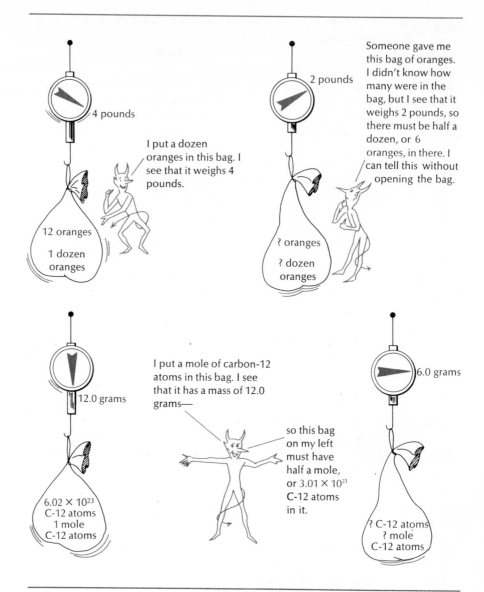

3.2 GRAM-ATOMIC WEIGHT

We've seen that atoms of different elements have different mass numbers, and therefore different masses. Then a mole of each kind of atom will have its own mass, which will be different from the mass of a mole of any other kind of atom. So, too, will a dozen oranges have a different weight from a dozen grapefruit or a dozen kumquats.

(We're about to begin working problems with numbers. In the examples that follow, we'll observe rules of significant figures as described in Appendix A.2, pp. 467–471.)

EXAMPLE 3.1: Given that the mass of an average egg white is 30 grams, an average egg yolk, 20 grams, and an average eggshell, 4 grams, calculate the mass of an egg. (Since eggs vary in mass, values with only one significant figure are given.)

Solution: An egg contains one white, one yolk, and one shell. We add up the parts:

$$
\begin{array}{l}
\text{1 egg white, each 30 grams} = 30 \text{ grams} \\
\text{1 egg yolk, each 20 grams} = 20 \text{ grams} \\
\underline{\text{1 eggshell, each 4 grams} = 4 \text{ grams}} \\
\phantom{\text{1 eggshell, each 4 grams} = 0}54 \text{ grams}
\end{array}
$$

Here, we must round off the 54 grams to 50 grams, since we're not allowed to have any significant figures beyond the first column that contains an uncertain digit, which in this case is the left column. The result is that the 4 grams is negligible (that is, we can neglect its mass) compared to the 50 grams. $50 + 4$ is still 50.

Answer: 50 grams.

The next example is the first of many we'll be doing that involve units and conversion factors. (Units and conversion factors are fully discussed in Appendix B, pp. 480–493. Working problems with conversion factors involves a few logical steps, which we'll always use. These steps are detailed in Section B.3, p. 484.)

EXAMPLE 3.2: Using the information in Example 3.1, calculate the mass, in grams, of one dozen eggs.

Solution:
Step 1: We want to convert one dozen eggs to grams.
$$\text{1 doz eggs} = \underline{} \text{ g}$$
Step 2: We need a conversion factor to convert dozen eggs to eggs (12 eggs/doz) and another to convert eggs to grams (50 g/egg).
Step 3:

$$\cancel{\text{1 doz eggs}} \times 12 \, \frac{\cancel{\text{eggs}}}{\cancel{\text{doz eggs}}} \times 50 \, \frac{\text{g}}{\cancel{\text{egg}}} = \underline{} \text{ g}$$

Notice that we may cancel "egg" with "eggs." It doesn't matter whether a given unit is singular or plural. The units check.

Answer: 600 grams.

EXAMPLE 3.3: If the mass of one dozen eggs is 600 grams, how many dozen eggs are in 1700 grams of eggs?

Solution:
Step 1: We want to convert 1700 grams of eggs to dozen.
$$\text{1700 g eggs} = \underline{} \text{ doz}$$

Step 2: One dozen eggs has a mass of 600 grams. That means that our conversion factor is 600 g eggs/doz. We'll want to invert this factor to 1 doz/600 g eggs, because we want g eggs to cancel. (For information on inverting conversion factors, see Appendix B.3, p. 484.)

Step 3:

$$1700 \text{ g eggs} \times \frac{1 \text{ doz}}{600 \text{ g eggs}} = \underline{\quad} \text{ doz}$$

Our units check, so we solve for the answer. The answer is 2.83, but we must round it to one significant figure.

Answer: 3 dozen.

Now, we're ready to do exactly the same kind of calculations with a carbon-12 atom. Then we'll see how we know that the mass of a mole of this kind of atom is 12.0 grams.

EXAMPLE 3.4: The mass of a proton is 1.67×10^{-24} grams (1 amu), a neutron, 1.67×10^{-24} grams (1 amu), and an electron, 9.11×10^{-28} grams $(4.86 \times 10^{-4}$ amu). What, then, is the mass in grams of one carbon-12 atom?

Solution: This is like the egg problem in Example 3.1, except that we have more significant figures and a carbon-12 atom has more than one of each component in it. If we look back at Table 2.2, we see that carbon has an atomic number of 6. That means it has 6 protons. Since the problem gives us the mass number of 12, this atom must also have 6 neutrons. The number of electrons in an atom is the same as the number of protons (also 6). Now, we multiply each part by 6 and add up the masses:

$$6 \text{ protons, each } 1.67 \times 10^{-24} \text{ g} = 10.0 \quad\quad \times 10^{-24} \text{ g}$$
$$6 \text{ neutrons, each } 1.67 \times 10^{-24} \text{ g} = 10.0 \quad\quad \times 10^{-24} \text{ g}$$
$$\underline{6 \text{ electrons, each } 9.11 \times 10^{-28} \text{ g} = \quad 0.00547 \times 10^{-24} \text{ g}}$$
$$20.00547 \times 10^{-24} \text{ g}$$

Again, we see that one of the components—this time, the electrons—has such a small mass compared with the rest that we neglect it. The number above has to be rounded off to one decimal place. This illustrates what we said in Chapter 2 about most of the mass of an atom consisting of the neutrons and protons.

Answer: 20.0×10^{-24} grams.

EXAMPLE 3.5: Given that the mass of a carbon-12 atom is 20.0×10^{-24} grams, calculate the mass in grams of 1.00 mole of carbon-12 atoms.

Solution: This is like the dozen problem of Example 3.2.

Step 1: We want to convert 1.00 mole of carbon-12 atoms to grams.

$$1.00 \text{ mole C-12} = \underline{\quad} \text{ g}$$

Step 2: We need a conversion factor to convert moles of carbon-12 atoms to numbers of carbon-12 atoms (6.02×10^{23} C-12 atoms/mole C-12) and another to convert C-12 atoms to grams (20.0×10^{-24} g/C-12 atom).

Step 3:

$$1.00 \text{ mole C-12} \times 6.02 \times 10^{23}\frac{\text{C-12 atoms}}{\text{mole C-12}} \times 20.0 \times 10^{-24}\frac{\text{g}}{\text{C-12 atom}} = \underline{\quad} \text{ g}$$

The units check, so we solve for our answer.

Answer: 12.0 grams.

The number of grams in a mole of carbon-12 atoms (12.0 g) turns out to be the same numerically as the mass number (12.0 amu). This is not an accident. The mole was chosen so that the mass number of any atom is the same numerically as the number of grams in a mole of the same kind of atom. The number 6.02×10^{23} is called *Avogadro's number,* in honor of an early chemist, Amadeo Avogadro, whom we'll say more about in Chapter 11.

Gram-atomic weight is the mass, in grams, of a mole of atoms of any element as it occurs in nature. By definition, the gram-atomic weight of carbon-12 is taken to be exactly 12.0000 grams, and an *atomic mass unit (amu)* is exactly 1/12 the mass of a carbon-12 atom. Then the gram-atomic weights of the elements are given in reference to this standard. These have been determined experimentally and are shown in Table 3.2.

One thing we notice right away is that the gram-atomic weight of the element carbon is 12.011, and not 12.0000. This is because any mole-sized sample of naturally occurring carbon atoms contains about 1 percent carbon-13 and a trace of carbon-14, in addition to carbon-12. When we calculated the mass of a mole of carbon-12 atoms, we knew that each carbon atom in our sample had the same mass. Atoms as they occur in nature don't have the same mass, though, any more than all eggs have exactly the same mass. We took care of this problem in the case of the eggs by using only one significant figure. With atoms, though, we'd like to be more exact. Masses of eggs vary randomly, but there are only a few isotopes of each element, and we know their masses. For any element, we always have a random assortment of isotopes with exactly the same proportion of each isotope. The element chlorine is always 75.5 percent chlorine-35 and 24.5 percent chlorine-37, no matter where we get the sample from or how large it is.

Avogadro's number

gram-atomic weight

atomic mass unit (amu)

EXAMPLE 3.6: What is the gram-atomic weight of naturally occurring chlorine?

Solution: We know what the percentages are, and we know what the mass of a mole of each isotope is (the same as its mass number). Then:

$$(0.755 \times 35.0 \text{ g}) + (0.245 \times 37.0 \text{ g})$$

or

$$= \quad 26.4 \text{ g} \quad + \quad 9.07 \text{ g}$$

Answer: 35.5 grams.

The gram-atomic weight given in Table 3.2 for chlorine is 35.453, whereas we got 35.5. This is because we carried our calculations to only three significant figures. When we're using gram-atomic weights, we'll usually find it convenient to round them to one decimal place, except for elements

TABLE 3.2
Atomic numbers and atomic weights of the elements[a]

Element	Sym-bol	Atomic Number	Atomic Weight	Rounded Value
Actinium	Ac	89	(227)	–
Aluminum	Al	13	26.98154	27.0
Americium	Am	95	(243)	–
Antimony	Sb	51	121.75	121.8
Argon	Ar	18	39.948	39.9
Arsenic	As	33	74.9216	74.9
Astatine	At	85	(210)	–
Barium	Ba	56	137.33	137.3
Berkelium	Bk	97	(249)	–
Beryllium	Be	4	9.01218	9.01
Bismuth	Bi	83	208.9804	209.0
Boron	B	5	10.81	10.8
Bromine	Br	35	79.904	79.9
Cadmium	Cd	48	112.41	112.4
Calcium	Ca	20	40.08	40.1
Californium	Cf	98	(251)	–
Carbon	C	6	12.011	12.0
Cerium	Ce	58	140.12	140.1
Cesium	Cs	55	132.9054	132.9
Chlorine	Cl	17	35.453	35.5
Chromium	Cr	24	51.996	52.0
Cobalt	Co	27	58.9332	58.9
Copper	Cu	29	63.546	63.5
Curium	Cm	96	(247)	–
Dysprosium	Dy	66	162.50	162.5
Einsteinium	Es	99	(254)	–
Erbium	Er	68	167.26	167.3

Element	Sym-bol	Atomic Number	Atomic Weight	Rounded Value
Mendelevium	Md	101	(256)	–
Mercury	Hg	80	200.59	200.6
Molybdenum	Mo	42	95.94	95.9
Neodymium	Nd	60	144.24	144.2
Neon	Ne	10	20.179	20.2
Neptunium	Np	93	237.0482	237.0
Nickel	Ni	28	58.70	58.7
Niobium	Nb	41	92.9064	92.9
Nitrogen	N	7	14.0067	14.0
Nobelium	No	102	(254)	–
Osmium	Os	76	190.2	190.2
Oxygen	O	8	15.9994	16.0
Palladium	Pd	46	106.4	106.4
Phosphorus	P	15	30.97376	31.0
Platinum	Pt	78	195.09	195.1
Plutonium	Pu	94	(242)	–
Polonium	Po	84	(210)	–
Potassium	K	19	39.0983	39.1
Praseodymium	Pr	59	140.9077	140.9
Promethium	Pm	61	(145)	–
Protactinium	Pa	91	231.0359	231.0
Radium	Ra	88	226.0254	226.0
Radon	Rn	86	(222)	–
Rhenium	Re	75	186.207	186.2
Rhodium	Rh	45	102.9055	102.9
Rubidium	Rb	37	85.4678	85.5
Ruthenium	Ru	44	101.07	101.1

Element	Symbol	Atomic Number	Atomic Mass	
Europium	Eu	63	151.96	152.0
Fermium	Fm	100	(253)	—
Fluorine	F	9	18.998103	19.0
Francium	Fr	87	(223)	—
Gadolinium	Gd	64	157.25	157.3
Gallium	Ga	31	69.72	69.7
Germanium	Ge	32	72.59	72.6
Gold	Au	79	196.9665	197.0
Hafnium	Hf	72	178.49	178.5
Hahnium	Ha	105	(260)	—
Helium	He	2	4.00260	4.00
Holmium	Ho	67	164.9304	164.9
Hydrogen	H	1	1.0079	1.01
Indium	In	49	114.82	114.8
Iodine	I	53	126.9045	126.9
Iridium	Ir	77	192.22	192.2
Iron	Fe	26	55.847	55.8
Krypton	Kr	36	83.80	83.8
Kurchatovium	Ku	104	(247)	—
Lanthanum	La	57	138.9055	138.9
Lawrencium	Lr	103	(257)	—
Lead	Pb	82	207.2	207.2
Lithium	Li	3	6.941	6.94
Lutetium	Lu	71	174.97	175.0
Magnesium	Mg	12	24.305	24.3
Manganese	Mn	25	54.9380	54.9
Samarium	Sm	62	150.4	150.4
Scandium	Sc	21	44.9559	45.0
Selenium	Se	34	78.96	79.0
Silicon	Si	14	28.0855	28.1
Silver	Ag	47	107.868	107.9
Sodium	Na	11	22.98977	23.0
Strontium	Sr	38	87.62	87.6
Sulfur	S	16	32.06	32.1
Tantalum	Ta	73	180.9479	180.9
Technetium	Tc	43	98.9062	98.9
Tellurium	Te	52	127.60	127.6
Terbium	Tb	65	158.9254	158.9
Thallium	Tl	81	204.37	204.4
Thorium	Th	90	232.0381	232.0
Thulium	Tm	69	168.9342	168.9
Tin	Sn	50	118.69	118.7
Titanium	Ti	22	47.90	47.9
Tungsten	W	74	183.85	183.9
Uranium	U	92	238.029	238.0
Vanadium	V	23	50.9444	50.9
Xenon	Xe	54	131.30	131.3
Ytterbium	Yb	70	173.04	173.0
Yttrium	Y	39	88.9059	88.9
Zinc	Zn	30	65.38	65.4
Zirconium	Zr	40	91.22	91.2
Name to be determined		106	(263)	—

[a]Based on carbon-12. Numbers in parentheses are the mass numbers of the most stable or best-known isotopes.

having atomic weights less than 10. We'll round the latter to two decimal places. Table 3.2 gives rounded values as well as full measured values. Gram-atomic weights can also be found in the tables inside the covers of this book.

atomic weight

The mass of a single "average" atom is expressed in atomic mass units, and is called the *atomic weight*. We can obtain the atomic weights of the elements just by taking the values in Table 3.2 to be atomic mass units. Chemists often speak of "atomic weight" when they mean "gram-atomic weight." This usually doesn't cause confusion, because their values are the same. Of course, the term "weight" is incorrect in both cases, since both refer to mass. However, "atomic weight" and "gram-atomic weight" have become so common in the working vocabulary of chemistry that any attempt to change would be futile. In these cases, we understand that "weight" means "mass."

Now that we know the mass of a mole of each element, we can do problems like the egg problem of Example 3.3.

EXAMPLE 3.7: How many moles are in 156 grams of carbon?

Solution:

Step 1: We want to convert 156 grams of carbon to moles.

$$156 \text{ g C} = \text{\_\_\_\_ moles}$$

Step 2: Our conversion factor is the atomic weight of carbon, which we get from Table 3.2. This is 12.0 g C/mole. We invert it to 1.00 mole/12.0 g C.

Step 3:

$$156 \text{ g C} \times \frac{1.00 \text{ mole}}{12.0 \text{ g C}} = \text{\_\_\_\_ moles}$$

The units are correct.

Answer: 13.0 moles.

EXAMPLE 3.8: How many grams are in 0.652 moles of chlorine atoms?

Solution:

Step 1: We want to convert 0.652 moles of Cl to grams.

$$0.652 \text{ moles Cl} = \text{\_\_\_\_ g}$$

Step 2: Our conversion factor, from Table 3.2, is 35.5 g/mole Cl.

Step 3:

$$0.652 \text{ moles Cl} \times 35.5 \frac{\text{g}}{\text{mole Cl}} = \text{\_\_\_\_ g}$$

The units check.

Answer: 23.1 grams.

3.3 TEMPERATURE AND HEAT

The elements' numerical properties of melting point, boiling point, and specific heat all depend on the key concepts of temperature and heat. The two go hand in hand: we can't change the temperature of something without also changing the amount of heat it has. But even though temperature and heat depend on each other, there is a difference between how hot something is (temperature) and how much heat it has (heat). The filament in an electric light bulb is at a much higher temperature than a red-hot electric stove burner, but we'd cook something on the burner and not on the light bulb filament. This is because the burner has more heat than the filament, although the filament is at a higher temperature than the stove burner. We'll see a little later that this is because the burner has more mass than the filament.

Heat is easier to define than temperature. Heat is a kind of energy. We haven't really defined energy yet, but earlier we defined matter as anything that takes up space and requires energy to be moved. Thus energy is what we need to move matter around. Sometimes *energy* is defined as the ability to do work. When we move matter around, we're doing work. There's a direct connection between heat and moving matter around. We define *heat* as the energy associated with the random motions of atoms and molecules. Things are hot because their atoms or molecules are moving fast.

energy

heat

We usually define temperature in terms of heat. The relationship between temperature and heat is that heat will flow from a body at a higher temperature to a body at a lower temperature. If we fill a hot frying pan with cold water, the frying pan cools off and the water warms up. If we left them alone, pretty soon they would both be at the same temperature. Heat would flow from the frying pan to the water because the frying pan was at a higher temperature than the water. We can define *temperature* as that quality of matter which causes heat to flow to or from it.

temperature

MEASURING TEMPERATURE WITH DEGREES.   Scientists
measure temperature with two scales: the *Celsius* (or centigrade) *scale* (C), and the *Kelvin* (or thermodynamic) *scale* (K). On the Celsius scale, the temperature at which water freezes is the 0° point, and the temperature at which water boils is the 100° point. (The symbol ° stands for "degree.") Between these two points are 100 divisions that measure degrees Celsius. A Celsius degree is thus 1/100 of the interval between the freezing point and the boiling point of water, and that's why it's also called the centigrade scale (*centi-* means "one hundredth"). The Kelvin scale is the official SI temperature scale. It's based on absolute zero, which is the lowest possible temperature and the temperature at which all motion stops ($-273.16°C$). The size of the Kelvin has been chosen to be the same size as the Celsius degree. As we'll see later, this makes it easy to convert between Kelvin and Celsius temperatures. Since the Kelvin scale has the lowest possible temperature as its zero point, we see that there's no such thing as a negative, or below zero, Kelvin temperature.

**Celsius
scale (C)**

**Kelvin
scale (K)**

The temperature scale commonly used in the U.S. at the time of this writing is the *Fahrenheit scale* (F). On it, the temperature at which water freezes is 32°F, and the temperature at which water boils is 212°F.

Right now we'll use the Celsius scale to describe melting and boiling

**Fahrenheit
scale (F)**

degree

points. The Kelvin scale will be used in Chapter 11 with gases. (A comparison of the three temperature scales, how to convert among them, and some practice problems are given in Appendix B.4, pp. 487–492.)

There's a difference between *temperature* and *degrees*. Degrees are used to measure temperature. If (or when) the United States changes to the Celsius scale, so that freezing weather starts at 0°C instead of 32°F, of course our weather won't get colder. Water freezes at the same point no matter what scale we use to measure that point. We do, however, express a certain temperature with different numbers of degrees according to the kind of thermometer we're using. The reason a temperature scale is necessary at all is so we can say something is at 10°C, or whatever, and people will understand us.

MEASURING HEAT WITH CALORIES.

In chemistry, we find it convenient to measure heat in calories. We use water as our standard of reference. One *calorie* (*cal* for short) is the amount of heat it takes to raise the temperature of one gram of water by one degree Celsius. In other words, if we had a sample of water weighing exactly 1.00 gram at a temperature of 14.5°C, we'd have to supply it with exactly 1.00 calorie to raise its temperature to 15.5°C. If we had 10.0 calories of heat available, we could either raise 1.00 gram of water 10.0°C or raise 10.0 grams of water 1.00°C. A larger unit of heat is the *kilocalorie* (*kcal* for short). A kilocalorie is 10^3 calories, or the amount of heat it takes to raise one kilogram of water by one degree Celsius. Neither of these units is an approved SI unit, but they are still used by chemists because of convenience. The proper SI unit is the *joule* (J), which is 0.239 calories.

calorie (cal)

kilocalorie (kcal)

joule (J)

We can use a formula to determine the number of calories needed to change the temperature of a given number of grams of water.

heat in calories = grams of water × temperature change in °C

EXAMPLE 3.9: You want to make a cup of tea. Your tap water is 21°C and you need to heat it to about 99°C. Your cup holds 230 grams of water. How many calories will it take to make the tea?

Solution: Use the formula.

Heat in calories = grams of water × temperature change in °C
Heat in calories = 230 g water × (99 − 21)°C
= 230 g water × 78°C

Answer: 1.8×10^4 calories, or 18 kilocalories.

The Calories that we count when we're trying to lose weight are really kilocalories. (Calories with a capital C means kilocalories.) Caloric values of foods are a measure of their available energy, and these values are measured by burning a sample of known weight. The amount of Calories given off when a sample of known weight is burned is the sample's caloric value. At first it might seem strange to find that something we think of as a unit of fat is really a unit of heat. This makes sense, though, since we "burn" the food in our bodies to make energy. If we consume more Calories' worth of food than we need to burn for energy, the extra energy is stored as future Calories (fat).

3.4 NUMERICAL PROPERTIES RELATED TO TEMPERATURE AND HEAT

Now that we know something about temperature and heat, we're ready to talk about melting point, boiling point, and specific heat—three numerical properties of the elements and of all substances.

MELTING POINT. The particles (atoms or molecules) of a solid are held together by attractive forces, which we'll be talking about in Chapter 10. Heating up a solid, such as a piece of ice, gives its molecules more energy and makes them move. Pretty soon they are moving fast enough to overcome the attractive forces that were holding them rigidly together in the solid. The temperature at which this happens is the *melting point* of the solid. When a liquid, such as water, is cooled, the reverse process happens. We take energy away from the molecules, and pretty soon the molecules are moving slowly enough for their attractive forces to hold them rigidly together again and form a solid. The temperature at which this happens is the *freezing point* of the liquid. Melting point and freezing point are really the same thing, approached from opposite directions. To melt a substance, we supply heat; to freeze it, we remove heat. While a solid is melting, its temperature stays constant at its melting point. Even though we keep heating a solid as it melts, we won't increase its temperature until all of the solid has changed to liquid. When a solid starts to melt, all of the heat that is put into it from then on goes into breaking up the attractive forces that hold the atoms or molecules together in the solid. When the solid is all melted, then the heat that is put in can once more go into increasing the temperature of the substance. The amount of heat that it takes to melt one gram of any substance at its melting point is called the *heat of fusion*. If we let the substance freeze, then it will give off heat in the amount of the heat of fusion. Freezing is a process that releases energy.

    Every substance has a melting (or freezing) point except diamond, which no one has been able to melt yet. The stronger the attractive forces that hold atoms or molecules together in the solid, the higher its melting (or freezing) point will be. The forces holding a diamond together in the solid state are so strong that they can't be overcome by heating. Most elements are solids at "room temperature," a vague term meaning a range of about 20°C to 30°C. A substance that's a solid at room temperature has a melting point higher than room temperature. Some substances are borderline, and they can be

melting point

freezing point

heat of fusion

either liquids or solids depending on the weather: we've all seen tar melt on a hot day. Olive oil will solidify (freeze) on a cold day. Table 3.3 shows the melting points of some elements.

BOILING POINT.

boiling point

In a liquid, the atoms or molecules are moving around, but there is still quite a bit of attraction among them. Heating a liquid, such as water, gives its molecules still more energy and makes them move even faster. When they are moving fast enough to overcome the attractive forces that keep them as a liquid, then they escape into the gas state. A liquid boils when its molecules escape into the gas state at the bottom of its container and form bubbles, which then rise to the top. This happens at the liquid's *boiling point*. While a liquid is boiling, its temperature stays at the boiling point no matter how much additional heat we supply. (See Figure 3.2.) As with melting, the heat that's put in goes into overcoming the molecules' attraction for each other. The amount of heat it takes to change

**TABLE 3.3
Numerical
properties
of selected
elements**

Element	Melting Point, °C	Boiling Point, °C	Specific Heat, cal/(g × °C)	Density, g/cm³ or g/l (for Gases)
Aluminum	660	2447	0.215	2.70
Argon	−189	−186	0.124	1.78[a]
Arsenic	817	613	0.0704	5.72
Barium	850	1537	0.068	3.59
Beryllium	1285	2970	0.436	1.86
Bismuth	271	1560	0.0303	9.80
Boron	2074	3675	0.252	2.48
Bromine	−7	59	0.107	3.12
Cadmium	321	767	0.0549	8.64
Calcium	851	1487	0.149	1.55
Carbon (graphite)	3550	3850	0.160	2.27
Cesium	29	670	0.048	1.88
Chlorine	−101	−34	0.115	2.98[a]
Chromium	1900	2640	0.110	7.20
Cobalt	1495	3550	0.109	8.90
Copper	1083	582	0.092	8.92
Fluorine	−220	−188	0.197	1.58[a]
Gallium	30	1980	0.080	5.91
Germanium	937	2830	0.074	5.32
Gold	1063	2707	0.031	19.3
Helium	−272	−269	1.24	0.18[a]
Hydrogen	−259	−253	3.41	0.0899[a]
Iodine	114	184	0.054	4.66
Iron	1530	3000	0.113	7.86
Krypton	−157	−153	0.059	3.74[a]

[a]Gas.

one gram of a liquid to a gas at its boiling point is the substance's *heat of vaporization*. The fact that energy is required to vaporize something lets you cool off on a hot day. You can get wet and let the water evaporate from your body. When the water changes to a gas (steam), it takes heat from your body, and your body cools off.

When a gas is cooled, it condenses (changes to a liquid) at its *condensation point*, which is the same temperature as the boiling point. When a gas condenses, it gives back the energy that it took to become a gas: its heat of vaporization. Thus both condensation and freezing are processes that give off heat. A steam burn is worse than a boiling water burn because steam gives off its heat of vaporization in addition to the heat it has because of being at 100°C.

If a substance's melting point is lower than room temperature, then it will be a liquid at room temperature. Table 3.3 shows that only two elements—bromine (melting point, −7°C; boiling point, 59°C) and mercury (melting point, −39°C; boiling point, 356°C)—are liquids at room temperature.

Element	Melting Point, °C	Boiling Point, °C	Specific Heat, cal/(g × °C)	Density, g/cm³ or g/l (for Gases)
Lead	327	1751	0.031	11.3
Lithium	179	1336	0.850	0.55
Magnesium	650	1117	0.243	1.74
Manganese	1244	2120	0.114	7.30
Mercury	−39	357	0.0331	13.6
Neon	−249	−246	0.246	0.900[a]
Nickel	1455	2840	0.106	8.90
Nitrogen	−210	−196	0.249	1.17[a]
Osmium	2727	4100	0.0313	22.6
Oxygen	−219	−183	0.219	1.33[a]
Phosphorus	44	280	0.190	1.82
Platinum	1774	3800	0.032	21.5
Potassium	64	758	0.188	0.87
Rubidium	39	700	0.086	1.53
Silicon	1415	2680	0.168	2.33
Silver	960	2177	0.0566	10.5
Sodium	98	883	0.293	0.97
Strontium	774	1366	0.0719	2.60
Sulfur	112	445	0.175	1.96
Tin	232	2687	0.0510	7.28
Titanium	1672	3260	0.142	4.51
Tungsten	3415	5000	0.034	19.4
Uranium	1132	3818	0.0276	19.1
Xenon	−112	−108	0.0378	5.90[a]
Zinc	419	907	0.0928	7.14

[a]Gas.

**FIGURE 3.2
Melting
and boiling
take place
at constant
temperatures**

0°C

Here's an experiment you can try at home, just like I'm doing. I'm melting some ice in this saucepan and taking its temperature. Right now I have a mixture of ice and water, and I'm stirring really well to make sure that it's always mixed. I'm really blasting it with heat—this burner is on full. But, as long as there is any ice left, the temperature stays at the melting point: 0°C.

100°C

This time I'm boiling some water. I still have the burner on full blast, and I see that I can't get the temperature above 100°C, which is the boiling point of water. I know that if I want to get water hotter than that, I have to use a pressure cooker. We'll see in Chapter 11 how a pressure cooker lets water boil at a temperature higher than 100°C.

Boiling points are usually measured relative to sea level. This is because they depend on atmospheric pressure, which varies at different altitudes. (We'll learn more about this in Chapter 11.) It takes longer to hard-boil an egg in the mountains than at the seashore, because water boils at a lower temperature at high altitudes. This is true of all other liquids as well. Figure 3.3 illustrates the changes from solid to liquid to gas.

✓ SPECIFIC HEAT.

If you're at the beach on a hot day, the sand might be so hot that you'd have to run to the water to keep from burning the bottoms of your feet. But the water might still be very cold. The water and the sand both received heat from the same sun, but the result is that the water is cold and the sand is hot. Water and sand have different abilities to store heat. Water can store more heat than sand without raising its temperature. Specific heat describes a substance's ability to store heat.

specific heat   *Specific heat* is the amount of heat that must be supplied to raise the temperature of a specific mass of a substance by a specified amount. In the metric system, the specific heat in calories is the number of calories needed to raise one gram of a substance one degree Celsius. The formula for finding specific heat is:

$$\text{specific heat} = \frac{\text{heat in calories}}{(\text{mass in grams}) \times (\text{temperature difference in °C})}$$

The units of specific heat are more interesting than some other units we've had so far. If we write the above equation in a more condensed form:

$$\text{specific heat} = \frac{\text{cal}}{\text{g} \times \text{°C}}$$

we see that the units are calories over grams times degrees Celsius, which we read, "calories per gram-degree."

To find the specific heat of water, we substitute 1.00 cal, 1.00 g, and 1.00°C into the formula and get 1.00 cal/(1.00 g × 1.00°C). This is because we used water to define the calorie in the first place. But other substances can have different specific heats, as shown in Table 3.3.

We can also express specific heat in terms of kilocalories and kilograms, as "kilocalories per kilogram-degree." The values in Table 3.3 can also be ex-

FIGURE 3.3   Conversion of solid to liquid to gas requires energy

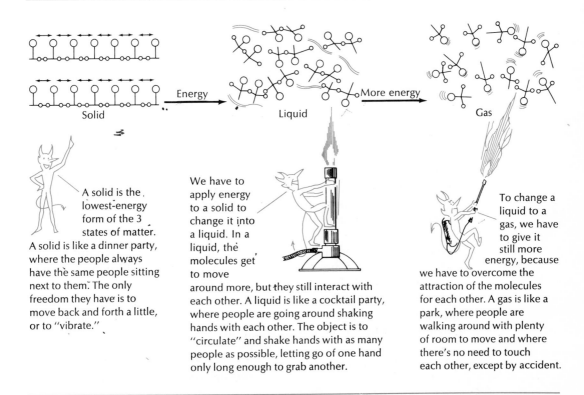

Solid   Energy →   Liquid   More energy →   Gas

A solid is the lowest-energy form of the 3 states of matter. A solid is like a dinner party, where the people always have the same people sitting next to them. The only freedom they have is to move back and forth a little, or to "vibrate."

We have to apply energy to a solid to change it into a liquid. In a liquid, the molecules get to move around more, but they still interact with each other. A liquid is like a cocktail party, where people are going around shaking hands with each other. The object is to "circulate" and shake hands with as many people as possible, letting go of one hand only long enough to grab another.

To change a liquid to a gas, we have to give it still more energy, because we have to overcome the attraction of the molecules for each other. A gas is like a park, where people are walking around with plenty of room to move and where there's no need to touch each other, except by accident.

pressed as kilocalories per kilogram-degree if this is more useful in solving a problem.

We can rearrange the specific heat equation like this:

heat in calories
= (specific heat) × (mass in grams) × (temperature change in °C)

This equation says that the amount of heat a substance can store depends on its specific heat, its mass, and the temperature difference. Now we can understand why the red-hot stove burner has more heat than the light bulb filament, even when the light bulb filament is at a higher temperature.

EXAMPLE 3.10: A light bulb filament made of tungsten weighs 1.00 gram and has a temperature of 1500°C. Calculate the amount of heat in calories released when the filament is cooled to 20°C.

Solution: In Table 3.3, the specific heat of tungsten is 0.034 cal/(g × °C). Substituting into the above equation gives us:

$$\text{Heat in calories} = 0.034 \frac{\text{cal}}{g \times °C} \times 1.00 \, g \times (1500 - 20) °C$$

The units below the line cancel with those above the line (g, °C).

Answer: 50 calories.

EXAMPLE 3.11: An electric stove burner made of iron weighs 750 grams and has a temperature of 550°C. Calculate the amount of heat in calories released when the burner is cooled to 20°C.

Solution: In Table 3.3, the specific heat of iron is 0.113 cal/(g × °C). Substituting into the equation gives us:

$$\text{Heat in cal} = 0.113 \frac{\text{cal}}{g \times °C} \times 750 \, g \times (550 - 20) °C$$

Answer: 4.5×10^4 calories, or 45 kilocalories.

The stove burner releases roughly a hundred times more calories than the tungsten filament. In this case, the larger mass of the burner is what gives it more heat. If we were comparing two substances of the same mass, then the one with the higher specific heat would have more heat.

Why is water used as a cooling agent—in automobile radiators, electronics industries, and chemical plants? Is it just because it's plentiful, cheap, and nontoxic? These are all good reasons, but another really good reason is water's high specific heat. Of the elements, only hydrogen and helium have higher specific heats than water. Water is a better cooling agent than antifreeze (ethylene glycol). We can illustrate this with still another rearrangement of the specific heat equation:

$$\text{temperature change in °C} = \frac{\text{heat in cal (or kcal)}}{\text{specific heat} \times \text{mass in g (or kg)}}$$

EXAMPLE 3.12:   Calculate the temperature change in 5 kg of water used to fill a radiator when 100 kcal of heat is supplied to it.

Solution: We substitute into the equation:

$$\text{temp. change in } °C = \frac{100 \text{ kcal}}{[1.00 \text{ kcal}/(\text{kg} \times °C)] \times 5 \text{ kg}} \qquad \left[\text{Note that } \frac{1}{(1/°C)} = °C\right]$$

Answer: 20°C. (See Appendix B, p. 482, for a discussion of inverting reciprocals.)

EXAMPLE 3.13:   Calculate the temperature change in 5 kg of ethylene glycol [specific heat 0.544 kcal/(kg × °C)] used to fill a radiator when 100 kcal of heat is supplied to it.

Solution: The specific heat of ethylene glycol is 0.544 kcal/(kg × °C). We substitute into the equation:

$$\text{temp. change in } °C = \frac{100 \text{ kcal}}{[0.544 \text{ kcal}/(\text{kg} \times °C)] \times 5 \text{ kg}}$$

Answer: 40°C.

We see that water is about twice as good a cooling agent as straight antifreeze.

Places that are near oceans or large lakes have more moderate climates than places far away from bodies of water. Why? Again, the high specific heat of water. Water's high specific heat causes it to resist changes in temperature. Globally, this serves the purpose of keeping our planet at relatively constant temperatures in spite of the alternation of sunlight and darkness. Later, we'll see what molecular characteristics of water cause it to have this conveniently high specific heat.

3.5 DENSITY

Fifty people jammed into an elevator will be more crowded than ten people in the same elevator. The elevator will also weigh more with fifty people in it than with ten people. The density of people in the first elevator is greater than the density of people in the second elevator. Also, if we compared two elevators—one with fifty fat people in it, and one with fifty skinny people in it—the one with the fifty fat people in it would weigh more.

The density of an element or other substance describes how closely its mass is packed into a given volume. This depends on the masses of the individual atoms and on how closely packed they are. When we talk about something being "light" or "heavy," we're talking about its density (see Figure 3.4). We define *density* as mass per unit volume. Or for liquids and solids, according to the metric system:

density

$$\text{density} = \frac{\text{mass in grams}}{\text{volume in cm}^3}$$

For gases, in metric system measurement, we can express density in the following way:

$$density = \frac{mass\ in\ grams}{volume\ in\ liters}$$

The densities of liquids and solids are expressed in grams per cubic centimeter (g/cm³) or grams per milliliter (g/ml). The two are the same,

FIGURE 3.4
How density works

I've poured 50 cubic centimeters of water and of mercury into each of two beakers. Of course, they don't balance, because the density of mercury is 13.6 times the density of water. Equal volumes don't have the same mass.

WATER : Density, 1.00 g/cm³
MERCURY : Density, 13.6 g/cm³

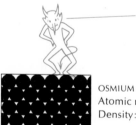

Mercury, though, is still a "lightweight" compared with osmium here. With its density of 22.6, osmium is the most dense element. Its atoms are very tightly packed together. More of them can get into a space.

OSMIUM
Atomic mass: 190.2 amu
Density: 22.6 g/cm³

Even though mercury atoms have more mass than osmium atoms, mercury is less dense than osmium because its atoms are less closely packed.

MERCURY
Atomic mass: 200.6 amu
Density: 13.6 g/cm³

because a cubic centimeter equals a milliliter. The densities of gases, which are much lighter than liquids or solids, are expressed in grams per liter (g/l).

EXAMPLE 3.14: What is the density of copper if 11.8 cm³ of it has a mass of 105.2 g?

Solution: Use the formula, density = mass/volume. Then:

$$\text{Density} = \frac{105.2 \text{ g}}{11.8 \text{ cm}^3}$$

Answer: 8.92 g/cm³.

EXAMPLE 3.15: What is the density of chlorine gas if 2.60 liters of it have a mass of 7.75 grams?

Solution: Use the density formula:

$$\text{Density} = \frac{7.75 \text{ g}}{2.60 \text{ l}}$$

Answer: 2.98 g/l.

Densities of some of the elements appear in Table 3.3, and Table 3.4 compares the densities of various elements with densities of other substances. Since a gram is defined as the mass of 1 cm³ of water (at 4°C), the density of water, by definition, is exactly 1 g/cm³. The densities of other substances tell how much more dense or less dense the substance is than water. Anything less dense than water ("lighter" than water) will float on water; any-

TABLE 3.4
Densities of some common substances[a]

Solids	Density, g/cm³	Liquids	Density, g/cm³	Gases	Density, g/l
Cork	0.21	Gasoline	0.70	Hydrogen	0.090
Lithium	0.54	Ethyl alcohol	0.79	Helium	0.18
Paper	0.70	Water (4°C)	1.00	Methane	0.72
Butter	0.86	Glycerine	1.26	Ammonia	0.77
Ice	0.92	Carbon		Neon	0.90
Sugar	1.59	tetrachloride	1.60	Carbon monoxide	1.25
Salt	2.16	Sulfuric acid	1.84	Nitrogen	1.17
Granite	2.60	Mercury	13.6	Air	1.29
Cement	2.70			Oxygen	1.33
Glass	2.50			Hydrogen chloride	1.63
Aluminum	2.70			Argon	1.78
Iron	7.86			Carbon dioxide	1.96
Copper	8.92			Chlorine	2.98
Lead	11.3				
Gold	19.3				
Osmium	22.6				

[a]Densities of liquids and solids are at 20°C, except for water and ice. Gases are at 0°C and 1 atmosphere.

Hmm—I see that helium doesn't make a good paperweight!

HELIUM PAPERWEIGHT

WHOOSH

HELIUM IS LESS DENSE THAN AIR.

JUMP

Ow! This experiment went over like a lead balloon!

SPLAT

LEAD IS MORE DENSE THAN AIR.

Good thing ice is less dense than water. Otherwise, it wouldn't be on top—and neither would I!

I'm making vinegar-and-oil salad dressing. As I pour this oil in, it'll sit on the top of the vinegar in a layer. That's because its density is less than the density of vinegar.

thing more dense ("heavier") will sink. It's the same with air, whose density is 1.29 g/l. Anything less dense than air ("lighter" than air) will rise in air; anything more dense ("heavier") will sink. (See Figure 3.5.)

Density is really another conversion factor. It lets us convert mass to volume and vice versa if we know what the substance is. We can invert it, too, as we can any conversion factor. For example, a density of 2.25 g/cm³ can be inverted as 1.00 cm³/2.25 g.

EXAMPLE 3.16: A backpacker wants to take a half liter (500 milliliters) of ethyl alcohol on his trip to see him through those cold mountain evenings. How much mass, in grams, will this add to his pack, excluding the container?

Solution:

Step 1: We want to convert 500 milliliters to grams.

$$500 \text{ ml} = \underline{\hspace{1cm}} \text{ g}$$

Step 2: Our conversion factor, from Table 3.4, is 0.79 g/cm³, the density of ethyl alcohol. Also, we need to recognize that a cubic centimeter is the same as a milliliter, so we use the conversion factor 1.00 cm³/ml.

Step 3:

$$500 \text{ ml} \times 1.00 \, \frac{\text{cm}^3}{\text{ml}} \times 0.79 \, \frac{\text{g}}{\text{cm}^3} = \underline{\hspace{1cm}} \text{ g}$$

The units are correct.

Answer: 400 g.

A useful feature of the metric system is that a density that's expressed in grams per cubic centimeter (g/cm³) can also be expressed in kilograms per liter (kg/l), with the same number. This is because we're multiplying the top and bottom of the factor by 10³.

EXAMPLE 3.17: Express a density of 3.73 g/cm³ in kilograms/liter (kg/l).

Solution:

Step 1: We want to convert 3.73 g/cm³ to kilograms/liter (kg/l).

$$3.73 \, \frac{\text{g}}{\text{cm}^3} = \underline{\hspace{1cm}} \frac{\text{kg}}{\text{l}}$$

Step 2: Our conversion factors (from Appendix Table B.4, p. 483) are 1.00 cm³/ml, 10³ ml/l, and 1 kg/10³ g.

Step 3:

$$3.73 \, \frac{\text{g}}{\text{cm}^3} \times 1.00 \, \frac{\text{cm}^3}{\text{ml}} \times 10^3 \, \frac{\text{ml}}{\text{l}} \times \frac{1.00 \text{ kg}}{10^3 \text{ g}} = \underline{\hspace{1cm}} \frac{\text{kg}}{\text{l}}$$

The units are correct.

Answer: 3.73 kg/l.

EXAMPLE 3.18: In early times, it was customary for underlords to pay homage to their king once a year by giving him his weight in gold. Kings often stuffed themselves with food just to be ready for this event. How many liters would be occupied by enough gold to buy the good graces of a 105-kilogram king?

Solution:

Step 1: We want to convert 105 kilograms of gold to liters of gold.

$$105 \text{ kg} = \underline{\hspace{1cm}} \text{ l}$$

Step 2: Our conversion factor is the density of gold, 19.3 g/cm³. As we showed in Example 3.17, this can also be written as 19.3 kg/l. We invert it to 1.00 l/19.3 kg to make the proper units cancel.

Step 3:

$$105 \text{ kg} \times \frac{1.00 \text{ l}}{19.3 \text{ kg}} = \underline{\hspace{1cm}} \text{ l}$$

The units are correct.

Answer: 5.44 l.

REVIEW QUESTIONS

Weighing as a Means of Counting

1. Why must we weigh atoms in order to count them?
2. What is a *mole?* Why do we need it in chemistry?
3. Express the mole both with and without exponential notation.
4. What are some metric units used in chemistry?
5. Explain how we can know the number of something without counting.

Gram-Atomic Weight

6. What is *gram-atomic weight?*
7. What is a unit? What is a conversion factor? How are they used?
8. What is *Avogadro's number?*
9. What is the chemist's *atomic weight?* Why are these atomic weights often not whole numbers?
10. Explain how atomic weight may be used as a conversion factor.

Temperature and Heat

11. How are *temperature* and *heat* related? How are they different?
12. What is *energy?* In what sense is heat a kind of energy?
13. Describe the three types of temperature scales.
14. What is the difference between temperature and *degrees?*
15. Which temperature scale is used to describe melting and boiling points?
16. What is a *calorie?* How are calories determined?
17. What are the Calories we count when we're dieting?

Numerical Properties Related to Temperature and Heat

18. What is *melting point?* What happens when something melts?
19. What is *freezing point?* What happens when something freezes?
20. Explain why heat is given off when something freezes.
21. What is room temperature? If something has a melting point above room temperature, is it a solid or a liquid?
22. Are most elements liquids, solids, or gases?
23. What is *boiling point?* What happens when something boils?
24. Why does the temperature remain constant at the melting and boiling points?
25. Explain why heat is given off when a gas condenses to a liquid.
26. How can you tell from a substance's melting and boiling points whether or not it is a liquid at room temperature?
27. Explain the difference between a solid, a liquid, and a gas.
28. What is *specific heat?* How is it related to the definition of the calorie?
29. What three factors determine how much heat an object has?
30. Why is water a good cooling agent? How does it help to keep the earth's climate relatively constant?

Density

31. What is *density?* Give the formula for calculating density.
32. In the metric system, what units do we use to express the density of solids, liquids, and gases?
33. What two factors determine the density of an element?
34. By definition, what is the density of water?
35. Will an object less dense than water float or sink on water?
36. Will an object more dense than air rise or sink in air?
37. Explain why we can express density in kilograms/liter with the same number we use for grams/cubic centimeter.

EXERCISES

1. Calculate the weight, in grams, of a dozen doughnuts, if each doughnut weighs 225 grams.
2. A dozen apples weighs 1.4 kg. How many kilograms will 2.5 dozen apples weigh?
3. A mole of hydrogen atoms weigh 1.01 grams. How many grams will 2.50 moles of hydrogen atoms weigh?
4. A mole of sodium atoms weighs 23.0 grams. How many grams will 10.0 moles of sodium atoms weigh?

5. Since hydrogen exists as diatomic molecules, how much will a mole of hydrogen molecules weigh?
6. Using the table of atomic weights (Table 3.2), make the following conversions.
   a. 10.0 moles of mercury to grams
   b. 4.00 grams of calcium to moles
   c. 0.500 moles of potassium to grams
   d. 354 grams of chlorine atoms to moles
   e. 1.00 moles of argon to grams
   f. 40.2 grams of neon to moles
7. A swimming pool contains 8×10^4 kg of water at 10°C. How many kilocalories are needed to heat the water to 25°C?

Consult Table 3.3 to answer Exercises 8 through 23.

8. What element in Table 3.3 has the largest liquid range; that is, the largest temperature span between its solid and gas states? What element has the smallest liquid range?
9. Why do you think tungsten, and no other metal, is used for electric light bulb filaments?
10. Thermometers containing alcohol instead of mercury have to be used below −39°C. Explain.
11. Compare the melting points of the Group IA and IIA metals and make a statement about their relative melting points.
12. How do the melting points of the first-row transition elements compare with the melting points of the Group IA and IIA metals?
13. What element on Table 3.3 has the highest melting point? The lowest?
14. If an iron frying pan weighing 2.5 kg is cooled from 210°C to 23°C, how many kilocalories will be released from it?
15. Five hundred calories of heat are supplied to 10-gram samples of both copper and aluminum. How many degrees Celsius does the temperature of each element change? Which element is better able to maintain a constant temperature (for example, in providing even heat to a cooking pot)?
16. What element on Table 3.3 has the lowest specific heat? The highest?
17. How many calories would be needed to heat 155 grams of zinc from 35.2°C to 58.4°C?

18. A 5.49-gram sample of a certain metal occupies 3.16 cm³. What is its density? What is the metal?
19. How many grams would 10.5 cm³ of bromine weigh?
20. Calculate the weight of 22.4 liters of argon.
21. How many cubic centimeters would be occupied by 95.2 grams of osmium?
22. How many liters would 4.00 grams of helium occupy?
23. Taking into account density and reactivity, select a metal that might make a good racing bicycle.
24. If 952 calories are supplied to 155 grams of water at 20.°C, what will its final temperature be?

Consult both Tables 3.3 and 3.4 to answer Exercises 25 through 31.

25. Choose some gases that could be used to float a balloon in air.
26. Explain why you can float in saltwater better than you can in pure water.
27. Oil spills on oceans can be cleaned up (with difficulty). How do the relative densities of oil and seawater explain this?
28. Name a substance that will not float on mercury.
29. If a fire extinguisher containing carbon dioxide were fired straight ahead, would the vapors rise to the ceiling or sink to the floor? Explain.
30. An airplane is in trouble and has to dump 2 metric tons (each 1000 kg) of its cargo, which is ethyl alcohol. About how many liters of ethyl alcohol will they have to dump?
31. To make her cooking easier, Grandma said, "A pint's a pound, the world around." In the metric system, we could translate this saying into, "A liter's a kilo, from Oshkosh to Hilo." Make some density observations, using butter, water, salt, and sugar, to prove or disprove Grandma's statement.
32. A method of storing heat from nuclear power plants during low-demand periods and using it in high-demand periods has been proposed that takes advantage of a substance's heat of fusion. The proposed process involves the melting and freezing of a substance, sodium nitrate. Explain how this might work.

4

Formulas and Names of Compounds

We saw in Chapter 2 that a compound is a substance made of more than one element, in which the atoms are joined by chemical bonds. There are over three million chemical compounds known today, and new ones are constantly being prepared and catalogued. Each compound has a name and a formula that describe it and let us know what particular compound we're talking about.

When we're talking about one person to another person, we'll have better luck getting across who we're talking about if we give the person's name, "Harry Robinson," instead of saying, "You know, the guy with blond hair who was talking to Sadie Smith at Louie's party." In the same way, if we wanted to buy a certain chemical compound, or discuss it in any way, we'd be better off giving its name, "hydrogen chloride," instead of saying, "You know, the colorless gas that burns your lungs and dissolves so well in water."

No one who is studying chemistry looks forward to the exercise of learning names and formulas of compounds. But, it could be worse. If names of chemicals were assigned as arbitrarily as names of people, learning them all would be a really discouraging and time-consuming activity. In the early days of chemistry, names were assigned according to how chemicals looked or what they did, or for various other reasons. As the number of known compounds grew, though, chemists had to figure out a more systematic way of naming them. This systematic way is what we use today. A lot of chemicals are still called by their nonsystematic or *common names*. We already know a lot of these common names. Table 4.1 shows some of them with their systematic names and formulas.

common name

The *formula* of a compound tells what elements are in it and the proportion, atom-for-atom or mole-for-mole, among those elements. For instance, the formula H_2SO_4 means that any sample of this particular compound (called sulfuric acid) contains the elements hydrogen, sulfur, and oxygen in the proportion two atoms of hydrogen to one atom of sulfur to four atoms of oxygen. It also means that one mole of the compound contains two moles of hydrogen, one mole of sulfur, and four moles of oxygen. If there is no subscript, "1" is understood.

formula

The *systematic name* of a compound tells what its formula is by using a certain set of rules, which we'll learn in this chapter. A different set of rules is

systematic name

TABLE 4.1
Common names, formulas, and systematic names of some familiar substances

Common Name	Formula	Systematic Name
Baking soda (bicarbonate of soda)	$NaHCO_3$	Sodium hydrogen carbonate
Washing soda	$Na_2CO_3 \cdot 10\,H_2O$	Sodium carbonate decahydrate
Milk of magnesia	$Mg(OH)_2$	Magnesium hydroxide
Lye	$NaOH$	Sodium hydroxide
Potash	K_2CO_3	Potassium carbonate
Borax	$Na_2B_4O_7 \cdot 10\,H_2O$	Sodium tetraborate decahydrate
Cream of tartar	$KHC_4H_4O_6$	Potassium hydrogen tartrate
Lime	CaO	Calcium oxide
Slaked lime	$Ca(OH)_2$	Calcium hydroxide
Table salt	$NaCl$	Sodium chloride

used according to whether the compound we want to name is ionic or covalent.

4.1 IONIC AND COVALENT COMPOUNDS

We'll be learning a lot more about ionic and covalent compounds in Chapters 7 and 8. Right now we want to know the basic differences between them and how to tell which is which, so we can name them properly.

Ionic compounds are made of *ions*. An ion is an electrically charged particle originating from one or more atoms. The charge comes about when an atom gains or loses electrons, so that it has more or fewer electrons than protons. *Negative ions* have more electrons than protons; *positive ions* have fewer electrons than protons. An ion may have a charge of more than one, and we write the charge in the upper right-hand corner of its symbol. A lone plus or minus sign, with no number, means a charge of one. Some examples are Na^+, Mg^{2+}, Al^{3+}, Cl^-, S^{2-}, N^{3-}. Usually metals form positive ions and nonmetals form negative ions.

ionic compounds

ions

negative ion

positive ion

An ionic compound is made of both positive ions (usually metals) and negative ions (usually nonmetals). The attractive force between unlike-charged particles is what holds an ionic compound together. The ions combine in such a way that the positive charges and negative charges exactly cancel (or to be precise, neutralize) each other. We say that such a compound is electrically neutral. For instance, the compound made of the ions Na^+ and Cl^- is NaCl. One plus charge neutralizes one minus charge. If we were given the formula NaCl (sodium chloride, or table salt), we'd know that it was ionic because we'd locate sodium on the periodic table and find it among the metals, whereas chlorine is found among the nonmetals.

Covalent compounds are molecules. Molecules have no electrical charge, and they are made of two or more atoms joined together. To make a compound, the atoms have to be different. For instance, water molecules, H_2O, each contain two hydrogen atoms and one oxygen atom. Covalent compounds usually form between two nonmetals. We know that H_2O is covalent because we find both hydrogen and oxygen among the nonmetals.

covalent compound

All of the rules for naming compounds depend on being able to tell whether a compound is ionic or covalent.

4.2 NAMES AND FORMULAS OF BINARY COMPOUNDS

A *binary compound* is one that's made of only two different elements (*bi-* means "two"). The examples NaCl and H_2O are both binary compounds.

binary compound

Although H_2O has three atoms per molecule, it has only two different kinds of atoms, H and O. We can have binary ionic compounds or binary covalent compounds. There are differences in how these two kinds are named, but they have one thing in common: All binary compounds, whether ionic or covalent, end in the suffix *-ide*.

BINARY COVALENT COMPOUNDS (OXIDES, ACIDS, AND OTHERS).

Since a covalent compound is one between non-metals, the elements that will participate in covalent compounds are only those to the right of the staircase-shaped line on the periodic table. There are several systems for naming covalent compounds. For now, we'll introduce just one. This system uses Greek prefixes to tell how many of each kind of atom there are. Table 4.2 shows the prefixes with some examples.

Using this Greek system, the name of the first element in the formula comes first, preceded by an appropriate prefix (where there is no chance for ambiguity, the prefix *mono-* is usually left off). Then comes the prefix for the second element, followed by its root name, and finished off by the suffix *-ide*. Table 4.3 gives some nonmetallic elements with their roots shown in italics, and also their roots plus *-ide*.

■ **EXAMPLE 4.1:** The compound P_4S_3 is used commercially to make match heads. Write its name.

Solution: We see that both phosphorus and sulfur are nonmetals. Looking in Tables 4.2 and 4.3 for appropriate prefixes and roots, and remembering that the name must end in *-ide,* we can write the name.

Answer: Tetraphosphorus trisulfide.

■ **EXAMPLE 4.2:** The compound carbon tetrachloride was used as a cleaning fluid until breathing the fumes was shown to cause liver damage. Write its formula.

TABLE 4.2
Greek prefixes and their use

Number of Atoms	Prefix	Sample	Name
1	*mono-*	CO	Carbon monoxide
2	*di-*	CO_2	Carbon dioxide
3	*tri-*	BF_3	Boron trifluoride
4	*tetra-*	N_2O_4	Dinitrogen tetroxide[a]
5	*penta-*	PCl_5	Phosphorus pentachloride
6	*hexa-*	SF_6	Sulfur hexafluoride
7	*hepta-*	Cl_2O_7	Dichlorine heptoxide[a]

Examples beyond seven are rare.

[a]Where an element root begins with a vowel, the a on the end of the Greek prefix is dropped for ease of pronunciation.

TABLE 4.3 **61**

Element, Root in Italics	Root	Root + -ide
Hydrogen	Hydr-	Hydride
Oxygen	Ox-	Oxide
Phosphorus	Phosph-	Phosphide
Sulfur	Sulf-	Sulfide
Nitrogen	Nitr-	Nitride
Chlorine	Chlor-	Chloride
Fluorine	Fluor-	Fluoride
Bromine	Brom-	Bromide
Iodine	Iod-	Iodide
Carbon	Carb-	Carbide

TABLE 4.3
Some
nonmetal names
and roots

Solution: We write first the symbol for carbon, C, and then the symbol for chlorine, Cl. The prefix *tetra-* means that there are four chlorines.

Answer: CCl_4.

One important class of binary covalent compounds is the set of the oxides of various nonmetals. An *oxide* is a compound of any element with oxygen. As we go through a few of them, we'll see that some are still known to us by their common names. Chemists would rather that everyone used systematic names, but many nonchemists (especially advertisers) don't pay any attention. We'll also see that the use of the prefix *mono-* usually depends on how many oxides of a particular element there are and what their numbers are.

oxide

EXAMPLE 4.3: There are two oxides of hydrogen: water, H_2O; and hydrogen peroxide, H_2O_2. Both of these names are common names. What are the systematic names?

Solution: Looking at the chart of Greek prefixes, we select the prefixes *mono-* and *di-* to distinguish these two oxides.

Answer: H_2O, dihydrogen monoxide; H_2O_2, dihydrogen dioxide.

EXAMPLE 4.4: There are two important oxides of carbon. One of them, carbon monoxide, is a poisonous gas that's part of automobile exhaust. It's poisonous because it reacts with the hemoglobin in blood and prevents the blood from carrying oxygen. Write the formula for carbon monoxide.

Solution: No prefix for carbon means one carbon; *mono-* means one oxygen.

Answer: CO.

EXAMPLE 4.5: The other oxide of carbon is carbon dioxide. This is a gas found in the atmosphere. It's a product of the burning of most fuels and of animal respiration. Write its formula.

Solution: Consult the table of Greek prefixes.

Answer: CO_2.

EXAMPLE 4.6: The term "NO$_x$" refers to automobile emissions and means mainly a mixture of two oxides of nitrogen, NO and NO$_2$. Give systematic names for these.

Solution: Consult the table of Greek prefixes.

Answer: NO, nitrogen monoxide; NO$_2$, nitrogen dioxide.

EXAMPLE 4.7: "Laughing gas," a dental anesthetic, is yet another oxide of nitrogen, having the formula N$_2$O. Give its systematic name.

Answer: Dinitrogen monoxide.

EXAMPLE 4.8: Altogether there are six oxides of nitrogen. Besides the oxides given in previous examples, there are also dinitrogen trioxide, dinitrogen tetroxide, and dinitrogen pentoxide. Write their formulas.

Answer: Dinitrogen trioxide, N$_2$O$_3$; dinitrogen tetroxide, N$_2$O$_4$; dinitrogen pentoxide, N$_2$O$_5$.

EXAMPLE 4.9: There are two oxides of sulfur, both of which are gases and air pollutants. Their formulas are SO$_2$ and SO$_3$. Give their systematic names.

Answer: SO$_2$, sulfur dioxide; SO$_3$, sulfur trioxide.

EXAMPLE 4.10: Ammonia is the common name for the gas nitrogen trihydride. It's an ingredient in household ammonia and is also used as a refrigerant and as an ingredient in fertilizer. Write its formula.

Answer: NH$_3$.

Table 4.4 shows all the substances discussed in these examples, with their systematic and common names.

Except for water, hydrogen peroxide, and ammonia, many binary com-

**TABLE 4.4
Common and
systematic names
of some binary
covalent
compounds**

Formula	Common Name	Systematic Name	Comments
H$_2$O	Water	Dihydrogen monoxide	Vital earth fluid
H$_2$O$_2$	Hydrogen peroxide	Dihydrogen dioxide	Disinfectant, bleach
CO	—	Carbon monoxide	Poisonous gas in car exhaust
CO$_2$	—	Carbon dioxide	Gas produced by burning most fuels
N$_2$O	Nitrous oxide	Dinitrogen monoxide	"Laughing gas," anesthetic
NO	Nitric oxide	Nitrogen monoxide	Colorless gas; air pollutant
NO$_2$	—	Nitrogen dioxide	Brownish gas; air pollutant

pounds of hydrogen with a nonmetal can be named in two ways. One way is according to the system we've just learned. Another way is to name them as *acids*. We'll be talking much more about acids later, but for now we'll just say that an acid is a compound of hydrogen with one or more nonmetals. (The reverse isn't true, however. Not *all* hydrogen-nonmetal compounds are acids.) Here, we're talking about *binary acids,* so it's just hydrogen plus one other nonmetal. Binary acids are always written with the hydrogen first. The name of a binary acid always begins with the prefix *hydro-*, followed by the root of the nonhydrogen element, then the suffix *-ic* and *acid.* For instance, HCl could be called hydrogen chloride, according to the Greek system, or it could be called hydrochloric acid. Table 4.5 gives some binary acids, with their names in both systems. Notice that HCN, hydrocyanic acid, follows these rules even though it's not a binary acid. Every now and then we'll come across an exception like this.

EXAMPLE 4.11: Give two names for HBr.

Solution: HBr is a compound of hydrogen with a nonmetal, and H comes first. Thus it's a binary acid. Looking at Table 4.5, or following the rules for naming binary acids, we have the answer.

Answer: Hydrobromic acid, or hydrogen bromide.

EXAMPLE 4.12: Dihydrogen sulfide is a foul-smelling, colorless gas that is characteristic of rotten eggs. The odors of sewage gas and intestinal gas are also caused largely by dihydrogen sulfide. Write its formula and its acid name.

Solution: The prefix *di-* means that there are two hydrogen atoms. No prefix on "sulfide" means only one sulfur. We can determine the acid name by following the rules or by referring to Table 4.5.

Answer: H_2S, hydrosulfuric acid.

Formula	Common Name	Systematic Name	Comments
N_2O_3	—	Dinitrogen trioxide	—
N_2O_4	—	Dinitrogen tetroxide	Always found with NO_2
N_2O_5	—	Dinitrogen pentoxide	—
SO_2	—	Sulfur dioxide	Choking gas; air pollutant
SO_3	—	Sulfur trioxide	Air pollutant; used for making sulfuric acid
NH_3	Ammonia	Nitrogen trihydride	Refrigerant; used to make fertilizers and household ammonia

**TABLE 4.5
Formulas and
names of some
binary acids**

Formula	Name, as an Acid	Name, Greek System
HF	Hydrofluoric acid	Hydrogen fluoride
HCl	Hydrochloric acid	Hydrogen chloride
HBr	Hydrobromic acid	Hydrogen bromide
HI	Hydriodic acid[a]	Hydrogen iodide
HCN[b]	Hydrocyanic acid	Hydrogen cyanide
H_2S	Hydrosulfuric acid	Dihydrogen sulfide (hydrogen sulfide)

[a]Here, we drop the o before the vowel to aid pronunciation.
[b]HCN is not a binary acid, but it is named according to the rules for binary acids.

Sometimes this sort of thing happens. HCN behaves a lot like the others above it, and so chemists named it like the ones above it, even though it's not a binary acid.

monatomic ion

MONATOMIC IONS.

An ion that originates from a single atom is a *monatomic ion*. Binary ionic compounds are composed of monatomic ions, and we need to know how to name these ions before we can name the compounds. Since a binary ionic compound is a compound of a metal and a nonmetal, the elements that will participate in a binary ionic compound will be found one on each side of the staircase-shaped line in the periodic table. The metal is the positive ion and the nonmetal is the negative ion. The basic difference between naming covalent compounds and ionic compounds lies in the way that we tell how many of each element are in the compound. With covalent compounds, we used Greek prefixes, but we don't do this with ionic compounds. In fact, the name doesn't tell *directly* how many of each there are. We have to figure it out, as we'll see.

To name a binary ionic compound, we simply put the name of the positive ion, then the name of the negative ion, and drop the word "ion" for each. For instance, the substance NaCl, composed of a sodium ion and a chloride ion, is called "sodium chloride." Clearly, the hardest part of this is learning how to name the ions themselves.

Naming negative ions is easier, so we'll take it up first and then get on to the more complicated positive ions. Names of monatomic negative ions are the root of the nonmetal, plus *-ide*, plus the word "ion." This is something like naming covalent compounds, but to write the formulas for ions, we take account of *charge*. Different nonmetals form negative ions with different charges, depending on how many electrons they take on. There are rules for this, derived from the periodic table.

Rule 1. *The negative charge on an ion formed from Groups IVA, VA, VIA, and VIIA is equal to 8 minus the group number.*
Rule 2. *The negative ion formed from hydrogen has a charge of 1—.*

When writing the formula of an ion, write the charge in the upper right-hand corner, preceded by the number of the charge. No number means a charge of 1. Some examples of monatomic negative ions are:

Cl^-	Chloride ion
O^{2-}	Oxide ion
N^{3-}	Nitride ion
C^{4-}	Carbide ion
H^-	Hydride ion

That's all there is to the names and charges of monatomic negative ions: Each nonmetal forms only one ion with one charge. Some metals, though, can form more than one positive ion, by losing different numbers of electrons. Not all metals lose different numbers of electrons, so we'll start with the ones that don't.

Fixed-charge, positive ions are ions that have only one possible charge, which is always the same. We can lay down some rules for these as we did for the negative ions, based on the periodic table.

fixed-charge, positive ion

Rule 1. *Positive ions formed from Group IA metals have charges of 1+.*
Rule 2. *Positive ions formed from Group IIA metals have charges of 2+.*
Rule 3. *The positive ion formed from aluminum has a charge of 3+: Al^{3+}*
Rule 4. *The positive ions formed from zinc and cadmium have charges of 2+: Zn^{2+}, Cd^{2+}.*
Rule 5. *The positive ion formed from silver has a charge of 1+: Ag^+.*

The names of these fixed-charge ions are easy to learn. The element's name is simply followed by the word "ion." For example, Zn^{2+} is called zinc ion, and the formula for zinc ion is Zn^{2+}. Because of the rules for fixed-charge ions, there's no doubt about the zinc ion's charge. Another example: If someone says "barium ion," we'll know better than to say, "Bury who?" We'll know that's the name for Ba^{2+}, because barium is in Group IIA of the periodic table and so has a charge of 2+ by the above rules.

Variable-charge, positive ions are ions that may have several possible charges. Usually the transition metals form variable-charge ions. The most important ones are listed below, along with their charges.

variable-charge, positive ion

Iron (Fe)	2+, 3+	Copper (Cu)	1+, 2+
Chromium (Cr)	2+, 3+, 6+	Tin (Sn)	2+, 4+
Manganese (Mn)	2+, 3+, 4+, 7+	Lead (Pb)	2+, 4+
Cobalt (Co)	2+, 3+	Mercury (Hg)	1+, 2+
Nickel (Ni)	2+, 3+		

There are two systems for naming variable-charge ions: the old system and the Stock system. In the old system, the root of the metal's name is used, sometimes the root of its Latin name if it has one. The suffix *-ic* is added to the root if the ion has the higher charge of two possibilities; the suffix *-ous* is added for the lower charge. Here's part of the above list of metals in the old system:

Fe^{2+}	Ferrous ion	Cr^{3+}	Chromic ion
Fe^{3+}	Ferric ion	Cr^{6+}	What do we do with Cr^{6+}?
Cr^{2+}	Chromous ion		

The truth is that the old system breaks down with metals that can have more than two charges. For these, a metal's ions after the first two have to be ignored. The system was invented before all the ions were discovered, and it's called "old" because chemists no longer use it.

The system chemists use now, the Stock system, is actually easier than the old system, as well as being more practical. All it requires is the name of the metal, followed by the number of the charge in Roman numerals in parentheses, and finished off with the word "ion." Table 4.6 shows the Stock system names for some of the most important variable-charge ions. To read these names, we say, for example, "iron-two ion" for iron(II) ion. Since the Stock system is relatively simple and a lot more useful than the old system, it should come as no surprise that it's the one we'll use in this book. Figure 4.1 shows fixed- and variable-charge positive ions, as well as negative ions.

BINARY IONIC COMPOUNDS (OXIDES AND BINARY SALTS).
Now that we know the rules for naming positive and negative monatomic ions, we can put them together to make compounds. We said that the attraction between positive and negative ions is what holds an ionic compound together. We also said that ionic compounds are electrically neutral, so the total number of positive charges must exactly balance the total number of negative charges. When we write the formula or name of an ionic compound, we always put the metal ion first. The name is a combination of the names of the two ions, with the word "ion" dropped from both.

EXAMPLE 4.13: A compound made from sodium ions (Na^+) and fluoride ions (F^-) is used in water fluoridation. Write the formula of this compound and name it.

Solution: Each ion has a charge of 1, with opposite sign, so one of each

**TABLE 4.6
Names and
formulas of some
variable-charge
ions**

Formula	Variable-Charge Ion	Formula	Variable-Charge Ion
Fe^{2+}	Iron(II) ion	Fe^{3+}	Iron(III) ion
Cr^{2+}	Chromium(II) ion	Cr^{3+}	Chromium(III) ion
Cr^{6+}	Chromium(VI) ion		
Mn^{2+}	Manganese(II) ion	Mn^{3+}	Manganese(III) ion
Mn^{4+}	Manganese(IV) ion	Mn^{7+}	Manganese(VII) ion
Cu^+	Copper(I) ion	Cu^{2+}	Copper(II) ion
Sn^{2+}	Tin(II) ion	Sn^{4+}	Tin(IV) ion
Pb^{2+}	Lead(II) ion	Pb^{4+}	Lead(IV) ion
Hg_2^{2+}	Mercury(I) ion[a]	Hg^{2+}	Mercury(II) ion

[a]The reason why Hg_2^{2+} is called mercury(I) ion is given in Section 4.3, page 74.

FIGURE 4.1
Periodic table showing charges of the ions of important elements

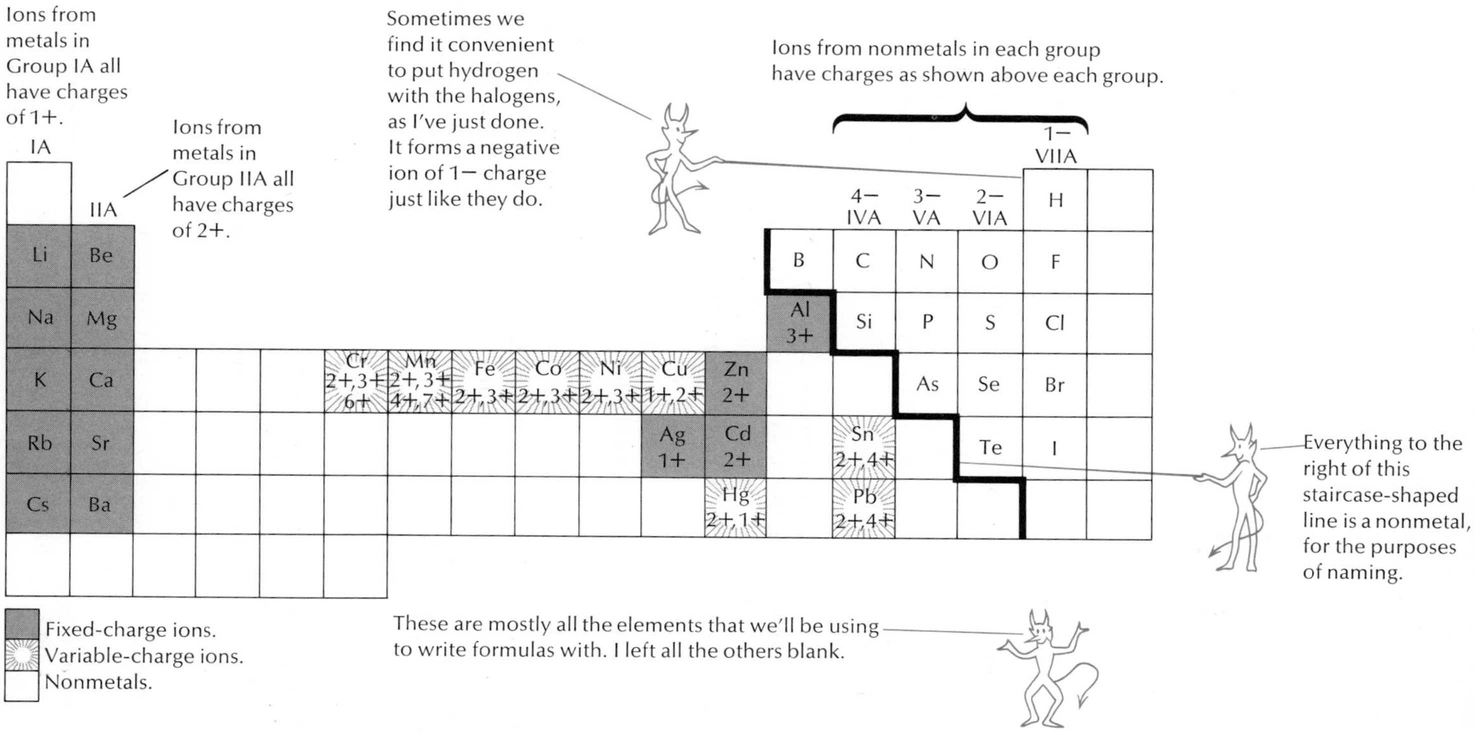

Ions from metals in Group IA all have charges of 1+.
Ions from metals in Group IIA all have charges of 2+.
Sometimes we find it convenient to put hydrogen with the halogens, as I've just done. It forms a negative ion of 1− charge just like they do.
Ions from nonmetals in each group have charges as shown above each group.
IA
IIA
4− IVA
3− VA
2− VIA
1− VIIA
H
Li
Be
B
C
N
O
F
Na
Mg
Al 3+
Si
P
S
Cl
K
Ca
Cr 2+,3+ 6+
Mn 2+,3+ 4+,7+
Fe 2+,3+
Co 2+,3+
Ni 2+,3+
Cu 1+,2+
Zn 2+
As
Se
Br
Rb
Sr
Ag 1+
Cd 2+
Sn 2+,4+
Te
I
Cs
Ba
Hg 2+,1+
Pb 2+,4+
Everything to the right of this staircase-shaped line is a nonmetal, for the purposes of naming.
Fixed-charge ions.
Variable-charge ions.
Nonmetals.
These are mostly all the elements that we'll be using to write formulas with. I left all the others blank.

makes the formula electrically neutral. Sodium comes first, since it's the metal. The name of the compound is "sodium ion" plus "fluoride ion," with "ion" dropped from both.

Answer: NaF, sodium fluoride.

EXAMPLE 4.14: Lime is a substance made of calcium ions (Ca^{2+}) and oxide ions (O^{2-}). Give its formula and name.

Solution: Putting one of each ion together will do the job, since the 2+ of the calcium ion will exactly balance the 2− of the oxide ion. The name comes from the two names of the ions, without "ion."

Answer: CaO, calcium oxide.

EXAMPLE 4.15: Fluoride ion helps prevent tooth decay by reacting chemically with the calcium in teeth. It forms a compound made of Ca^{2+} and F^-. Write its formula and name.

Solution: Things get a bit stickier here. The single negative charge of F^- isn't enough to balance the two positive charges of Ca^{2+}. We still need another negative charge. The solution is to combine two fluoride ions with a single calcium ion, and to show this by using a subscript 2.

Answer: CaF_2, calcium fluoride.

An easy way of writing formulas is just to switch the charge numbers between the positive and the negative ion, and use them for subscripts. Above, we used the 2 from the charge of calcium ion for the subscript of F, and the 1 from the charge of the fluoride ion for the subscript of Ca. Similarly, for a compound between K^+ and O^{2-}, we switch the numbers and the formula is K_2O, potassium oxide. A compound between Al^{3+} and Cl^- is $AlCl_3$ and is called aluminum chloride. For Ca^{2+} and N^{3-}, the formula is Ca_3N_2 (two of the threes and three of the twos). Figure 4.2 shows why this always works.

To write the formula of a binary ionic compound from its name, first decide what the charges are on the positive and the negative ions. Then, switch the numbers and write them as subscripts. As we saw in Example 4.14, it's sometimes necessary to reduce subscripts to the lowest common multiple: CaO and not Ca_2O_2.

EXAMPLE 4.16: Silver sulfide is the black tarnish on silverware. Write its formula.

Solution: Silver ion is on the list of fixed-charge ions, and its formula is Ag^+. Sulfur is found in Group VIA, so the formula for the sulfide ion is S^{2-}. We switch the charge numbers around and make them subscripts.

Answer: Ag_2S.

EXAMPLE 4.17: Galena, a lead ore, contains the compound lead(II) sulfide. Write its formula.

Solution: Since there is a Roman numeral after lead, we know without looking it up that lead is a variable-charge ion and that its charge is 2+. We know sulfur is in Group VIA (and besides, we just used it above), so the sulfide ion is S^{2-}. Switching the charge numbers around, we get Pb_2S_2, which we then simplify.

Answer: PbS.

To write the name of a binary ionic compound from its formula, first decide whether the metal ion is a fixed- or a variable-charge ion. If it's a fixed-charge ion, then no Roman numerals are needed. If it's a variable-charge ion, we must decide which charge is involved and use the appropriate Roman numeral. The negative ion will always end in *-ide*. We put the two names together and drop the word "ion" from both.

EXAMPLE 4.18: Manganese is an ingredient in some types of steel. One source of manganese is from the ore pyrolusite, which contains the compound MnO_2. Write the name for this compound.

Solution: We find manganese in the list of variable-charge ions: 2+, 3+, 4+, or 7+. We know oxygen has a fixed charge of 2−, so we use it to figure out what the charge of manganese is. Two oxide ions, at 2− each, give us a total of 4−. The formula has only one manganese ion, so its charge must be 4+.

Answer: Manganese(IV) oxide.

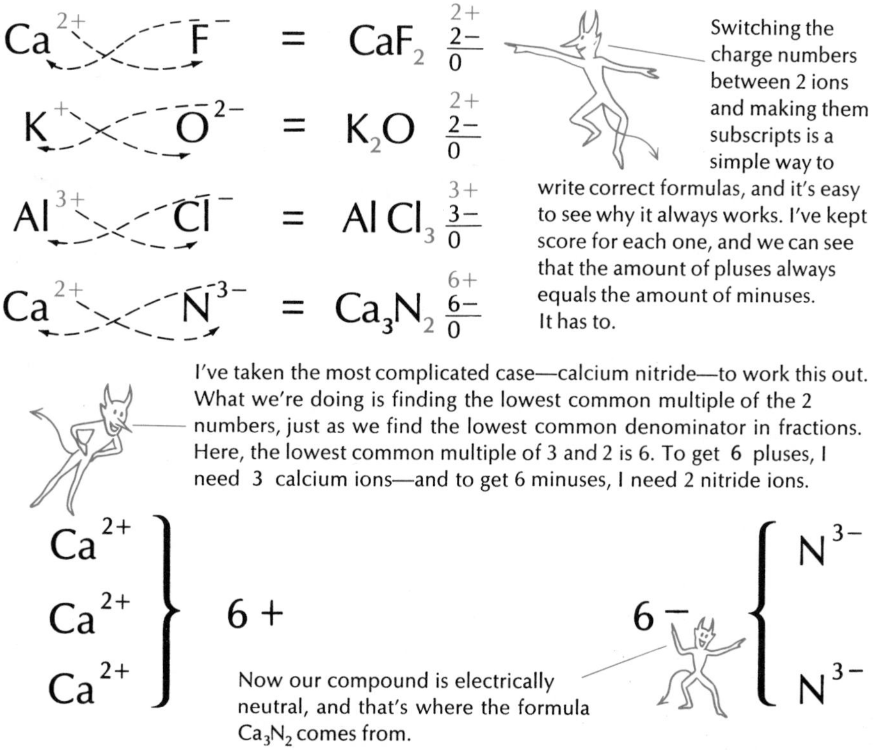
Ca^{2+} F^{-} = CaF_2 2+ 2− 0
K^{+} O^{2-} = K_2O 2+ 2− 0
Al^{3+} Cl^{-} = $AlCl_3$ 3+ 3− 0
Ca^{2+} N^{3-} = Ca_3N_2 6+ 6− 0
Switching the charge numbers between 2 ions and making them subscripts is a simple way to write correct formulas, and it's easy to see why it always works. I've kept score for each one, and we can see that the amount of pluses always equals the amount of minuses. It has to.
I've taken the most complicated case—calcium nitride—to work this out. What we're doing is finding the lowest common multiple of the 2 numbers, just as we find the lowest common denominator in fractions. Here, the lowest common multiple of 3 and 2 is 6. To get 6 pluses, I need 3 calcium ions—and to get 6 minuses, I need 2 nitride ions.
Ca^{2+} Ca^{2+} Ca^{2+} 6 +
6 − N^{3-} N^{3-}
Now our compound is electrically neutral, and that's where the formula Ca_3N_2 comes from.

FIGURE 4.2 Formulas of ionic compounds must show that the compound is electrically neutral

Note: Because their names are so similar, manganese and magnesium are easily confused. Magnesium is a Group IIA metal, and so its charge is always 2+. Manganese is a transition metal and has variable charge.

EXAMPLE 4.19: A thick, white cream, used to prevent sunburn and also used for clown makeup, contains the compound ZnO. Write its name.

Solution: We find zinc among the fixed-charge ions. Since a fixed-charge ion has no Roman numeral in its name, the answer is simple.

Answer: Zinc oxide.

EXAMPLE 4.20: Chalcocite is a copper ore that also contains sulfur. When this ore is smelted, a great deal of SO_2 (sulfur dioxide) air pollution results. The formula for the compound between copper and sulfur in this ore is Cu_2S. Write its name.

Solution: Copper is among the variable-charge ions: it's 1+ or 2+. The sulfide ion (S^{2-}) is always the same, however. Since this formula requires two copper ions for one sulfide ion, each copper ion must be 1+, or copper(I) ion.

Answer: Copper(I) sulfide.

Table 4.7 shows some binary ionic compounds with their names and formulas. Binary ionic compounds where the negative nonmetal ion is an element other than oxygen are called *binary salts*. If the nonmetal ion is oxygen, the compound is called an *oxide*.

binary salt
oxide

TABLE 4.7
Names and
formulas of some
binary
ionic compounds

Here's a compound you've heard of by its old system name, stannous fluoride. It's the ingredient in some fluoride toothpastes, and in advertising it's never called "tin(II) fluoride." Sometimes it's called "Fluoristan." Chemists are bad enough when it comes to naming, but there's no telling what name an advertiser will invent!

Formula	Name	Comment
Oxides		
FeO	Iron(II) oxide	
Fe_2O_3	Iron(III) oxide	This is rust.
CrO	Chromium(II) oxide	
Cr_2O_3	Chromium(III) oxide	Green dye used in manufacture of paper money.
PbO	Lead(II) oxide	This is "white lead."
PbO_2	Lead(IV) oxide	This is "red lead," used in lead-based industrial paint pigments.
Binary Salts		
Cu_2S	Copper(I) sulfide	Chalcocite ore.
CuS	Copper(II) sulfide	
SnF_2	Tin(II) fluoride	Ingredient in fluoride toothpaste.
SnF_4	Tin(IV) fluoride	
$HgCl_2$	Mercury(II) chloride	

4.3 NAMES AND FORMULAS OF TERNARY COMPOUNDS

A *ternary compound* is a compound that contains three elements. Usually (but not always) one of the elements is either a metal or hydrogen, another element is a nonmetal, and the third element is oxygen. When one of the elements is hydrogen and not a metal, the ternary compound is covalent. Ternary compounds containing metals (and not hydrogen) are ionic. Whether ternary compounds are covalent or ionic, though, they will include polyatomic ions, so we need to take these up first.

ternary compound

POLYATOMIC IONS. A bonded group of atoms with an overall charge is a *polyatomic ion*. If the molecule has more electrons than protons, then the polyatomic ion is negative. If the molecule has fewer electrons than protons, then the polyatomic ion is positive.

polyatomic ion

Negative polyatomic ions usually consist of a *central atom* and one or more oxygen atoms. The whole thing has a negative charge of $1-$, $2-$, or $3-$. To name these ions, we use the root of the central atom plus the suffix *-ite* or *-ate*. Sometimes we also add the prefix *hypo-* or *per-*.

central atom

Unfortunately, there really isn't much system to these names. In general (though not always), the most common of several polyatomic ions formed by the same central atom is the *-ate* ion. The ion having one less oxygen atom than the *-ate* ion is the *-ite* ion. The ion having one more oxygen atom than the *-ate* ion keeps the suffix *-ate* and adds the prefix *per-*. The ion having one less oxygen atom than the *-ite* ion keeps that suffix and takes the prefix *hypo-*. This may be made clearer by Table 4.8. Fortunately, all of the possible ions don't exist.

Then, there are some negative polyatomic ions that don't follow even the complicated rules above. These are shown in Table 4.9, along with two important *positive* polyatomic ions. The six ions given in the table really have to be memorized, since their names don't follow any rules.

We might expect the positive mercury(I) ion to be simply Hg^+. Instead, two of these single ions join together and make one ion, and the whole thing has a charge of $2+$. Each mercury atom has an average charge of $1+$, though, and that's why it's called the mercury(I) ion.

The ammonium ion, NH_4^+, behaves a lot like the Group IA metal ions, Li^+, Na^+, K^+, Rb^+, Cs^+, and it is often spoken of in the same breath with them.

TERNARY COVALENT COMPOUNDS (OXYACIDS).

Most ternary covalent compounds—usually made of hydrogen, a nonmetal, and oxygen—are *oxyacids*. (Some ternary covalent compounds are not acids, and some ternary acids are not oxyacids. But oxyacids are more common and more important.)

oxyacid

TABLE 4.8
Names and formulas of some negative polyatomic ions

Most Common Ion		1 Less O Atom		2 Less O Atoms		1 More O Atom	
ClO_3^-	Chlorate ion	ClO_2^-	Chlorite ion	ClO^-	Hypochlorite ion	ClO_4^-	Perchlorate ion
BrO_3^-	Bromate ion	BrO_2^-	Bromite ion	BrO^-	Hypobromite ion	BrO_4^-	Perbromate ion
IO_3^-	Iodate ion	IO_2^-	Iodite ion	IO^-	Hypoiodite ion	IO_4^-	Periodate ion
SO_4^{2-}	Sulfate ion	SO_3^{2-}	Sulfite ion		None	SO_5^{2-}	Persulfate ion
NO_3^-	Nitrate ion	NO_2^-	Nitrite ion		None		None
PO_4^{3-}	Phosphate ion	PO_3^{3-}	Phosphite ion		None		None
CrO_4^{2-}	Chromate ion[a]		None		None		None
$Cr_2O_7^{2-}$	Dichromate ion[a]		None		None		None
MnO_4^{2-}	Manganate ion[a]		None		None	MnO_4^-	Permanganate ion[a,b]
CO_3^{2-}	Carbonate ion		None		None		None

[a]Note that these ions contain metals rather than nonmetals.
[b]This is an exception to the rule. Permanganate ion does not have more oxygen atoms than manganate ion. Instead, it has one less negative charge.

TABLE 4.9 **73**
Some negative
and positive
polyatomic ions

Negative		Positive	
CN^-	Cyanide ion	Hg_2^{2+}	Mercury(I) ion[a]
OH^-	Hydroxide ion	NH_4^+	Ammonium ion
$C_2H_3O_2^-$	Acetate ion		
O_2^{2-}	Peroxide ion[a]		

[a]Strictly speaking, the peroxide ion and mercury(I) ion aren't polyatomic ions, since they're made of only one element. But they behave like polyatomic ions and thus are classed as such.

We arrive at the formula of an acid by taking a negative polyatomic ion, putting as many hydrogen atoms in front of it as the ion has negative charges, and dropping the charge. For example, the acid made from the sulfate ion, SO_4^{2-}, is H_2SO_4; from the phosphate ion, PO_4^{3-}, it's H_3PO_4.

Acids can have two names. First, we can call them hydrogen compounds of the polyatomic ions, by putting "hydrogen" in front of the ion's name and dropping "ion." In this system, H_2SO_4 is hydrogen sulfate, and H_3PO_4 is hydrogen phosphate. Second, we can name them as acids. If the polyatomic ion ends in -*ate*, its corresponding acid drops the -*ate* and ends with -*ic* and *acid*. If the polyatomic ion ends in -*ite*, its corresponding acid drops the -*ite* and adds -*ous* and *acid*. In acids containing sulfur and phosphorus, the root changes slightly from the one that's used in the polyatomic ion. Table 4.10 shows some ternary acids with their names and the ions from which they're derived.

TERNARY IONIC COMPOUNDS (TERNARY SALTS AND METAL HYDROXIDES).

Ternary ionic compounds are compounds between metal (or ammonium) ions and negative polyatomic ions. A *ternary salt* is a ternary ionic compound where the negative polyatomic ion is *not* hydroxide. A *metal hydroxide,* as you might expect, is a ternary ionic compound where the negative ion is hydroxide (OH^-).

ternary salt

metal hydroxide

We've already done the hard part. We know how to name metal ions, and we know how to name polyatomic ions. All we have to do is put these together into formulas and name them.

To write the formula for a ternary ionic compound, we use the same technique as we used for the binary ionic compounds. We put the two ions together, switch their charges, and make the charges subscripts. A compound of Na^+ and SO_4^{2-} is Na_2SO_4; a compound of Ca^{2+} and SO_4^{2-} is $CaSO_4$. But a compound of Al^{3+} and SO_4^{2-} is $Al_2(SO_4)_3$. To avoid confusion, we put parentheses around a polyatomic ion when it's used with a subscript. When parentheses are used, we read the formula, "A-l-two-S-O-four taken three times."

To name a ternary ionic compound, we name the positive ion, then the negative ion, and drop "ion" from each. Thus Na_2SO_4 is sodium sulfate, $CaSO_4$ is calcium sulfate, and $Al_2(SO_4)_3$ is aluminum sulfate.

TABLE 4.10

Names and formulas of some common oxyacids and their corresponding polyatomic ions

Poly-atomic Ion	Name	Acid	Name, as Acid	Name, as Hydrogen Compound
NO_3^-	Nitrate ion	HNO_3	Nitric acid	Hydrogen nitrate
NO_2^-	Nitrite ion	HNO_2	Nitrous acid	Hydrogen nitrite
SO_4^{2-}	Sulfate ion	H_2SO_4	Sulfuric acid	Hydrogen sulfate
SO_3^{2-}	Sulfite ion	H_2SO_3	Sulfurous acid	Hydrogen sulfite
PO_4^{3-}	Phosphate ion	H_3PO_4	Phosphoric acid	Hydrogen phosphate
PO_3^{3-}	Phosphite ion	H_3PO_3	Phosphorous acid	Hydrogen phosphite
CO_3^{2-}	Carbonate ion	H_2CO_3	Carbonic acid	Hydrogen carbonate
ClO_4^-	Perchlorate ion[a]	$HClO_4$	Perchloric acid[a]	Hydrogen perchlorate[a]
ClO_3^-	Chlorate ion[a]	$HClO_3$	Chloric acid[a]	Hydrogen chlorate[a]
ClO_2^-	Chlorite ion[a]	$HClO_2$	Chlorous acid[a]	Hydrogen chlorite[a]
ClO^-	Hypochlorite ion[a]	$HClO$	Hypochlorous acid[a]	Hydrogen hypochlorite[a]
$C_2H_3O_2^-$	Acetate ion	$HC_2H_3O_2$	Acetic acid	Hydrogen acetate

[a]Acids and polyatomic ions containing bromine and iodine are named in the same way as acids and polyatomic ions containing chlorine.

EXAMPLE 4.21: The compound $(NH_4)_3PO_4$ is an excellent fertilizer, which gives plants the nitrogen and the phosphorus necessary for their growth. Name this compound.

Solution: We know that NH_4^+ is the ammonium ion. From Table 4.8, we also see that PO_4^{3-} is the phosphate ion.

Answer: Ammonium phosphate.

EXAMPLE 4.22: "Chrome yellow," a yellow paint pigment, has the formula $PbCrO_4$. Name this compound.

Solution: Going back to the naming of metal ions, we find that lead (Pb) is among the variable-charge ions. We have to decide whether it's 2+ or 4+ in this compound. To do this, we look at the negative ion (Table 4.8) and see that its name is chromate ion with a charge of 2−. Since there is only one lead ion for one chromate ion, the charge on the lead ion must be 2+, and the name is lead(II) ion.

Answer: Lead(II) chromate.

EXAMPLE 4.23: Calomel, an important substance used in electrodes for various industrial processes, has the formula Hg_2Cl_2. Name this compound.

Solution: We find mercury (Hg) among the variable-charge ions. We know that chloride ion (Cl^-) has a charge of 1−, so the mercury must be in the form of the polyatomic positive ion, Hg_2^{2+}, or mercury(I) ion.

Answer: Mercury(I) chloride.

To write a formula from a name, follow the same procedure as for binary salts. Decide what the charges of the positive and negative ions are by consulting the appropriate tables, and then switch the charges and make subscripts out of them. Don't forget to put parentheses around polyatomic ions if more than one of them is needed in the formula.

EXAMPLE 4.24: Saltpeter is potassium nitrate. It was once used for making gunpowder but is now used for making glass and ceramics and also for curing meat. Write its formula.

Solution: Potassium is a fixed-charge ion (K^+). From Table 4.8, we see that nitrate ion is NO_3^-.

Answer: KNO_3.

EXAMPLE 4.25: Bones are largely composed of calcium phosphate. Write its formula.

Solution: Calcium is a fixed-charge ion (Ca^{2+}). Phosphate ion is PO_4^{3-}. We switch charge numbers, make them subscripts, and put parentheses around PO_4.

Answer: $Ca_3(PO_4)_2$.

EXAMPLE 4.26: A copper ore, called "azurite" because of its beautiful azure color, is a mixture of copper(II) carbonate and copper(II) hydroxide. Write formulas for these two compounds.

Solution: From its name, we know that the copper(II) ion is Cu^{2+}. Carbonate ion is CO_3^{2-}, and hydroxide ion is OH^-.

Answer: Copper(II) carbonate, $CuCO_3$; copper(II) hydroxide, $Cu(OH)_2$.

4.4 NAMING COMPOUNDS WITH MORE THAN THREE ELEMENTS

We've seen that we can make the oxyacid H_2SO_4 by combining the sulfate ion (SO_4^{2-}) with two hydrogens. Also, we can make the ternary salt Na_2SO_4 by combining SO_4^{2-} with two sodium ions (Na^+). We can also combine SO_4^{2-} with one hydrogen and one sodium ion to get $NaHSO_4$. This compound is partly an acid, because it still has a hydrogen atom, and partly an ionic compound, because it contains a metal ion and a negative ion. Mixed compounds like this are easy to name. We name the metal ion, then hydrogen, then the negative ion: sodium hydrogen sulfate. We see that this compound is made of a sodium ion, Na^+, and an HSO_4^-, a negative ion derived from the sulfate ion, called a "hydrogen sulfate ion." Any polyatomic ion (like SO_4^{2-}) with more than one negative charge can take fewer hydrogen atoms than it needs to form an oxyacid, and form instead an intermediate ion (HSO_4^-).

Another possibility is to combine both Na^+ and K^+ with SO_4^{2-}, to get $NaKSO_4$. This is called simply sodium potassium sulfate. In short, we can have any combination of metal ions or hydrogen that adds up to the charge on the negative ion. Some mixed compounds are shown in Table 4.11.

4.5 NAMING HYDRATES

hydrate

Hydrates are ionic compounds that have water molecules in their cyrstal structures. Since there is usually a fixed amount of water, we can write formulas for hydrates. Copper(II) sulfate forms a hydrate that has this formula:

$$CuSO_4 \cdot 5\,H_2O \quad \text{or} \quad CuSO_4 \times 5\,H_2O$$

This is named copper(II) sulfate pentahydrate, or copper(II) sulfate

**TABLE 4.11
Some mixed
compounds**

Acid	Ion	Name	Mixed Compound	Name
H_2CO_3	HCO_3^-	Hydrogen carbonate ion	$NaHCO_3$	Sodium hydrogen carbonate
			$NaKCO_3$	Sodium potassium carbonate
H_2SO_4	HSO_4^-	Hydrogen sulfate ion	$KHSO_4$	Potassium hydrogen sulfate
			$LiNH_4SO_4$	Lithium ammonium sulfate
H_2SO_3	HSO_3^-	Hydrogen sulfite ion	$Ca(HSO_3)_2$	Calcium hydrogen sulfite
H_3PO_4	HPO_4^{2-}	Hydrogen phosphate ion	K_2HPO_4	Potassium hydrogen phosphate
			$CaHPO_4$	Calcium hydrogen phosphate
	$H_2PO_4^-$	Dihydrogen phosphate ion	LiH_2PO_4	Lithium dihydrogen phosphate
			$Ca(H_2PO_4)_2$	Calcium dihydrogen phosphate
			$MgNH_4PO_4$	Magnesium ammonium phosphate
			$LiNaKPO_4$	Lithium sodium potassium phosphate
H_2S^a	HS^-	Hydrogen sulfide ion	$NaHS$	Sodium hydrogen sulfide

[a]H_2S is a binary acid, but it's included here because it forms the same kind of mixed compounds as the ternary acids.

5-hydrate. First comes the name of the salt itself, and then either Greek prefixes or numbers can be used to say how many water molecules there are.

■ **EXAMPLE 4.27:** Plaster of paris hardens to form gypsum, which has the formula $CaSO_4 \cdot 2\,H_2O$. Name this substance.

Solution: First, we must name the salt. Then we add the two water molecules.

Answer: Calcium sulfate dihydrate, or calcium sulfate 2-hydrate.

4.6 NAMES AND FORMULAS: GENERAL EXAMPLES

$Na_2B_2O_5$

We've set down a lot of rules for naming each kind of substance. When we're faced with a compound to name, or a formula to write from a name, the compound won't be categorized for us. Our first problem will be to decide which class of compounds it belongs in. Having done that, then we can follow the rules for that particular class.

■ **EXAMPLE 4.28:** KCN is an important ingredient in murder mysteries. Write its name.

Solution: First, we classify the compound. We see that it's a metal plus two nonmetals, so it's a ternary ionic compound. We find in Table 4.9 that the name for CN^- is cyanide ion.

Answer: Potassium cyanide.

■ **EXAMPLE 4.29:** The compound responsible for the sour taste in vinegar is $HC_2H_3O_2$. What is its name?

Solution: Since the formula begins with hydrogen, we classify it as an acid and find its name in Table 4.10.

Answer: Acetic acid, or hydrogen acetate.

■ **EXAMPLE 4.30:** Glass is SiO_2. Give the systematic name of this substance.

Solution: This compound is made of two nonmetallic elements, so it's a binary covalent compound. We name it according to those rules.

Answer: Silicon dioxide.

■ **EXAMPLE 4.31:** Sodium hypochlorite is an ingredient in chlorine bleach. Write its formula.

Solution: This compound contains a metal ion (sodium), so it must be a salt. The prefix *hypo* and suffix *-ite* in "hypochlorite" tell us that it's a polyatomic ion. We find the hypochlorite ion in Table 4.8, with the formula ClO^-.

Answer: NaClO.

EXAMPLE 4.32: Baking soda is sodium hydrogen carbonate. Write its formula.

Solution: We see that this compound has more than three elements, so we follow the rules for these. Table 4.11 gives the hydrogen carbonate ion as HCO_3^-.

Answer: $NaHCO_3$.

EXAMPLE 4.33: Carbon disulfide is a smelly, inflammable liquid. Write its formula.

Solution: The name ends in -*ide,* and both carbon and sulfur are nonmetals, so we must be dealing with a binary covalent compound.

Answer: CS_2.

REVIEW QUESTIONS

1. What does the *formula* of a compound tell us?
2. Why do we need *systematic names* for compounds?
3. What is the difference between a *common name* and a systematic name?

Ionic and Covalent Compounds
4. What is an *ionic compound?*
5. What is an *ion?*
6. How do we show the charge of an ion? Give an example.
7. Do metals usually form *positive ions* or *negative ions*? What about nonmetals?
8. How can we tell whether or not a given compound is ionic?
9. What do we mean by "electrically neutral"?
10. What are *covalent compounds?*
11. How can we tell whether we have a covalent compound or not?

Names and Formulas of Binary Compounds
12. What is a *binary compound?*
13. What ending goes on the name of all binary compounds?
14. What are *oxides?*
15. Give the formulas and the common names and systematic names for the two oxides of hydrogen.
16. How many oxides of carbon are there? Give their names and formulas.
17. Give the names and formulas of the two oxides of nitrogen that are present in automobile emissions.
18. What is the formula for ammonia?
19. What is a *binary acid?*
20. State the rules for naming binary acids.
21. Why does HCN appear among the binary acids?

22. What is a *monatomic ion?*
23. What ending appears on the name of all negative monatomic ions?
24. How are the charges of negative ions related to their positions in the periodic table?
25. Do metals or nonmetals form negative ions?
26. What are *fixed-charge ions?*
27. Which fixed-charge, positive ions are related to their positions in the periodic table? Which are not?
28. What are *variable-charge ions?* List them and their charges.
29. Why do we use the Stock system of naming rather than the old system?
30. How do we write the formula of an ionic compound so that it's electrically neutral?
31. Why does switching the charges between two ions and using them for subscripts work in writing formulas?
32. What is the difference between magnesium and manganese?
33. What is a *binary salt?* How does it differ from an oxide?

Names and Formulas of Ternary Compounds
34. What is a *ternary compound?*
35. What is a *polyatomic ion?*
36. What do negative polyatomic ions usually consist of? How do we name them?
37. What are the names and formulas of the negative polyatomic ions that don't follow the rules?
38. What are the names and formulas of the positive polyatomic ions?
39. Why isn't the mercury(I) ion written Hg^+?
40. What polyatomic ion is often grouped with the Group·IA metal ions?

41. What are *oxyacids*? What are the two ways of naming them?
42. What is a *ternary salt*? A *metal hydroxide*?
43. How do we name and write the formula of a ternary ionic compound?

Naming Compounds with More than Three Elements
44. Explain how a compound may have more than three elements.

45. What are the rules for naming these compounds? Give an example.

Naming Hydrates
46. What is a *hydrate*?
47. How do we designate the number of water molecules in a hydrate?

EXERCISES

1. Identify the following compounds as ionic or covalent.
   a. carborundum, SiC
   b. washing soda, $Na_2CO_3 \cdot 10 H_2O$
   c. table salt, NaCl
   d. phosphine, PH_3
   e. ammonia, NH_3
   f. potash, K_2CO_3

2. Write formulas for these binary covalent compounds.
   a. nitrogen trichloride
   b. carbon tetrafluoride
   c. sulfur dichloride
   d. diboron hexahydride

3. Name these binary covalent compounds.
   a. OF_2
   b. Cl I
   c. N_2H_4
   d. SF_6

4. Give two names for each binary acid.
   a. H_2S
   b. HCN
   c. HI
   d. HCl

5. Write formulas for these binary acids.
   a. hydrosulfuric acid
   b. hydrogen bromide
   c. hydrofluoric acid
   d. hydrogen selenide

6. Name each monatomic ion.
   a. Na^+
   b. S^{2-}
   c. H^-
   d. P^{3-}
   e. Cu^{2+}
   f. Al^{3+}

7. Write formulas for these monatomic ions.
   a. oxide ion
   b. silver ion
   c. nitride ion
   d. potassium ion
   e. bromide ion
   f. strontium ion

8. Classify the following binary compounds as ionic or covalent, and give their names or formulas.
   a. Cl_2O
   b. ZnS
   c. magnesium nitride
   d. BBr_3
   e. tetraphosphorus hexoxide
   f. mercury(I) oxide
   g. Ca_2C
   h. copper(I) chloride
   i. dihydrogen telluride
   j. BaF_2

9. Name these binary ionic compounds.
   a. LiH
   b. BeO
   c. FeS
   d. $NiCl_2$
   e. K_3N
   f. $HgBr_2$

10. Write formulas for these binary ionic compounds.
    a. tin(IV) oxide
    b. barium sulfide
    c. potassium bromide
    d. chromium(II) chloride
    e. cadmium fluoride
    f. lead(II) iodide

Try to answer Exercises 11 through 14 from memory, consulting appropriate tables only when necessary.

11. Give names for these polyatomic ions.
    a. SO_4^{2-}
    b. NO_2^-
    c. ClO_4^-
    d. MnO_4^-

12. Write formulas for these polyatomic ions.
    a. nitrate ion
    b. chromate ion
    c. hypochlorite ion
    d. phosphite ion

13. Write formulas for these oxyacids.
    a. sulfuric acid
    b. nitrous acid
    c. iodic acid
    d. phosphorous acid

14. Give two names for these oxyacids.
    a. HNO_3
    b. H_3PO_4
    c. $HBrO_2$
    d. H_2CO_3

15. Name these ternary ionic compounds.
    a. $KClO_4$
    b. $FeSO_4$
    c. $(NH_4)_2Cr_2O_7$
    d. $AgC_2H_3O_2$
    e. Na_3PO_4
    f. $CuCO_3$

16. Write formulas for these ternary ionic compounds.
    a. calcium hypochlorite
    b. ammonium nitrate
    c. barium chromate
    d. magnesium hydroxide
    e. sodium cyanide
    f. ammonium carbonate

17. Classify each of the following ternary compounds as ionic or covalent, and give their names or formulas.
    a. nitric acid
    b. Li_2SO_3
    c. chromium(III) hydroxide
    d. H_2SO_4
    e. $(NH_4)_3PO_4$
    f. $HClO_3$
    g. hydrogen sulfate
    h. lead(II) carbonate
    i. HIO
    j. potassium permanganate

18. Name these mixed compounds.
    a. $LiAl(SO_4)_2$
    b. $KHCO_3$
    c. $Mg(HSO_3)_2$
    d. Li_2HPO_4

19. Write formulas for compounds formed between these positive and negative ions (use the appropriate lines to write the formulas).

	OH^-	CN^-	SO_4^{2-}	PO_4^{3-}	HCO_3^-	NO_3^-	ClO_2^-	O_2^{2-}
NH_4^+	—	—	—	—	—	—	—	—
Co^{2+}	—	—	—	—	—	—	—	—
K^+	—	—	—	—	—	—	—	—
Hg_2^{2+}	—	—	—	—	—	—	—	—
Mn^{2+}	—	—	—	—	—	—	—	—
Pb^{4+}	—	—	—	—	—	—	—	—
Sn^{2+}	—	—	—	—	—	—	—	—
Ca^{2+}	—	—	—	—	—	—	—	—
Li^+	—	—	—	—	—	—	—	—

20. Write formulas for binary ionic compounds formed between these metals and nonmetals (use the appropriate lines to write the formulas).

	O	F	N	S	Cl	Br	I
Zn	—	—	—	—	—	—	—
Li	—	—	—	—	—	—	—
Na	—	—	—	—	—	—	—
Al	—	—	—	—	—	—	—
Ca	—	—	—	—	—	—	—
Fe^{3+}	—	—	—	—	—	—	—
Sr	—	—	—	—	—	—	—
Mg	—	—	—	—	—	—	—
K	—	—	—	—	—	—	—
Cr^{2+}	—	—	—	—	—	—	—
Hg^{2+}	—	—	—	—	—	—	—

21. Write formulas for these mixed compounds.
   a. sodium dihydrogen phosphate
   b. ammonium hydrogen sulfate
   c. sodium potassium sulfite
   d. aluminum hydrogen carbonate

22. Classify and write formulas for these compounds.
   a. sodium peroxide
   b. aluminum sulfide
   c. phosphoric acid
   d. nitrogen monoxide

   e. ammonia
   f. cadmium
      hypochlorite

   g. carbon dioxide
   h. copper(II)
      sulfate

23. Classify and name these compounds.
   a. $CrSO_4 \cdot 4\,H_2O$
   b. $HClO_4$
   c. $NaKSO_3$
   d. PF_5
   e. SiO_2
   f. NH_4CN
   g. $BaCrO_4$
   h. SO_3

5

Chemical Reactions and Equations

In this chapter, we're going to look at some of the ways elements and compounds react with each other to free other elements and form other compounds. Before we start, though, we need to know something about the word "react."

We had a crude definition of chemical reaction in Chapter 2. Now we'll modify it to make it a little more specific. We'll have occasion to modify it again later when we have more knowledge to build on. At this point, we'll define a *chemical reaction* as a process by which one or more chemical substances are converted into different chemical substances by breaking or forming chemical bonds. When chemicals react, they participate in a chemical reaction.

chemical reaction

Chemical reactions are the basis of chemistry and of life as we know it. Chemical reactions are going on around us all the time. The burning of fuel, the rusting of iron, our bodily processes—all these are chemical reactions. In later chapters, we'll look at the nature of chemical bonds and see why they break and form the way they do. For now, we're interested in the *what* before the *why*.

We saw in the last chapter that formulas are a shorthand way of telling what a compound's made of. We also have a shorthand way of describing chemical reactions: with chemical equations.

For instance, in the steel industry, coke, which is largely carbon, is used as a fuel. We could describe the burning of coke in this way: "Carbon reacts with oxygen (burns) to form carbon dioxide." We've already seen, though, that chemists don't like to write things out if they don't have to. Instead of describing a reaction in a sentence, they'd rather translate it into symbols and formulas (their "words"), and equations (their "sentences").

In this chapter, we'll learn how to translate chemistry to English and vice versa. We'll learn how to write complete, correct equations and predict the products of some types of reactions.

5.1 READING AND WRITING EQUATIONS

chemical equation

A *chemical equation* is the chemist's shorthand for describing what happens in a chemical reaction. The reaction we talked about earlier is an easy one that we can translate into chemistry from English.

English: "Carbon reacts with oxygen to yield carbon dioxide."
Chemistry: $C + O_2 \longrightarrow CO_2$

reactant

product

yields

The "before" substances on the left, C and O_2, are the *reactants*. The "after" substance on the right, CO_2, is the *product* of the reaction. The arrow between them means *yields*.

$$\text{reactants} \longrightarrow \text{products}$$
$$\text{yield}$$

Now we'll see how to do the English-chemistry translation. It involves several steps. Here's another simple example.

English: "Iron reacts with sulfur to yield iron(II) sulfide."

We'll translate this sentence into chemistry, using the steps that follow.

Step 1: *Find out what all the formulas are.*
The formula for iron is Fe; for sulfur, S; and for iron(II) sulfide, FeS. If we're not sure of a formula, we should always go back to Chapter 4 and check. The equation won't be right if the formulas aren't right, any more than a sentence would be right if the words weren't right.

Step 2: *Decide what the reactants are and what the products are.*
The English sentence says, "Iron reacts with sulfur . . . ," so iron and sulfur must be the reactants. The English goes on: ". . . to yield iron(II) sulfide." Iron(II) sulfide must therefore be the product.

Step 3: *Write the equation.*
The reactants go on the left, and the products go on the right. The arrow goes in between them in place of the word "yields."

$$Fe + S \longrightarrow FeS$$

EXAMPLE 5.1: Translate this English into chemistry: "Sodium hydroxide reacts with hydrochloric acid to yield sodium chloride and water."

Solution:
Step 1: Sodium hydroxide is NaOH; hydrochloric acid is HCl; sodium chloride is NaCl; water is H_2O.
Step 2: Sodium hydroxide and hydrochloric acid are reactants; sodium chloride and water are products.
Step 3: NaOH and HCl go on the left; NaCl and H_2O go on the right.
Answer: $NaOH + HCl \longrightarrow NaCl + H_2O$

5.2 BALANCING EQUATIONS

The equations we've looked at so far are simpler than most equations used in chemistry. Here's an English-chemistry translation that presents a new problem.

English: "Nitrogen reacts with hydrogen to yield ammonia."
Chemistry: $N_2 + H_2 \longrightarrow NH_3$

The equations we've had before were correct at this point. This one, though, isn't quite right. As it stands now, it's violating the _Law of Conservation of Matter,_ which states that matter can neither be destroyed nor created in a chemical reaction. In a chemical reaction, atoms begin by being joined in a certain way. During the reaction, the atoms are taken apart, and at the end of the reaction, they end up being joined in a different way. But the Law of Conservation of Matter says that none of them can be lost in the process,

**Law of
Conservation
of Matter**

nor can new ones be introduced. We have to have the same number of each kind of atom at the end as we had at the beginning of the reaction. However, at the end, the atoms will probably belong to different elements or compounds than they belonged to at the beginning. Also, one kind of atom can't change to another kind.

Let's see how this applies to the equation we've written,

$$2N \quad 6H$$
$$N_2 + 3H_2 \longrightarrow 2NH_3$$

This equation says that one molecule of nitrogen, containing two atoms of nitrogen, reacts with one molecule of hydrogen, containing two atoms of hydrogen, to yield one molecule of ammonia, containing one atom of nitrogen and three atoms of hydrogen. Somehow we've lost an atom of nitrogen, which we're not allowed to do, and we've gained an atom of hydrogen, which we're not allowed to do either. We can't fix things by changing a nitrogen to a hydrogen. That's against the rules too.

We can fix things by making another ammonia molecule out of the extra nitrogen molecule on the left. We were already short one hydrogen atom, so we'll have to use more molecules of hydrogen to do the job. Altogether, to make two molecules of ammonia at three hydrogen atoms apiece, we need six hydrogen atoms, or three hydrogen molecules each containing two hydrogen atoms. This is illustrated in Figure 5.1.

We can reflect all this very simply in the chemistry translation.

$$2N \quad 6H$$

Chemistry: $N_2 + 3 H_2 \longrightarrow 2 NH_3$
English: "One molecule of nitrogen reacts with three molecules of hydrogen to yield two molecules of ammonia."

balancing   The original equation needed *balancing,* because it violated the Law of Conservation of Matter. We balanced it by putting numbers in front of the formulas so that the equation would have the same number of each kind of atom on both sides. A number in front of a formula means that everything in that formula is multiplied by the number. If there is no number, "1" is understood.

There are four main steps involved in balancing an equation. To illustrate them, we'll use this unbalanced equation as an example:

$$H_2 + Cl_2 \longrightarrow HCl$$

From now on, we'll use this kind of an arrow to show an unbalanced equation:

$$\longrightarrow$$

Step 1: *Count the atoms on each side of the equation.*
    Left: 2 H   Right: 1 H
           2 Cl   1 Cl
Step 2: *Decide which atom or atoms are unbalanced.*
    Both H and Cl are.
Step 3: *Balance the equation by putting appropriate numbers in front of the formulas.*

FIGURE 5.1
A balanced
equation
obeys the law
of conservation
of matter

85

Hmm—I wanted to make a molecule of ammonia, but all I could find were these diatomic molecules of nitrogen and hydrogen. If I take them apart and try to make ammonia, then for each nitrogen atom, I'll need three hydrogen atoms. For these two nitrogens, I'll need six hydrogens—or three molecules of hydrogen. Then I'll end up with two molecules of ammonia instead of one.

Here's the chemistry translation of what I just said. The "3" in front of H_2 means three molecules of hydrogen. The "2" in front of NH_3 means two molecules of ammonia. Since there's no number in front of N_2, there's only one molecule of nitrogen.

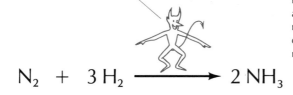

$$N_2 + 3H_2 \longrightarrow 2NH_3$$

I've taken everything apart now and sorted the atoms by elements. Each side has two nitrogens and six hydrogens. Matter has been neither created nor destroyed, only rearranged.

Put a "2" in front of HCl on the right:

$$H_2 + Cl_2 \longrightarrow 2HCl$$

Step 4: *Count atoms again, as a final check.*
    Left: 2 H   Right: 2 H
              2 Cl   2 Cl

The equation is balanced.

Of course, if the final check shows the equation *still* to be unbalanced, then more steps will be involved.

It's important to note that we always balance equations by putting numbers in front of formulas and not by changing subscripts in formulas. We might be tempted, for instance, to write "H_2Cl_2" as the product instead of "2 HCl," or to write "H + Cl" instead of "$H_2 + Cl_2$," in an attempt to balance the equation. This would be contrary to another rule, which is that *formulas must not be violated.*

A formula tells how many of each kind of atom belong in a set, and we can't break up the set. A deck of cards is also a set—of fifty-two. If you lose the jack of hearts, you no longer have a complete set. To replace the card, you have to buy a whole new deck. You'll have more than you need of every card except the jack of hearts, but that's the way it goes. A deck of cards is a set, and that's that. In nature, hydrogen and chlorine also come in sets— two each, or "two-packs"—and that's how they enter into chemical reactions. Since we have to use two of each, we end up with two molecules of hydrogen chloride instead of just one. We can't tamper with the formula for hydrogen chloride either. HCl is HCl: one molecule contains one atom of hydrogen and one atom of chlorine. H_2Cl_2 would mean that one molecule contained two atoms of hydrogen and two atoms of chlorine, and that's wrong.

The only way to balance an equation is to change the total quantity of one substance or another, by placing a number *before* it.

Now, let's follow through on some more examples of balancing equations.

EXAMPLE 5.2: Calcium, a rather active metal, soon tarnishes if it is left out in the air. Here's the equation for that reaction:

$$2\,Ca + O_2 \longrightarrow 2\,CaO$$

Balance this equation.

Solution:

Step 1: Left: 1 Ca   Right: 1 Ca
             2 O   1 O

Step 2: O is unbalanced.

Step 3: Put a "2" in front of CaO.

$$Ca + O_2 \longrightarrow 2\,CaO$$

Left: 1 Ca   Right: 2 Ca
          2 O   2 O

Now Ca is unbalanced, so more work is needed. Put a "2" in front of Ca on the left.

$$2\,Ca + O_2 \longrightarrow 2\,CaO$$

Step 4: Final atom check.

Left: 2 Ca   Right: 2 Ca
          2 O   2 O

Answer: $2\,Ca + O_2 \longrightarrow 2\,CaO$.

EXAMPLE 5.3: Potassium chlorate gives off oxygen when it is heated. This makes it particularly useful in the fireworks industry and in the space industry where a solid source of oxygen is desired. Here's what happens when potassium chlorate is heated:

$$KClO_3 \longrightarrow KCl + 2\,O_2$$

Balance the equation.

Solution:

Step 1: Left: 1 K   Right: 1 K
             1 Cl   1 Cl
             3 O   2 O

Step 2: O is unbalanced.

Step 3: To balance a 3 with a 2, use the lowest common multiple, which is

6 (two of the threes and three of the twos). Put a "2" in front of $KClO_3$ and a "3" in front of O_2.

$$2\ KClO_3 \not\longrightarrow KCl + 3\ O_2$$

Left: 2 K   Right: 1 K
           2 Cl   1 Cl
           6 O   6 O

K and Cl are unbalanced now. Put a "2" in front of KCl.

$$2\ KClO_3 \longrightarrow 2\ KCl + 3\ O_2$$

Step 4: Final atom check.

Left: 2 K   Right: 2 K
           2 Cl   2 Cl
           6 O   6 O

Answer: $2\ KClO_3 \longrightarrow 2\ KCl + 3\ O_2$.

We should remember that a number in front of a formula means that everything in the formula is multiplied by that number to get the atom count. We multiply the number times a subscript if there is one, as in $KClO_3$ above. The number of oxygens in $2\ KClO_3$ is $2 \times 3 = 6$ oxygens.

EXAMPLE 5.4: Aluminum occurs naturally as Al_2O_3 in bauxite ore. A new process for getting the aluminum out of the ore involves treating the ore with sulfuric acid as a first step. Here's the equation for what happens:

$$Al_2O_3 + H_2SO_4 \not\longrightarrow Al_2(SO_4)_3 + H_2O$$

Balance the equation.

Solution:

Step 1: Left: 2 Al   Right: 2 Al
            3 O   1 O
            2 H   2 H
            1 SO_4 3 SO_4

Notice that when a polyatomic ion like sulfate (SO_4^{2-}) remains intact from one side of the equation to the other, we count the ion once instead of counting its atoms (1 S, 4 O).

Step 2: O and SO_4 are unbalanced.

Step 3: Where more than one thing is unbalanced, it's a good idea to start with the most complicated difference in subscripts, which in this case is SO_4 with a difference of 3 and 1. Start by putting a "3" in front of H_2SO_4 to balance the sulfates.

$$Al_2O_3 + 3\ H_2SO_4 \not\longrightarrow Al_2(SO_4)_3 + H_2O$$

Left: 2 Al   Right: 2 Al
           3 O   1 O
           6 H   2 H
           3 SO_4 3 SO_4

Now H and O are unbalanced. Again, we choose the most complicated difference, which is H with 6 and 2. Put a "3" in front of H_2O to balance H.

$$Al_2O_3 + 3\ H_2SO_4 \longrightarrow Al_2(SO_4)_3 + 3\ H_2O$$

Step 4: Left: 2 Al   Right: 2 Al
              3 O   3 O
              6 H   6 H
              3 SO_4 3 SO_4

The equation is balanced. Note that when we balanced H, we also automatically balanced O. This often happens.

Answer: $Al_2O_3 + 3 H_2SO_4 \longrightarrow Al_2(SO_4)_3 + 3 H_2O$.

EXAMPLE 5.5: Balance this equation:

$$Fe_2(SO_4)_3 + Ca(OH)_2 \nrightarrow Fe(OH)_3 + CaSO_4$$

Solution:

Step 1: Left: 2 Fe   Right: 1 Fe
              3 SO_4 1 SO_4
              1 Ca   1 Ca
              2 OH   3 OH

Step 2: Everything is unbalanced except Ca.

Step 3: We start with the most complicated difference in subscripts, which is OH, with 2 on the left and 3 on the right. Find the lowest common multiple (6). Put a "3" in front of $Ca(OH)_2$ and a "2" in front of $Fe(OH)_3$.

$$Fe_2(SO_4)_3 + 3 Ca(OH)_2 \nrightarrow 2 Fe(OH)_3 + CaSO_4$$

Left: 2 Fe   Right: 2 Fe
          3 SO_4 1 SO_4
          3 Ca   1 Ca
          6 OH   6 OH

Ca and SO_4 are now unbalanced. Each is 3 to 1. A careful look will show us that we can fix both at once by putting a "3" in front of $CaSO_4$.

$$Fe_2(SO_4)_3 + 3 Ca(OH)_2 \longrightarrow 2 Fe(OH)_3 + 3 CaSO_4$$

Step 4: Left: 2 Fe   Right: 2 Fe
              3 SO_4 3 SO_4
              3 Ca   3 Ca
              6 OH   6 OH

Answer: $Fe_2(SO_4)_3 + 3 Ca(OH)_2 \longrightarrow 2 Fe(OH)_3 + 3 CaSO_4$

We can see from these last examples that some unbalanced equations need several tries before they'll balance out. If we go at it systematically enough, we'll always triumph in the end.

Let's summarize the guidelines for balancing a chemical equation.

1. Adjust the numbers in front of each formula so that the same number of each kind of atom appears on each side of the equation.
2. In general, first balance the most complicated difference in subscripts, and thereafter, the most complicated difference in atoms.
3. Consider polyatomic ions as single entities as long as they stay that way on both sides of the equation.
4. Count atoms on each side of the equation as a final check.

5. Remember that matter must be conserved, formulas must not be violated, and a number in front of a formula applies to the whole formula.

Other Symbols
Used in
Equations

89

5.3 OTHER SYMBOLS USED IN EQUATIONS

Often, we want to convey more in a chemical equation than just the chemical species involved. We want to specify whether each is a gas, a liquid, or a solid, or is dissolved in water. (A substance dissolved in water is in *aqueous solution* and is often called "aqueous.") We might also want to say that heat is being supplied in the reaction. These symbols are shown in Table 5.1.

**aqueous
solution**

We'll now go back through all the equations we've had so far, in order, and get some practice both in understanding these new symbols and in doing chemistry-English translations.

EXAMPLE 5.6: Translate into English:

$$C(s) + O_2(g) \longrightarrow CO_2(g)$$

Solution: We say "solid carbon." We can say either "gaseous oxygen" or "oxygen gas" (same for carbon dioxide).

Answer: "Solid carbon reacts with oxygen gas to yield (or to form) carbon dioxide gas."

EXAMPLE 5.7: Translate into English:

$$Fe(s) + S(s) \longrightarrow FeS(s)$$

Solution: For a metal, like iron, we can also say "iron metal" instead of "solid iron." Both are correct.

Answer: "Solid iron (or iron metal) reacts with solid sulfur to yield solid iron(II) sulfide."

Meaning	Symbol[a]	Other Symbol
Substance is a solid	(s)	$\downarrow$
Substance is a liquid	(l)	
Substance is a gas	(g)	$\uparrow$
Aqueous solution (substance dissolved in water)	(aq)	
Heat is supplied	Δ	

TABLE 5.1
Some symbols
used in writing
equations

[a]These symbols are the ones used in this book. The others may be used elsewhere and are listed for information only.

EXAMPLE 5.8: Translate into English:
$$NaOH(aq) + HCl(aq) \longrightarrow NaCl(aq) + H_2O(l)$$

Solution: Everything besides water is in aqueous solution, and liquid water itself is produced. That means that the whole thing takes place dissolved in water. We can say that just once for the whole reaction. Also, we'll call HCl "hydrochloric acid" and not "hydrogen chloride." Naming it as an acid means that it's dissolved in water.

Answer: "Sodium hydroxide and hydrochloric acid react in aqueous solution to yield sodium chloride and water."

EXAMPLE 5.9: Translate into English:
$$N_2(g) + 3 H_2(g) \longrightarrow 2 NH_3(g)$$

Answer: "Nitrogen gas (gaseous nitrogen) reacts with hydrogen gas (gaseous hydrogen) to yield ammonia gas (gaseous ammonia)."

EXAMPLE 5.10: Translate into English:
$$H_2(g) + Cl_2(g) \longrightarrow 2 HCl(g)$$

Solution: We have HCl again, but this time we're told that it's a gas, not in aqueous solution as it was in Example 5.8. When it's a gas, we call it hydrogen chloride and not hydrochloric acid.

Answer: "Hydrogen gas reacts with chlorine gas to yield hydrogen chloride gas."

EXAMPLE 5.11: Translate into English:
$$2 Ca(s) + O_2(g) \longrightarrow 2 CaO(s)$$

Answer: "Calcium metal reacts with oxygen gas to produce solid calcium oxide."

EXAMPLE 5.12: Translate into English:
$$2 KClO_3(s) \xrightarrow{\Delta} 2 KCl(s) + 3 O_2(g)$$

Solution: $KClO_3$ is decomposing (see Section 5.4, pp. 91–92) into simpler substances, with the aid of heat. We call this *thermal decomposition*.

thermal decomposition

Answer: "Solid potassium chlorate undergoes thermal decomposition (or, decomposes thermally) to produce solid potassium chloride and gaseous oxygen."

EXAMPLE 5.13: Translate into English:
$$Al_2O_3(s) + 3 H_2SO_4(aq) \longrightarrow Al_2(SO_4)_3(aq) + 3 H_2O(l)$$

Solution: Here we have another reaction in aqueous solution. Al_2O_3 is said to be a solid, though, so we have to say so. Some things don't dissolve in water, and Al_2O_3 is one of them. We're not supposed to know instinctively which things dissolve in water and which don't; that's what the symbol (s) is there to tell us.

Answer: "Solid aluminum oxide reacts with sulfuric acid (not hydrogen sulfate) to yield aluminum sulfate and water in aqueous solution."

EXAMPLE 5.14: Translate into English:

$$Fe_2(SO_4)_3(aq) + 3\,Ca(OH)_2(aq) \longrightarrow 2\,Fe(OH)_3(s) + 3\,CaSO_4(aq)$$

Solution: Here one of the products is a solid, so we have to say so. A solid that is formed from a reaction in solution is called a *precipitate*. We could say, "a precipitate of $Fe(OH)_3$ is formed," or, "$Fe(OH)_3$ precipitates out." This latter is the most common usage, but it wouldn't be wrong to say simply "solid $Fe(OH)_3$."

Answer: "Iron(III) sulfate reacts with calcium hydroxide in aqueous solution to form calcium sulfate and a precipitate of iron(III) hydroxide."

Note from these examples that we can use "forms," "is formed," "produces," or "is produced" interchangeably with "yields" or "to yield."

5.4 TYPES OF CHEMICAL REACTIONS AND THEIR EQUATIONS

It's usually easier for us to learn things if we know something about the classes they belong to. We'll divide chemical reactions into four categories: combination, decomposition, single replacement, and double replacement.

COMBINATION REACTIONS. In combination reactions, two elements, two compounds, or an element and a compound react to form a single compound. That is, two substances combine to yield a single different substance.

$$A + B \longrightarrow AB$$

Examples

Two elements: $C(s) + O_2(g) \longrightarrow CO_2(g)$
Two elements: $Hg(l) + S(s) \longrightarrow HgS(s)$
Two compounds: $CaO(s) + CO_2(g) \longrightarrow CaCO_3(s)$
Element + compound: $O_2(g) + 2\,SO_2(g) \longrightarrow 2\,SO_3(g)$

DECOMPOSITION REACTIONS. In a decomposition reaction, a compound decomposes either into the elements that make it up, or into simpler compounds, or into some of each.

$$AB \longrightarrow A + B\,(+C + \cdots)$$

Decomposition usually (though not always) occurs with the help of heat. We've seen in the previous section that the Greek letter delta (Δ) is used to show that heat is supplied.

I like to call them "dances"!

Swing your partner!

CRUNCH

That number's over. Time to sit down again.

Examples

Elements formed: $2 HgO(s) \xrightarrow{\Delta} 2 Hg(l) + O_2(g)$

Compounds formed: $NiCO_3(s) \xrightarrow{\Delta} NiO(s) + CO_2(g)$

Eléments + compounds formed:

$$(NH_4)_2Cr_2O_7(s) \xrightarrow{\Delta} N_2(g) + Cr_2O_3(s) + 4 H_2O(g)$$

May I cut in?

SINGLE REPLACEMENT REACTIONS.

In a single replacement reaction, a compound reacts with an element to yield another compound and another element. Either the positive part or the negative part of the compound can be replaced.

$$AB + C \longrightarrow AC + B$$

Here's what happens when either of these parts is replaced.

Positive part is replaced:

$$CuCl_2(aq) + Zn(s) \longrightarrow ZnCl_2(aq) + Cu(s)$$
$$2 HCl(aq) + Mg(s) \longrightarrow MgCl_2(aq) + H_2(g)$$
$$2 H_2O(l) + 2 Na(s) \longrightarrow 2 NaOH(aq) + H_2(g)$$

Negative part is replaced:

$$2 NaI(aq) + Cl_2(g) \longrightarrow 2 NaCl(aq) + I_2(s)$$
$$CaH_2(s) + 2 H_2O(l) \longrightarrow Ca(OH)_2(aq) + 2 H_2(g)$$
$$PbS(s) + O_2(g) \longrightarrow Pb(s) + SO_2(g)$$

Everybody change partners!

DOUBLE REPLACEMENT REACTIONS.

In a double replacement reaction, two compounds just exchange their positive or negative parts.

$$AB + CD \longrightarrow AD + BC$$

Examples

$$HCl(aq) + NaOH(aq) \longrightarrow NaCl(aq) + H_2O(l)$$
$$Pb(NO_3)_2(aq) + Na_2SO_4(aq) \longrightarrow PbSO_4(s) + 2 NaNO_3(aq)$$
$$FeCl_3(aq) + 3 KOH(aq) \longrightarrow Fe(OH)_3(s) + 3 KCl(aq)$$

5.5 PREDICTING PRODUCTS AND WRITING EQUATIONS

Sometimes we have to write a complete equation when we know only the reactants. This means that we'll have to figure out what the products are. If we have a set of rules to follow, we can do this for the types of simple reactions we've listed above. Chemical reactions have many more types than these, however, and the rules aren't meant to cover everything. Nor are they meant to be memorized. But by referring to them when we need to, we'll be able to write a lot of equations.

When writing chemical equations, always put in the physical state (*g, l, s, aq*) if you know it. Knowing this for the elements is no problem; Chapter 2 outlined which elements were gases, liquids, and solids at room temperature. Assume that all ionic compounds are solids; if they're aqueous, the problem will say so. Covalent compounds can be solids, liquids, or gases, and there's no good rule right now for telling what a given covalent compound will be. We know a few of them, though, to be gases: hydrogen chloride, ammonia, and the important oxides of carbon, nitrogen, and sulfur. We know that water and hydrogen peroxide are liquids. Compounds named as acids are aqueous. If a compound is encountered that isn't easily classified by any of the above comments, then leave its physical state out.

In the examples that follow, we'll always put all the physical states in, and we'll indicate when a substance's physical state couldn't have been predicted.

WRITING COMBINATION REACTIONS.

Rule 1. A metal reacting with a nonmetal yields a binary ionic compound. For variable-charge metals, choose the compound for which the metal has the lowest charge, unless you have information to the contrary.

EXAMPLE 5.15: Cadmium reacts with sulfur to produce a yellow substance used in paint pigments. Write the equation.

Solution: Cadmium is a fixed-charge ion ($2+$); sulfur forms the ion S^{2-} The only product possible by the rules we know is CdS, cadmium sulfide. Since it's ionic, we know it's a solid.

Answer: $Cd(s) + S(s) \longrightarrow CdS(s)$

EXAMPLE 5.16: The filament in flashbulbs is magnesium. When the bulb flashes, magnesium is burning in the air. Write the equation.

Solution: When a substance *burns in air*, it combines with oxygen to form an oxide (it oxidizes). As we saw in Chapter 4, oxides are binary compounds, although they occur so frequently that they are often placed in a category of their own. Magnesium is a fixed-charge ion, so only one product is possible.

burning in air

Answer: $2 Mg(s) + O_2(g) \longrightarrow 2 MgO(s)$

EXAMPLE 5.17: When steel is made, the iron that makes up a large part of it is heated to very high temperatures. The outside of the finished steel becomes oxidized. Write the equation for the reaction of iron with oxygen.

Solution: The word "oxidized" tells us that iron is reacting with oxygen.

(We'll find another meaning for the word in Chapter 14.) Iron has variable charge: 2+ or 3+. We choose 2+, since we have no other information.

Answer: $2\,Fe(s) + O_2(g) \longrightarrow 2\,FeO(s)$.

Rule 2. *When the lower oxide of an element reacts with oxygen, the next higher oxide of that element is formed.*

EXAMPLE 5.18: Sulfuric acid is the Number One chemical produced and used in the United States. The saying goes that a country's industrial prowess is measured by the amount of sulfuric acid it produces. The first step in the production of sulfuric acid is to allow sulfur dioxide to react with oxygen. Write the equation.

Solution: We know that sulfur has two oxides: SO_2 and SO_3. When oxygen reacts with the lower one, SO_2, the higher one, SO_3, is formed. All are gases, as we know.

Answer: $2\,SO_2(g) + O_2(g) \longrightarrow 2\,SO_3(g)$.

Rule 3. *Some nonmetal oxides react with water to produce acids whose formulas consist of one or more water molecules combined with the original nonmetal oxide formula.*

EXAMPLE 5.19: The next step in the production of sulfuric acid is to allow sulfur trioxide to react with water. Write the equation.

Solution: We know that sulfuric acid is the product. One water molecule combined with SO_3 adds two hydrogens and one oxygen to SO_3: H_2SO_4. We add the new oxygen in with the oxygen the SO_3 already had.

Answer: $H_2O(l) + SO_3(g) \longrightarrow H_2SO_4(aq)$.

EXAMPLE 5.20: Write the equation for the reaction of $N_2O_5(l)$ with water.

Solution: This problem is a little more difficult. We know, though, that an oxyacid of nitrogen is going to be formed, and there are only two of them: HNO_3 and HNO_2. We have to choose one of them, but neither of them contains *two* nitrogen atoms, as does N_2O_5. We therefore have to make two acid molecules from one oxide molecule. If we add one water molecule to N_2O_5, we get 2 H, 2 N, and 6 O: exactly enough for two HNO_3 molecules.

Answer: $N_2O_5(l) + H_2O(l) \longrightarrow 2\,HNO_3(aq)$.
Here we couldn't have known, unless told, that N_2O_5 is a liquid.

Rule 4. *The oxide of a metal reacts with water to produce a metal hydroxide in which the metal has the same charge that it had in the oxide.*

EXAMPLE 5.21: Lime, CaO, is slaked by adding it to water. Write the equation.

Solution: The hydroxide of calcium will be formed in this reaction. Calcium is a fixed-charged ion, so there is no choice but $Ca(OH)_2$.

Answer: $CaO(s) + H_2O(l) \longrightarrow Ca(OH)_2(aq)$.
Note: Since we are adding water, we assume that the product is aqueous.

Rule 5. *Some metal oxides and some nonmetal oxides react with each other to form ternary salts.*
   Case A. Metal oxides react with carbon dioxide to form carbonates.

EXAMPLE 5.22: Write the equation for lithium oxide reacting with carbon dioxide.
Answer: $Li_2O(s) + CO_2(g) \longrightarrow Li_2CO_3(s)$.

   Case B. Metal oxides react with sulfur dioxide to form sulfites.

EXAMPLE 5.23: Write the equation for the reaction between barium oxide and sulfur dioxide.
Answer: $BaO(s) + SO_2(g) \longrightarrow BaSO_3(s)$.

   Case C. Metal oxides react with sulfur trioxide to form sulfates.

EXAMPLE 5.24: Write the equation for the reaction of calcium oxide with sulfur trioxide.
Answer: $CaO(s) + SO_3(g) \longrightarrow CaSO_4$.

WRITING DECOMPOSITION REACTIONS. We'll find that
many decomposition reactions are just the reverse of many of the combination reactions, except that some decompositions require heat.

Rule 6. *When a binary compound decomposes, the separate elements are the products, unless information to the contrary is given.* (This is nearly the reverse of Rule 1; this rule includes all binary compounds, whereas Rule 1 only included binary ionic compounds.)

EXAMPLE 5.25: Silver iodide is an ingredient in photographic film. When light hits it, it decomposes and the film is exposed. Write the equation.
Solution: Silver iodide is AgI. Its separate elements are Ag and I_2.
Answer: $2\,AgI(s) \longrightarrow 2\,Ag(s) + I_2(s)$.

EXAMPLE 5.26: Solid nitrogen triiodide is very unstable, and it decomposes noisily when struck. A favorite pastime of some chemists is to smear a paste of it on the bottoms of their shoes. As they walk down the hall, they are accompanied by the crackling noise of the compound decomposing with each step. Write the equation.
Solution: Nitrogen triiodide is NI_3. We were given the information that it's a solid; we wouldn't have known it otherwise.
Answer: $2\,NI_3(s) \longrightarrow N_2(g) + 3\,I_2(s)$.

Rule 7. *Some oxyacids decompose to form water and the corresponding nonmetal oxide.* (This is the reverse of Rule 3.) The acids that do this easily are H_2CO_3, H_2SO_3, and HNO_2. H_2SO_4 and HNO_3 do it, too, but with more difficulty (they have to be heated to a high temperature).

EXAMPLE 5.27: When a carbonated drink warms up, it loses its carbonation, because carbonic acid has decomposed. Write the equation.

Solution: Carbonic acid is H_2CO_3, and its corresponding nonmetal oxide is CO_2.

Answer: $H_2CO_3(aq) \xrightarrow{\Delta} CO_2(g) + H_2O(l)$

Rule 8. *A metal hydroxide decomposes, usually with heat, to yield a metal oxide and water. The metal keeps the charge it had in the hydroxide.* (This is the reverse of Rule 4.)

EXAMPLE 5.28: When blue copper(II) hydroxide is heated, a solid black substance is formed. Write the equation.

Solution: Copper(II) hydroxide is $Cu(OH)_2$. The fact that the product is black is of no help to us in knowing what compound it is, but we do know that the copper ion keeps a charge of $2+$. The oxide is thus CuO.

Answer: $Cu(OH)_2(s) \xrightarrow{\Delta} CuO(s) + H_2O(g)$

Note: We are heating solid $Cu(OH)_2$, and the water is driven off as steam, hence the "$H_2O(g)$."

Rule 9. *Some ternary salts decompose with heat to yield the corresponding nonmetal oxides and metal oxides.* (This is the reverse of Rule 5.)
   Case A. Metal carbonates decompose to form metal oxides and carbon dioxide.

EXAMPLE 5.29: Limestone is calcium carbonate. It is converted to lime, which is used in many industrial processes, by roasting the limestone in a lime kiln. Write the equation.

Answer: $CaCO_3(s) \xrightarrow{\Delta} CaO(s) + CO_2(g)$

   Case B. Metal sulfites decompose to form metal oxides and sulfur dioxide.

EXAMPLE 5.30: Write the equation for the thermal decomposition of potassium sulfite.

Answer: $K_2SO_3(s) \xrightarrow{\Delta} K_2O(s) + SO_2(g)$

   Case C. Metal sulfates decompose with strong heating to form metal oxides and sulfur trioxide.

EXAMPLE 5.31: Write the equation for the thermal decomposition of lead(II) sulfate.

Solution: Lead is a variable-charge metal, and it must keep the charge it has (2+). Therefore the product will be PbO.

Answer: $PbSO_4(s) \xrightarrow{\Delta} PbO(s) + SO_3(g)$

WRITING SINGLE REPLACEMENT REACTIONS.

Rule 10. *Alkali metals and alkaline earth metals (except beryllium and magnesium) react with water to produce the corresponding metal hydroxide and hydrogen gas.*

EXAMPLE 5.32: One way to make sodium hydroxide (lye) is to extract sodium metal from seawater (by a process we'll talk about in Chapter 14) and then let the sodium react with water. Write the equation for this last reaction.

Answer: $2 Na(s) + 2 H_2O(l) \longrightarrow 2 NaOH(aq) + H_2(g)$

Rule 11. *Active metals (all the metals that we showed in Figure 4.1, p. 67, except Ag, Au, Cu, and Hg) react with acids to produce corresponding metal salts and hydrogen gas.*

EXAMPLE 5.33: A common laboratory preparation of hydrogen gas allows zinc to react with hydrochloric acid. Write the equation.

Solution: The salt that is formed is between zinc ion and chloride ion. The hydrogen has been replaced by zinc.

Answer: $Zn(s) + 2 HCl(aq) \longrightarrow ZnCl_2(aq) + H_2(g)$.

EXAMPLE 5.34: Sulfuric acid will dissolve an aluminum pan. Write the equation.

Solution: The salt that is formed is between aluminum ion and sulfate ion. The numbers here are a bit more complicated than in the example above.

Answer: $2 Al(s) + 3 H_2SO_4(aq) \longrightarrow Al_2(SO_4)_3(aq) + 3 H_2(g)$

Rule 12. *Some metals react with some salts to produce the salt of the new metal and the old metal as a free element.* In this chapter, we'll only consider reactions of this type that work as we've described them. In Chapter 14, we'll see that there are rules for deciding which metals will replace which metal ions.

EXAMPLE 5.35: Copper is recovered from ore by first dissolving the ore in sulfuric acid to form an aqueous solution of copper(II) sulfate. Then the copper(II) sulfate solution is treated with scrap iron. Write the equation for this last reaction.

Solution: Iron can be Fe^{2+} or Fe^{3+}. Since we don't know which it is, we assume that it's the lower one, Fe^{2+}.

Answer: $CuSO_4(aq) + Fe(s) \longrightarrow FeSO_4(aq) + Cu(s)$

Rule 13. *Some nonmetals react with some salts to produce the salt of the new nonmetal and the old nonmetal as a free element.* Again, in this chapter, we'll only consider the ones that work as we've described them.

EXAMPLE 5.36: Iodine is recovered from seawater by treating the seawater with chlorine. Seawater contains potassium iodide, which reacts with the chlorine. Write the equation.

Solution: Chlorine replaces the iodide part of potassium iodide. The iodine is released as the free element.

Answer: $2\ KI(aq) + CL_2(g) \longrightarrow 2\ KCl(aq) + I_2(s)$

WRITING DOUBLE REPLACEMENT REACTIONS.

Rule 14. *An acid reacts with a metal hydroxide to yield a salt plus water.* The salt is composed of the metal ion and the negative ion from the acid.

EXAMPLE 5.37: An upset stomach is often caused by "excess stomach acid," which is hydrochloric acid. A popular medicine for an upset stomach contains aluminum hydroxide. Write the equation for the reaction between aluminum hydroxide in the medicine and hydrochloric acid.

Solution: Aluminum hydroxide is $Al(OH)_3$; hydrochloric acid is HCl. The aluminum will make a salt with the chloride ion: $AlCl_3$.

Answer: $2\ Al(OH)_3(s) + 6\ HCl(aq) \longrightarrow 2\ AlCl_3(aq) + 6\ H_2O$
$$(6\ HOH)$$

Note: Sometimes we find it convenient to write water as HOH instead of H_2O, to show that the "H" part came from the acid and the "OH" part came from the hydroxide.

Rule 15. *An acid reacts with a metal oxide to yield a salt plus water.* This is almost the same as Rule 14, except that less water is produced.

EXAMPLE 5.38: Steel surfaces, after manufacture, have a layer of iron(II) oxide on them. (See Example 5.17.) This oxide layer is removed by "pickling," which means dissolving the iron(II) oxide in sulfuric acid. Write the equation for this reaction.

Solution: Iron(II) oxide is FeO; sulfuric acid is H_2SO_4. The iron(II) ion will combine with the sulfate ion to form $FeSO_4$.

Answer: $FeO(s) + H_2SO_4(aq) \longrightarrow FeSO_4(aq) + H_2O$

Rule 16. *An acid reacts with a metal sulfide to produce a salt and hydrogen sulfide.* This is similar to Rule 15, except that hydrogen sulfide is produced instead of water.

EXAMPLE 5.39: In Example 5.35, we said that the first step in the recovery of copper from its ores is to dissolve the ore in sulfuric acid. If the compound in copper ore is CuS, write the equation for this reaction.

Solution: Copper is in the 2+ state, so it will stay that way.

Answer: $CuS(s) + H_2SO_4(aq) \longrightarrow CuSO_4(aq) + H_2S(g)$

Rule 17. *An acid reacts with a metal carbonate or a sulfite to yield a metal salt, water, and either carbon dioxide or sulfur dioxide.*

EXAMPLE 5.40: If you add vinegar to baking soda, it will fizz. This is because the acetic acid in vinegar is reacting with sodium hydrogen carbonate (baking soda). Write the equation.

Solution: Hydrogen carbonates behave just like carbonates in this kind of reaction.

Answer: $HC_2H_3O_2(aq) + NaHCO_3 \longrightarrow NaC_2H_3O_2(aq) + H_2O(l) + CO_2(g)$

EXAMPLE 5.41: Write the equation for the reaction of phosphoric acid with calcium sulfite.

Solution: Here sulfur dioxide will be the product. The salt is calcium phosphate.

Answer: $2\,H_3PO_4(aq) + 3\,CaSO_3(s) \longrightarrow$
$$Ca_3(PO_4)_2(aq) + 3\,SO_2(g) + 3\,H_2O(l)$$

Rule 18. *When two ionic compounds react with each other, the positive ions exchange negative ions.*

EXAMPLE 5.42: At Lake Tahoe, California, phosphate pollution is removed from sewage by introducing calcium hydroxide. Calcium phosphate, a precipitate, can then be removed. Write the equation for the reaction between sodium phosphate and calcium hydroxide.

Solution: Sodium phosphate is Na_3PO_4; calcium hydroxide is $Ca(OH)_2$. If we switch negative ions, we'll get NaOH and $Ca_3(PO_4)_2$.

Answer: $2\,Na_3PO_4(aq) + 3\,Ca(OH)_2(aq) \longrightarrow Ca_3(PO_4)_2(s) + 6\,NaOH(aq)$

MISCELLANEOUS. There are many, many chemical reactions that don't follow any of these rules, or don't fall neatly into the four categories we've outlined. There are a couple that do follow some rules but don't fit any of our categories.

Rule 19. *When a binary compound burns in oxygen or air, the products are oxides of both elements.*

EXAMPLE 5.43: Write the equation for the burning of dihydrogen sulfide in air.

Solution: The oxide of hydrogen is water. Sulfur has two oxides: SO_2 and SO_3. We choose the lower one.

Answer: $2\,H_2S(g) + 3\,O_2(g) \longrightarrow 2\,H_2O(g) + 2\,SO_2(g)$

Note: Since we're burning H_2S, the water produced will be steam.

EXAMPLE 5.44: Write the equation for the burning of copper(I) sulfide in air.

Solution: Each element has two oxides. We choose the lower one of each.

Answer: $2 Cu_2S(s) + 3 O_2(g) \longrightarrow 2 Cu_2O(s) + 2 SO_2(g)$

Rule 20. Carbon, or any compound containing carbon, when it burns can yield either carbon monoxide or carbon dioxide as the oxide of carbon. If it burns in insufficient oxygen or air, carbon monoxide will form. If it burns in sufficient or excess oxygen or air, then carbon dioxide will form.

EXAMPLE 5.45: Write equations for carbon burning in sufficient air and in insufficient air.

Answer: $C(s) + O_2(g) \longrightarrow CO_2(g)$ (sufficient air)
$2 C(s) + O_2(g) \longrightarrow 2 CO(g)$ (insufficient air)

EXAMPLE 5.46: Write equations that show acetylene, $C_2H_2(g)$, burning in sufficient air and in insufficient air.

Solution: Acetylene is a compound we haven't had before, but we have its formula, so writing the equations is no problem.

Answer: $2 C_2H_2(g) + 5 O_2(g) \longrightarrow 4 CO_2(g) + 2 H_2O(g)$ (sufficient air)
$2 C_2H_2(g) + 3 O_2(g) \longrightarrow 4 CO(g) + 2 H_2O(g)$ (insufficient air)

UNPREDICTABLE REACTIONS.

There are still a lot of reactions that can't be predicted by any of the rules we've had so far. In these cases, the problem will tell us what the products are. There are a lot of cases where this is true.

Case A. Reactions between most nonmetals can't be predicted.

EXAMPLE 5.47: Sulfur reacts with chlorine to produce disulfur dichloride (*l*). Write the equation.

Solution: We would have no way of knowing what this product is, unless the problem told us, as it did. We have rules for predicting metals plus nonmetals, but not two nonmetals (except when one of them is oxygen).

Answer: $2 S(s) + Cl_2(g) \longrightarrow S_2Cl_2(l)$

Case B. When the simplest compound, or the compound where a metal has its lowest charge, isn't formed, the reaction can't be predicted.

EXAMPLE 5.48: Sodium metal burns in air to form sodium peroxide. Write the equation.

Solution: Here we'd expect sodium oxide to be the product, unless we had information to the contrary, which we do. The fact is that when sodium is burned, sodium peroxide and not sodium oxide is the product.

Answer: $2 Na(s) + O_2(g) \longrightarrow Na_2O_2(s)$

Case C. Some reactions are more involved than the simple categories we've had, or are even combinations of several types of reactions at once.

EXAMPLE 5.49: In the paper industry, pulp is bleached with a solution made by passing chlorine gas through limewater, $Ca(OH)_2(aq)$. Calcium hypochlorite, the active bleaching agent, is produced, along with calcium chloride and water. Write the equation.

Solution: There is no way that we could have predicted these products from any of the rules we've had, but the problem gives them to us, so we can write the equation.

Answer:

$$2\,Cl_2(g) + 2\,Ca(OH)_2(aq) \longrightarrow Ca(ClO)_2(aq) + CaCl_2(aq) + 2\,H_2O(l)$$

EXAMPLE 5.50: "Superphosphate" fertilizer is made by treating phosphate rock, $Ca_3(PO_4)_2$, with sulfuric acid. Calcium dihydrogen phosphate and calcium sulfate are the products. Write the equation.

Solution: This is similar to a double replacement reaction, but it is not exactly identical. However, since we have the products, we can write the equation.

Answer: $Ca_3(PO_4)_2(s) + 2\,H_2SO_4(aq) \longrightarrow Ca(H_2PO_4)_2(aq) + 2\,CaSO_4(aq)$

REVIEW QUESTIONS

1. What is a *chemical reaction?*
2. What is the chemist's shorthand way of describing chemical reactions?

Reading and Writing Equations

3. What are *reactants* and *products?* On which side of a chemical equation is each found?
4. What is the symbol for *yields* in a chemical equation?
5. What are the steps involved in translating English into chemistry?

Balancing Equations

6. What is the *Law of Conservation of Matter?*
7. What do we mean by a *balanced* equation?
8. Why must we balance equations?
9. What does a number in front of a formula mean in an equation?
10. What are the steps involved in balancing equations?
11. Why may we not balance equations by putting numbers in as subscripts?
12. What should always be the final step in balancing an equation?
13. How do we deal with polyatomic ions when balancing equations?

14. When several atoms are unbalanced, how do we choose which to balance first?
15. What are the guidelines for balancing a chemical equation?

Other Symbols Used in Equations

16. What are the symbols for gas, solid, liquid, aqueous solution, and heat?
17. What does "gaseous oxygen" mean?
18. How do we name HCl to specify that it's in aqueous solution?
19. What do we mean by *thermal decomposition?*
20. What is a *precipitate?*
21. What are some synonyms for "yields"?

Types of Chemical Reactions and Their Equations

22. What are the four basic types of chemical reactions?
23. Give an example for each of the four types of reactions.
24. How do we show that heat is required in a reaction?
25. In your own words, tell what the difference is between the following: (a) a combination reaction and a decomposition reaction; (b) a single

replacement reaction and a double replacement reaction.

Predicting Products and Writing Equations

26. How can we know the physical state of a substance?
27. What class of compounds are mostly solids?
28. How will we know whether or not a substance is in aqueous solution?
29. What products are usually formed by the following combination reactions?
    a. a metal reacting with a nonmetal
    b. the lower oxide of an element reacting with oxygen
    c. a nonmetal oxide reacting with water
    d. a metal oxide reacting with water
    e. a metal oxide reacting with a nonmetal oxide
30. What products are usually formed by these decomposition reactions?
    a. a binary compound decomposing
    b. an oxyacid decomposing
    c. a metal hydroxide decomposing
    d. a ternary salt decomposing
31. What products are usually formed by these single replacement reactions?
    a. an alkali metal reacting with water
    b. an active metal reacting with an acid

c. a metal reacting with a salt
d. a nonmetal reacting with a salt
32. What products are usually formed by these double replacement reactions?
    a. an acid reacting with a metal hydroxide
    b. an acid reacting with a metal oxide
    c. an acid reacting with a metal sulfide
    d. an acid reacting with a metal carbonate or sulfite
    e. a salt reacting with another salt
33. What products are usually formed by these miscellaneous reactions?
    a. a binary compound burning in air
    b. carbon burning in insufficient air
34. In the case of a variable-charge ion, which charge do we choose if we have no information?
35. What do we mean by *oxidized*?
36. How can we decide what acid is formed when a given nonmetal oxide reacts with water?
37. How do we know when water is driven off as steam?
38. Why do we sometimes write water "HOH" instead of "H_2O"?
39. What are some kinds of reactions that can't be predicted by the rules in this chapter?
40. What information must we have if we are to write and balance an equation that can't be predicted by our rules?

EXERCISES

1. State which of the following English-chemistry translations are incorrect and correct them:
   a. *English:* "Calcium reacts with chlorine to form calcium chloride."
      Chemistry: $Ca + Cl_2 \longrightarrow CaCl_2$.
   b. *English:* "Sodium reacts with bromine to yield sodium bromide."
      Chemistry: $Na + Br_2 \longrightarrow NaBr_2$.
   c. *English:* "Silicon reacts with oxygen to yield silicon dioxide."
      Chemistry: $S + O_2 \longrightarrow SO_2$.
   d. *English:* "Mercury(II) oxide reacts to form mercury and oxygen."
      Chemistry: $HgO \longrightarrow Hg + O$.
   e. *English:* "Sodium chloride reacts with silver nitrate to yield silver chloride and sodium nitrate."
      Chemistry: $NaCl + AgNO_3 \longrightarrow AgCl + NaNO_3$.
2. Translate the following English sentences into chemistry.
   a. "Lithium reacts with nitrogen to yield lithium nitride."

   b. "Ammonia reacts with oxygen to yield nitrogen monoxide and water."
   c. "Zinc reacts with copper(II) nitrate to yield copper and zinc nitrate."
   d. "Phosphorus reacts with oxygen to yield tetraphosphorus hexoxide."
   e. "Ammonium sulfide reacts with mercury(II) bromide to yield ammonium bromide and mercury(II) sulfide."
3. Which of the following equations are balanced?
   a. $2 K + Br_2 \longrightarrow 2 KBr$
   b. $N_2 + O_2 \longrightarrow NO$
   c. $CaCO_3 + 2 HCl \longrightarrow CaCl_2 + CO_2 + H_2O$
   d. $3 Fe + 2 O_2 \longrightarrow Fe_2O_3$
   e. $H_2O_2 \longrightarrow H_2O + O_2$
4. Balance each of the unbalanced equations in Exercise 3.
5. What is wrong with each of these "balanced" equations?
   a. $2 H + O \longrightarrow H_2O$
   b. $FeS + HBr \longrightarrow FeBr + HS$
   c. $H_2 + F_2 \longrightarrow H_2F_2$

d. $Na_2CO_3 + CaCl_2 \longrightarrow CaCO_3 + Na_2Cl_2$

e. $BCl_3 \longrightarrow B + Cl_3$

f. $Li_2O + H_2O \longrightarrow Li_2(OH)_2$

g. $Al + 2\,HCl \longrightarrow AlCl_2 + H_2$

h. $PbNO_3 + KCl \longrightarrow PbCl + KNO_3$

i. $KClO_4 \longrightarrow KCl + O_4$

6. Write correct, balanced equations for each of the incorrect equations in Exercise 5.

7. Balance these equations.

a. $P + Cl_2 \nrightarrow PCl_3$

b. $Mg_3N_2 + H_2O \nrightarrow Mg(OH)_2 + NH_3$

c. $Fe + O_2 \nrightarrow Fe_2O_3$

d. $Ni(OH)_2 + H_2SO_4 \nrightarrow NiSO_4 + H_2O$

e. $Fe + AgNO_3 \nrightarrow Fe(NO_3)_2 + Ag$

f. $BaCl_2 + (NH_4)_2CO_3 \nrightarrow BaCO_3 + NH_4Cl$

g. $NaNO_2 + H_2SO_4 \nrightarrow HNO_2 + Na_2SO_4$

h. $NaOH + CO_2 \nrightarrow Na_2CO_3 + H_2O$

i. $B + F_2 \nrightarrow BF_3$

j. $HNO_2 \nrightarrow N_2O_3 + H_2O$

8. Translate the following from English to chemistry, and balance the equations.

a. "Ammonia reacts with sulfuric acid to yield ammonium sulfate."

b. "Methane, CH_4, burns in air to yield carbon dioxide and water."

c. "Dinitrogen trioxide reacts with water to yield nitrous acid."

d. "Barium carbonate decomposes with heat to yield barium oxide and carbon dioxide."

e. "Silicon reacts with chlorine to form silicon tetrachloride."

9. Translate from chemistry into English.

a. $Ca(s) + 2\,HBr(aq) \longrightarrow CaBr_2(aq) + H_2(g)$

b. $2\,HI(g) \longrightarrow H_2(g) + I_2(s)$

c. $2\,Be(s) + O_2(g) \longrightarrow 2\,BeO(s)$

d. $Mn(NO_3)_2(aq) + Na_2S(aq) \longrightarrow$
$$MnS(s) + 2\,NaNO_3(aq)$$

e. $Cl_2O_7(l) + H_2O(l) \longrightarrow 2\,HClO_4(aq)$

10. Translate from English to chemistry (put in s, l, g, aq, Δ), and balance the equations.

a. "Solid boron reacts with oxygen gas to yield solid diboron trioxide."

b. "Lead metal reacts with solid sulfur to yield solid lead(II) sulfide."

c. "Nitrogen gas reacts with chlorine gas to yield nitrogen trichloride gas."

d. "Hydrogen gas reacts with liquid bromine to yield gaseous hydrogen bromide."

e. "Aqueous potassium hydroxide reacts with nitric acid to yield water and aqueous potassium nitrate."

f. "Solid zinc sulfide reacts with sulfuric acid to yield dihydrogen sulfide gas and aqueous zinc sulfate."

g. "Solid ammonium nitrite decomposes thermally to yield nitrogen gas and steam."

h. "Aqueous chlorine reacts with aqueous potassium bromide to yield aqueous bromine and potassium chloride."

i. "Solid sodium hydrogen carbonate reacts with hydrochloric acid to yield aqueous sodium chloride, water, and carbon dioxide gas."

j. "Aqueous barium chloride reacts with aqueous ammonium sulfate to yield aqueous ammonium chloride and a precipitate of barium sulfate."

11. Classify the following reactions as combination, decomposition, single replacement, or double replacement.

a. $4\,Al(s) + 3\,O_2(g) \longrightarrow 2\,Al_2O_3$

b. $CaI_2(aq) + Hg(NO_3)_2(aq) \longrightarrow$
$$Ca(NO_3)_2(aq) + HgI_2(s)$$

c. $Mg(s) + 2\,HC_2H_3O_2(aq) \longrightarrow$
$$Mg(C_2H_3O_2)_2(aq) + H_2(g)$$

d. $CoSO_3(s) \overset{\Delta}{\longrightarrow} CoO(s) + SO_2(g)$

e. $FeO(s) + C(s) \longrightarrow Fe(s) + CO(g)$

f. $2\,Cu(s) + S(s) \longrightarrow Cu_2S(s)$

g. $2\,AgNO_3(aq) + K_2CrO_4(aq) \longrightarrow$
$$Ag_2CrO_4(s) + 2\,KNO_3(aq)$$

h. $Sr(OH)_2(aq) + H_2SO_4(aq) \longrightarrow$
$$SrSO_4(s) + 2\,H_2O(l)$$

i. $Pb(NO_3)_2(s) \overset{\Delta}{\longrightarrow} PbO(s) + 2\,NO_2(g)$

j. $2\,NH_3(g) + H_2SO_4(aq) \longrightarrow (NH_4)_2SO_4(aq)$

12. Translate each of the equations in Exercise 11 into English.

13. Complete and balance each of the following equations for combination reactions.

a. $Li(s) + Cl_2(g) \longrightarrow$

b. $Cr(s) + O_2(g) \longrightarrow$

c. $NO(g) + O_2(g) \longrightarrow$

d. $CO_2(g) + H_2O(l) \longrightarrow$

e. $K_2O(s) + H_2O(l) \longrightarrow$

f. $BeO(s) + CO_2(g) \longrightarrow$

g. $ZnO(s) + SO_2(g) \longrightarrow$

h. $Rb_2O(s) + SO_3(g) \longrightarrow$

14. Complete and balance each of the following equations for decomposition reactions.

a. $Ag_2O(s) \overset{\Delta}{\longrightarrow}$ e. $SnCO_3(s) \overset{\Delta}{\longrightarrow}$

b. $PCl_5(l) \overset{\Delta}{\longrightarrow}$ f. $MgSO_3(s) \overset{\Delta}{\longrightarrow}$

c. $H_2SO_3(aq) \overset{\Delta}{\longrightarrow}$ g. $CuSO_4(s) \overset{\Delta}{\longrightarrow}$

d. $Fe(OH)_3(s) \overset{\Delta}{\longrightarrow}$

15. Complete and balance the following equations for single replacement reactions.

a. $Ca(s) + H_2O(l) \longrightarrow$

b. $Rb(s) + H_2O(l) \longrightarrow$

c. $Cr(s) + HCl(aq) \longrightarrow$

d. $Cd(s) + H_3PO_4(aq) \longrightarrow$

e. $Ni(s) + Hg(NO_3)_2(aq) \longrightarrow$

f. $Zn(s) + CuCl_2(aq) \longrightarrow$

g. $KBr(aq) + F_2(aq) \longrightarrow$

h. $BaI_2(aq) + Br_2(aq) \longrightarrow$

i. $K_2S(aq) + I_2(s) \longrightarrow$

16. Complete and balance the following equations for double replacement reactions.
    a. $HBr(aq) + KOH(aq) \longrightarrow$
    b. $Zn(OH)_2(s) + HClO_4(aq) \longrightarrow$
    c. $CdO(s) + HF(aq) \longrightarrow$
    d. $MgCO_3(s) + H_3PO_4(aq) \longrightarrow$
    e. $NaHSO_3(aq) + HCl(aq) \longrightarrow$
    f. $AgNO_3(aq) + Na_2SO_4(aq) \longrightarrow$
    g. $SnCl_2(aq) + (NH_4)_2S(aq) \longrightarrow$

17. For each of the following equations, state which rule you would use to predict the products, or state that you have insufficient information to write the products by any of the rules given.
    a. $P(s) + O_2(g) \not\longrightarrow$
    b. $Na(s) + As(s) \not\longrightarrow$
    c. $Pb(NO_3)_2(aq) + KCl(aq) \not\longrightarrow$
    d. $Al(s) + H_3PO_4(aq) \not\longrightarrow$
    e. $C_2H_6(g) + O_2(g) \not\longrightarrow$
    f. $NiCO_3 \xrightarrow{\Delta}$
    g. $HC_2H_3O_2(aq) + Li_2O(s) \not\longrightarrow$
    h. $Mg(CN)_2(aq) + HCl(aq) \not\longrightarrow$
    i. $PCl_5(s) + H_2O(l) \not\longrightarrow$
    j. $Mg(ClO_3) \xrightarrow{\Delta}$

18. Complete and balance the equations in Exercise 17 for which you have sufficient information.

19. Many metals occur in ores as sulfides and are recovered by roasting the ore in air (burning). When zinc sulfide is roasted, zinc oxide and sulfur dioxide are obtained. When mercury(II) sulfide is roasted, free mercury and sulfur dioxide are the products. Write balanced equations for these two reactions and point out the difference in reaction type.

20. The Solvay process is an important commercial process of manufacturing sodium bicarbonate (sodium hydrogen carbonate). (a) Limestone ($CaCO_3$) is heated to give lime (CaO) and carbon dioxide. (b) The lime is added to water to form slaked lime [$Ca(OH)_2$]. (c) Ammonia is brought in and allowed to react with water and carbon dioxide to form aqueous ammonium hydrogen carbonate. (d) Aqueous sodium chloride is brought in and allowed to react with the ammonium hydrogen carbonate solution to give aqueous sodium hydrogen carbonate (the product) and aqueous ammonium chloride. (e) The ammonium chloride is changed back into ammonia gas, which can be reused, by this reaction: Ammonium chloride reacts with the slaked lime solution to produce ammonia, calcium chloride, and water. Write balanced equations for all reactions and state the reaction type for each.

21. "Nitrogen fixation" is an important process for the survival of plant life. Nitrogen in the atmosphere is in the form N_2, elemental nitrogen. Plants can't use it in this form, yet nitrogen is an essential part of their nutrition. To absorb nitrogen, the plants must receive it in some combined form, as a chemical compound. One way that nitrogen fixation occurs in nature begins with electrical storms. (a) Lightning causes nitrogen to react with oxygen and form nitrogen monoxide. (b) The nitrogen monoxide reacts further with oxygen in the air to form nitrogen dioxide. (c) Water vapor combines with nitrogen dioxide to form nitric acid and nitrogen monoxide. The nitric acid washes down with rain and becomes part of the soil. Write balanced equations for these reactions and state the reaction type for each.

22. In Exercise 19, we saw that zinc sulfide was converted to zinc oxide by roasting. The free zinc metal is obtained from zinc oxide by treating it with carbon monoxide, which is converted to carbon dioxide. Write a complete, balanced equation for this reaction.

23. A good way to clean silver is to put the silver into an aluminum pan full of saltwater. The aluminum reacts with the silver tarnish, Ag_2S, and replaces the silver. Write a complete, balanced equation for this reaction. (The salt only facilitates the reaction; it doesn't enter into the equation.)

24. Hydrazine, N_2H_4, is a rocket fuel. Write a balanced equation for its burning in oxygen. Nitrogen monoxide is one product.

25. An old way of making lye (NaOH) was to mix slaked lime [$Ca(OH)_2$] with plant ash (Na_2CO_3) in water solution. Write a complete, balanced equation for this reaction.

26. One form of iron ore is Fe_2O_3. Iron can be obtained as the free metal by heating with coke (C). Write a complete, balanced equation for this reaction.

6

Calculations with Formulas and Equations

We encounter problems every day that involve knowing or being able to tell how much of something it takes to make how much of something else. How much dry cement does it take to mix up enough concrete to mortar a 6-foot high brick wall 20 feet wide? How many eggs should we buy to make enough cookies for fifty girl scouts? Problems in chemistry are just like these. A chemist in an industrial plant might have to figure out, say, how much calcium carbonate will absorb enough harmful sulfur dioxide from the plant's emissions so as to comply with the Environmental Protection Agency's sulfur dioxide emission standards.

To solve these problems, the bricklayer, the baker, and the chemist need recipes. The chemist's recipe is a chemical equation, which tells what amounts of calcium carbonate and sulfur dioxide react to give what amounts of calcium sulfate and carbon dioxide.

$$2 \, CaCO_3(s) + 2 \, SO_2(g) + O_2(g) \longrightarrow 2 \, CaSO_4(s) + 2 \, CO_2(g)$$

Once the equation is known, the chemist can change the quantities of reactants and products to get (or in this case, to get rid of) the desired amounts of each.

In the last chapter, we interpreted chemical equations in terms of atoms and molecules. Now we want to interpret them in terms of moles and finally in terms of grams, so that we can work with them in a practical way. The chemist in an industrial plant can't count out atoms one-by-one. We have to make use of a concept we've introduced earlier: weighing as a means of counting. (See Section 3.1 p. 32.) We'll see that both formulas and equations can be expressed in terms of weight with numbers, and that's a chemistry-arithmetic translation. We'll learn how to do chemistry-arithmetic translations, and how to solve problems with conversion factors which we get from balanced chemical equations.

6.1 THE QUANTITATIVE MEANING OF FORMULAS

We saw that a formula means how many of each kind of atom are in a given chemical compound. For instance, the formula H_2SO_4 means that one molecule of the compound contains two atoms of hydrogen, one atom of sulfur, and four atoms of oxygen. That's one chemistry-English translation. We need to look at another chemistry-English translation, and learn how to get to a chemistry-arithmetic translation.

THE MOLE REVISITED. A mole is 6.02×10^{23} things: in particular, we're interested in counting atoms, molecules, and ions with this number. The phrase "one mole of neon atoms" means 6.02×10^{23} neon atoms. It also means 20.2 grams, because the gram-atomic weight of neon is 20.2 grams per mole. So, one arithmetic translation of the English phrase "one mole of neon," is "20.2 grams of neon."

In the same way, "two moles of neon" translates into "40.4 grams of neon." "One-half mole of neon" translates to "10.1 grams of neon," and so on. Since these mean, respectively, 12.0×10^{23} neon atoms and 3.01×10^{23} neon atoms, we can use either moles or grams to count atoms. When the chips are down and we actually have to make a measurement, we use grams instead of moles, because we don't have any kind of scale or balance that lets us measure moles directly. The gram-atomic weight of an element is one arithmetic translation of its symbol.

MOLECULAR WEIGHT.
What if we have a diatomic gas, such as oxygen (O_2)? A mole of O_2 means a mole of diatomic O_2 molecules: 6.02×10^{23} molecules. Since each molecule contains two atoms, then a mole of O_2 molecules will contain 12.0×10^{23} O atoms. The mass of a mole of diatomic O_2 molecules is twice the mass of a mole of O atoms. Since each mole of O atoms has a mass of 16.0 grams, a mole of O_2 molecules has a mass of 32.0 grams ($2 \times 16.0 = 32.0$). The arithmetic translation of "one mole of O_2," is "32.0 grams."

We can reinterpret the formula H_2SO_4. Another translation is this: "One mole of H_2SO_4 contains two moles of H, one mole of S, and four moles of O." To understand how this works, let's look at a simple analogy.

A red wagon has these parts: four wheels, one handle, and one body. Two red wagons have eight wheels, two handles, and two bodies. One dozen red wagons have four dozen wheels, one dozen handles, and one dozen bodies. *And,* one mole of red wagons has four moles of wheels, one mole of handles, and one mole of bodies. If we knew what each part weighed, we could calculate the weight of one mole of red wagons by adding up the weight of four moles of wheels, one mole of handles, and one mole of bodies.

In the same way, we can get the mass of a mole of H_2SO_4 molecules by adding up the masses of two moles of H, one mole of S, and four moles of O. The mass, in grams, of a mole of molecules is called the *gram-molecular weight,* or simply *molecular weight.* We get the molecular weight of a substance by adding up the gram-atomic weights of all the atoms that are in it. Molecular weight of a substance is the arithmetic translation of its molecular formula.

**gram-
molecular
weight**

EXAMPLE 6.1: What is the molecular weight of H_2SO_4?

Solution: Add up the gram-atomic weights.

$$
\begin{array}{ll}
\text{2 H atoms, each 1.01 g/mole} = & 2.02 \ \text{g/mole} \\
\text{1 S atom, each 32.1 g/mole} = & 32.1 \ \ \text{g/mole} \\
\text{4 O atoms, each 16.0 g/mole} = & \underline{64.0 \ \ \text{g/mole}} \\
& 98.12 \ \text{g/mole}
\end{array}
$$

The answer must be rounded off to one decimal place.

Answer: 98.1 g/mole.

Just as with gram-atomic weight, molecular weight is a conversion factor that lets us convert between grams and moles. Numbers of atoms in a formula are pure numbers. The formula H_2SO_4 means that *exactly* one mole contains *exactly* two moles of H, one mole of S, and four moles of O—no more and no less. Our molecular weight will only be limited in significant figures by the individual atomic weights. We'll usually agree to carry out molecular weights to one decimal place.

EXAMPLE 6.2: How many grams are in 2.50 moles of H_2SO_4?

Solution: We want to convert 2.50 moles of H_2SO_4 to grams. We saw above that the molecular weight of H_2SO_4 is 98.1 g/mole. This is our conversion factor. Here's the setup:

$$2.50 \text{ moles } H_2SO_4 \times 98.1 \frac{\text{g } H_2SO_4}{\text{mole } H_2SO_4}$$

Answer: 245 g H_2SO_4.

EXAMPLE 6.3: How many moles are in 545 grams of H_2SO_4?

Solution: We want to convert 545 grams of H_2SO_4 to moles. Our conversion factor is still 98.1 g/mole, which we have to invert to 1.00 mole/98.1 g to do this conversion.

$$545 \text{ g } H_2SO_4 \times \frac{1.00 \text{ mole } H_2SO_4}{98.1 \text{ g } H_2SO_4}$$

Answer: 5.56 moles H_2SO_4.

FORMULA WEIGHT.

Since ionic compounds are not molecules, we can't very well talk about their molecular weight. Instead, we talk about *gram-formula weight*. Gram-formula weight, or simply *formula weight*, means the mass, in grams, of one mole of any substance as determined by its formula. The formula weight of a compound is one arithmetic translation of its formula.

gram-formula weight

For instance, "one mole of the ionic compound Na_2SO_4" can be translated as "two moles of sodium ions and one mole of sulfate ions" as well as "two moles of Na, one mole of S, and four moles of O." We get the formula weight in exactly the same way as we get the molecular weight: add up the atomic weights of all the atoms in the compound. If the compound is a hydrate, the water is added in too.

EXAMPLE 6.4: What is the formula weight of $CuSO_4 \cdot 5\,H_2O$?

Solution: Here, the "$5\,H_2O$" means five water molecules, or $5 \times 2 = 10$ H atoms and $5 \times 1 = 5$ O atoms. We add these into the formula weight.

$$
\begin{array}{llr}
1 \text{ Cu, each } 63.5 \text{ g/mole} = & 63.5 \text{ g/mole} \\
1 \text{ S, each } 32.1 \text{ g/mole} = & 32.1 \text{ g/mole} \\
4 \text{ O, each } 16.0 \text{ g/mole} = & 64.0 \text{ g/mole} \\
10 \text{ H, each } 1.01 \text{ g/mole} = & 10.1 \text{ g/mole} \\
5 \text{ O, each } 16.0 \text{ g/mole} = & \underline{80.0 \text{ g/mole}} \\
& 249.7 \text{ g/mole}
\end{array}
$$

Answer: 249.7 g/mole.

Formula weight and molecular weight are really the same, since they're derived in the same way. Formula weight is the more common usage, and it can also include molecular weight. We'll usually find it more convenient to use formula weight. Again, as with gram-atomic weight, we find "weight" used incorrectly to mean "mass."

6.2 THE QUANTITATIVE MEANING OF EQUATIONS

We said that chemical equations were the chemist's recipes. For instance, the following equation is the chemist's recipe for making water:

$$2 H_2 + O_2 \longrightarrow 2 H_2O$$

(In this chapter, we won't use the symbols showing the physical state [g, l, s, aq]; they might confuse or obscure the arithmetic translations we're trying to emphasize.) We can translate the above equation like this: "Two moles of hydrogen react with one mole of oxygen to yield two moles of water." The numbers in front of the formulas in a chemical equation are pure numbers, too, like the subscripts in the formulas themselves.

To do the chemistry-arithmetic translation, we use the arithmetic translations of the individual formulas, namely, the formula weights. By using the formula weight of each substance, we can translate the equation into arithmetic as follows: "4.04 grams of hydrogen react with 32.0 grams of oxygen to yield 36.0 grams of water."

How do we get this translation? The formula weight of H_2 is 2×1.01 g/mole $= 2.02$ g/mole; O_2 is 2×16.0 g/mole $= 32.0$ g/mole; H_2O is 2.02 g/mole $+ 16.0$ g/mole $= 18.0$ g/mole. In the balanced equation, the quantities of both hydrogen and water are doubled (two moles of each). The masses of hydrogen and water are also doubled, so that the total mass on one side of the equation (36.0 grams) equals the total mass on the other side (36.0 grams). Figure 6.1 shows these different translations of the equation for water. Figure 6.2 shows a comparison between chemical equations and nonchemical recipes.

6.3 CALCULATIONS WITH CHEMICAL EQUATIONS

We've seen how to get the arithmetic translations of chemical equations, and we've also seen that formula weights are conversion factors. Now we'll see how to put them together to do calculations.

FIGURE 6.1
Translations of a chemical equation

These are all different ways of writing the recipe for water. In *A*, I've written the equation in terms of molecules. Then, in *B*, I multiplied the whole thing by 6.02 × 10²³, and I ended up with *C*. *D* is just *C* divided by 6.02 × 10²³ molecules/mole, which gives us moles.

$$2\,H_2 \quad + \quad O_2 \quad \longrightarrow \quad 2\,H_2O$$

A		2 molecules H_2	+	1 molecule O_2	$\dashrightarrow$ 2 molecules H_2O
B	6.02×10^{23}	(2 molecules H_2	+	1 molecule O_2	$\dashrightarrow$ 2 molecules H_2O)
C		$\left(\dfrac{12.04 \times 10^{23}}{\text{molecules } H_2}\right)$	+	$\left(\dfrac{6.02 \times 10^{23}}{\text{molecules } O_2}\right)$	$\dashrightarrow$ $\left(\dfrac{12.04 \times 10^{23}}{\text{molecules } H_2O}\right)$
D		2 moles H_2	+	1 mole O_2	$\dashrightarrow$ 2 moles H_2O
E		2(1.01 g + 1.01 g)	+	(16.0 g + 16.0 g)	$\dashrightarrow$ 2(1.01 g + 1.01 g + 16.0 g)
F		4.04 g H_2	+	32.0 g O_2	$\dashrightarrow$ 36.0 g H_2O
G		40.4 g H_2	+	320 g O_2	$\dashrightarrow$ 360 g H_2O
H		20 moles H_2	+	10 moles O_2	$\dashrightarrow$ 20 moles H_2O

After *D*, I used formula weights to get number of grams from number of moles. In *E*, I got the formula weight by adding the gram-atomic weights and multiplying by the number of moles. That gives us *F*, where we can see that the total mass of matter on both sides is 36.0 grams.

In *G* and *H*, I fooled with the recipe to show how it can be increased. In *G*, I needed 360 grams of water, not 36.0 grams, so I increased all the ingredients 10 times. In *H*, I did the same thing using moles.

EQUATIONS AS SOURCES OF CONVERSION FACTORS.
We're going to use the information contained in chemical equations for conversion factors. Let's look at an example.

Chlorine gas is made commercially by the electrolytic decomposition of salt from seawater, according to this unbalanced equation:

$$2\,NaCl \longrightarrow 2\,Na + Cl_2$$

We want to know how many moles of sodium chloride must decompose to get 5.00 moles of chlorine. There are five steps involved in solving problems like this one.

Step 1. *Check to be sure that the equation is balanced.* (You can't get a correct answer unless the equation is balanced.) The balanced equation:

$$2\,NaCl \longrightarrow 2\,Na + Cl_2$$

Step 2. *Figure out what units are to be converted to what other units.* We want to convert 5.00 moles of chlorine to moles of sodium chloride.

Step 3. *Write the number, with its units, on the left side of the calculation space. Write the units of the desired answer on the right.*

$$5.00 \text{ moles } Cl_2 = \underline{\quad} \text{ moles } NaCl$$

Step 4. *Pick a conversion factor from the balanced equation.* We want a conversion factor that contains Cl_2 and NaCl, so we only look at these two quantities. We see that two moles of NaCl yield one mole of Cl_2. We want to trade "moles NaCl" for "moles Cl_2," so we arrange our conversion factor so that "moles Cl_2" is on the bottom and will cancel out. Our conversion factor is:

$$\frac{2 \text{ moles } NaCl}{\text{mole } Cl_2}$$

This is the *mole ratio.* The numbers in front of formulas in equations are

mole ratio

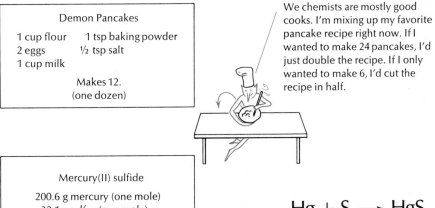

Demon Pancakes

1 cup flour   1 tsp baking powder
2 eggs   ½ tsp salt
1 cup milk

Makes 12.
(one dozen)

We chemists are mostly good cooks. I'm mixing up my favorite pancake recipe right now. If I wanted to make 24 pancakes, I'd just double the recipe. If I only wanted to make 6, I'd cut the recipe in half.

Mercury(II) sulfide

200.6 g mercury (one mole)
32.1 g sulfur (one mole)

Makes 232.7 g HgS.
(one mole)

$$Hg + S \longrightarrow HgS$$

Now, I'm mixing up the only recipe for mercury(II) sulfide. I got this recipe from the equation up there. The equation says that 1 mole of mercury (200.6 g) will react with 1 mole of sulfur (32.1 g) to yield 1 mole of mercury(II) sulfide (232.7 g). If I wanted 23.27 g of HgS, I'd use one-tenth of the recipe. If I wanted 465.4 g of HgS, I'd double the recipe.

**FIGURE 6.2
Comparison of
nonchemical
recipes and
chemical
equations**

pure numbers. We write them as digits and understand that they won't limit the number of significant figures that our answer can have.

Step 5. *Set up the problem and check units. Find the answer.*

$$5.00 \text{ moles } \cancel{Cl_2} \times \frac{2 \text{ moles NaCl}}{\cancel{\text{mole } Cl_2}} = \underline{\quad} \text{ moles NaCl}$$

The units check. The answer is 10.0 moles NaCl.

MOLE-TO-MOLE CONVERSIONS.

The preceding example was a mole-to-mole conversion. We converted moles of one substance to moles of another, using the mole ratio as a conversion factor. We'll do a few more examples of this kind of conversion.

EXAMPLE 6.5: If 6.87 moles of chlorine are produced by the above equation, how many moles of sodium are also produced?

Solution:
Step 1: The equation is already balanced.
Step 2: We want to convert 6.87 moles Cl_2 to moles Na.
Step 3: 6.87 moles Cl_2 = ____ moles Na
Step 4: Our conversion factor is 2 moles Na/mole Cl_2.
Step 5:

$$6.87 \text{ moles } \cancel{Cl_2} \times \frac{2 \text{ moles Na}}{\cancel{\text{mole } Cl_2}} = \underline{\quad} \text{ moles Na}$$

The units check.

Answer: 13.7 moles Na.

EXAMPLE 6.6: Nitric acid is prepared commercially by this equation:

$$NO_2 + H_2O \xrightarrow{\quad} HNO_3 + NO$$

How many moles of nitric acid can be made from 0.831 moles of NO_2?

Solution:
Step 1: The equation is not balanced, so we balance it.

$$3\,NO_2 + H_2O \longrightarrow 2\,HNO_3 + NO$$

Step 2: We want to convert 0.831 moles of NO_2 to moles of HNO_3.
Step 3: 0.831 moles NO_2 = ____ moles HNO_3
Step 4: From the equation, our conversion factor is 2 moles HNO_3/3 moles NO_2.
Step 5:

$$0.831 \text{ moles } \cancel{NO_2} \times \frac{2 \text{ moles } HNO_3}{3 \text{ moles } \cancel{NO_2}} = \underline{\quad} \text{ moles } HNO_3$$

The units check.

Answer: 0.554 moles HNO_3.

MOLE-TO-MASS AND MASS-TO-MOLE

CONVERSIONS. In these slightly more complex conversions, we begin to use formula weights as conversion factors, in addition to the mole ratio.

EXAMPLE 6.7: In the preparation of nitric acid (Example 6.6), how many grams of nitric acid can be made from 0.831 moles of NO_2?

Solution:
Step 1: The equation is already balanced.
Step 2: We want to convert 0.831 moles NO_2 to grams of nitric acid.
Step 3: 0.831 moles NO_2 = ____ grams HNO_3.
Step 4: We need two conversion factors. The mole ratio, 2 moles HNO_3/3 moles NO_2, gets us from moles of NO_2 to moles of HNO_3, as in Example 6.6. We need another conversion factor to get from moles of HNO_3 to grams of HNO_3: the formula weight of HNO_3.

$$
\begin{array}{lll}
\text{H:} & 1(1.01 \text{ g/mole}) = & 1.01 \text{ g/mole} \\
\text{N:} & 1(14.0 \text{ g/mole}) = & 14.0 \text{ g/mole} \\
\underline{O_3:} & \underline{3(16.0 \text{ g/mole}) =} & \underline{48.0 \text{ g/mole}} \\
HNO_3: & & 63.0 \text{ g/mole}
\end{array}
$$

This conversion factor is 63.0 g/mole HNO_3.
Step 5: Our setup:

$$
0.831 \text{ moles } NO_2 \times \frac{2 \text{ moles } HNO_3}{3 \text{ moles } NO_2} \times \frac{63.0 \text{ g}}{\text{mole } HNO_3} = \underline{\quad} \text{ g } HNO_3
$$

The units check.

Answer: 34.9 g HNO_3.

EXAMPLE 6.8: The rusting of iron is represented by the following un-balanced equation:

$$Fe + O_2 \longrightarrow\!\!\!/ \ Fe_2O_3$$

11.5 grams of rust are scraped off a rusty tool. How many moles of iron are lost from the tool?

Solution:
Step 1: The equation is not balanced, so we balance it:

$$4 Fe + 3 O_2 \longrightarrow 2 Fe_2O_3$$

Step 2: We want to convert 11.5 grams of Fe_2O_3 to moles of Fe.
Step 3: 11.5 g Fe_2O_3 = ____ moles Fe.
Step 4: Again, we need two conversion factors. This time, we first need the formula weight of Fe_2O_3 to change grams of Fe_2O_3 to moles of Fe_2O_3; then we need the mole ratio to change moles of Fe_2O_3 to moles of Fe. Our formula weight:

$$
\begin{array}{lll}
Fe_2: & 2(55.8 \text{ g/mole}) = & 111.6 \text{ g/mole} \\
\underline{O_3:} & \underline{3(16.0 \text{ g/mole}) =} & \underline{48.0 \text{ g/mole}} \\
Fe_2O_3: & & 159.6 \text{ g/mole}
\end{array}
$$

The formula weight is 159.6 g Fe_2O_3. The mole ratio, from the balanced equation, is 4 moles Fe/2 moles Fe_2O_3, which simplifies to 2 moles Fe/mole Fe_2O_3.

Step 5: Our setup:

$$11.5 \text{ g Fe}_2\text{O}_3 \times \frac{1 \text{ mole Fe}_2\text{O}_3}{159.6 \text{ g Fe}_2\text{O}_3} \times \frac{2 \text{ moles Fe}}{\text{mole Fe}_2\text{O}_3} = \underline{\quad} \text{ moles Fe}$$

The units check.

Answer: 0.144 moles Fe.

MASS-TO-MASS CONVERSIONS.

In these calculations, we'll use two formula weight conversion factors plus a mole ratio.

EXAMPLE 6.9: In the rusting of iron (Example 6.8), how many grams of rust are formed from 2.36 grams of iron lost from the tool?

Solution:

Step 1: The equation is already balanced.

Step 2: We want to convert 2.36 g Fe to grams of Fe_2O_3.

Step 3: 2.36 g Fe = _____ g Fe_2O_3.

Step 4: We need a conversion factor to get from grams of iron to moles of iron (the atomic weight of iron); one to get from moles of iron to moles of Fe_2O_3 (the mole ratio); and one to get from moles of Fe_2O_3 to grams of Fe_2O_3 (the formula weight). Our conversion factors are 55.8 g Fe/mole Fe; 2 moles Fe/mole Fe_2O_3; and 159.6 g Fe_2O_3/mole Fe_2O_3.

Step 5: Our setup:

$$2.36 \text{ g Fe} \times \frac{1 \text{ mole Fe}}{55.8 \text{ g Fe}} \times \frac{1 \text{ mole Fe}_2\text{O}_3}{2 \text{ moles Fe}} \times \frac{159.6 \text{ g Fe}_2\text{O}_3}{\text{mole Fe}_2\text{O}_3} = \underline{\quad} \text{ g Fe}_2\text{O}_3$$

The units check.

Answer: 3.38 g Fe_2O_3.

EXAMPLE 6.10: A major source of sulfur dioxide pollution comes from the smelting of copper sulfide ore. One equation for this is:

$$CuS + O_2 \longrightarrow Cu + SO_2$$

How many metric tons of sulfur dioxide will be released into the atmosphere as a result of smelting 555 metric tons of CuS?

Solution:

Step 1: The equation is balanced.

Step 2: We want to convert 555 metric tons of CuS to metric tons of SO_2.

Step 3: 555 metric tons CuS = _____ metric tons SO_2.

Step 4: We're given a new unit here: a metric ton (t) is 1000 kg; it is 10 percent heavier than the 2000-pound English ton. However, since the answer is asked for in the same units, we don't have to know anything about metric tons to solve the problem. We can express formula weights in metric tons instead of grams if we want to, because formula weights can have any units. We usually understand them to be gram-formula weights, but here we'll express them in ton-formula weights, or ton moles (t-mole). When we add up the formula weights, we can use the same numbers we would use for grams. We can get away with this if we stick to the same units all the way through the problem. (See Figure 6.3.)

CuS: Cu: 63.5 t/t-mole   SO$_2$:   S: 32.1 t/t-mole
       S: 32.1 t/t-mole   O$_2$: (2 × 16.0) = 32.0 t/t-mole
       CuS: 95.6 t/t-mole   SO$_2$:   64.1 t/t-mole

Our conversion factors are 95.6 t CuS/t-mole CuS; 1 t-mole CuS/t-mole SO$_2$; and 64.1 t SO$_2$/t-mole SO$_2$.

Step 5: Our setup:

$$555 \text{ t CuS} \times \frac{1 \text{ t-mole CuS}}{95.6 \text{ t CuS}} \times \frac{1 \text{ t-mole SO}_2}{\text{t-mole CuS}} \times \frac{64.1 \text{ t SO}_2}{\text{t-mole SO}_2} = \underline{\quad} \text{ t SO}_2$$

The units check.

Answer: 372 t SO$_2$.

EXAMPLE 6.11: In the beginning of this chapter, we discussed the removal of SO$_2$ pollution from smokestack emissions as follows:

$$2\,CaCO_3 + 2\,SO_2 + O_2 \longrightarrow 2\,CaSO_4 + 2\,CO_2$$

FIGURE 6.3
Formula weights may have any units

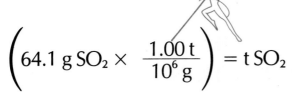

$$\left(95.6 \text{ g CuS} \times \frac{1.00 \text{ t}}{10^6 \text{ g}} \right) = \text{t CuS}$$

To convert grams to metric tons, we'd have to multiply the formula weights of *both* CuS and SO$_2$ by this conversion factor.

$$\left(64.1 \text{ g SO}_2 \times \frac{1.00 \text{ t}}{10^6 \text{ g}} \right) = \text{t SO}_2$$

$$555 \text{ t CuS} \times \frac{64.1 \text{ g SO}_2 \times \dfrac{1.00 \text{ t}}{10^6 \text{ g}}}{95.6 \text{ g CuS} \ \dfrac{1.00 \text{ t}}{10^6 \text{ g}}} = 372 \text{ t SO}_2$$

So you see, when we put it into the setup, all the complicated conversion units cancel right out! I think that's really neat. Think of all the trouble we save by using metric tons from the start. We just have to be sure we use them all the way through.

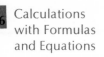
How many metric tons of $CaCO_3$ will it take to absorb the 372 metric tons of SO_2 produced in Example 6.10?

Solution:

Step 1: The equation is balanced.

Step 2: We want to convert metric tons of SO_2 to metric tons of $CaCO_3$.

Step 3: 372 metric tons SO_2 = _____ metric tons $CaCO_3$.

Step 4: We add up the formula weights.

$$
\begin{array}{llll}
SO_2\text{:} & S\text{:} & & 32.1 \text{ t/t-mole} \\
 & O_2\text{:} & 2(16.0) = & 32.0 \text{ t/t-mole} \\ \hline
 & SO_2\text{:} & & 64.1 \text{ t/t-mole} \\
\end{array}
$$

$$
\begin{array}{llll}
CaCO_3\text{:} & Ca\text{:} & & 40.1 \text{ t/t-mole} \\
 & C\text{:} & & 12.0 \text{ t/t-mole} \\
 & O_3\text{:} & 3(16.0) = & 48.0 \text{ t/t-mole} \\ \hline
 & CaCO_3\text{:} & & 100.1 \text{ t/t-mole} \\
\end{array}
$$

Our conversion factors are 64.1 t SO_2/t-mole SO_2; 2 t-moles $CaCO_3$/2 t-moles SO_2 (simplifies to 1 t-mole $CaCO_3$/t-mole SO_2); and 100.1 t $CaCO_3$/t-mole $CaCO_3$.

Step 5: Our setup:

$$372 \text{ t } SO_2 \times \frac{1 \text{ t-mole } SO_2}{64.1 \text{ t } SO_2} \times \frac{1 \text{ t-mole } CaCO_3}{\text{t-mole } SO_2} \times \frac{100.1 \text{ t } CaCO_3}{\text{t-mole } CaCO_3}$$

$$= \underline{\quad} \text{ t } CaCO_3$$

The units check.

Answer: 581 t $CaCO_3$.

6.4 HEAT AS PART OF CHEMICAL REACTIONS

In Chapter 5, we saw that some chemical reactions need heat to make them go. We used the Greek letter delta (Δ) to show this in a qualitative way. Heat can also be given off in a chemical reaction, although we don't have any simple way of showing that. In fact, most chemical reactions involve heat, either by needing heat to make them go or by giving off heat. We can measure how much heat is involved in any chemical reaction, and we can use these numbers just like formula weights when we're doing chemical calculations.

exothermic reaction

A reaction that gives off heat is called an *exothermic reaction,* and the amount of heat is written on the right side of the equation. In this case, heat is a product of the reaction. A reaction that requires heat is called an *endo-*

endothermic reaction

thermic reaction, and the amount of heat is written on the left side of the equation. In that case, heat is a reactant. Here are two examples:

$$2 H_2 + O_2 \longrightarrow 2 H_2O + 136 \text{ kcal} \quad \text{(exothermic)}$$
$$N_2 + O_2 + 43.2 \text{ kcal} \longrightarrow 2 NO \quad \text{(endothermic)}$$

The amount of heat involved is called the *heat of reaction* and is expressed in kilocalories (kcal). The heat of reaction is fixed for a given reaction, and we always get this heat, whether we want it or not. Some chemical reactions are used for the sole purpose of generating heat. The burning of natural gas, coal, oil, and other fuels are examples of this.

EXAMPLE 6.12: When natural gas (methane, CH_4) is burned, 213 kcal/ mole of heat is produced according to this equation:

$$CH_4 + 2\,O_2 \longrightarrow CO_2 + 2\,H_2O + 213 \text{ kcal}$$

How much heat will be produced by the burning of 454 grams of natural gas?

Solution:

Step 1: The equation is balanced.

Step 2: We want to convert 454 grams of methane to kilocalories.

Step 3: 454 g CH_4 = _____ kcal.

Step 4: Our conversion factors are the formula weight of CH_4 and the ratio 1 mole CH_4/213 kcal from the equation. We add up the formula weight of CH_4:

$$
\begin{array}{lll}
C: & & 12.0 \text{ g/mole} \\
H_4: & (4 \times 1.01) = & \underline{4.04 \text{ g/mole}} \\
CH_4: & & 16.0 \text{ g/mole}
\end{array}
$$

Step 5: Our setup:

$$454 \text{ g } CH_4 \times \frac{1 \text{ mole } CH_4}{16.0 \text{ g } CH_4} \times \frac{213 \text{ kcal}}{\text{mole } CH_4} = \underline{\quad} \text{ kcal}$$

The units check.

Answer: 6040 kcal.

Sometimes we *don't* want the heat of reaction. In a gasoline engine, for instance, the heat of reaction is a nuisance. We have to have radiators or other cooling systems to continually get rid of the heat of reaction when gasoline burns. All we really want the gasoline to do is to make gases— carbon dioxide, carbon monoxide, and water vapor—and make the mixture expand so that the pistons are pushed and the car runs. But the heat of reaction is just as much a part of the reaction as the chemical substances are, and we have to take it whether we want it or not.

EXAMPLE 6.13: One ingredient in gasoline is octane, C_8H_{18}. It burns according to this equation:

$$2\,C_8H_{18} + 25\,O_2 \longrightarrow 16\,CO_2 + 18\,H_2O + 2614 \text{ kcal}$$

How many grams of octane would have to be burned to produce enough heat to boil the water in a 12-liter radiator (about 6480 kcal)?

Solution:

Step 1: The equation is balanced.

Step 2: We want to convert 6480 kcal to grams of octane.

Step 3: 6480 kcal = _____ g octane.

Step 4: We add up the formula weight of octane:

$$C_8: \quad 8(12.0) = \quad 96.0 \text{ g/mole}$$
$$\underline{H_{18}: \quad 18(1.01) = \quad 18.2 \text{ g/mole}}$$
$$C_8H_{18}: \qquad\qquad\quad 114.2 \text{ g/mole}$$

Our conversion factors are 2 moles C_8H_{18}/2614 kcal and 114.2 g C_8H_{18}/mole C_8H_{18}.

Step 5: Our setup:

$$6480 \text{ kcal} \times \frac{2 \text{ moles } C_8H_{18}}{2614 \text{ kcal}} \times \frac{114.2 \text{ g } C_8H_{18}}{\text{mole } C_8H_{18}} = \underline{\quad} \text{ g } C_8H_{18}$$

The units check.

Answer: 566 g C_8H_{18}.

In chemical plants, many chemical reactions are going on at the same time, some giving off heat, and some requiring heat. A challenging problem that chemical engineers face is to design the plant so that the heat from the exothermic reactions is used to make the endothermic reactions go. This is done through heat exchangers. Usually the numbers don't exactly match up, though, and so some heat has to be supplied or gotten rid of.

6.5 PROBLEMS INVOLVING PERCENTAGES

percent

Percent means parts per hundred parts. We have a number of instances where we need to use percent in chemical calculations. We can express a compound in terms of percentages by weight of its elements. We can talk about the percent purity of a compound. In a chemical reaction, we might not actually obtain all of the product that our calculations led us to believe we would. In that case, we would calculate a percent yield. We'll learn to work with all of these things in this section.

PERCENTAGES AND FORMULAS. A chemical formula can be used to calculate the percentages of all the elements in it. For instance, the compound lead(II) sulfide is 86.6 percent lead and 13.4 percent sulfur, by weight. We'll see a little later how we calculate this, but first let's look at weight percentage with a simple example.

Suppose we own the following creatures:

> 2 elephants, at 4055 pounds apiece
> 2 aardvarks, at 50.5 pounds apiece

We sell these animals to two different parties in the same city. A zoo buys the elephants, and a private collector buys the aardvarks. They agree to pay the shipping charge, by railroad. How should we divide the shipping bill between the two purchasers?

One way to look at it would be to divide the bill in half. We could say that the load is 50 percent elephants and 50 percent aardvarks. But if our shipping charge is computed by weight (which it is), we have to look at the situation differently, because elephants weigh so much more than aardvarks. To determine the fair amount of the bill to be paid by each buyer, we should calculate the *percentage-by-weight* of each pair of animals. To do this, we compute the total weight, divide the sum into each of the individual weights, and multiply by 100. Like this:

**percentage-
by-weight**

$$2 \text{ elephants, at } 4055 \text{ pounds each} = 8110 \text{ pounds}$$
$$2 \text{ aardvarks, at } 50.5 \text{ pounds each} = \underline{\quad 101 \text{ pounds}}$$
$$\text{Total} \quad 8211 \text{ pounds}$$

Percentage-by-weight of elephants:

$$\frac{8110 \text{ lb}}{8211 \text{ lb}} \times 100. = 98.8\%$$

Percentage-by-weight of aardvarks:

$$\frac{101 \text{ lb}}{8211 \text{ lb}} \times 100. = 1.2\%$$

The answers total 100 percent. We always add up the percentages when the problem is finished, just to check the answers. If they're right, they'll always add up to 100 percent.

So, the answer is that the recipient of the aardvarks should pay 1.2 percent of the shipping bill; the new owner of the elephants gets stuck with 98.8 percent.

Now we're ready to do the same thing in chemistry.

EXAMPLE 6.14: Let's go back to lead(II) sulfide and calculate the percentages by weight of lead and of sulfur in this compound.

Solution: First, write the correct formula: PbS. Then add up the atomic weights to get the formula weight.

$$\begin{array}{ll} \text{Pb:} & 207.2 \\ \text{S:} & \underline{32.1} \\ \text{PbS:} & 239.3 \end{array}$$

Divide each individual weight by the total weight, and multiply by 100 (10^2).

$$Pb = \frac{207.2}{239.3} \times 10^2 = 86.59\% \ (86.6\%)$$

$$S = \frac{32.1}{239.3} \times 10^2 = 13.4\%$$

Finally, be sure the answers add to 100%.

$$86.6\% + 13.4\% = 100.0\%$$

The results check.

Answer: 86.6% Pb; 13.4% S.

Expressing elements in compounds as percentages is called *percent composition.*

**percent
composition**

EXAMPLE 6.15: Iron pills, for iron-deficiency anemia, usually contain iron in the form of iron(II) sulfate. Calculate its percent composition to two decimal places.

Solution: The formula of iron(II) sulfate is $FeSO_4$. The formula weight is:

$$
\begin{array}{ll}
Fe: & 55.85 \\
S: & 32.06 \\
4\,O: & 64.00 \\
\hline
FeSO_4: & 151.91
\end{array}
$$

Compute the percent composition of each element.

$$Fe = \frac{55.85}{151.91} \times 10^2 = 36.77\%$$

$$S = \frac{32.06}{151.91} \times 10^2 = 21.10\%$$

$$O = \frac{64.00}{151.91} \times 10^2 = 42.13\%$$

The percentages add up to 100.00%.

Answer: 36.77% Fe; 21.10% S; 42.13% O.

Sometimes we are given percent composition and asked to determine the formula of a compound. This means we must figure out the whole-number ratio of elements in the compound. This is easy to do, as we'll see in the following example.

EXAMPLE 6.16: A compound has the following percent composition: 56.68% K, 8.68% C, and 34.73% O. What is its formula?

Solution: Remember that percent means parts per hundred, and in this case it means grams per 100 grams. If we keep in mind that we're talking about 100 grams of the compound, then we may express the percentages as grams and divide each by the atomic weight of the element.

$$K: \quad \frac{56.68 \text{ g}}{39.10 \text{ g/mole}} = 1.450 \text{ moles K}$$

$$C: \quad \frac{8.68 \text{ g}}{12.0 \text{ g/mole}} = 0.723 \text{ moles C}$$

$$O: \quad \frac{34.73 \text{ g}}{16.00 \text{ g/mole}} = 2.171 \text{ moles O}$$

This gives us the relative numbers of moles of each element in the formula. We *could* write $K_{1.450}C_{0.723}O_{2.171}$, but it wouldn't be very useful. Instead, we get a whole-number answer by dividing each number of moles by the smallest one. In this case, the smallest number is 0.723 moles C. When we do this, we're saying, "Okay, what if we have *one* carbon atom? Then how many of the others do we have?"

$$\frac{1.450 \text{ moles K}}{0.723 \text{ moles C}} = 2.00 \text{ moles K/mole C}$$

$$\frac{0.723 \text{ moles C}}{0.723 \text{ moles C}} = 1.00 \text{ moles C/mole C}$$

$$\frac{2.171 \text{ moles O}}{0.723 \text{ moles C}} = 3.00 \text{ moles O/mole C}$$

For every one mole of carbon, we have two moles of potassium and three of oxygen. We use this ratio to write the formula.

Answer: K_2CO_3.

For covalent compounds, we have to make a distinction between empirical formula and molecular formula. The *empirical formula* is a formula that tells the simplest ratio of the elements in the compound. The *molecular formula* tells how many of each kind of atom are in a molecule. Sometimes these are the same, but sometimes they're different. For instance, the formula H_2O is both an empirical formula and a molecular formula. It's the simplest ratio, in whole numbers, between hydrogen and oxygen, and it also tells us that there are two atoms of hydrogen and one atom of oxygen in a water molecule.

However, the compound acetylene has the molecular formula C_2H_2. This says that there are two atoms of carbon and two atoms of hydrogen in a molecule of acetylene. We could divide each by two and get CH, which is the empirical formula. For this compound and many others, the empirical formula is different from the molecular formula. When we're given percentages and asked to find formulas, what we'll get will be the empirical formula. We won't run into this problem with ionic compounds, as in Example 6.15, because for an ionic compound there's no such thing as a molecular formula. To tell the difference between the empirical formula and the molecular formula for a covalent compound, though, we need more information than the percentages. We need the molecular weight.

**empirical
formula**

✓ ■ **EXAMPLE 6.17:** A compound has this percent composition: 92.24% C, 7.76% H. Its molecular weight is 78.06. What is its molecular formula?

Solution: First, find the empirical formula.

$$C: \quad \frac{92.24 \text{ g}}{12.01 \text{ g/mole}} = 7.680 \text{ moles C}$$

$$H: \quad \frac{7.76 \text{ g}}{1.01 \text{ g/mole}} = 7.68 \text{ moles H}$$

Since these two numbers are the same, we have a 1-to-1 ratio of carbon to hydrogen. This gives us the empirical formula of CH, which we need to change to the molecular formula. If the empirical formula, CH, were the molecular formula, it would have a molecular weight of 12.01 g/mole + 1.01 g/mole = 13.02 g/mole. It doesn't, though. The molecular weight is 78.06 g/mole. The molecular formula has to be some multiple of the empirical formula. To find out what multiple this is, we divide the weight of the empirical formula into the molecular weight:

$$\frac{78.06 \text{ g/mole}}{13.02 \text{ g/mole}} = 6$$

Our molecular formula is thus 6 times the empirical formula.

Answer: C_6H_6.

PERCENT PURITY. Chemicals usually occur in nature mixed with other chemicals. Separating the chemicals wanted from the chemicals not wanted provides many real problems for chemists to solve. To know what **percent purity** we're up against, we use *percent purity* to tell us how many parts of the stuff we want is contained in 100 parts of the total mixture, including the stuff we don't want. Sometimes we don't bother to separate it, but just use it the way it is, in its impure state. If we do that, then we have to use more of the impure substance than we'd have to use if it were pure.

EXAMPLE 6.18: A silver ore is 21.0 percent silver. How many grams of ore are needed to produce 10.0 grams of pure silver?

Solution:

Step 1: We want to convert 10.0 grams of silver to grams of ore.

Step 2: 10.0 g Ag = _____ g ore.

Step 3: We need a conversion factor to go from grams of silver to grams of ore. The percentage is our conversion factor. It means that a 100-gram sample of ore contains 21.0 grams of silver, or 21.0 g Ag/100. g ore. This is the same as 0.210 grams of silver per 1 gram of ore, and we'll use this figure. Since we want the "g Ag" to cancel out, we'll put it on the bottom. Then our conversion factor is:

$$\frac{1.00 \text{ g ore}}{0.210 \text{ g Ag}}$$

Step 4:

$$10.0 \text{ g Ag} \times \frac{1.00 \text{ g ore}}{0.210 \text{ g Ag}} = \text{_____ g ore}$$

Answer: 47.6 g ore.

EXAMPLE 6.19: Coal is mostly carbon. If a given coal sample is 75.0 percent carbon, how many kilograms of carbon dioxide will be formed when 1.00 kg of coal is burned?

Solution:

Step 1: The balanced equation is:

$$C + O_2 \longrightarrow CO_2$$

Step 2: We want to convert kilograms of coal to kilograms of CO_2.

Step 3: 1.00 kg coal = _____ kg CO_2.

Step 4: We need *two* conversion factors: one to convert kilograms of coal to kilograms of carbon, and another to convert kilograms of carbon to kilograms of CO_2. The percent purity is our first conversion factor. 75.0 percent carbon means that 100 parts of coal contain 75.0 parts of carbon, so our conversion factor is 75.0 kg C/100 kg coal, or 0.750 kg C/kg coal. Here's what we have so far:

$$1.00 \text{ kg coal} \times \frac{0.750 \text{ kg C}}{\text{kg coal}} = \text{_____ kg } CO_2$$

We get the other conversion factors from the chemical equation and from the atomic and formula weights, as we did earlier in this chapter. Remember that formula weights may be expressed in any units we choose so long as we use the same units throughout the problem. We get the formula weights in kilograms (kg-moles):

C: 12.0 kg/kg-mole CO_2:   C: 12.0 kg/kg-mole

O_2: $2(16.0) = 32.0$ kg/kg-mole

CO_2:   44.0 kg/kg-mole

Our conversion factors are 12.0 kg C/kg-mole C, 1 kg-mole C/kg-mole CO_2, and 44.0 kg CO_2/kg-mole CO_2.

Step 5: Our finished setup:

$$1.00 \text{ kg-coal} \times \frac{0.750 \text{ kg C}}{\text{kg-coal}} \times \frac{1 \text{ kg-mole C}}{12.0 \text{ kg C}} \times \frac{1 \text{ kg-mole } CO_2}{\text{kg-mole C}} \times \frac{44.0 \text{ kg } CO_2}{\text{kg-mole } CO_2}$$
$$= \underline{} \text{ kg } CO_2$$

The units check.

Answer: 2.75 kg CO_2.

PERCENT YIELD.

We've done calculations that tell us how much of something will be produced by a certain amount of something else in a chemical reaction. This number is called the *theoretical yield*. This is the maximum amount that we should expect. However, in the working applications of chemistry, we hardly ever get as much product as the equation says we should. There are lots of reasons for this. We might lose some of the material in the process of separating it from other products. The reaction may not have gone to completion (we'll talk about this more in Chapter 15). Maybe the starting materials weren't as pure as we thought. This doesn't mean that the Law of Conservation of Matter is being violated. That extra material is *somewhere*—we just don't have it. The amount that we do get is the *actual yield*. We get the *percent yield* by dividing the actual yield by the theoretical yield.

theoretical yield

actual yield
percent yield

EXAMPLE 6.20: Acetylene (C_2H_2) is made commercially by adding calcium carbide, CaC_2, to water according to this equation:

$$CaC_2 + 2 H_2O \longrightarrow C_2H_2 + Ca(OH)_2$$

2550 kg of calcium carbide is treated with an excess of water, and 867 kg of acetylene is obtained. Calculate the percent yield.

Solution: First, "an excess of water" means that we can have as much water as we want. The theoretical yield of acetylene thus depends on the amount of calcium carbide we have; we say that calcium carbide is the *limiting reactant*. Its amount limits the amount of product we can get.

limiting reactant

To calculate percent yield, first we must calculate the theoretical yield in the usual way.

Step 1: The equation is balanced.
Step 2: We want to convert kilograms of CaC_2 to kilogram of C_2H_2.
Step 3: 2550 kg CaC_2 = _____ kg C_2H_2.
Step 4:

Ca:	40.0 kg/kg-mole	C_2:	$2(12.0) = 24.0$ kg/kg-mole
C_2:	$2(12.0) = 24.0$ kg/kg-mole	H_2:	$2(1.01) = 2.02$ kg/kg-mole
CaC_2:	64.1 kg/kg-mole	C_2H_2:	26.0 kg/kg-mole

Our conversion factors are 64.1 kg CaC_2/kg-mole CaC_2; 1 kg-mole CaC_2/kg-mole C_2H_2; and 26.0 kg C_2H_2/kg-mole C_2H_2.

Step 5: Our setup:

$$2550 \text{ kg CaC}_2 \times \frac{1 \text{ kg-mole CaC}_2}{64.1 \text{ kg CaC}_2} \times \frac{1 \text{ kg-mole C}_2H_2}{\text{kg-mole CaC}_2} \times \frac{26.0 \text{ kg C}_2H_2}{\text{kg-mole C}_2H_2}$$
$$= \_\_\_\_ \text{ kg C}_2H_2$$

The units check. The answer here is 1030 kg C_2H_2. But the problem told us we got 867 kg. Thus we have to calculate the percent yield.

$$\frac{867 \text{ kg}}{1030 \text{ kg}} \times 10^2 = \_\_\_\_ \text{ percent yield}$$

Answer: 84.2 percent yield.

EXAMPLE 6.21: The calcium carbide in the previous reaction is made by heating lime (calcium oxide) in an excess of coke (carbon):

$$CaO + 3 C \xrightarrow{\Delta} CaC_2 + CO$$

This reaction gives 67.9 percent yield. What would be the actual yield of calcium carbide if 9550 kg of lime were used?

Solution: Again, we must first calculate the theoretical yield.

Step 1: The equation is balanced.

Step 2: We want to convert kilograms of calcium oxide to kilograms of calcium carbide.

Step 3: 9550 kg CaO = ____ kg CaC_2.

Step 4: We know that the formula weight of CaC_2 is 64.1 kg.

$$\begin{array}{ll} \text{Ca:} & 40.1 \text{ kg/kg-mole} \\ \underline{\text{O:} \quad 16.0 \text{ kg/kg-mole}} \\ \text{CaO:} & 56.1 \text{ kg/kg-mole} \end{array}$$

Our conversion factors are 64.1 kg CaC_2/kg-mole CaC_2 (from Example 6.20); 56.1 kg CaO/kg-mole CaO; and 1 kg/mole CaC_2/kg-mole CaO.

Step 5: Our setup:

$$9550 \text{ kg CaO} \times \frac{1 \text{ kg-mole CaO}}{56.1 \text{ kg CaO}} \times \frac{1 \text{ kg-mole CaC}_2}{\text{kg-mole CaO}} \times \frac{64.1 \text{ kg CaC}_2}{\text{kg-mole CaC}_2}$$
$$= \_\_\_\_ \text{ kg CaC}_2$$

The units check. The answer, 1.09×10^4 kg CaC_2, is the theoretical yield. Since:

$$\text{percent yield} = \frac{\text{actual yield}}{\text{theoretical yield}} \times 10^2$$

then

$$\text{actual yield} = \frac{\text{percent yield} \times \text{theoretical yield}}{10^2}$$

$$\text{actual yield} = \frac{67.9 \times 1.09 \times 10^4 \text{ kg CaC}_2}{10^2}$$

$$= \_\_\_\_ \text{ kg CaC}_2$$

Answer: 7.40×10^3 kg CaC_2.

REVIEW QUESTIONS

1. What is the chemist's recipe?

The Quantitative Meaning of Formulas
2. Why must we use grams to count atoms?
3. What is the arithmetic translation of an element's symbol?
4. What do we mean by *gram-molecular weight?* How do we calculate it?
5. How do we convert grams to moles?
6. What is *gram-formula weight?* How does it compare with gram-molecular weight?
7. How do we calculate formula weight?

The Quantitative Meaning of Equations
8. Explain how a chemical equation can be translated into arithmetic.
9. How is a chemical equation like a nonchemical recipe? How is it different?
10. Why must the total mass on one side of an equation equal the total mass on the other side?

Calculations with Chemical Equations
11. How is a chemical equation a source of conversion factors?
12. What are the steps involved in doing calculations with chemical equations?
13. What conversion factors are used in mole-to-mole conversions?
14. What conversion factors are used in mole-to-mass conversions? How do we get these conversion factors?
15. What conversion factors are used in mass-to-mass conversions?
16. Can we use other mass units besides grams in mass-to-mass conversions? How?
17. How can we simplify a conversion factor when the two formulas have the same mole numbers in the equation?

Heat as Part of Chemical Reactions
18. Is heat always needed to make a chemical reaction go?

19. What are *exothermic* reactions and *endothermic* reactions?
20. What is *heat of reaction?* What units do we normally measure it in?
21. How do we treat heat of reaction in chemical calculations?
22. Can we change the heat of reaction for a given equation?
23. How is heat of reaction useful? How is it not useful?

Problems Involving Percentages
24. What does *percent* mean?
25. What is *percentage-by-weight?* What units can it have?
26. How is a chemical formula used to calculate percentage-by-weight of the elements in it?
27. How can we figure out the formula for a substance from the *percent composition?*
28. What is the difference between *empirical formula* and *molecular formula?* Are these always different?
29. What information do we need to find a compound's molecular formula? How do we use this information?
30. What is *percent purity?*
31. How is percentage a conversion factor?
32. When an impure substance is used as a reactant, how does this affect the amount of it that must be used to get a specific amount of product?
33. What are the steps involved in doing a chemical calculation where the starting material is impure?
34. What is *theoretical yield;* How do we get it?
35. Do we always obtain the theoretical yield? Why?
36. What is *percent yield?*
37. What are the steps involved in calculating the percent yield for a reaction where the *actual yield* is given?
38. What is meant by a *limiting reactant?*
39. What does an "excess" of a reactant mean?

EXERCISES

1. How many atoms are contained in each of the following?
   a. 1/3 mole of helium
   b. 3.21 grams of sulfur
   c. 6 moles of argon
   d. 20.0 grams of argon
   e. 2 moles of O_2
   f. 0.100 moles of sodium

2. How many molecules are in each of the following? (Assume that fractional and whole numbers of moles are pure numbers and do not limit the number of significant figures in the answer.)
   a. 1/2 mole of NO
   b. 2 moles SO_2
   c. 1/4 mole O_3
   d. 1 mole N_2O_5
   e. 1/10 mole H_2O
   f. 1/3 mole of P_4O_{10}

3. How many nitrogen atoms are contained in each part of Exercise 2?

4. Calculate the following.
   a. the number of moles of table legs in one mole of tables
   b. the number of moles of legs, wings, and antennae in one-half mole of butterflies
   c. the number of moles of phosphorus atoms in one mole of P_4 molecules
   d. the number of moles of each kind of atom in one mole of H_3PO_4
   e. the number of total moles of ions in one-half mole of $Al_2(SO_4)_3$

5. Calculate the molecular weight or formula weight of each of the following.
   a. N_2
   b. HNO_3
   c. Na_2SO_4
   d. $C_6H_{12}O_6$
   e. $CaSO_4 \cdot 2 H_2O$
   f. $(NH_4)_3PO_4$

6. Calculate the number of moles in the following.
   a. 22.4 grams of neon
   b. 107 grams of NaBr
   c. 14.9 grams of Cl_2
   d. 46.2 grams of Li_2SO_4

7. Calculate the number of grams in the following.
   a. 2.00 moles of I_2
   b. 1.57 moles of $HClO_3$
   c. 0.122 moles of Fe
   d. 10.0 moles of NO_2
   e. 5.93 moles of Cr_2O_3
   f. 0.500 moles of C_3H_8

8. State the number of moles of each kind of atom for each of the following.
   a. 2 $Fe(OH)_3$
   b. 3 Ca_3N_2
   c. 4 N_2O_5
   d. 3 NH_4KCO_3

9. Give the six mole-to-mole conversion factors that can be found from each equation.
   a. $2 C_2H_2 + 5 O_2 \longrightarrow 4 CO_2 + 2 H_2O$
   b. $Fe_2O_3 + 3 CO \longrightarrow 2 Fe + 3 CO_2$
   c. $3 Cl_2 + CH_4 \longrightarrow CHCl_3 + 3 HCl$

10. How many moles of the first product in each of the following equations would be obtained by using 0.175 moles of the first reactant? (Equations are not necessarily balanced.)
    a. $CuO + HCl \nrightarrow CuCl_2 + H_2O$
    b. $Al + Cl_2 \nrightarrow AlCl_3$
    c. $NH_3 + H_2SO_4 \nrightarrow (NH_4)_2SO_4$
    d. $NaNO_3 \nrightarrow NaNO_2 + O_2$

11. In 1970, ammonia was second in the U.S. to sulfuric acid in amount produced, which was 1.18×10^{13} grams. Ammonia is produced by the Haber process:

    $$N_2 + 3 H_2 \longrightarrow 2 NH_3$$

    a. How many moles of ammonia were produced in 1970?

    b. How many moles of hydrogen and of nitrogen would have to be used to produce this many moles of ammonia?

12. How many moles of the first reactant in each of the following equations would be needed to produce 785 grams of the first product? (Check that equation is balanced.)
    a. $Zn + Pb(NO_3)_2 \nrightarrow Pb + Zn(NO_3)_2$
    b. $AgNO_3 + H_2S \nrightarrow Ag_2S + HNO_3$
    c. $P + O_2 \nrightarrow P_4O_{10}$
    d. $PbO_2 \longrightarrow Pb + O_2$

13. Butane, C_4H_{10}, is one kind of bottled gas. How many moles of oxygen are used when 1050 grams of butane are burned to yield carbon dioxide and water?

14. How many grams of the first reactant in each of the following equations would be needed to react with 2.34 grams of the second reactant?
    a. $S + Cl_2 \nrightarrow SCl_2$
    b. $Ba(NO_3)_2 + (NH_4)_2CO_3 \nrightarrow BaCO_3 + NH_4NO_3$
    c. $Cr(OH)_3 + HCl \nrightarrow CrCl_3 + H_2O$
    d. $Zn + AgNO_3 \nrightarrow Zn(NO_3)_2 + Ag$

15. The decomposition of ammonium dichromate occurs as follows:

    $$(NH_4)_2Cr_2O_7 \longrightarrow Cr_2O_3 + N_2 + 4 H_2O$$

    The green chromium(III) oxide is the pigment used in paper money. How many grams of ammonium dichromate would a counterfeiter have to use to produce 50.0 grams of chromium(III) oxide?

16. An art student runs out of yellow pigment on a Sunday. A chemistry major friend offers to make some yellow pigment in the form of lead(II) chromate ("chrome yellow"):

    $$K_2CrO_4 + Pb(NO_3)_2 \longrightarrow PbCrO_4 + 2 KNO_3$$

    How many grams of potassium chromate and of lead(II) nitrate does the chemistry major need to produce 3.50 grams of lead(II) chromate?

17. Sugar ferments to produce alcohol according to this equation:

    $$C_6H_{12}O_6 \longrightarrow 2 C_2H_5OH + 2 CO_2$$

    How many grams of alcohol and of carbon dioxide are produced from the fermentation of 5.00 kg of sugar?

18. Part of a water purification technique uses this reaction (equation is not balanced):

    $$Al_2(SO_4)_3(aq) + Ca(OH)_2(aq) \nrightarrow$$
    $$Al(OH)_3(s) + CaSO_4(aq)$$

    The aluminum hydroxide is a fluffy, white precipitate that can trap tiny particles suspended in water. When the aluminum hydroxide is removed from the water, the particles are removed too.

    a. How many kilograms of aluminum sulfate are needed to produce 255 kg of aluminum hydroxide?

b. How many kilograms of the by-product, calcium sulfate, will also be produced?

19. Dihydrogen sulfide is a common problem in industrial waste. One source of dihydrogen sulfide is bacterial conversion of sulfates, which frequently appear in industrial wastes, according to this equation:

$$H_2SO_4 \xrightarrow{\text{bacteria}} H_2S + 2\,O_2$$

However, the dihydrogen sulfide can be eliminated by treating it with hydrogen peroxide:

$$H_2O_2 + H_2S \longrightarrow 2\,H_2O + S$$

a. How many metric tons of dihydrogen sulfide would be produced by 5.00 metric tons of sulfuric acid?

b. How many metric tons of hydrogen peroxide would it take to get rid of the resulting dihydrogen sulfide?

20. Calculate the amount of heat, in kilocalories, that would be produced in each of the following exothermic reactions if 75.0 grams of the first reactant are used.

a. $Zn + S \longrightarrow ZnS + 148.5$ kcal

b. $2\,C_2H_6 + 7\,O_2 \longrightarrow 4\,CO_2 + 6\,H_2O + 736$ kcal

21. In each of the following endothermic reactions, calculate the number of grams of the first product that would be produced if 855 kcal were supplied.

a. $2\,KClO_3 + 21.4$ kcal $\longrightarrow 2\,KCl + 3\,O_2$

b. $CaCO_3 + 42$ kcal $\longrightarrow CaO + CO_2$

22. Natural gas (CH_4), propane (C_3H_8), and butane (C_4H_{10}) are all used as fuels in the home. They burn according to these equations:

$$CH_4 + 2\,O_2 \longrightarrow CO_2 + 2\,H_2O + 192 \text{ kcal}$$
$$C_3H_8 + 5\,O_2 \longrightarrow 3\,CO_2 + 4\,H_2O + 489 \text{ kcal}$$
$$2\,C_4H_{10} + 13\,O_2 \longrightarrow 8\,CO_2 + 10\,H_2O + 1270\,\text{kcal}$$

Calculate the number of kilocalories per gram of each fuel and decide, on that basis, which is the best fuel.

23. Determine the percent composition: HgI_2, NO, $Ca_3(PO_4)_2$. Use two decimal places.

24. Determine the formulas from these percent compositions.

a. 41.82% Na, 58.18% O

b. 1.48% H, 51.78% Cl, 46.74% O

c. 60.05% K, 18.43% C, 21.52% N

25. Ammonium nitrate is used as a fertilizer; so is ammonia. Compute the percent nitrogen in each. If they both cost the same amount of money per kilogram, which one is the better buy in terms of nitrogen content?

26. A poisonous gas called cyanogen is 46.14% C and 53.86% N. Its molecular weight is 52.02. What is its empirical formula and its molecular formula?

27. A gaseous fuel is 85.59% C and 14.41% H. Its molecular weight is 56.08. Give its empirical formula and its molecular formula.

28. Magnetite ore is 27.0% Fe_3O_4, and it is a source of iron metal.

a. How much pure Fe_3O_4 is contained in 1.00 metric ton of magnetite?

b. How many metric tons of iron are contained in 1.00 metric ton of magnetite?

29. "Fools gold" is pyrite ore, and it contains beautiful gold crystals of FeS_2. This is also a source of iron metal, and so it is somewhat valuable even though it isn't gold. If a certain pyrite ore is 32.8% FeS_2, how much of this ore must be used to obtain 255 kg of pure iron?

30. An older method of manufacturing chlorine gas was to treat pyrolusite ore with hydrochloric acid. The active ingredient in pyrolusite ore is MnO_2, and this is the reaction:

$$MnO_2 + 4\,HCl \longrightarrow Cl_2 + MnCl_2 + 2\,H_2O$$

If the pryolusite ore is 55.7% MnO_2, how much chlorine can be obtained from 5.54 metric tons of pyrolusite ore?

31. Limestone and marble are mostly made of calcium carbonate. When the atmospheric pollutant sulfur trioxide combines with rainwater, the resulting sulfuric acid can damage buildings and statues made out of limestone or marble. This is because sulfuric acid dissolves calcium carbonate. The equation for the reaction of sulfur trioxide and rainwater to produce sulfuric acid is:

$$SO_3(g) + H_2O(l) \longrightarrow H_2SO_4(aq)$$

The equation for sulfuric acid's dissolving of calcium carbonate is:

$$CaCO_3(s) + H_2SO_4(aq) \longrightarrow$$
$$CaSO_4(aq) + H_2O(l) + CO_2(g)$$

If, over a period of time, rain containing 1.00 kg of sulfur trioxide falls on a statue weighing 545 kg, what percentage of the statue will be dissolved (assuming the statue is 100% $CaCO_3$)?

32. The Ostwald process for making nitric acid begins with converting ammonia to nitrogen monoxide:

$$4\,NH_3 + 5\,O_2 \xrightarrow{\Delta} 4\,NO + 6\,H_2O$$

This reaction goes with a 80.3 percent yield. What is the actual yield of nitrogen monoxide from 10.7 metric tons of ammonia and an excess of oxygen?

7

Why Ionic Compounds Form

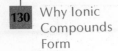

In this chapter and the next two chapters, we'll find out the reasons behind some rules and facts we've been talking about. We know how to tell the difference between ionic compounds and covalent compounds so that we can write their formulas and name them. We know that metals form positive ions and nonmetals form negative ions, and we know how to use the staircase-shaped line on the periodic table to tell which is which. We know how to find an ion's charge by its group in the periodic table. We know that some elements are so reactive that they don't exist in nature as free elements but as parts of compounds. We also know that, on the other hand, the noble gases are very unreactive.

Energy lies at the bottom of all of these facts and rules. A certain process will happen because it can be in a state of lower potential energy afterward. In this chapter, we'll look at chemical reactions in general and then see how the elements achieve a lower energy by forming ionic compounds. In the course of doing this, we'll also find out the connection between group number and charge, the reason for the staircase-shaped line, and what it really means to be a metal or a nonmetal. But first we need to find out about potential energy.

7.1 ENERGY AND CHEMICAL REACTIONS

energy

In Chapter 3, we said that energy is what's needed to move matter. Moving matter requires work, so we can define *energy* as the ability to do work. This doesn't mean that energy has to do work; only that it can. We usually talk about energy according to whether it is being made available now or later.

potential energy

POTENTIAL ENERGY. Stored energy, energy that's being saved for later, is *potential energy*. For instance, water above a dam has potential energy. It has the potential to do work at a later time. We know that if we open the spillway and let the water go through, we can get the water to do work for us. When we do open the spillway, the water will flow spontaneously to the bottom. Anything that happens spontaneously usually does so because it goes from a higher to a lower potential energy state. The water above the dam is in a higher potential energy state than it is below the dam.

We say "higher than" and "lower than" because we always have to talk about potential energy states relative to each other. The water above the dam has potential energy relative to the water below it. But what if there's a lower dam further downstream? Then the water at the bottom of the first dam would have potential energy relative to the bottom of the second dam. The water at the bottom of the first dam is in a state of lower potential energy relative to the top of the first dam, but it is in a state of higher potential energy relative to the bottom of the second dam. Figure 7.1 illustrates these relative potential energy states.

FIGURE 7.1
131
Relative
potential
energy states

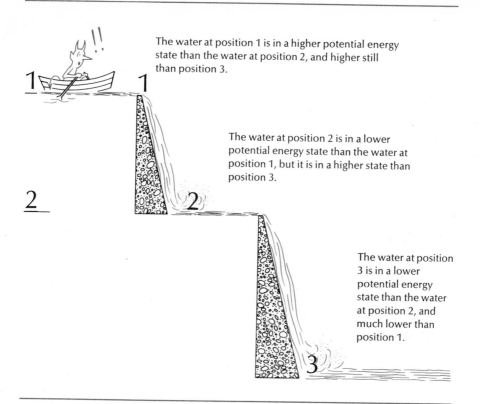

The water at position 1 is in a higher potential energy state than the water at position 2, and higher still than position 3.

The water at position 2 is in a lower potential energy state than the water at position 1, but it is in a higher state than position 3.

The water at position 3 is in a lower potential energy state than the water at position 2, and much lower than position 1.

When the water goes from the top to the bottom of the dam, it releases its potential energy. We could make it turn a turbine and make electricity for us, but we don't have to. It will release its energy in either case. When something happens spontaneously, energy is usually released.

REACTIVITY.   Now we can look at chemical elements. When we say that an element is *reactive,* we really mean that it is in a state of higher potential energy as the free element than it is in most of its compounds. Of course, if we keep the element confined in an inert container all by itself, it can't react. But if we turn it loose outside, it will quickly find something to react with, just as a sailor on leave after a six-month cruise will quickly find a date. If we put a piece of sodium out on a tabletop, it will find plenty of things to react with just in that one spot: the air, the water in the air, or possibly even the tabletop itself.

    The elements sodium and chlorine are very reactive. If we talk about their reaction with one another, then we can say that they're in a state of high potential energy relative to their product, sodium chloride. Figure 7.2 illustrates by analogy the relative high potential energy states of the elements sodium and chlorine.

    When sodium and chlorine react, energy is released in the form of heat.

reactivity

FIGURE 7.2 Separate reactive elements have high potential energy

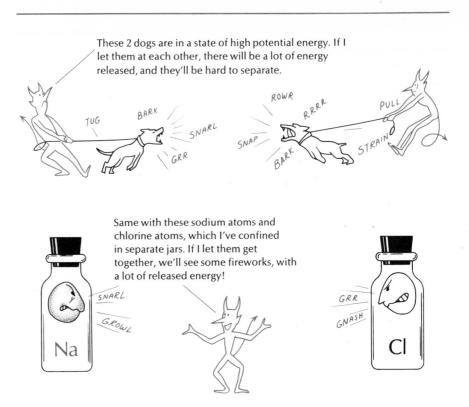

The elements are giving up potential energy as they go from a higher to a lower potential energy state. Or, translating what we just said into chemistry:

$$Na(s) + \tfrac{1}{2}Cl_2(g) \longrightarrow NaCl(s) + 98.3 \text{ kcal}$$

In Chapter 5, we called this kind of reaction, where energy is a product, an exothermic reaction. Most spontaneous reactions are exothermic. A *spontaneous reaction* is one that proceeds all by itself, like this one. All we had to do was to get the elements together, and they did the rest. Sometimes, though, we have to give a spontaneous reaction a push to get it started. Magnesium will sit out in the air without reacting with it. If we light a match to the magnesium, it will burn and form magnesium oxide in an exothermic reaction. From then on, it will proceed by itself. The total energy produced by the reaction is much more than the energy provided by the match. Ionic compounds are usually formed by exothermic reactions, for reasons that we'll see later in this chapter.

The energies that are involved in forming ionic compounds from elements are mostly electrostatic in nature. That means that the energies have to do with the attraction or repulsion of charged particles for one another. We'll look at this kind of energy next.

spontaneous reaction

ELECTROSTATIC ENERGY. We saw in Chapter 2 that unlike charges attract each other. If two unlike charges are already together, it takes energy to separate them, because of the force of attraction between them. Conversely, if two unlike charges are apart and come together, energy is released. When we're talking about two unlike charges, this is energy of attraction. The *electrostatic energy of attraction* is the energy released when two unlike charges come together from infinitely far apart to a certain final distance.

electrostatic energy of attraction

We also saw that like charges repel each other. If two like charges are apart, it takes energy to push them together. If they are together, they will fly apart and release energy. When we're talking about two like charges, this is energy of repulsion. The *electrostatic energy of repulsion* is the energy required to push two like charges together to a certain distance from infinitely far apart. These electrostatic energies are illustrated in Figure 7.3.

electrostatic energy of repulsion

7.2 THE FORMATION OF IONIC COMPOUNDS

When an ionic compound is formed from its elements, more than one individual process is involved. At least five separate events, each with its own energy, contribute to the total reaction. First we'll see what these energies are and how they fit together. Then we'll look at the three most important energies one at a time.

THE SODIUM-CHLORINE REACTION IN SLOW MOTION.
When sodium and chlorine react to form sodium chloride, it happens very fast. But if we could slow the process down, we'd see that the energy (heat) of reaction is really what's left over after a series of individual processes have happened.

When an ionic compound forms, these things have to happen.

1. The atoms of each element have to be converted into separate, gaseous atoms. For a solid like sodium, this means vaporizing it; for a diatomic gas like chlorine, this means taking the molecules apart.
2. The gaseous atoms have to be changed into gaseous ions by removing electrons from the metal atoms and putting them onto the nonmetal atoms.
3. The resulting gaseous ions then come together to form the ionic crystal.

Each of these processes either requires or releases energy.

Figure 7.4 gives us a slow motion look at this reaction. We see that the resulting compound, NaCl, has its ions arranged in an orderly, geometric structure. Such a structure is called a *crystal lattice* and is typical of ionic

crystal lattice

compounds. The force of attraction that holds ions together in a crystal is an *ionic bond*. This regular arrangement happens because the unlike-charged ions try to get as close to each other as possible, and the like-charged ions try to get as far away from each other as possible. The particular geometric arrangement of a given ionic compound depends on the sizes and charges of the individual ions. The structure shown for NaCl is a cubic structure, so named because its particles resemble cubes. A piece of salt with a volume of about 10^{-2} mm^3 looks like a little cube under a microscope and

FIGURE 7.3
Energy is released when two unlike charges come together, and when two like charges separate

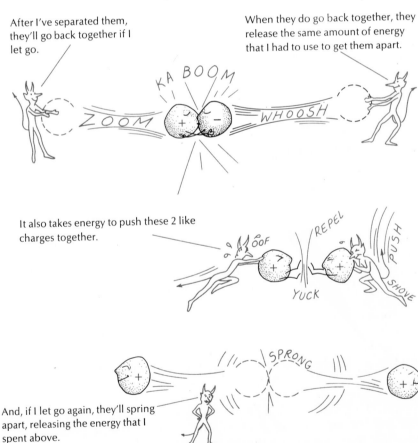

FIGURE 7.4
Energies involved in the formation of an ionic crystal

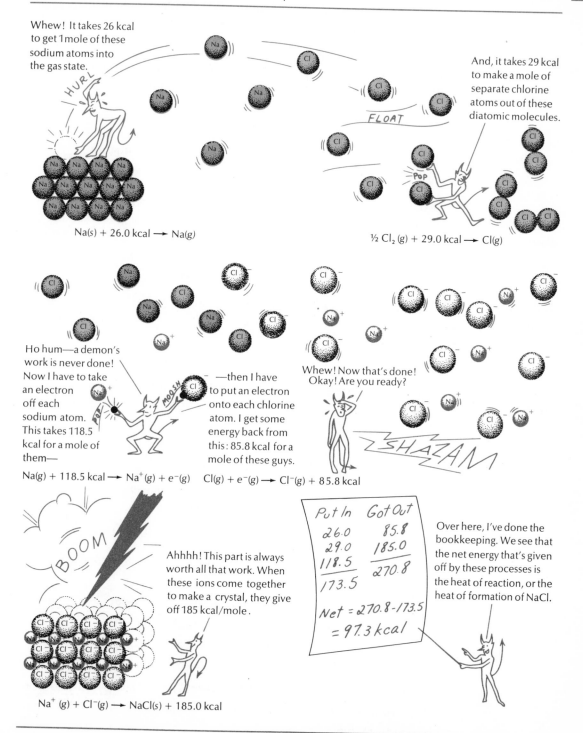

Whew! It takes 26 kcal to get 1 mole of these sodium atoms into the gas state.

HURL

Na(s) + 26.0 kcal ⟶ Na(g)

And, it takes 29 kcal to make a mole of separate chlorine atoms out of these diatomic molecules.

FLOAT

POP

½ Cl₂ (g) + 29.0 kcal ⟶ Cl(g)

Ho hum—a demon's work is never done! Now I have to take an electron off each sodium atom. This takes 118.5 kcal for a mole of them—

—then I have to put an electron onto each chlorine atom. I get some energy back from this: 85.8 kcal for a mole of these guys.

Na(g) + 118.5 kcal ⟶ Na⁺(g) + e⁻(g)   Cl(g) + e⁻(g) ⟶ Cl⁻(g) + 85.8 kcal

Whew! Now that's done! Okay! Are you ready?

SHAZAM

BOOM

Ahhhh! This part is always worth all that work. When these ions come together to make a crystal, they give off 185 kcal/mole.

Na⁺ (g) + Cl⁻(g) ⟶ NaCl(s) + 185.0 kcal

Put In   Got Out
26.0   85.8
29.0   185.0
118.5   ─────
─────   270.8
173.5

Net = 270.8 - 173.5
    = 97.3 kcal

Over here, I've done the bookkeeping. We see that the net energy that's given off by these processes is the heat of reaction, or the heat of formation of NaCl.

contains about 2×10^{17} each of sodium ions and chloride ions. Since there can be arbitrary numbers of ions, depending on the crystal size, we don't speak of a NaCl molecule. But we understand that any sample always contains the same number of sodium ions as chloride ions.

The sodium-chlorine reaction wouldn't happen if the net result didn't release energy. We see that some of the individual processes require energy, and some release energy. For the compound to form, the total energy released has to be greater than the total energy required. The energy for each process has a name.

First, the energy that's needed to change a solid into separate, gaseous atoms is the substance's *heat of sublimation*. For sodium, the heat of sublimation is 26.0 kcal/mole. We could write this as an equation.

**heat of
sublimation**

$$Na(s) + 26.0 \text{ kcal} \longrightarrow Na(g)$$

Next, the energy that's needed to make separate, gaseous atoms by taking molecules apart is the *heat of dissociation*. For chlorine, it's 29.0 kcal per mole of chlorine atoms (or per one-half mole of diatomic chlorine molecules). Or, writing this as an equation:

**heat of
dissociation**

$$\tfrac{1}{2}Cl_2(g) + 29.0 \text{ kcal} \longrightarrow Cl(g)$$

Next, the *ionization energy* is needed to take electrons off gaseous atoms and make gaseous ions out of them. For sodium, this is 118.5 kcal/mole, and the equation is:

**ionization
energy**

$$Na(g) + 118.5 \text{ kcal} \longrightarrow Na^+(g) + e^-(g)$$

Next, when electrons are added to gaseous atoms to make gaseous negative ions, the energy that's released is the *electron affinity*. For chlorine, this is 85.8 kcal/mole, and the equation is:

**electron
affinity**

$$Cl(g) + e^-(g) \longrightarrow Cl^-(g) + 85.8 \text{ kcal}$$

Finally, when gaseous positive and negative ions come together to form a solid crystal, energy is given off, and this is the *lattice energy*. For NaCl, the lattice energy is 185.0 kcal/mole, and the equation is:

lattice energy

$$Na^+(g) + Cl^-(g) \longrightarrow NaCl(s) + 185.0 \text{ kcal}$$

We can summarize all these processes by writing their equations all together.

Heat of Sublimation	$Na(s) + 26.0 \text{ kcal} \longrightarrow Na(g)$
Heat of Dissociation	$\tfrac{1}{2}Cl_2(g) + 29.0 \text{ kcal} \longrightarrow Cl(g)$
Ionization Energy	$Na(g) + 118.5 \text{ kcal} \longrightarrow Na^+(g) + e^-(g)$
Electron Affinity	$Cl(g) + e^-(g) \longrightarrow Cl^-(g) + 85.8 \text{ kcal}$
Lattice Energy	$Na^+(g) + Cl^-(g) \longrightarrow NaCl(s) + 185.0 \text{ kcal}$
Heat of Reaction (Heat of Formation)	$Na(s) + \tfrac{1}{2}Cl_2(g) \longrightarrow NaCl(s) + 97.3 \text{ kcal}$

To add a series of equations like this, we cancel all terms that appear on both the right and the left of the arrows, regardless of which equations they are in. We add the energies on each side, then subtract one total from another, as in Figure 7.4. The equation we end up with is the equation for the formation of solid sodium chloride from solid sodium and gaseous chlorine. The heat of reaction is 97.3 kcal/mole. When a reaction produces a compound from elements, the heat of reaction is also called the compound's *heat of formation*. Even though we've listed all of these processes separately so that we can look at them, they happen all at once (simultaneously). In this way, chemistry is like a business. To keep producing, a business has to have at least as much money coming in as it is spending. Businesses receive and spend money at the same time (simultaneously).

**heat of
formation**

We see that if the processes that require energy can't be paid for by the processes that release energy, the compound won't form. Next we'll look at the three larger energies—ionization energy, electron affinity, and lattice energy—and see what factors cause them to be large or small.

IONIZATION ENERGY AND THE FORMATION OF POSITIVE IONS.

It takes energy to remove an electron from an atom, because of the electrostatic attraction between the electron and the nucleus of the atom. We saw that the ionization energy of sodium is 118.5 kcal/mole; for chlorine, it's 299 kcal/mole. A sodium atom, and not a chlorine atom, loses an electron in the reaction, because it takes less energy to remove an electron from a sodium atom. In general, nonmetals have higher ionization energies than metals, and that's why metals tend to lose electrons and nonmetals don't.

If we take a second electron off, we get the atom's second ionization energy, and so on. For sodium, we'd write the equations for the first and second ionizations like this:

First: $Na(g) + 118.5 \text{ kcal} \longrightarrow Na^+(g) + e^-(g)$
Second: $Na^+(g) + 1091 \text{ kcal} \longrightarrow Na^{2+}(g) + e^-(g)$

Now we see why compounds of Na^{2+} don't form. The second ionization energy is nearly ten times the first, and apparently it is too large to be paid for by any processes that would release energy. For all the Group IA metals, the second ionization energy is much higher than the first, and this is why all Group IA metals form ions of only 1+ charge. These and other ionization energies are shown in Figure 7.5. We see that for each metal, there is a sharp increase in ionization energy for removing one electron beyond the element's group number.

For the Group IIA metals in Figure 7.5—beryllium, magnesium, and calcium—we see that the second ionization energies are a bit larger than the first, but that the third is at least ten times the first. These metals can afford to lose two electrons but not three electrons. We find their ionization energies for removing two electrons by adding the separate equations:

**FIGURE 7.5
Ionization
energies for
selected metals**

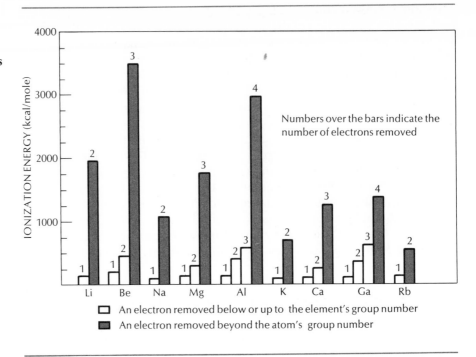

$$Mg(g) + 176 \text{ kcal} \longrightarrow Mg^+(g) + e^-(g)$$
$$Mg^+(g) + 345 \text{ kcal} \longrightarrow Mg^{2+}(g) + e^-(g)$$
$$\overline{Mg(g) + 521 \text{ kcal} \longrightarrow Mg^{2+}(g) + 2\,e^-(g)}$$

For aluminum, which loses three but not four electrons, we'd add its three ionization energies in the same way. It takes a total of 1222 kcal/mole to remove three electrons from aluminum.

It's always harder to take the second and subsequent electrons off. It takes more energy to remove a negatively charged electron from a doubly charged ion than from a singly charged ion, as shown in Figure 7.6.

ELECTRON AFFINITY AND THE FORMATION OF NEGATIVE IONS.
Energy is usually released when one electron is added to a neutral atom, because of the attraction of the positively charged nucleus for the new electron. Electron affinity has a positive sign if energy is released. The electron affinity of sodium is only 28.0 kcal/mole. Clearly, we'd rather add an electron to chlorine and get 85.1 kcal/mole. This is why chlorine, and not sodium, gains an electron in the reaction. In general, nonmetals have higher electron affinities than metals, and that's why nonmetals form negative ions and metals don't.

We can talk about second and higher electron affinities, just as we did for ionization energies. For oxygen, we'd write two equations like this:

$$O(g) + e^-(g) \longrightarrow O^-(g) + 33.9 \text{ kcal}$$
$$\underline{O^-(g) + e^-(g) \longrightarrow O^{2-}(g) - 211.0 \text{ kcal}}$$
$$O(g) + 2\,e^-(g) \longrightarrow O^{2-}(g) - 177.1 \text{ kcal}$$

The negative sign for the second electron affinity means that energy is required, not released. This is because of the repulsion between the second electron and the already negative ion, as shown in Figure 7.7. A total of 177.1 kcal/mole must be supplied to get the two electrons on. We could write this in our usual way, with the energy on the left:

$$O(g) + 2\,e^-(g) + 177.1 \text{ kcal} \longrightarrow O^{2-}(g)$$

Putting three or more electrons onto oxygen or the other Group VIA elements takes too much energy, and ions like O^{3-} don't form. Ions of elements in Group VIIA stop at 1− because putting two electrons on takes too much energy.

It's easy for me to take this electron off this potassium atom. It has an ionization energy of a mere 100 kcal/mole.

Group IA

The first electron comes off magnesium fairly easily, too, with an ionization energy of only 176 kcal/mole.

Group IIA

Whew! There! I got the second electron off, but it wasn't as easy as the first. I had to pull it off a positive charge. This second electron has an ionization energy of 345 kcal/mole.

Hmm—I see from aluminum's group number that it needs to lose 3 electrons. Judging from magnesium up there, I'd say that getting that third electron off aluminum will be a real bear, since I'll have to pull it off a 2+ charge. The third ionization energy of aluminum is 633 kcal/mole.

Group IIIA

**FIGURE 7.6
Increased
amounts
of energy
are needed
to remove
successive
electrons from
an atom**

FIGURE 7.7
**Energy is needed
to add successive
electrons
to an atom**

See how easily this first electron goes onto this oxygen atom? The nucleus attracts the electron, and there's a release of energy. Now the oxygen has a 1− charge.

Oof! It sure is hard to put this second electron on this ion now that it already has a negative charge. It will go on if I exert enough energy (211 kcal/mole), but it sure won't release any energy.

Whew, I did it. But I'd hate to try putting a third one on.

LATTICE ENERGY AND THE STABILITY OF IONIC COMPOUNDS.

The lattice energy is the difference between the energy of attraction of the unlike-charged ions and the energy of repulsion between the like-charged ions. There has to be a net lattice energy for the crystal to stay together, and this means that the energy of attraction has to be greater than the energy of repulsion. The energy of attraction depends on two things: charge and distance. The higher the ionic charge, the greater the attraction; and the shorter the distance (the closer the ions), the greater the attraction.

Figure 7.8 is a graph showing lattice energy plotted against closeness for some ionic compounds. We define *closeness* as 1 over the minimum possible distance between ions. This minimum possible distance is the sum of the ions' radii (the distances from their nuclei to their outer electrons). First, we notice that the compounds we've plotted fall into two groups, labeled A and B. The A line is four times as steep as the B line, because the A group contains only doubly charged ions. Doubly charged ions have four times the attraction for each other as singly charged ions. An ionic compound made from doubly charged ions has about four times the lattice energy of one made from singly charged ions having the same closeness.

closeness

Second, we notice that in either group the lattice energy is greater for greater closeness. This is because the minimum distance between ions decreases as ionic size (radius) decreases. The smaller the ions, the larger the lattice energy.

Higher lattice energy means greater stability. We also see that usually the higher the lattice energy, the higher the melting point. This is because part of the lattice energy must be overcome to melt an ionic compound and separate its ions from each other. We'll see also in Chapter 12 that compounds with low lattice energy (for example, NaCl) dissolve in water more easily than compounds with high lattice energy (for example, MgO).

To summarize, we see that ionic compounds that form from doubly or triply charged ions pay for their larger ionization energies and electron

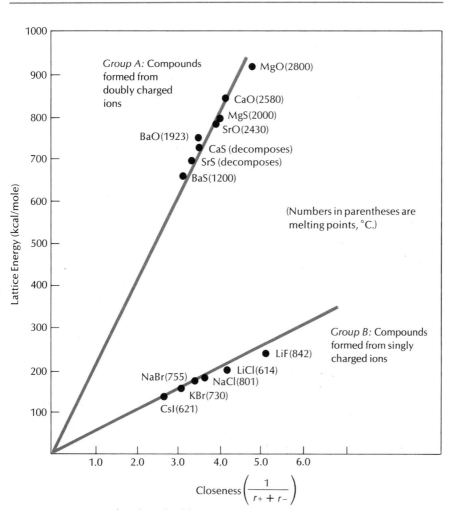

Group A: Compounds formed from doubly charged ions

MgO (2800)
CaO (2580)
MgS (2000)
SrO (2430)
BaO (1923)
CaS (decomposes)
SrS (decomposes)
BaS (1200)

(Numbers in parentheses are melting points, °C.)

Group B: Compounds formed from singly charged ions

LiF (842)
LiCl (614)
NaBr (755)
NaCl (801)
KBr (730)
CsI (621)

Lattice Energy (kcal/mole)

1000
900
800
700
600
500
400
300
200
100

1.0   2.0   3.0   4.0   5.0   6.0

$$\text{Closeness}\left(\frac{1}{r_+ + r_-}\right)$$

r_+ and r_-, the radii of the positive and negative ions, are in nanometers.

affinities with larger lattice energies. Generally, small, highly charged ions form more stable crystals with higher lattice energy, higher melting point, and less water solubility than compounds made from large, singly charged ions.

7.3 IONIC TRENDS IN THE PERIODIC TABLE

We've seen that charge and distance are the important factors in the formation of an ionic compound. Ionization energy and electron affinity determine charge, and ionic radii determine distance. Figure 7.9 shows these three quantities for the representative elements.

IONIZATION ENERGY. We see from Figure 7.9 that first ionization energies increase from left to right in the periodic table, and they decrease as we go down any group. Also, we see that the total energy necessary for an atom to lose the same number of electrons as its group number increases greatly from left to right. As we cross the staircase-shaped line, this energy increases sharply—for instance, from 630 for beryllium to 1636 for boron. Thus the line is actually an energy line that tells at what point the energy becomes too great for an element to lose electrons. We define metals as elements that lose electrons, and nonmetals as elements that gain electrons in forming ionic compounds. Thus metallic character increases as ionization energy decreases.

Let's start with Group IA and see what happens to the ionization energy as we go toward the bottom of the periodic table, and, in particular, what happens when we cross the staircase-shaped line. In Group IA, hydrogen, the only nonmetal, has an ionization energy of 312—too high to form H^+. As we cross the staircase-shaped line down to lithium, we note a large drop in ionization energy to 124. After that, the ionization energy decreases slightly but steadily as we progress down the group. Cesium has the lowest ionization energy of all the elements and is therefore the most metallic element. In Group IIA, all are metals, and we see that the ionization energy for two electrons decreases steadily from 630 for beryllium to 349 for barium, but there are no abrupt changes. In Group IIIA, the metalloid boron has a large ionization energy for three electrons (too large for B^{3+} to form). As we cross the line to aluminum, the ionization energy drops sharply to 1221 and fluctuates but stays fairly constant around 1200 kcal to 1300 kcal for the other members of the group. In Group IVA, the nonmetal carbon has a very large ionization energy for four electrons. This drops quite a bit for the metalloids silicon and germanium, then drops further for the metals tin and lead. We see that these last two elements have the option of losing only two electrons instead of four, for an expenditure of fewer kilocalories of energy. We recall that these both have variable-charge ions of $2+$ and $4+$.

FIGURE 7.9   Ionization energies, electron affinities, and atomic and ionic radii for some representative elements

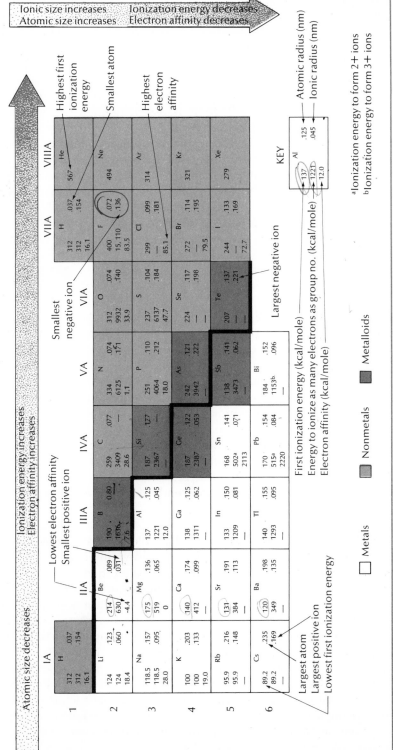

In Group VA, we start with a large ionization energy for five electrons for nitrogen. The differences between the remaining elements isn't very great, but we see that bismuth does have the option of saving energy by forming a 3+ ion. In Group VIA, most of the important elements are nonmetals with high ionization energies, and in Group VIIA, they all are. We can summarize by saying that it takes more energy to remove electrons from elements at the top of the periodic table than from elements at the bottom.

Now let's look at the trends going across the periodic table. We've already seen what happens in Period 2; in Period 3, we see an increase in total ionization energy for the metals sodium, magnesium, and aluminum. As we cross the line to silicon, this energy increases sharply, and the rest of the elements in the period are nonmetals. In Period 4, the sharp increase happens at both metalloids germanium and arsenic. In Period 5, there is a sharp increase between tin and antimony. In general, we can say that both first and total ionization energy increase as we go across a period from left to right, but that towards the middle of the table there is some skipping around and less of a regular trend. This is just another example of the increased "fuzziness" that we find toward the middle of the table.

ELECTRON AFFINITY. Electron affinities have less regularity than ionization energies, but we can notice a few general things. Although there are a lot of ups and downs on the way, the electron affinities of the Group VIIA nonmetals are considerably higher than those of the Groups IA and IIA metals. (In fact, beryllium has a negative electron affinity.) Higher electron affinity as well as higher ionization energy causes nonmetals to gain rather than to lose electrons.

Electron affinities are much more difficult to measure than ionization energies, and so not much information is available for electron affinities. For this reason, second and higher electron affinities are not shown, nor are electron affinities shown for noble gases. We can say, though, that electron affinities follow the same general trends as ionization energies.

ATOMIC AND IONIC RADII. We can make a few general statements about the atomic and ionic radii shown in Figure 7.9. First, we see that the radii of positive ions are always smaller than the radii of their corresponding atoms. For example, the radius of the neutral sodium atom is 0.157 nm, whereas the radius of the positive sodium ion is 0.095 nm. We also see that the radii of negative ions are always greater than the radii of their corresponding atoms. For example, the fluorine atom's radius is 0.072 nm, whereas the negative fluoride ion's radius is 0.136 nm. Thus, with a few exceptions, most positive ions are smaller than most negative ions.

Next, we see some trends with both atomic and ionic radii. Beginning at the top of Group IA and moving down, we find that each atom and its corresponding ion has a larger radius than the atom and ion above it. We see this trend in Group VIIA and in the other groups also.

Beginning at the left of Period 2 and moving right, we also see that each atom has a smaller radius than the atom to its left. With ions, we see a decrease in size with increasing amount of positive charge: Be^{2+} is smaller than singly charged Li^+. With the negative ions in Period 2, we find that size decreases as the amount of charge decreases: N^{3-} is larger than O^{2-}, which is larger than F^-. We'll learn in Chapter 9 the reasons for these variations.

7.4 ELECTRONS AND CHEMICAL REACTIONS

An element's reactivity depends on how its electrons are arranged. The noble gases are very unreactive because their electrons are arranged in extremely stable, low potential energy states. Other elements have electrons in higher potential energy states. When ionic compounds form, elements lose or gain electrons in order to achieve a stable, noble gas electronic arrangement.

VALENCE ELECTRONS.   Not all of an atom's electrons are involved in chemical reactions. Only the outer, or valence electrons, participate. We can add to our definition of a *chemical reaction* and say that it is an interaction involving atoms' valence electrons, in which chemical bonds are broken or formed, or both. For the representative elements—the only ones we'll discuss in this chapter—we'll define *valence electrons* as the outer electrons of a representative element, as indicated by the element's group number. Elements in Group IA have one valence electron; IIA, two, and so on. Representative elements are so called because we can discuss their valence electrons in this simple way. In Chapter 9, we'll see why the transition elements don't fit this classification.

chemical reaction

valence electron

LEWIS, OR ELECTRON-DOT, STRUCTURES.   In 1916, the chemist G. N. Lewis invented what he called "electron-dot" structures to explain chemical bonding, and we still find them useful today. A *Lewis structure* consists of the element's symbol plus dots to represent the number of valence electrons.

   According to Lewis, each element can be thought of as having a possible *octet* (*oct-* means "eight") of electrons around it. Imagine that the element's symbol has a square around it, with places for two electrons on each side, like this:

Lewis structure

octet

Symbol of element → E → Places for electrons

Each element's valence electrons are placed around its symbol. Each side receives one electron until the four sides are used up; then the electrons are paired. Lewis structures of the representative elements are shown in Figure 7.10. In this figure, we've put the noble gases in twice: once on the left side and once on the right side. Some chemists prefer to call the noble gases Group 0; others prefer Group VIIIA. Right now we prefer both. We'll see why by looking at a simple analogy.

ELECTRONS AND THE PERIODIC TABLE.

The word "period" means the completion of a recurring cycle. The week is a period of time seven days long. When one week is finished, a new week starts, and the period repeats. Some people think that Sunday is the end of the week; others think it is the beginning. It doesn't matter, because in either case there are always seven days from one Sunday to the next.

Since the periodic table lists the elements by increasing atomic number, we can think of the table as a building up of electrons, just as a week is a building up of days. That is, any element has one more electron than the element just before it. In Figure 7.10, a horizontal row is a period eight electrons long. When a period is finished, a new one starts, and the period repeats. Some people think that the noble gases are the end of the period; others think they are the beginning. In either case, there are eight valence electrons from one noble gas to the next. We can say that a noble gas has a stable electronic arrangement of either eight valence electrons or none, depending on whether we're considering it to be at the end or at the beginning of a period.

As far as the metals are concerned, the noble gases are the beginning of the periods. By definition, metals lose electrons to form positive ions. Representative metals usually lose as many valence electrons as they have, because in this way each metal atom can get down to the valence electron arrangement (none) of the noble gas that comes before it. Of course, the ion that's formed has the same amount of positive charge as the metal had valence electrons.

If we look at our modified periodic table in Figure 7.10, we see that the staircase-shaped line cuts diagonally through the elements. The distribution of metals and nonmetals is different for each period. Period 1 has no metals in it; Period 6 has five. This is because it takes more energy to remove electrons from elements in the lower-numbered periods, as we saw earlier.

We'll use Period 6 as an illustration because it has the most metals in it, even though some of them are relatively unfamiliar. We start with cesium, which has one valence electron. It can lose that electron to become Cs^+ and have the xenon structure. The last metal is bismuth, which has five valence electrons to lose. Here are Lewis structures of atoms and ions formed from metals that have lost all their valence electrons:

$$\text{Atoms:} \quad Cs\cdot \quad Ba\cdot \quad \cdot Tl\cdot \quad \cdot Pb\cdot \quad \cdot Bi\cdot$$

$$\text{Ions:} \quad Cs^+ \quad Ba^{2+} \quad Tl^{3+} \quad Pb^{4+} \quad Bi^{5+}$$

FIGURE 7.10 147
Lewis structures of the representative elements

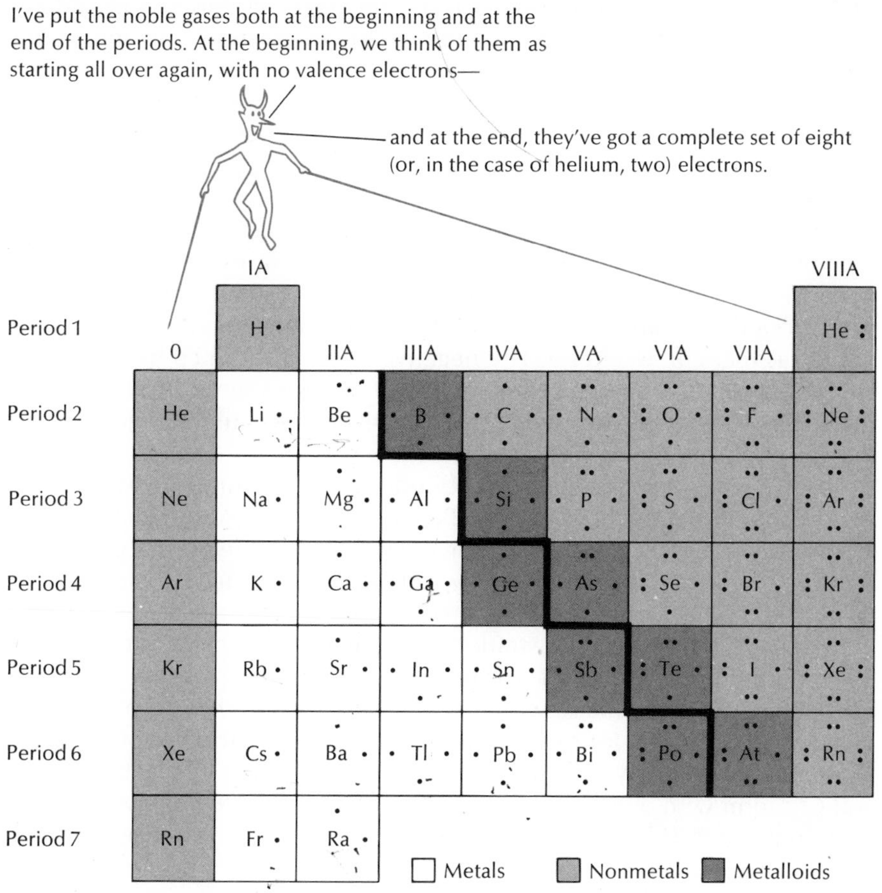

I've put the noble gases both at the beginning and at the end of the periods. At the beginning, we think of them as starting all over again, with no valence electrons—

—and at the end, they've got a complete set of eight (or, in the case of helium, two) electrons.

	IA							VIIIA
Period 1	H ·							He :
	0		IIA	IIIA	IVA	VA	VIA	VIIA
Period 2	He	Li ·	Be ·	· B ·	· C ·	· N ·	: O ·	: F ·	: Ne :
Period 3	Ne	Na ·	Mg ·	· Al ·	· Si ·	· P ·	: S ·	: Cl ·	: Ar :
Period 4	Ar	K ·	Ca ·	· Ga ·	· Ge ·	· As ·	: Se ·	: Br ·	: Kr :
Period 5	Kr	Rb ·	Sr ·	· In ·	· Sn ·	· Sb ·	: Te ·	: I ·	: Xe :
Period 6	Xe	Cs ·	Ba ·	· Tl ·	· Pb ·	· Bi ·	: Po ·	: At ·	: Rn :
Period 7	Rn	Fr ·	Ra ·						

☐ Metals   ▨ Nonmetals   ▩ Metalloids

In Chapter 4, though, we learned that lead is a variable-charge metal; it can form Pb^{2+} as well as Pb^{4+}. Several of the representative metals with fairly many valence electrons have variable charge. Lead and tin, in Group IVA, need to lose four electrons each for their noble gas structures. They do form these 4+ ions, when enough energy is available (2220 kcal/mole for lead, 2113 kcal/mole for tin). Otherwise they form 2+ ions, because it takes less energy to remove two electrons (515 kcal/mole for lead, 502 kcal/mole for tin). Bismuth forms a 3+ ion in addition to its 5+ ion, for similar reasons. In Chapter 9, we'll see why these elements have these particular options.

The lower-charge ions don't have noble gas structures. We'll rarely have occasion to write their Lewis structures, but here they are:

Atoms: · Sn ·,   · Pb ·   : Bi ·

Ions: Sn $^{2+}$ Pb $^{2+}$ Bi $^{3+}$

We see that the Lewis structure of a metal ion whose metal atom has lost *all* its valence electrons is the same as its ionic formula, superscript and all. For these last three, though, the Lewis structures show the remaining valence electrons.

Now we can explain the sharp increase in ionization energy shown in Figure 7.5. Removing an electron beyond an element's group number means removing an electron from a noble gas structure. Since noble gas structures are the ultimate in low energy, destroying them in any way—either by removing or adding electrons—will always require a great deal of energy.

As far as the nonmetals are concerned, the noble gases are the end of the periods. By definition, nonmetals gain electrons to form negative ions. This way, a nonmetal can get up to the electronic arrangement (eight) of the noble gas that comes after it. The negative ion that's formed has the same amount of negative charge as the number of electrons the atom gained, and that's why we can get the charge of a negative ion by subtracting the nonmetal's group number from eight.

Again, if we look at the modified periodic table in Figure 7.10, we see that Period 2 has four nonmetals in it and Period 6 has none. (Although the noble gases are nonmetals, we don't count them because they don't gain electrons.) A nonmetal atom will usually gain as many electrons as it needs to give it the higher noble gas structure.

We'll use Period 2 as an illustration because it has the most nonmetals in it. Working from right to left, we see that fluorine has seven electrons. It can gain one and become F^- with the neon structure. At the end of the nonmetals, carbon needs four electrons to form C^{4-} with the neon structure. Again, it's increasingly difficult to gain a larger number of electrons. N^{3-} and C^{4-} form with difficulty, but they don't form variable-charge, negative ions similar to Pb^{2+}, Sn^{2+}, and Bi^{3+}. The metalloid boron, however, can form a negative ion in which it gains only three electrons, but it doesn't gain the five that it needs for the neon structure. Lewis structures for the nonmetal ions, plus boron, in Period 2 are shown below.

$$\text{Atoms:} \quad :\!\ddot{F}\!\cdot \quad \cdot\ddot{O}\!\cdot \quad \cdot\dot{N}\!\cdot \quad \cdot\dot{C}\!\cdot \quad \dot{B}\!\cdot$$

$$\text{Ions:} \quad :\!\ddot{F}\!: {}^- \quad :\!\ddot{O}\!: {}^{2-} \quad :\!\ddot{N}\!: {}^{3-} \quad :\!\ddot{C}\!: {}^{4-} \quad \dot{B}\!: {}^{3-}$$

We see that B^{3-} doesn't have a noble gas structure, and also that its Lewis structure doesn't obey the rule of single electrons where possible. Again, we see why nonmetals don't gain more electrons than would be predicted by their group numbers. To do so would be to destroy a noble gas structure, which takes a great deal of energy.

The helium electronic structure is an exception to the rule of eight electrons to a period. The helium structure has two electrons. Hydrogen forms the helium structure by gaining an electron; lithium and beryllium form it by losing one and two electrons, respectively. (Boron would have to lose three for the helium structure, but this takes too much energy.) Lewis structures for atoms and their ions that have the helium structure are as follows:

$$\text{Atoms:} \quad H\!\cdot \quad Li\!\cdot \quad Be\!\cdot$$

$$\text{Ions:} \quad H\!:{}^- \quad Li^+ \quad Be^{2+}$$

The metalloids, along the staircase-shaped line that separates metals from nonmetals, are in an awkward position when it comes to losing or gaining electrons. They have too many to lose, and too many to gain. Some can form ions with difficulty, but whether they lose or gain depends on other energy factors. We can see why it is difficult to classify them. Often they form covalent bonds instead of becoming ions.

In this chapter, we've seen that the low potential energy of the noble gas electronic structure is the underlying reason for the formation of most ionic compounds. In the next chapter, we'll be looking at covalent bonding, which is another way for elements to achieve noble gas structures.

REVIEW QUESTIONS

Energy and Chemical Reactions

1. What is *energy*? What is *potential energy*? Give an example of potential energy.
2. What do we mean by a reactive element? What are some reactive elements?
3. What is a *spontaneous reaction*? Give an example.
4. What are *electrostatic energies of attraction and repulsion*?

The Formation of Ionic Compounds

5. What is a *crystal lattice*? How does it come about?
6. What is an *ionic bond*?
7. What are the separate events that contribute to the formation of an ionic compound?
8. Why don't we speak of a NaCl molecule?
9. What are *ionization energy, electron affinity,* and *lattice energy*? How do we use these, with *heat of sublimation* and *heat of dissociation,* to calculate the heat of reaction of sodium with chlorine to produce sodium chloride?
10. Why does a sodium atom, and not a chlorine atom, lose an electron?
11. Why does sodium lose only one electron? Why does magnesium lose two?
12. Explain, in terms of ionization energies, why an element's group number has a relation to its ionic charge.
13. Explain why each successive ionization energy for a given element is higher than the first.
14. Explain why an element's first electron affinity may be positive, but the second is always negative.
15. Explain, in terms of ionization energy and electron affinity, why metals form positive ions and nonmetals form negative ions.
16. Why must an ionic crystal have a net lattice energy? What are the two factors that determine lattice energy?
17. How does lattice energy vary with ionic size

(radius)? What is the general relationship of lattice energy with melting point?
18. Explain how ionic compounds containing doubly or triply charged ions may form, even though large amounts of energy are required.

Ionic Trends in the Periodic Table

19. How do first and total ionization energies vary down a group and across a period of the periodic table?
20. What happens when we cross the staircase-shaped line? What does this line really mean?
21. Explain the following, in terms of ionization energies.
   a. Al^{3+} but not B^{3+} forms
   b. H is a nonmetal but Li is a metal
   c. Cs is the most metallic element
   d. aluminum is a metal, but silicon is a metalloid
22. In general, are negative ions or positive ions larger? What is the relationship in size between an atom and its corresponding ion?
23. How do the sizes of atoms vary down a group? Across a period? What is the smallest atom and what is the largest atom?
24. How do the sizes of ions vary with charge? Going down a group? What is the smallest positive ion? The smallest negative ion?

Electrons and Chemical Reactions

25. What is the potential energy state of a noble gas's electrons relative to other elements' electrons?
26. What is our current definition of *chemical reaction*?
27. What are *valence electrons*? How do we find out how many valence electrons a given element has?
28. What is a *Lewis structure*? Give an example.
29. Why are the noble gases sometimes called Group 0 and sometimes Group VIIIA?

30. What does the word "period" mean? How does it relate to the periodic table?
31. How can metals achieve a noble gas arrangement of valence electrons? What about nonmetals?
32. Write Lewis structures for one sample representative element in each group of the periodic table.
33. How do we write Lewis structures for metal ions whose atoms have lost all of their valence electrons? Give some examples.
34. Write Lewis structures for the three metal ions that have not lost all of their valence electrons.
35. How do we write Lewis structures for negative ions that have achieved noble gas structures? Give some examples.
36. What is the helium noble gas structure? Write Lewis structures for all ions that form the helium structure.
37. Why is it difficult for metalloids to lose or gain electrons?
38. Explain the ionization energies of Figure 7.5 in terms of noble gas structures.
39. What do we mean by an *octet* of electrons? What negative ion doesn't have an octet?
40. Explain, in terms of noble gas structures, why ions like O^{3-} and F^{2-} don't form.

EXERCISES

1. Which one of each of the following pairs has higher potential energy?
   a. a bowling ball on the fourth floor or one on eighth floor of a building
   b. a bullet that has been fired or one that hasn't
   c. separate samples of sodium and chlorine, or a sample of sodium chloride
   d. a sample of helium, or a sample of hydrogen
   e. separate Na^+ and Cl^- ions, or the same ions that are together.
2. The heat of sublimation of lithium metal is 33.2 kcal/mole. The lattice energy of LiF is 240 kcal/mole, and the heat of dissociation of F_2 is 37.7 kcal/mole. Using a similar set of equations to those on page 136, calculate the heat of formation of LiF. (Consult Figure 7.9 for the necessary ionization energies and electron affinities.)
3. The heat of dissociation of O_2 is 118.9 kcal/mole, and the lattice energy of Na_2O is 602 kcal/mole. Write equations and calculate the heat of formation of Na_2O, using 26.0 kcal/mole as the heat of sublimation of sodium, and other appropriate information from Figure 7.9. Hint: Consider $2(Na[s] + 26.0 \text{ kcal} \rightarrow Na[g])$. The electron affinity of oxygen for two electrons is -177 kcal/mole.
4. Calcium has a first ionization energy of 140.0 kcal/mole and a second ionization energy of 272.0 kcal/mole. Write equations that show these two processes, add them, and calculate the ionization energy of calcium for losing two electrons.
5. Sulfur has a first electron affinity of 46 kcal/mole and a second electron affinity of -118 kcal/mole. Write equations that show these two processes, add them, and calculate the electron affinity of sulfur for two electrons.

6. The compound MgTe does not exist. With reference to appropriate energies, speculate as to possible reasons for its nonexistence.
7. Which, in the following sets of pairs, would you expect to have the higher lattice energy? Give a reason for each choice.
   a. NaH or BeO   d. CsI or LiI
   b. CsF or CsI   e. BeO or BaO
   c. AlN or BeS   f. NaCl or $CaCO_3$
8. Give explanations for each of the following statements.
   a. NaI has a lower melting point than NaF.
   b. LiCl has a higher melting point than CsCl.
   c. CaO has a lower lattice energy than MgO.
   d. AlN has a higher melting point than ZnS.
   e. BeO has a higher melting point than CsI.
9. Which, in the following sets of pairs, would be the most metallic?
   a. C or Li   d. Sb or Bi
   b. Be or Ca   e. Sn or I
   c. Al or Tl   f. Ge or Sn
10. State the group in the periodic table that has, in general:
    a. the highest first ionization energy
    b. the lowest first ionization energy
    c. the highest electron affinity.
11. Looking at the periodic table inside the covers of this book, but without consulting the numbers in Figure 7.9, predict which of the following would have a higher first ionization energy.
    a. Na or Rb   d. Ba or Ca   g. B or Al
    b. Al or Ar   e. N or Bi   h. Mg or O
    c. Kr or He   f. As or Br   i. Al or Cl
12. Looking at the periodic table inside the covers of this book, but without consulting the numbers in Figure 7.9, write the symbol for the element whose electron affinity is the following:

a. higher than N but lower than F
b. the lowest in Group IA
c. the highest in the third period
d. less than S but greater than Al
e. the lowest in Group VIIA

13. Looking at the periodic table inside the covers of this book, but without consulting the numbers in Figure 7.9, predict which of the following species is the larger (has the larger radius).

a. Li or Li^+ e. H or H^- i. Mg^{2+} or Al^{3+}
b. S or S^{2-} f. Cl^- or I^- j. Cl^- or S^{2-}
c. N^{3-} or F^- g. Mg^{2+} or Ba^{2+} k. Be^{2+} or O^{2-}
d. He or Kr   h. K^+ or Br^-

14. Francium, the last member of the alkali metals group, is not shown on Figure 7.9. From the trend of ionic size, predict whether FrCl would have a higher melting point or a lower melting point than CsCl.

15. Without consulting Figure 7.10, and using the letter "E" for element, write Lewis structures that represent an element in each "A" group of the periodic table. Example: Group IA, $E\cdot$.

16. Write the charge of the ion that would be formed from an atom having each of the following numbers of valence electrons.

a. one valence electron
b. six valence electrons
c. seven valence electrons
d. two valence electrons

17. In what groups do we find at least one atom that gains electrons and at least one atom that loses electrons?

18. Write Lewis structures for these ions.

a. Ca^{2+} d. Br^- g. B^{3-}
b. S^{2-} e. K^+ h. Sn^{4+}
c. Ga^{3+} f. P^{3-}

19. Carbon and lead are both in Group IVA and therefore each has four valence electrons. Explain why carbon gains four electrons to form C^{4-}, but lead loses four to form Pb^{4+}.

8

Why Covalent Compounds Form

We know that elements react with each other in an attempt to achieve a lower-energy, noble gas electronic structure. There are two ways that an element can do this. One way is to lose or gain electrons and form ions, as we saw in the last chapter. Another way is to share electrons and form covalent bonds, which we'll see in this chapter.

Nonmetals react with nonmetals to form covalent compounds. This happens because there is an overall release of energy when the resulting covalent compound is formed. Nonmetals have no choice when they're reacting with each other. They can't form ions, because all they want to do is to accept electrons and there's no atom around that wants to donate them. So, sharing electrons is the answer.

Because of the different kind of bonding involved, covalent compounds behave a lot differently than ionic compounds. We'll see some of the characteristics of covalent compounds in this chapter.

8.1 MOLECULES AND COVALENT BOND FORMATION

molecule

covalent bond

We can expand our definition of a molecule now. A *molecule* is a particle of matter made of two or more atoms joined by covalent bonds. A *covalent bond* is a shared electron pair. Two atoms can cooperate to achieve noble gas structures, by forming a covalent bond. Each atom contributes a single electron to the formation of an electron pair. Then the two atoms share the pair, and each atom counts both electrons in the pair toward its noble gas structure. Some atoms can do this more than once, if they need to, in order to have an octet of electrons.

DIATOMIC MOLECULES IN ELEMENTS. We saw in Chapter 2 that some elements exist as diatomic molecules. They do this because being joined puts them in a lower energy state than does being single atoms. Now we'll find out why.

The halogens all have seven valence electrons. They each need one more electron to achieve a noble gas structure. Fluorine, for instance, needs one more electron for the neon structure. Let's look at the Lewis structure of a fluorine atom. When two electrons are together on a side, we say that these electrons are paired, or that they form an electron pair. If an electron is alone on a side, we say that it's an unpaired electron.

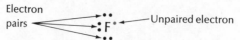

In covalent bond formation, fluorine can get the electron it needs by bonding to another element or by bonding to another fluorine. Two fluorine atoms can contribute each of their unpaired electrons to form a pair, and then they share the pair. The pair then belongs to them both equally, and not to one or the other. Then each atom has eight electrons, or four pairs, just like neon. We can use Lewis structures to see how this might happen.

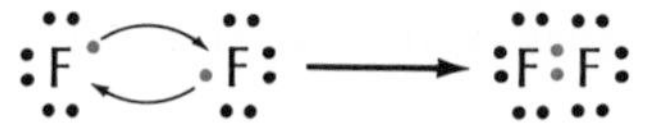

$$:\ddot{F}\cdot\quad\cdot\ddot{F}: \longrightarrow :\ddot{F}\!:\!\ddot{F}:$$

The two dots between the two fluorine atoms now represent a shared electron pair, or covalent bond. The other pairs that aren't involved in bonding are called *nonbonding electron pairs*. The structure on the right is the Lewis structure for the F_2 molecule. Lewis structures for Cl_2, Br_2, and I_2 are the same as for F_2.

nonbonding electron pair

Let's look at hydrogen. Since it has only one electron, hydrogen's nearest noble gas configuration is that of helium, with two electrons. To achieve this structure by covalent bond formation, hydrogen can bond to another element, or it can form a diatomic molecule by bonding with another hydrogen atom, like this:

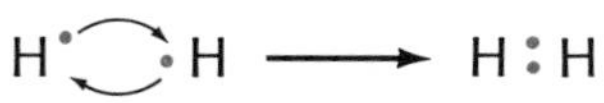

$$H\cdot\quad\cdot H \longrightarrow H\!:\!H$$

Notice that a diatomic hydrogen molecule has no nonbonding electron pairs.

F_2 and H_2 form *single* covalent bonds, since there is only one electron pair involved in the bond. Oxygen, which has six valence electrons, has two unpaired electrons. To achieve its octet when bonding with another oxygen atom, it forms a *double* bond, like this:

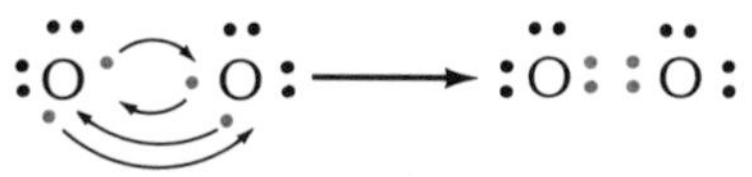

$$:\ddot{O}\cdot\quad\cdot\ddot{O}: \longrightarrow :\ddot{O}\!:\!:\!\ddot{O}:$$

The four dots between the two oxygen atoms stand for two single bonds, or one double bond. Notice that the Lewis structure of the O_2 molecule no longer has two electrons on a side, as atoms do. Instead, the four dots that represent two covalent bonds between the two atoms are owned equally by both atoms, so that each has an octet. The molecule has four nonbonding electron pairs, two on each O.

Nitrogen is an element whose diatomic molecule, N_2, has a *triple* bond between atoms. It does this because it has only five valence electrons, with three unpaired. It must pair three electrons to achieve the noble gas structure.

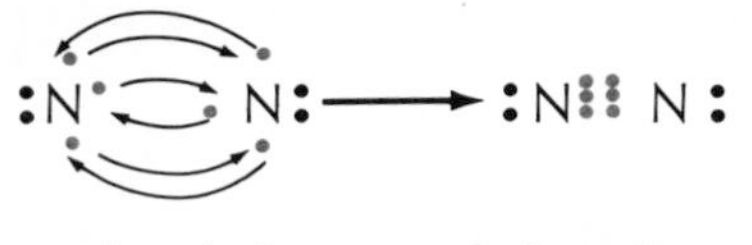

$$:N\cdot\quad\cdot N: \longrightarrow :N\!\vdots\!\vdots\!N:$$

The resulting nitrogen molecule has a triple bond, as shown by the six dots between the nitrogen atoms, and two nonbonding electron pairs (one on each N).

MOLECULES FORMED FROM TWO ELEMENTS. Up to now, we've seen how an atom of a single element can bond to another atom of the same element. Now we'll see how atoms of different elements can bond to each other.

The electron-dot formulas of hydrogen and fluorine are as follows:

$$\text{H} \cdot \quad \cdot \ddot{\underset{\cdot\cdot}{\text{F}}}\colon$$

Each atom has one unpaired electron. If they share their unpaired electrons, each will achieve a noble gas structure, and a molecule will be formed.

$$\text{H}\colon\!\ddot{\underset{\cdot\cdot}{\text{F}}}\colon$$

This, of course, is hydrogen fluoride, HF. HCl, HBr, and HI all have the same Lewis structure as HF.

Let's look at the Lewis structures of hydrogen and of oxygen:

$$\text{H} \cdot \quad \cdot \ddot{\underset{\cdot\cdot}{\text{O}}} \cdot$$

Hydrogen has one unpaired electron and oxygen has two. One of oxygen's electrons will form a bond with hydrogen's one electron, but that will leave oxygen with an unpaired electron:

$$\text{H}\colon\!\ddot{\underset{\cdot\cdot}{\text{O}}} \cdot$$

That electron can form a bond with another hydrogen and its electron, like this:

$$\text{H}\colon\!\ddot{\underset{\cdot\cdot}{\text{O}}}\colon\!\text{H}$$

We see that the simplest molecule formed from hydrogen and oxygen has one oxygen atom bonded to two hydrogen atoms, to make a molecule of water. Water has two single covalent bonds and two nonbonding electron pairs on the oxygen. H_2S, H_2Se, and H_2Te have the same Lewis structure as H_2O.

At this point, it's worth saying that these Lewis structures aren't meant to represent the shape or geometry of these molecules. They only show which atoms are bonded to which, how many electron pairs are used in bonding, and how many nonbonding electron pairs each atom has. Therefore, the bonds and the nonbonding electron pairs can be written on any side of the atom they belong to. All of the following structures would be all right for water, and they would all mean the same thing.

$$\text{H}\colon\!\ddot{\underset{\cdot\cdot}{\text{O}}}\colon\!\text{H} \quad \text{H}\colon\!\ddot{\underset{\cdot\cdot}{\text{O}}}\colon \quad \overset{\text{H}}{\underset{\text{H}}{\colon\!\ddot{\text{O}}\colon\!\text{H}}} \quad \overset{\text{H}}{\underset{\text{H}}{\colon\!\ddot{\text{O}}\colon}}$$

Nitrogen has three unpaired electrons. With this structure, nitrogen can

combine with three hydrogen atoms (one electron apiece) to form a molecule of ammonia.

$$H:\overset{..}{\underset{\underset{H}{|}}{N}}:H$$

Ammonia is a strong-smelling, choking gas. Dissolved in water, it makes
household ammonia. It's also used as an ingredient in fertilizers and as a
refrigerant. PH_3, AsH_3, and SbH_3 have the same Lewis structures.

Carbon has four unpaired electrons. In the simplest combination of
carbon and hydrogen, one carbon atom will bond to four hydrogen atoms
to form a molecule of CH_4.

$$\overset{H}{\underset{H}{H:\overset{..}{C}:H}}$$

The common name for CH_4 is methane. Methane is natural gas, or marsh
gas, and it is used as a fuel. Again, this is the simplest molecule containing
carbon and hydrogen. There are many, many other combinations of the two
elements, which we'll see in Chapter 17. SiH_4 and GeH_4 have the same Lewis
structure as CH_4.

Now that we know that two dots means a covalent bond or nonbonding
electron pair, we can switch to the simpler bar notation for Lewis structures.
In this notation, we use a straight line between atoms to represent a bond,
and lines parallel to the edges of the letter used for the atom represent
nonbonding electron pairs. We still use single dots to show unpaired electrons. Here are all the structures we've talked about so far, written in bar
notation.

$$|\overline{F}-\overline{F}| \quad |O=O| \quad |N≡N| \quad H-\overline{F}| \quad H-\overline{O}-H \quad H-\overline{N}-H$$
$$\underset{H}{|}$$

$$H-H \quad H-\overset{H}{\underset{H}{\overset{|}{\underset{|}{C}}}}-H$$

We've worked our way across the periodic table, from right to left, and
seen how the Period 2 nonmetal elements bond to hydrogen. The number
of bonds to hydrogen reflects the total number of covalent bonds that each
element can form. For these elements, the number of single bonds formed is
equal to the number of unpaired electrons each element has. Hydrogen and
fluorine, each with only one unpaired electron, form only one single bond.
Oxygen, with two unpaired electrons, can form two single bonds or one
double bond. Nitrogen can form three single bonds, or one single bond and
one double bond, or one triple bond. Carbon can form four single bonds,
two single bonds and a double bond, two double bonds, or one single bond
and one triple bond. (There's no such thing as a quadruple bond.) We can
represent these elements, with the bonds they can form, like this:

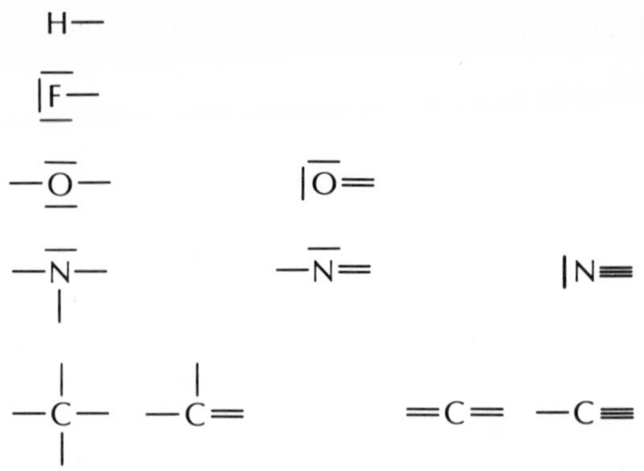

H—

|F—

—O— |O=

—N—   —N= |N≡

—C— —C=   =C= —C≡

Elements in higher-numbered periods bond this way, too, each having the
same number of possible bonds as the Period 2 element in the same group.
However, elements in periods beyond Period 2 aren't limited to this number
of bonds. We can only predict compounds where elements do follow the
system of Period 2.

EXAMPLE 8.1: Write the Lewis structure for the most likely compound
between chlorine and sulfur.

Solution: We see that chlorine has one unpaired electron and, like
fluorine, can form one single bond. Sulfur has two unpaired electrons
and can form two single bonds. Therefore, the most likely compound
between chlorine and sulfur would be the one where sulfur makes single
bonds to one of each of two chlorine atoms.

Answer:

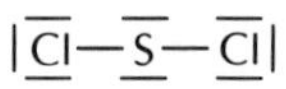

|Cl—S—Cl|

EXAMPLE 8.2: Write the Lewis structure for the most likely compound between silicon and fluorine.

Solution: We see that silicon has four unpaired electrons, like carbon.
Fluorine has one. Therefore, one silicon can bond to four fluorine atoms.

Answer:

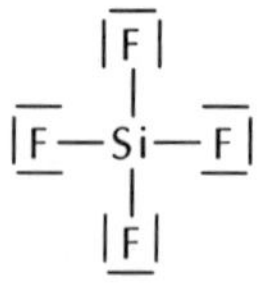

|F|
|
|F—Si—F|
|
|F|

EXAMPLE 8.3: Write the Lewis structure for the most likely compound
between carbon and oxygen.

Solution: Carbon has four unpaired electrons; oxygen has two. We can
form a molecule where carbon forms two double bonds with each of
two oxygens:

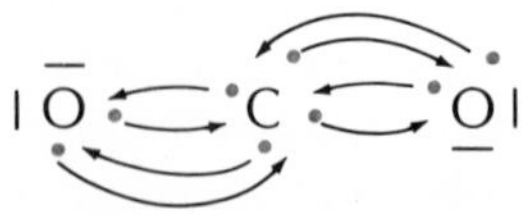

|O≡≡C≡≡O|

Answer:

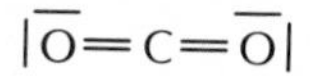

$$|\overline{O}{=}C{=}\overline{O}|$$

COORDINATE COVALENT BONDING.

We've seen that, in ordinary covalent bonding, each atom involved contributes one electron to a pair, and then each atom shares the pair. That's fair.

Coordinate covalent bonding, on the other hand, allows an atom that's missing an entire electron pair to share the nonbonding electron pair on another bond. A *coordinate covalent bond* is a shared electron pair where both electrons have been contributed by one of the atoms.

Coordinate covalent bonding is best illustrated by example. Here are the Lewis structures of fluorine and of boron:

**coordinate
covalent bond**

$$:\!\overset{\cdot\cdot}{\underset{\cdot\cdot}{F}}\!\cdot \qquad \overset{\cdot}{\underset{\cdot}{B}}\!\cdot$$

Each of boron's three unpaired electrons can bond to one fluorine atom, like this:

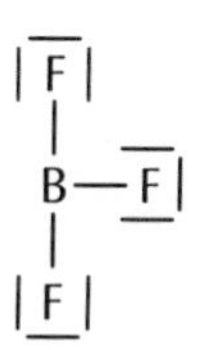

$$
\begin{array}{c}
|\overline{F}| \\
| \\
B{-}\overline{F}| \\
| \\
|\overline{F}|
\end{array}
$$

Notice that in this compound, boron trifluoride, boron doesn't have an octet. (Recall that B^{3-} doesn't have an octet either.) It does the best it can by pairing up all three of its valence electrons, but it still doesn't have a noble gas structure. Nevertheless, BF_3 is a fairly stable compound by itself. If it is allowed to come in contact with a molecule that has nonbonding electron pairs, though, it can react with it to form a coordinate covalent bond and complete its octet.

Ammonia is a molecule that reacts with BF_3. Ammonia can donate its pair of nonbonding electrons to boron, which in turn shares the pair back with ammonia. The resulting molecule, called boron trifluoride-ammonia adduct, can be written like this:

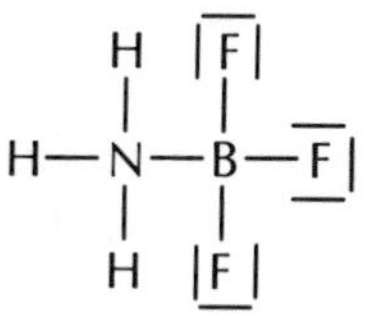

$$
\begin{array}{ccc}
H & |\overline{F}| & \\
| & | & \\
H{-}N{-}B{-}\overline{F}| \\
| & | & \\
H & |\overline{F}| &
\end{array}
$$

Boron, with its three valence electrons, might seem likely to be a metal and lose all three for the helium structure. We saw, though, that its ionization energy is too large. It can't form B^{5-}, either, which would give it the neon structure. Adding all those electrons takes too much energy. What it can do is to pair up its three electrons, as in B^{3-} or in covalent compounds like BF_3. These compounds are stable, showing us that three bonds—or three electron pairs—are better than none. We see, though, that if it does get a chance to achieve an octet by using another atom's nonbonding electrons, it will do so.

We've used boron to illustrate coordinate covalent bonding, but other atoms can bond this way too. This kind of bonding is important in oxyacids and polyatomic ions.

8.2 CHARACTERISTICS OF COVALENT BONDS

Just as we used lattice energies and ionic radii to describe ionic compounds, we now use bond strengths and bond lengths to describe covalent compounds.

BOND ENERGY. Covalent bonds form when the potential energy state of the bonded atoms is lower than the potential energy state of the unbonded atoms. Therefore, when a covalent bond is formed, there is a release of energy. The *bond energy* is the amount of energy, per mole, released when a covalent bond is formed from separate, gaseous atoms. The bond energy of a hydrogen molecule is 103 kcal/mole. Translating this into an equation:

bond energy

$$H(g) + H(g) \longrightarrow H_2(g) + 103 \text{ kcal}$$

This same amount of energy would be required to take a diatomic H_2 molecule apart into its separate, gaseous atoms. The amount of energy required is thus a measure of the bond strength. We sometimes use the term *bond strength* interchangeably with the term bond energy.

bond strength

Why should there be a release of energy when a covalent bond is formed? The answer lies in the attraction of the positive nuclei for additional electrons. When a covalent bond is formed, each nucleus can share two electrons in place of the one it had as a separate atom. We remember from Chapter 7 that energy is released when an electron is added to a neutral atom to form an ion (electron affinity). Energy is released when a covalent bond is formed for much the same reason.

For diatomic molecules where there is only one covalent bond, the bond energy is the same as the energy of formation of the molecule. We realize, though, that the bond energy of, say, one carbon-hydrogen bond is one-fourth the energy released when a mole of methane (CH_4) is formed from separate, gaseous atoms. This is because each molecule of CH_4 contains four carbon-hydrogen bonds.

$$C(g) + 4\,H(g) \longrightarrow CH_4(g) + 399 \text{ kcal}$$

Here the energy of one C—H bond is therefore 99.8 kcal/mole. When we speak of bond energy, we mean the energy of one bond, regardless of how many bonds there might be in a molecule.

BOND LENGTH.   The distance between nuclei of two atoms joined by a covalent bond is the *bond length,* and it is expressed in nanometers (nm). There is a relation between bond length and bond strength. There is also a relation between both of these properties and the multiplicity of the bond—that is, whether it is a double or triple bond.

bond length

Table 8.1 shows some trends in bond length and bond strength. In Series 1, the bond length increases from H—F to H—I. This is in keeping with the increasing atomic size from F to I that we saw in Chapter 7. We also note that as the bond length increases, the bond energy decreases. Again, this reflects a decreased attraction with decreased closeness, as we saw for lattice energies in Chapter 7. Series 2 shows the effect of multiple bonds. The single F—F bond has the greatest bond length and smallest bond energy. The double O=O bond has shorter length and greater energy. And the triple N≡N bond has the shortest length and greatest energy. This trend is also shown in Series 3, for carbon-carbon single, double, and triple bonds. We usually find that increasing bond energy goes with decreasing bond length. It's as if the atoms were being pulled closer together by more pieces of string. Shorter bonds are stronger.

Bond	Bond Length (nanometers)	Bond Energy (kcal/mole)
Series 1		
H—F	0.0917	135
H—Cl	0.127	102
H—Br	0.141	86.5
H—I	0.161	70.5
Series 2		
F—F	0.142	33
O=O	0.121	118
N≡N	0.110	225
Series 3		
—C—C—	0.154	85
—C=C—	0.135	125
—C≡C—	0.120	230
Series 4		
H—H	0.0741	103
F—F	0.142	33
Cl—Cl	0.199	57.2
Br—Br	0.228	45.4
I—I	0.267	35.6

**TABLE 8.1
Some bond
lengths and
bond energies**

In Series 4, we see that bond length increases with atomic size in the halogens, but there's not much relation between bond length and bond energy in this series.

8.3 LEWIS STRUCTURES

We've seen that there are some simple molecules that we could predict just on the basis of the number of unpaired electrons their atoms have. Having done that, we could write the Lewis structure of the molecule. Most molecules that we'll encounter aren't so easily predicted, though, because many of them use coordinate covalent bonds where we might not necessarily expect them. For instance, the molecule carbon monoxide, CO, bonds one carbon with only one oxygen. If we look at the Lewis structures of these, we can easily see how carbon could form a double bond with oxygen:

$$\cdot \overset{\cdot}{C} \,\,\,\, \overset{\cdot \cdot}{\underset{\cdot \cdot}{O}} \colon \longrightarrow \cdot \overset{\cdot}{C} = \overset{\cdot \cdot}{O} \colon$$

However, this leaves carbon with only six electrons, two of them unpaired. Carbon pairs these, like this:

$$\overset{\curvearrowright}{\underset{\cdot}{\cdot}} C = \overset{\cdot \cdot}{O} \colon \longrightarrow \colon C = \overset{\cdot \cdot}{O} \colon$$

Oxygen uses one of its nonbonding electron pairs to make a coordinate covalent bond with carbon. Oxygen has its octet, and so does carbon:

$$\colon C \overset{\frown}{=} \overset{\cdot \cdot}{O} \colon \longrightarrow \colon C \vdots \vdots O \colon \quad \left(| C \equiv O | \right)$$

This is one of the rare instances where oxygen forms a triple bond. We couldn't have predicted this from what we know about valence electrons and how they bond. Fortunately, now that we understand that there are many compounds that don't bond in the simple way discussed in Section 8.2, we don't have to be able to figure out where the electrons came from. We can write Lewis structures without knowing which bonds are coordinate covalent or how the electron pairing took place. We'll look at some rules for covalent compounds and for polyatomic ions.

central atom

COVALENT COMPOUNDS. We can write the Lewis structure of any covalent compound if we know its formula and if we know which atoms are bonded to which. We start by figuring out what the *central atom* is—that is, the atom that has the most other atoms bonded to it. Here are some rules for writing Lewis structures.

1. For binary covalent compounds, the central atom is the one that appears only once in the formula. For instance, in PCl_3, CS_2, and SiF_4, the central

atoms are P, C, and Si. The other atoms in each formula are bonded to the central atom and not to each other.

2. For oxyacids and polyatomic ions, the atom other than hydrogen or oxygen is the central atom. The hydrogens in an oxyacid are bonded to the oxygens, and not to the central atom. For instance, in H_2SO_4, NO_3^-, and $HClO_3$, the central atoms are S, N, and Cl. In H_2SO_4 and $HClO_3$, the hydrogens are bonded to the oxygens, like this:

$$H-O-\underset{\underset{O}{|}}{\overset{\overset{O}{||}}{S}}-O-H \qquad\qquad H-O-\underset{\underset{O}{|}}{Cl}-O$$

We haven't drawn in the nonbonding electron pairs, because we're just trying to show the way the atoms are bonded. These aren't finished Lewis structures.

3. The octet rule should be obeyed whenever possible. The *octet rule* states that each atom except hydrogen and boron attempts to achieve an octet of electrons. (Molecules do exist where atoms violate the octet rule, but we won't consider them here.)

octet rule

4. The finished Lewis structure of a molecule has to have the same number of electrons as the total of the valence electrons of the atoms that make it up. Since molecules are electrically neutral, no electrons have been added or subtracted. All we do is to rearrange the electrons that the atoms have. For instance, in the molecule CCl_4, we have this many valence electrons altogether:

$$\begin{array}{ll} \text{C:} & \text{4 valence electrons} \\ \text{4(Cl):} & \underline{\text{28 valence electrons}} \\ & \text{32 valence electrons, or 16 pairs} \end{array}$$

Now, if we write a finished Lewis structure for CCl_4, it can't have more or fewer than sixteen electron pairs. If we write this Lewis structure for this compound:

$$\begin{array}{c} ..\\ :\ddot{Cl}: \\ .. \quad .. \\ :\ddot{Cl}:C:\ddot{Cl}: \\ .. \quad .. \\ :\ddot{Cl}: \\ .. \end{array}$$

we find that it has sixteen pairs, and we've obeyed this rule.

5. If too many electrons would be used trying to satisfy octets, then the molecule makes multiple bonds. A double bond uses two fewer electrons; a triple bond uses four fewer. For instance, in the structure:

$$H-\overline{\overline{C}}-\overline{\overline{N}}|$$

an electron count shows the following

Individual atoms

$$\begin{array}{ll} \text{H:} & \text{1 valence electron} \\ \text{C:} & \text{4 valence electrons} \\ \text{N:} & \underline{\text{5 valence electrons}} \\ & \text{10 electrons, 5 pairs} \end{array}$$

Our Lewis structure uses seven pairs, but we are only supposed to use five. We can get rid of two pairs by making a triple bond between carbon and nitrogen.

$$H-C\equiv N|$$

Now we have used only five pairs. This works because a shared electron pair counts toward the octet of both of the atoms that share it. A nonbonding pair only counts for the atom it's on.

Now we can go through the steps in writing a Lewis structure. Suppose that we are asked to write the Lewis structure of SO_2.

Step 1. *Decide what the central atom is and how the other atoms are bonded.* We decide that S is the central atom (Rule 1) and the two O's are bonded to it.

Step 2. *Write out the central atom and the others that are bonded to it. Make single bonds between them.*

$$O-S-O$$

Step 3. *Count the total number of valence electrons contributed by all atoms in the molecule.*

$$
\begin{array}{rl}
S: & 6 \text{ valence electrons} \\
2(O): & \underline{12} \text{ valence electrons} \\
& 18 \text{ electrons, 9 pairs}
\end{array}
$$

Step 4. *Subtract from the total the electron pairs that have already been used to make the single bonds. Assign the electron pairs that are left to atoms in the molecule, forming octets where possible. (Rules 3, 4, and 5.)* We've made two single bonds, so seven pairs are left. We'd need eight pairs if all of them were nonbonding, so we make a double bond between S and one of the O's.

$$|\overline{O}=\overline{S}-\overline{O}|$$

Step 5. *Check the number of electrons again, and make sure that the octet rule is satisfied.*

Electron count: 9 pairs, 18 electrons
Octet rule: O has 8; S has 8; O has 8

Our Lewis structure is correct.

Sometimes, as in writing chemical equations, we might have to repeat Steps 4 and 5 until we get the right structure.

Now we can look at some more examples.

EXAMPLE 8.4: Write the Lewis structure of HNO_3.

Solution:
Step 1: We have an acid here, so we know that N is the central atom. The three O's are each bonded to the N, and the H is bonded to one of the O's.

Step 2:

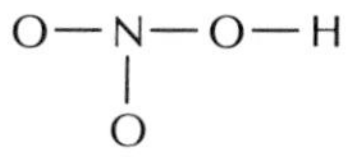

$$O-N-O-H$$
$$\ \ \ \ \ \ \ \ |$$
$$\ \ \ \ \ \ \ \ O$$

Here it doesn't matter which O we decide to attach the H to.
Step 3:

$$\begin{aligned}
\text{N:} &\quad \text{5 valence electrons}\\
\text{3(O):} &\quad \text{18 valence electrons}\\
\text{H:} &\quad \underline{\text{1 valence electron}}\\
&\quad \text{24 electrons, or 12 electron pairs}
\end{aligned}$$

Step 4: We've used four pairs in bonding, so eight are left to assign. Again, we see that just putting nonbonding electron pairs all around would require nine pairs, and we only have eight. So, we make a double bond between N and one of the O's, but not the O that's bonded to the H. That would give O too many bonds.

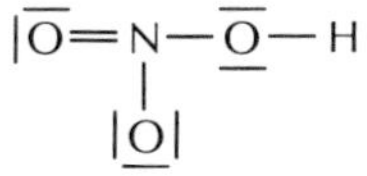

$$|\overline{O}=N-\overline{O}-H$$
$$\ \ \ \ \ \ \ \ \ \ |$$
$$\ \ \ \ \ \ \ \ \ \ |\underline{O}|$$

Step 5:

Electron count: 12 pairs, or 24 electrons.
Octet rule: All satisfied except that H has two electrons, which is correct.

Answer:

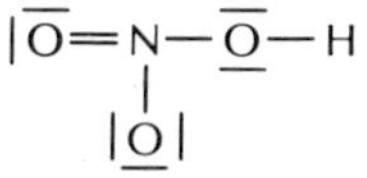

$$|\overline{O}=N-\overline{O}-H$$
$$\ \ \ \ \ \ \ \ \ \ |$$
$$\ \ \ \ \ \ \ \ \ \ |\underline{O}|$$

EXAMPLE 8.5: Write the Lewis structure of H_2O_2. The two oxygen atoms are bonded together, and one hydrogen is bonded to each oxygen.

Solution:
Step 1: Here there is no central atom, so our simple rules don't apply. However, the problem has told us how the atoms are bonded.
Step 2:

$$H-O-O-H$$

Step 3:

$$\begin{aligned}
\text{2(O):} &\quad \text{12 valence electrons}\\
\text{2(H):} &\quad \underline{\text{2 valence electrons}}\\
&\quad \text{14 electrons, or 7 pairs}
\end{aligned}$$

Step 4: We've used three pairs in bonding, so that leaves four to assign. If we put two nonbonding pairs on each oxygen, that will be exactly four.

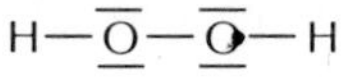

$$H-\overline{\underline{O}}-\overline{\underline{O}}-H$$

Step 5:

Electron count: 14 electrons, or 7 pairs.
Octet rule: Each O has eight electrons; each H has two electrons.

Answer:

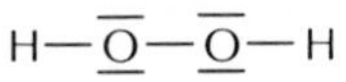

$$H-\overline{\underline{O}}-\overline{\underline{O}}-H$$

POLYATOMIC IONS. Polyatomic ions are really charged molecules. That is, they contain covalent bonds, but they have a positive or a negative charge. Rules for writing Lewis structures for polyatomic ions are the same as for covalent compounds, except that the charge must be taken into account during the electron count.

EXAMPLE 8.6: Write the Lewis structure of the phosphate ion, PO_4^{3-}.

Solution:

Step 1: P is the central atom, and the four O's are each bonded to it.

Step 2:

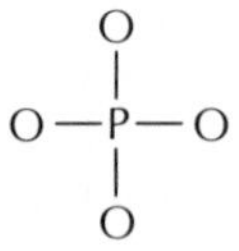

$$
\begin{array}{c}
O \\
| \\
O - P - O \\
| \\
O
\end{array}
$$

Step 3: Phosphate ion is PO_4^{3-}. The $3-$ means that the ion has three more electrons than the total of the electrons provided by its individual atoms. So, we have to add these three electrons in.

$$
\begin{array}{ll}
\text{P:} & 5 \text{ valence electrons} \\
4(\text{O}): & 24 \text{ valence electrons} \\
3-: & \underline{3 \text{ valence electrons}} \\
& 32 \text{ electrons, or 16 pairs}
\end{array}
$$

Step 4: We've used four pairs in bonding, so twelve are left. If we give each oxygen atom three nonbonding pairs, that exactly does it.

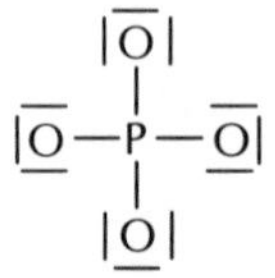

$$
\begin{array}{c}
|\overline{O}| \\
| \\
|\overline{O} - P - \overline{O}| \\
| \\
|\overline{O}|
\end{array}
$$

Step 5:

Electron count: 16 pairs, or 32 electrons.
Octet rule: All satisfied.

Answer:

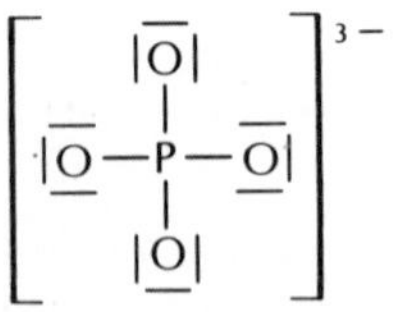

$$
\left[
\begin{array}{c}
|\overline{O}| \\
| \\
\cdot |\overline{O} - P - \overline{O}| \\
| \\
|\overline{O}|
\end{array}
\right]^{3-}
$$

EXAMPLE 8.7: Write the Lewis structure of the ammonium ion.

Solution:

Step 1: N is the central atom; the four H's are attached to it.

Step 2:

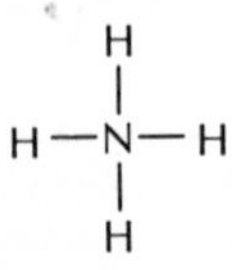

$$
\begin{array}{c}
H \\
| \\
H - N - H \\
| \\
H
\end{array}
$$

Step 3: Ammonium ion is NH_4^+. The $+$ means that the ion has one less electron than the total of the electrons provided by its individual atoms. So, we have to subtract one electron.

$$\begin{array}{ll} \text{N:} & \text{5 valence electrons} \\ \text{4(H):} & \text{4 valence electrons} \\ \text{1+:} & \underline{-1 \text{ valence electron}} \\ & \text{8 electrons, or 4 pairs} \end{array}$$

Step 4: We've used four pairs in bonding, so none are left. The formula is correct as it stands.

Step 5:

Electron count: 4 pairs, or 8 electrons.
Octet rule: N has eight, H has two.

Answer:

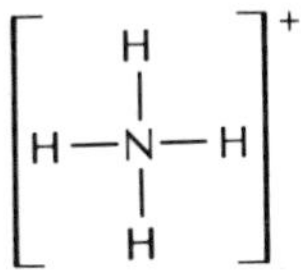

$$\left[\begin{array}{c} \text{H} \\ | \\ \text{H}-\text{N}-\text{H} \\ | \\ \text{H} \end{array} \right]^{+}$$

Note that the charge is part of the Lewis structure of a polyatomic ion. Lewis structures of polyatomic ions without the charge on them are incorrect.

EXAMPLE 8.8: Write the Lewis structure for the nitrate ion.

Solution:

Step 1: N is the central atom.

Step 2:

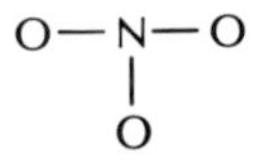

$$\begin{array}{c} \text{O}-\text{N}-\text{O} \\ | \\ \text{O} \end{array}$$

Step 3:

$$\begin{array}{ll} \text{N:} & \text{5 electrons} \\ \text{3(O):} & \text{18 electrons} \\ \text{1-:} & \underline{\text{1 electron}} \\ & \text{24 electrons, or 12 pairs} \end{array}$$

Step 4:

$$\begin{array}{c} \overline{\text{|O}}{=}\text{N}{-}\overline{\text{O|}} \\ | \\ \underline{\text{|O|}} \end{array}$$

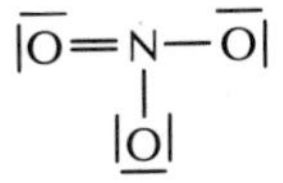

Step 5: 24 electrons, or 12 pairs.
Octet rule is satisfied.

Answer:

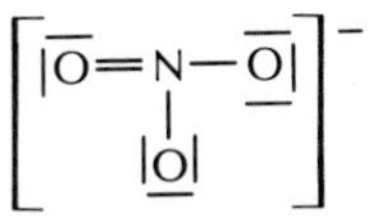

$$\left[\begin{array}{c} \overline{\text{|O}}{=}\text{N}{-}\overline{\text{O|}} \\ | \\ \underline{\text{|O|}} \end{array} \right]^{-}$$

We should notice the relationship between the Lewis structures of oxyacids and their corresponding polyatomic ions. For example, nitrate ion and nitric acid:

$$\left[\overline{|O} {=} N {-} \overline{O|} \right]^{-} \qquad |\overline{O} {=} N {-} \overline{O} {-} H$$

$$\underset{|O|}{|} \qquad \underset{|O|}{|}$$

We see that they have the same numbers of electron pairs. One of the non-bonding electron pairs on the nitrate ion has turned into a bonding pair when it bonds to hydrogen in the acid. This is why the nitrate ion has a negative charge. It's missing the hydrogen.

8.4 BOND POLARITY

So far, we've talked about compounds as being either ionic or covalent. We've used the staircase-shaped line on the periodic table as a guide in deciding whether a given compound is one or the other. This works fine for general cases and for naming compounds, but actually elements don't let themselves be classified so easily. We already know that there's a fuzzy region around the metalloids.

For instance, if cesium, with low ionization energy and low electron affinity, reacts with fluorine, with high ionization energy and high electron affinity, we'll get an ionic compound. The fluorine takes an electron completely away from the cesium. Two elements that have about the same high ionization energy and electron affinity, like phosphorus and hydrogen, produce a covalent compound. But what if we have two elements that both have ionization energies and electron affinities that are too high for them to lose electrons, but they are quite different in value from each other? We'll still get a covalent compound, but the bond will be sort of in between covalent and ionic. We call this a polar covalent bond. We describe and explain polar covalent bonds by using a concept called electronegativity.

**electro-
negativity**

ELECTRONEGATIVITY. Hydrogen's electron affinity is 16.1 kcal/mole. Fluorine's is 83.5 kcal/mole—much higher than hydrogen's. When they bond, fluorine tries to take the electron completely away from hydrogen. It can't, though, because hydrogen's ionization energy is too high. The result is a tug-of-war between hydrogen and fluorine, with the electron pair in between—and with fluorine almost winning. (See Figure 8.1.)

The chemist Linus Pauling proposed a concept called electronegativity to explain inequalities of bonding. *Electronegativity* is related to electron affinity and ionization energy, and it is defined as the tendency of an element to hold bonding electrons.

Pauling calculated his values from bond energies. Whereas we might expect the bond energy of HF to be about the average of H_2 and F_2 bond energies, in fact it isn't. The HF bond energy is higher than the averages.

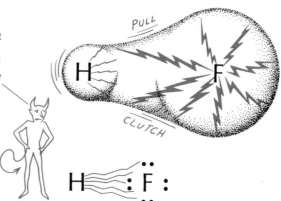

How do you like that? Why, that poor hydrogen atom with its electron affinity of only 16.1 doesn't have a *chance* at that electron pair against fluorine's electron affinity of 83.5! You or I would have the same problem if we had to share a small blanket with a football tackle on a cold night! I guess they're stlll "sharing" it, but fluorine has the lion's share.

Pauling used differences like these to calculate electronegativity values, shown in Figure 8.2. The values were adjusted so that fluorine, the highest, has an electronegativity of 4.0. Oxygen is the next most electronegative element.

POLAR BONDS.

In a covalent bond, atoms share electron pairs "equally," but some atoms are more equal than others.[1] For instance, in a chlorine molecule, the electron pair is exactly shared between the two chlorine atoms. Neither one has any more control over it than the other. There is no doubt here about the sharing, because the bond is between atoms of the same element.

We can use the electronegativity values to decide how the electron-pair bond would be shared between various elements. A bond between two elements with about the same electronegativity values, such as nitrogen and chlorine, will be shared equally by the elements. Such a bond is called *nonpolar covalent,* because its centers of positive and negative charge are in the same place. We consider bonds between atoms whose electronegativity difference is between 0 and 0.6 to be nonpolar covalent.

nonpolar covalent bond

Most nonmetals have high electronegativity values and are said to be *electronegative.* Metals have low electronegativity values and are said to be *electropositive.* When an electropositive element like cesium (0.7) reacts with an electronegative element like fluorine (4.0), the electron pair will be shared so unequally that fluorine will own the whole thing, and the bond will be ionic. We usually consider ionic bonds to be those where the difference in electronegativity values between the two elements is greater than 2.0, but again this is an arbitrary classification.

electronegative element

electropositive element

A bond between two elements where the electronegativity difference is

1. A paraphrase from George Orwell's *Animal Farm.*

FIGURE 8.2
Electronegativity values for the elements (exclusive of inner transition elements)

ELECTRONEGATIVITY DECREASES →

↑ ELECTRONEGATIVITY INCREASES

Most electronegative element

Most electropositive elements

H 2.1																	He —
Li 1.0	Be 1.5											B 2.0	C 2.5	N 3.0	O 3.5	F 4.0	Ne —
Na 0.9	Mg 1.2											Al 1.5	Si 1.8	P 2.1	S 2.5	Cl 3.0	Ar —
K 0.8	Ca 1.0	Sc 1.3	Ti 1.5	V 1.6	Cr 1.6	Mn 1.5	Fe 1.8	Co 1.8	Ni 1.8	Cu 1.9	Zn 1.6	Ga 1.6	Ge 1.8	As 2.0	Se 2.4	Br 2.8	Kr —
Rb 0.8	Sr 1.0	Y 1.2	Zr 1.4	Nb 1.6	Mo 1.8	Tc 1.9	Ru 2.2	Rh 2.2	Pd 2.2	Ag 1.9	Cd 1.7	In 1.7	Sn 1.8	Sb 1.9	Te 2.1	I 2.5	Xe —
Cs 0.7	Ba 0.9	La 1.1	Hf 1.3	Ta 1.5	W 1.7	Re 1.9	Os 2.2	Ir 2.2	Pt 2.2	Au 2.4	Hg 1.9	Tl 1.8	Pb 1.8	Bi 1.9	Po 2.0	At 2.2	Rn —
Fr 0.7	Ra 0.9	Ac 1.1	Ku —	Ha —	106 —												

■ Nonmetals   ■ Metalloids

between 0.6 and 2.0 is considered to be a polar covalent bond. A *polar covalent bond* is one in which the centers of positive and negative charge are in different places. For instance, the electronegativity difference between hydrogen and fluorine is 1.9. This means that fluorine will control the electron pair much more than hydrogen, as we saw it doing in Figure 8.1. When discussing polarity, we sometimes use a crossed arrow to indicate a polar covalent bond. The arrow points to the more electronegative element.

$$H \longmapsto F$$

The reason this kind of bond is called polar is that it has two poles: a positive and a negative. Such a charge separation is called a *dipole*.

dipole

The greater the electronegativity difference, the more polar the bond, until at the extreme, the electron pair comes off completely and we have an ionic bond. An ionic bond can be thought of as the extreme of bond polarity. (See Figure 8.3.)

Fluorine, oxygen, nitrogen, and chlorine are the "big four" electronegative elements. Bonds between these and the more electropositive nonmetals will usually be polar.

FIGURE 8.3
Greater electronegativity differences cause greater bond polarity

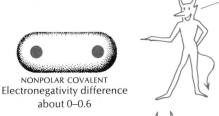

NONPOLAR COVALENT
Electronegativity difference
about 0–0.6

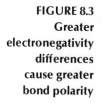

Now, that's what I call sharing! These two atoms have about the same electronegativities, so each has a fair share of the electron pair. In these pictures, I've used red circles to mean nuclei of atoms, and the shaded cloud to mean the electron pair.

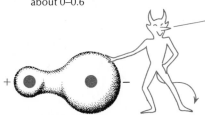

POLAR COVALENT
Electronegativity difference
about 0.6–2.0

Electronegative elements are *electron hogs*. Watch how this electronegative element I'm leaning on hogs the electron pair! The less electronegative element can barely hold on!

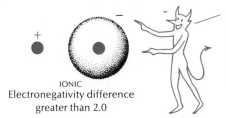

IONIC
Electronegativity difference
greater than 2.0

And here we have the ultimate in electron hoggishness: an ionic bond! This electronegative element has the whole electron pair. That's why it has this negative charge, as we know from the last chapter.

---

polar molecule

POLAR MOLECULES.

A consequence of polar bonds is that entire molecules can be polar, too. We define a *polar molecule* as a molecule whose centers of positive and negative charge aren't in the same place. Although a molecule is electrically neutral overall, within it there can be such a separation of charge.

Whether a molecule is polar or nonpolar can determine some of the properties of a particular compound in bulk. Compounds whose molecules are polar tend to have higher melting points and boiling points in general than compounds whose molecules are nonpolar. Many of water's unique properties, including its ability to dissolve ionic compounds, are due to the fact that its molecules are polar. More about this in Chapter 12.

It takes more than just polar bonds to cause a molecule to be polar. HF, CF_4, H_2O, and CO_2 all contain polar bonds, but only HF and H_2O are polar molecules. What makes the difference is the shape of the molecule. Symmetrical molecules can't be polar, even though they might contain polar bonds. This is the case with CF_4 and CO_2. In both cases, the polar bonds pulling against one another exactly cancel, and there is no *net* dipole, as shown in Figure 8.4.

center of symmetry

Both CO_2 and CF_4 have *centers of symmetry*. This means that if we start

**FIGURE 8.4
Polar bonds
acting
unsymmetrically
cause
polar molecules;
polar bonds
acting
symmetrically
cause nonpolar
molecules**

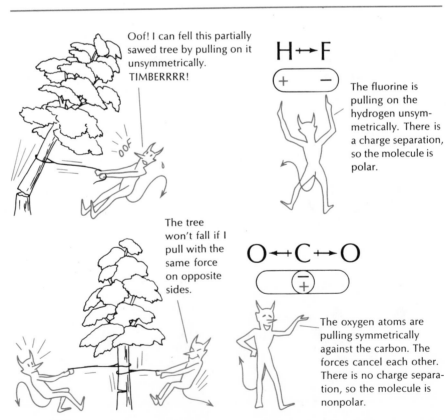

Oof! I can fell this partially sawed tree by pulling on it unsymmetrically. TIMBERRRR!

H↦F

The fluorine is pulling on the hydrogen unsymmetrically. There is a charge separation, so the molecule is polar.

The tree won't fall if I pull with the same force on opposite sides.

O↤C↦O

The oxygen atoms are pulling symmetrically against the carbon. The forces cancel each other. There is no charge separation, so the molecule is nonpolar.

FIGURE 8.5
CF_4 has a center
of symmetry;
H_2O has none

173

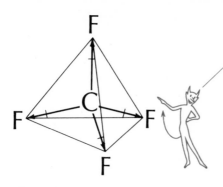

This CF_4 molecule has a center of symmetry. If I climbed inside to the carbon atom and crawled along each bond, I'd find a fluorine atom the same distance from the center in each direction.

This water molecule has no center of symmetry. If I crawled along each line starting with the oxygen atom in the center, sometimes I'd find a hydrogen atom, and sometimes I'd find a nonbonding electron pair.

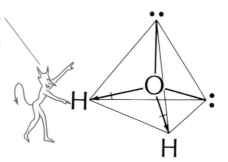

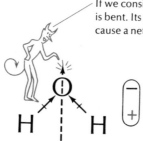

If we consider just the atoms, we see that water is bent. Its polar bonds pulling unsymmetrically cause a net dipole in this direction.

at the central atom and move out any one of the bonds, we will always encounter the same structure. CO_2 is a linear molecule with carbon in the center of two oxygens; CF_4 is tetrahedral, with carbon in the middle of the tetrahedron and each of the four fluorines at a corner.

It's easy to see why HF is polar. It contains only one bond, and that bond is polar. It lacks a center of symmetry. Water also lacks a center of symmetry, because the molecule is bent so that both polar bonds are on the same side. Figure 8.5 shows symmetrical molecules and unsymmetrical molecules.

To summarize, a polar molecule must have *both* of these things:

1. polar bond or bonds
2. no center of symmetry

But how do we know what shape any molecule has?

8.5 MOLECULAR SHAPE

We've seen how to tell whether a molecule is polar or not if we know its shape. Now we'll see how to find out a molecule's shape if we know its Lewis structure. The arrangement around a central atom is determined by the electron groups that are attached to it. These groups try to get as far away from each other as possible, because electrons repel one another. This is stated by the *VSEPR (Valence Shell Electron Pair Repulsion) theory,* which explains why molecules have certain shapes.

VSEPR theory

electron group

electron group number

ELECTRON GROUPS.
Electron groups attached to a central atom include bonds (single, double, or triple) and nonbonding electron pairs. The *electron group number* is thus the number of bonds (or number of bonded atoms) plus the number of nonbonding electron pairs. For the molecules we'll consider in this book, the electron group number will be 2, 3, or 4. Each of these numbers indicates a specific geometry because of electron pair repulsion. Two groups around a central atom have a linear arrangement. Three groups go to the corners of a triangle. Four go to the corners of a tetrahedron. (See Figure 8.6.)

electronic geometry

molecular shape

MOLECULAR MODELS.
Electron groups give us a central atom's *electronic geometry,* which is what the drawings in Figure 8.6 show. If each electron group contains a bonded atom, then the shape of the molecule will be the same as the central atom's electronic geometry. However, if one or more of the electron groups are nonbonding pairs, the molecular shape will be different from the electronic geometry. This is because *molecular shape* is the geometry of a molecule's atoms, not of its atoms *and* nonbonding electron pairs. (See Figure 8.7.)

bond angle

BOND ANGLES.
The angle formed by the bonds from a central atom to two other atoms is the *bond angle.* The angle is 180° when two atoms are attached to a central atom with linear geometry. For a triangular molecule, it's 120°. For a tetrahedral molecule, it's 109°. These angles are found in a molecule where the bonded atoms are all the same.

For molecules that contain nonbonding electron pairs, these bond angles will be slightly less than the ones predicted above. This is because nonbonding electron pairs are more repulsive than bonding ones. For a pyramidal molecule like ammonia, the greater repulsion of the one nonbonding pair will push the three hydrogens together slightly. The observed bond angle for ammonia is 107° instead of 109°. (See Figure 8.7.) For water, which contains two nonbonding pairs, the two hydrogen atoms are pushed still closer together. The observed bond angle in water is 105°.

FIGURE 8.6 175

Geometric arrangement of two, three, and four electron groups around a central atom

Watch what happens when I let go of these two negatively charged balls.

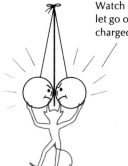

They really want to get away from each other. This is as far as they can get. Down here I've shown this linear arrangement of two electron pairs and a central atom.

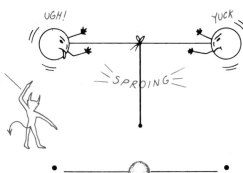

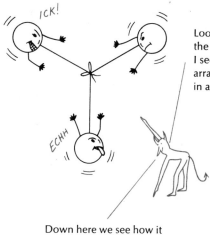

Looking down from the top of the stick, I see that three balls arrange themselves in a triangle.

Down here we see how it looks with electron pairs.

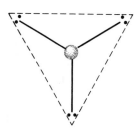

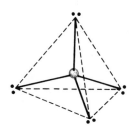

Four, and we have a tetrahedron. Down there is the structure with electron pairs.

FIGURE 8.7
Molecular shapes with all electron groups as bonded atoms and with nonbonding electron pairs (central atoms are shown in color)

Here we see models of molecules where all electron groups are bonded atoms. The electronic geometry and molecular shape are the same.

LINEAR ELECTRONIC GEOMETRY

LINEAR MOLECULE (ball-and-stick model)

LINEAR MOLECULE (space-filling model)

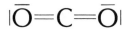

LINEAR MOLECULE CO_2

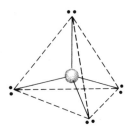

TETRAHEDRAL ELECTRONIC GEOMETRY

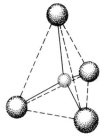

TETRAHEDRAL MOLECULE (ball-and-stick model)

TETRAHEDRAL MOLECULE (space-filling model)

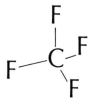

TETRAHEDRAL MOLECULE CF_4

Here, though, the molecules contain nonbonding electron pairs. The nonbonding electrons influence the geometry of the molecule, but they aren't counted in the molecular shape. Thus the electronic geometry and molecular shape are different.

TRIANGULAR ELECTRONIC GEOMETRY

BENT MOLECULE (ball-and-stick model)

BENT MOLECULE (space-filling model)

BENT MOLECULE SO_2

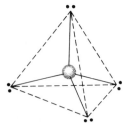

TETRAHEDRAL ELECTRONIC GEOMETRY

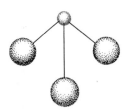

PYRAMIDAL MOLECULE (ball-and-stick model)

PYRAMIDAL MOLECULE (space-filling model)

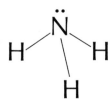

PYRAMIDAL MOLECULE NH_3

MOLECULAR SHAPE FROM LEWIS STRUCTURES.

To find out a molecular shape, we first find the electron group number and then consult Table 8.2 to get the electronic geometry and molecular shape. As an

Electron Group Number	Electronic Geometry	Number of Nonbonding Electron Pairs	Molecular Shape	Bond Angle
2	Linear	0	Linear	180°
2	Linear	1	Linear	180°
3	Triangular	0	Triangular	120°
3	Triangular	1	Bent	Less than 120°
4	Tetrahedral	0	Tetrahedral	109°
4	Tetrahedral	1	Pyramidal	Less than 109°
4	Tetrahedral	2	Bent	Still less than 109°

example, let's find the electronic geometry and molecular shape of SO_2. First, we write the Lewis structure.

$$|\overline{O}-\overline{S}=\underline{O}|$$

Then we find the electron group number of the central atom (S). The electron group number is the sum of its bonded atoms (2) plus its nonbonding pairs (1)—a total of 3. Table 8.2 shows that a molecule having an electron group number of 3, with one nonbonding electron pair, has triangular electronic geometry and bent molecular shape. Such a molecule also has a bond angle slightly less than 120°, because of the nonbonding electron pair.

Table 8.3 shows some molecules and polyatomic ions with their electronic geometries and molecular shapes. We should be able to see how these were obtained by following the steps laid out above.

TABLE 8.3
Electronic geometries and molecular shapes of some molecules and polyatomic ions

Formula	Central Atom	Electron Group Number	Electronic Geometry	Number of Nonbonding Electron Pairs	Molecular Shape	Predicted Bond Angle
CO_2	C	2	Linear	0	Linear	180°
CO	C	2	Linear	1	Linear	—
BF_3	B	3	Triangular	0	Triangular	120°
NO_3^-	N	3	Triangular	0	Triangular	120°
NO_2^-	N	3	Triangular	1	Bent	Less than 120°
NH_4^+	N	4	Tetrahedral	0	Tetrahedral	109°
CF_4	C	4	Tetrahedral	0	Tetrahedral	109°
SO_3	S	3	Triangular	0	Triangular	120°
H_2SO_4	S	4	Tetrahedral	0	Tetrahedral	109°
NH_3	N	3	Tetrahedral	1	Pyramidal	Less than 109°
PO_4^{3-}	P	4	Tetrahedral	0	Tetrahedral	109°
H_2O	O	4	Tetrahedral	2	Bent	Less than 109°

REVIEW QUESTIONS

Molecules and Covalent Bond Formation

1. How do we now define a *molecule*? A *covalent bond*?
2. How is it possible for an atom to achieve an octet by covalent bond formation?
3. Why do hydrogen and the halogens exist as diatomic molecules? Draw Lewis structures for a diatomic hydrogen molecule and for one of the halogens.
4. What are double and triple covalent bonds? Give an example of each.
5. Write Lewis structures for compounds formed between hydrogen and the following: fluorine, oxygen, nitrogen, carbon.
6. What are *nonbonding electron pairs*? How many nonbonding electron pairs do each of the molecules in Question 5 have?
7. What is bar notation? Write Lewis structures for the compounds in Question 5 in bar notation.
8. How do the valence electrons of an element determine how many bonds it forms? Give the number of bonds for H, F, O, N, and C.
9. What is a *coordinate covalent bond*? Give an example. What other substances form coordinate covalent bonds?
10. Explain why boron may have an incomplete octet.

Characteristics of Covalent Bonds

11. What is *bond energy*? How do we translate it into an equation?
12. Why is energy released when a covalent bond is formed?
13. How do we find the bond energy if a molecule contains more than one bond?
14. What is *bond length*? What units do we use to measure it?
15. How are bond strength and bond length related?

Lewis Structures

16. Can we always predict compounds on the basis of the number of unpaired electrons atoms have? Give an example.
17. Do we have to know which bonds are coordinate covalent in order to write a Lewis structure?
18. How do we decide what the *central atom* is in a structure?

19. What is the *octet rule*?
20. Why do we add up the electrons of the individual atoms in a molecule?
21. How do we get rid of two electrons at a time if we've used too many in a Lewis structure?
22. What are the steps involved in writing a Lewis structure of a molecule? Give an example.
23. How are polyatomic ions different from molecules? How do we count electrons for polyatomic ions?
24. How are the Lewis structures of polyatomic ions and their corresponding oxyacids related?

Bond Polarity

25. Is the division between ionic compounds and covalent compounds a clear-cut one?
26. What happens when two nonmetals bond that have large differences in electron affinity?
27. What is *electronegativity*? Which element has the highest electronegativity?
28. In general, where on the periodic table do we find the most *electronegative elements*? The most *electropositive elements*?
29. What is a *nonpolar covalent bond*? A *polar covalent bond*? Give examples of each, and describe them.
30. Why is a polar bond so called? What notation do we often use to indicate a polar bond?
31. Explain the relationship between nonpolar, polar, and ionic bonds.
32. What are the "big four" electronegative elements?
33. What is a *polar molecule*? A nonpolar molecule? What must a molecule have in order to be polar?
34. Give some examples of polar molecules.

Molecular Shape

35. What is the *VSEPR theory*? State its main assumptions.
36. What is *electronic geometry*? What are the three basic types?
37. What is *molecular shape*? When is it different from electronic geometry, and when is it the same?
38. What is a *bond angle*? What are the bond angles for the basic electronic geometries?
39. What is an *electron group number*? How do we use it to determine geometry and molecular shape?

EXERCISES

1. Write Lewis structures for Cl_2, Br_2, and I_2.
2. The halogens can form diatomic molecules with each other. These are called *interhalogen compounds*. Write Lewis structures for the interhalogen compounds ICl, BrF, ClF.
3. The diatomic molecule S_2 exists, but it's not very stable. Write its Lewis structure.
4. Write Lewis structures for compounds of hydrogen with Cl, S, P, and Si. Use both dot and bar notation.
5. Write Lewis structures for the most likely compounds formed between the following pairs:
   a. O and F   c. B and Cl
   b. P and Br   d. C and S
6. BF_3 can react with water to form a coordinate covalent bond. Write the Lewis structure for such a compound.
7. BF_3 can also react with a fluoride ion, F^-, and complete boron's octet by forming a polyatomic negative ion, BF_4^-. Write its Lewis structure.
8. When H_2O is formed from its separate, gaseous atoms, we can write this equation:

$$2\ H(g) + O(g) \longrightarrow H_2O(g) + 221\ kcal$$

   What is the bond energy of an O—H bond?
9. The energy of an N—H bond is 93.4 kcal/mole. How much energy is needed, per mole, to take NH_3 apart into separate, gaseous atoms?
10. Without looking at Table 8.1, state which compound of each of the following pairs has greater bond length and which has greater bond energy.
    a. HF or HI   b. O_2 or N_2 c. O_2 or F_2
11. Would you expect At_2 to have a longer or shorter bond than I_2? Why?
12. What is wrong with these Lewis structures?

    a. $H-\overline{\underset{|\underline{O}|}{\overset{|\overline{O}|}{Cl}}-\overline{O}|$ for $HClO_3$

    b. $|\overline{O}-\underset{|\underline{O}|}{S}-\overline{O}|$ for SO_3

    c. $|\overline{O}-\underset{|\underline{O}|}{N}=\overline{O}$ for NO_3^-

    d. $H-\overline{O}-\underset{|\underline{O}|}{C}-\overline{O}-H$ for H_2CO_3

    e. $H-H-\overline{O}-\underset{|\underline{O}|}{\overset{|\overline{O}|}{S}}-\overline{O}|$ for H_2SO_4

    f. $\left[|\overline{O}=\overline{N}=\overline{O}|\right]^-$ for NO_2^-

13. Write correct Lewis structures for the substances in Exercise 12.
14. Boric acid, used diluted as an eyewash, has the formula H_3BO_3. Write its Lewis structure. (Boron does not have a complete octet.)
15. Write Lewis structures for H_2SO_4, HSO_4^-, and SO_4^{2-}. Show their similarities.
16. Write Lewis structures for SO_4^{2-}, PO_4^{3-}, ClO_4^-, and CCl_4. Point out their similarities.
17. Write Lewis structures of NO_3^-, CO_3^{2-}, and SO_3. Point out their similarities.
18. Write Lewis structures for NO_2^- and ClO_2^-. Point out their differences.
19. Hydrazine, N_2H_4, is used for rocket fuel. The two nitrogen atoms are bonded together, and two hydrogen atoms are bonded to each nitrogen. Write its Lewis structure.
20. Teflon is made from tetrafluoroethylene, C_2F_4. The two carbon atoms are bonded to each other, and two fluorine atoms are bonded to each carbon atom. Write its Lewis structure.
21. Write Lewis structures for these compounds.
    a. formaldehyde, CH_2O (C is the central atom, and all other atoms are bonded to it.)
    b. ethane, C_2H_6 (The two carbon atoms are bonded together.)
    c. vinyl chloride, C_2H_3Cl (The two carbon atoms are bonded together. Two hydrogen atoms are bonded to one carbon atom, and a hydrogen and a chlorine are bonded to the other carbon atom.)
22. Write Lewis structures for these polyatomic ions.
    a. OH^- c. SH^- e. HCO_3^-
    b. CN^- d. O_2^{2-} f. ClO^-

23. Without looking at Figure 8.2, arrange each of the following sets in order of increasing electronegativity.
    a. S, Cl, Se, F   b. Rb, I, F, Sr   c. B, Li, N, F

24. Using the values in Figure 8.2, classify the bonds that would be formed between the following elements as nonpolar, polar covalent, or ionic.
    a. Al and Si   e. C and O
    b. Ba and Br   f. H and O
    c. C and Cl   g. S and I
    d. Be and Se   h. Pb and S

25. For the polar covalent bonds in Exercise 24, write out the bonds with the crossed arrow pointing at the more electronegative element.

26. We've seen that the distinctions between ionic and covalent compounds are not cut-and-dried; they are only guidelines. To prove this, select a pair of atoms in each of the following categories (use Figure 8.2).
    a. a metal and a nonmetal, whose bond would be predicted to be polar covalent (by electronegativity difference) instead of ionic
    b. a nonmetal and a metalloid on the right-hand side of the staircase-shaped line, whose bond would be predicted to be ionic (by electronegativity difference) instead of covalent

27. State whether the following molecules are polar or nonpolar, and show reasoning. Molecular geometries are given in parentheses.
    a. CH_4 (tetrahedral)   e. CH_2O (triangular)
    b. $CHCl_3$ (tetrahedral)   f. H_2S (bent)
    c. CO (linear)   g. HCl (linear)
    d. BCl_3 (triangular)

28. From molecular shape and bond polarities, state whether the following would be expected to be polar or nonpolar.
    a. SO_3 c. PH_3
    b. SO_2 d. F_2O

29. For all species in Exercises 12 through 18, give the electronic geometries and molecular shapes.

9

Atomic Structure

We've been promising to say more about our model of the atom. That model wasn't produced overnight. Before it was developed, other models also gained wide acceptance by scientists. Each model was subjected to experiment (remember the scientific method?) and some parts of each were discarded while other parts were kept and improved on. (See A Brief History of the Atom, below.)

quantum mechanical atom

The result to date is what we call the *quantum mechanical atom*. This model hasn't been disproved by experiment yet, but that doesn't mean it won't be someday. Scientists are very active in this field, and they are constantly discovering new particles smaller than protons, neutrons, and electrons. Quite likely, a newer model of the atom will be proposed sometime in the future. Meanwhile, the quantum mechanical atom works very well to explain everything we'll deal with in this book.

A BRIEF HISTORY OF THE ATOM

Time	Persons Involved	Events
500 B.C.	Leucippus Democritus	Proposed that matter is made of tiny particles (atoms) that are fundamental to all substances and that cannot be divided.
400 B.C.	Aristotle	Refuted the idea of atoms. Proposed instead that matter is made of four "elements": earth, air, fire, and water. His influence and reputation caused the idea of atoms to be submerged for many centuries.
400 B.C.–1661 A.D.		The "dark ages" of atomic theory. Alchemy and superstition prevailed. The alchemists recognized three "elements": sulfur, mercury, and salt. Although many discoveries were made that eventually contributed to chemical knowledge, the idea of atoms as fundamental particles remained in obscurity.
1661	Robert Boyle	Expressed skepticism about both Greek and alchemical "elements," and suggested that there might be much more fundamental particles.

1804	John Dalton	Formalized the atomic theory of Democritus, and improved upon it by experimentation. Reawakened the concept of atoms as fundamental, small, indivisible particles that compose all matter.
1886	William Crookes	Discovered electrons, but didn't know what they were.
1897	J. J. Thomson	Characterized the electron. Realized that electrons are part of atoms, and that atoms also had a positive part that was left when the electrons were stripped away. Showed, therefore, that atoms are not indivisible. Proposed his "plum pudding" model of the atom.
1898	William Wien	Discovered the proton and established it as part of an atom.
1900	Max Planck	Introduced his quantum theory, which states that some kinds of energy are given off not continuously but in discrete lumps (quanta).
1908	Albert Einstein	Extended Planck's quantum theory to describe electrons in atoms. Proposed that electrons in atoms occupy quantized "energy levels."
1911	Ernest Rutherford	Disproved Thomson's "plum pudding" model. Proposed, instead, that most of an atom's mass and all of its positive charge are concentrated in a very small center: the nucleus. The electrons were seen to occupy a large volume of mostly empty space, but it wasn't known how the electrons were arranged in that space.

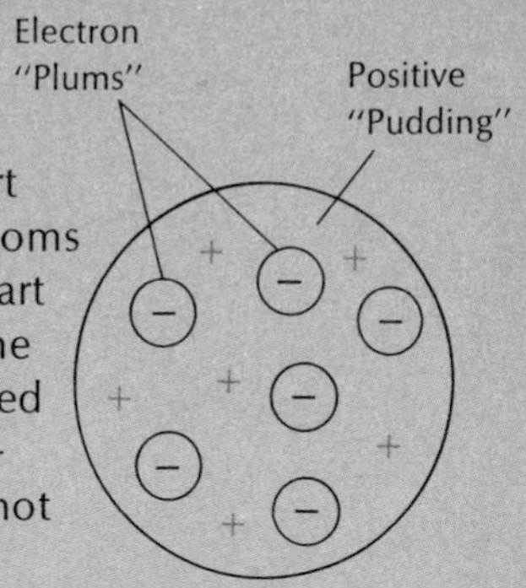

Electron "Plums"

Positive "Pudding"

Thomson's "Plum Pudding" model

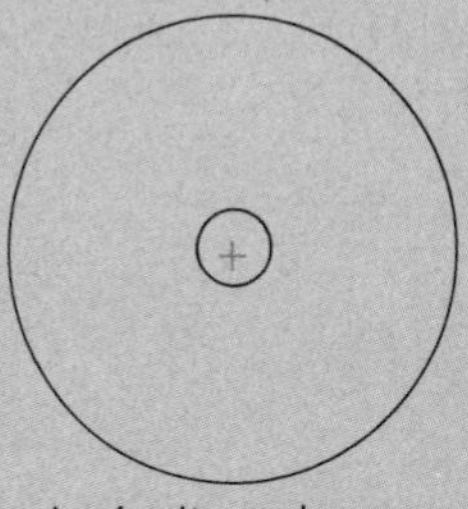

Rutherford's nuclear atom

continued

1913	Niels Bohr	Proposed a planetary model of the atom. The nucleus was in the center, and the electrons occupied orbits. The orbits had certain energies and were certain specific distances from the nucleus. The elec- trons were supposed

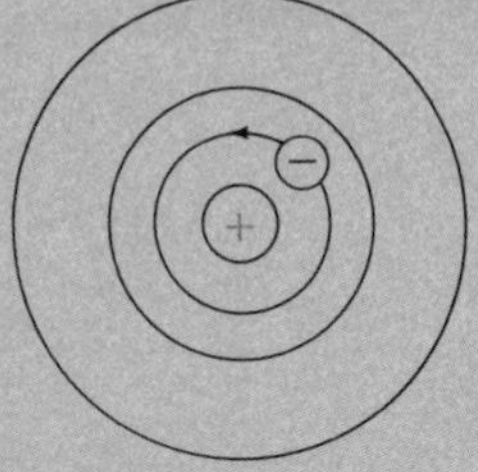

Bohr's model of the hydrogen atom

to be held in place by electrostatic attraction, which in turn was balanced by centrifugal force. The orbits were calculated on the basis of the electrons' momentum as they orbited the nucleus. Unfortunately, the Bohr atom did not adequately explain atoms more complex than hydrogen.

1924	Louis de Broglie	Discovered that moving electrons behave like waves. Therefore, he proposed that electrons in motion around nuclei must be treated as waves.
1925	Werner Heisenberg	Developed his uncertainty principle, which says in essence that it is not possible to know exactly where rapidly moving particles like electrons are at any time. One can only know their probable positions.
1926	Erwin Schrödinger	Combined de Broglie's and Heisenberg's find- ings into the develop- ment of the Schrödinger equation. This equation treated electrons in atoms like waves. The solutions to his equa- tion give regions around atoms that are likely to have

Model of the hydrogen atom resulting from the Schrödinger equation

electrons in them. These regions—called orbitals—are quantized.

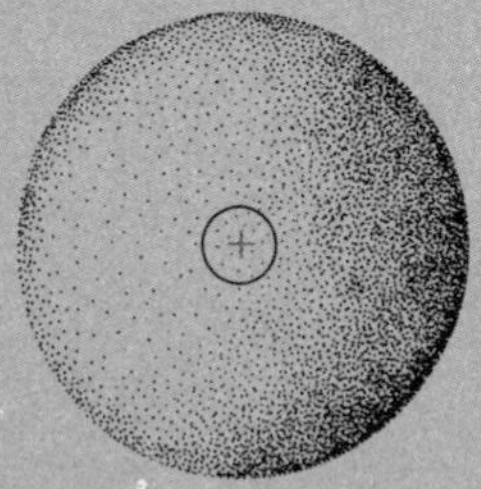

1930	W. Bothe and H. Becker	Discovered the neutron. Although neutrons were assumed to exist before this, the actual proof was not supplied until this late date in atomic history.

9.1 THE QUANTUM MECHANICAL ATOM

The main feature of the quantum mechanical atom is that it explains how electrons are arranged in atoms. This explanation agrees with the way the atoms behave, as we'll soon see. According to this model, electrons are arranged in quantized energy levels.

QUANTIZED ENERGY LEVELS.

Something that is separated into finite parts is said to be *quantized*. A staircase is quantized into steps that are a certain distance apart. The opposite of quantized is continuous. A ramp is continuous, whereas a staircase is quantized. (See Figure 9.1.)

quantized

Electrons in atoms are arranged in layers, called *principal energy levels*. These energy levels correspond to different distances from the nucleus. We know that the closer two unlike-charged particles can get to each other, the more energy will be released. Therefore, the energy level closest to the nucleus has the lowest energy. Electrons can go from one energy level to another, but they can't be anywhere in between. If we ride an elevator, we can get off at any floor, but we can't get off between floors. Electrons can't either; they have to be at one energy level or another. If we want to move an

**principal
energy level**

**FIGURE 9.1
Continuous and
quantized energy**

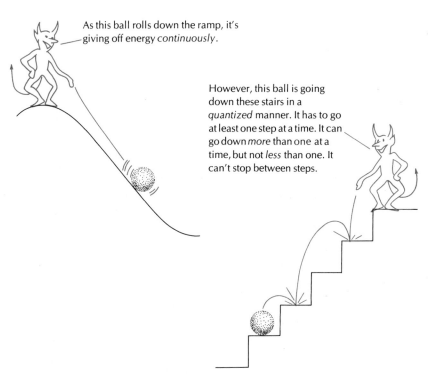

As this ball rolls down the ramp, it's giving off energy *continuously*.

However, this ball is going down these stairs in a *quantized* manner. It has to go at least one step at a time. It can go down *more* than one at a time, but not *less* than one. It can't stop between steps.

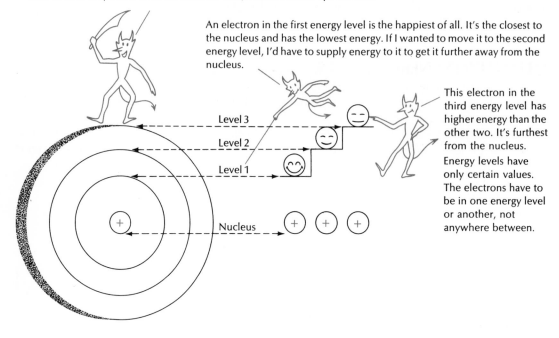

I've sliced an atom in half again, so that we can see the shells, or energy levels. There are really a lot more than this, as we'll see later. But this will give us an idea of how they work. Over on the other side, I've lined them up like stairs.

An electron in the first energy level is the happiest of all. It's the closest to the nucleus and has the lowest energy. If I wanted to move it to the second energy level, I'd have to supply energy to it to get it further away from the nucleus.

This electron in the third energy level has higher energy than the other two. It's furthest from the nucleus.

Energy levels have only certain values. The electrons have to be in one energy level or another, not anywhere between.

Level 3
Level 2
Level 1

Nucleus

electron to a higher energy level (further from the nucleus), we have to supply energy. If an electron goes from a higher to a lower energy level, it gives off energy.

We describe these principal energy levels with whole numbers. The first (lowest) energy level is given the number 1; the second is given the number 2; and so on. Sometimes these energy levels are called *shells*. We can think of the energy levels as being one inside of another, like a child's set of nesting blocks. (See Figure 9.2.) The energy levels are each divided into smaller levels, called sublevels.

shell

SUBLEVELS. Imagine a dresser that's divided into drawers, which are further divided into smaller compartments for socks, handkerchieves, and so forth. An atom is like the dresser. The drawers are like the principal energy levels, and the compartments are like the sublevels. A *sublevel* is an energy level within the principal energy level. These sublevels have the notations *s, p, d,* and *f,* and their energy increases in that order. Every principal energy level does not have all four sublevels, though. Level 1 has only the *s* sub-

sublevel

level. Level 2 has *s* and *p*. Level 3 has *s, p,* and *d*. And Level 4 and beyond have all four: *s, p, d,* and *f*. Each sublevel contains different numbers of orbitals.

ORBITALS. A region in space around an atom that has a high probability of containing one or two electrons is called an *orbital*. An orbital can also be called an "electron probability volume." To see how probability enters into the picture, let's look at a simple analogy.

orbital

We can read the label on an automobile tire when the tire is standing still. When the tire is moving, though, the writing becomes a fuzzy band. If we wanted to describe where a certain letter—say, a "G"—was at any instant on the moving tire, we'd have a hard time doing it. But we could definitely say that it was more likely to be inside the fuzzy band than outside it. The band is the region of high probability of finding the "G"; the "G" spends most of its time somewhere within that band. (See Figure 9.3.)

**FIGURE 9.3
An orbital
is an electron
probability
volume**

We can easily see where the "G" is on this tire that's standing still.

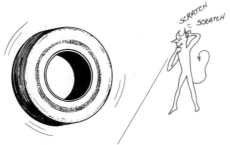

Hmmm—but where is it now? I'll bet it's somewhere in that fuzzy band, but that's about the best I can say. It's tracing out a path of where it's been, and inside that path is where we'd probably find it. We can call this a "probability band."

This orbital is a fuzzy piece of space that has an electron in it somewhere. It's tracing out a three-dimensional path of where it's been, and in there is where we'd probably find it. We can call this a "probability volume."

Electrons in atoms never stand still. We'd have just as hard a time trying to say exactly where any one electron was at any given instant as we had trying to pinpoint the "G" on the tire. Like the white band on the tire, though, an orbital is a region of high probability of finding the electron. The electron spends most of its time somewhere in the orbital. Orbitals are fuzzy, like the probability band on the tire. That's why we call them probability volumes.

Orbitals have the same notations as the sublevels: *s, p, d,* and *f.* Each kind of orbital has its own shape, and each sublevel contains a certain number of orbitals. The *s* sublevel contains one *s* orbital. The *p* sublevel contains three *p* orbitals. The *d* sublevel contains five *d* orbitals. And the *f* sublevel contains seven *f* orbitals.

Figure 9.4 shows the shapes of the *s, p,* and *d* orbitals. The *s* orbital is the simplest, being just a sphere. The shapes get more interesting with the *p* and *d* orbitals. We see that these have different parts, or lobes. One *p* orbital has two lobes. If an electron is in a *p* orbital, it occupies both lobes at the same time. The three *p* orbitals are mutually perpendicular, which means that they're 90° from each other. Most of the *d* orbitals have four lobes, and one electron in a *d* orbital would occupy all four lobes at the same time.

Each orbital can hold two electrons. Given the choice, two electrons will each occupy a separate orbital instead of both occupying the same one, because of their like charge. But as we'll see later, two separate orbitals are sometimes not available, and the electrons have to pair up.

9.2 DESCRIBING ELECTRONIC CONFIGURATIONS

electronic configuration

An element's *electronic configuration* is a statement of how many electrons it has in each orbital. For example, the electronic configuration of carbon can be stated in words like this: "Carbon has two electrons in the *s* orbital of the first energy level, two electrons in the *s* orbital of the second energy level, and one in each of two *p* orbitals in the second energy level."

Like many other things we've encountered, this is an obvious place to use some kind of shorthand notation. First of all, instead of saying "the *s* orbital of the first energy level," we say simply 1*s*. Similarly, a 2*p* orbital means a *p* orbital in the second energy level.

We use these number-letter names for sublevels and orbitals in the two types of shorthand notation that follow.

box notation

BOX NOTATION. We use square boxes to represent orbitals and arrows to represent electrons in *box notation.* The box-notation translation of the sentence describing carbon's configuration is as follows:

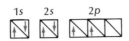

Here we see that the arrows point up and down in the orbitals where there are two electrons. The diagonal slashes in each box indicate that each orbital can be occupied by two electrons. We see that two of the *p* orbitals have single electrons in them, and one *p* orbital is empty.

SPECTRAL NOTATION.

spectral notation

In *spectral notation,* we use the number-letter designations of the orbitals, along with superscripts to show the num-

FIGURE 9.4
Shapes of *s*, *p*, and *d* orbitals

These orbitals are probability volumes, just like the fuzzy band on the tire was a probability band. Orbitals are much more interesting than the band on the tire, though. This *s* orbital in my right hand is like a ball, and the *p* orbital in my left is like a dumbbell.

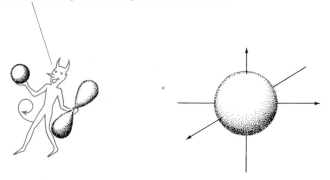

Each *p* orbital has two parts. We call these *lobes.* The three *p* orbitals are arranged on different axes, so they're all perpendicular to each other.

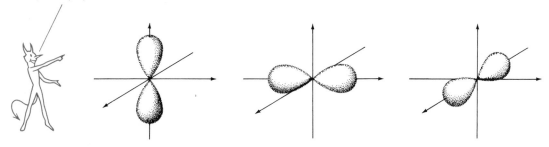

These *d* orbitals are even more interesting! Four of them have four lobes each and they look like cloverleaves. The last one looks like a *p* orbital with a collar.

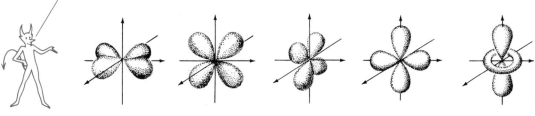

ber of electrons in each sublevel. The spectral-notation translation of carbon's configuration is as follows:

$$1s^2 2s^2 2p^2$$

In spectral notation, we don't list each orbital separately. Hence the designation "$2p^2$" means that there are two electrons in the p sublevel, but it doesn't say that they occupy separate orbitals. Each single designation has this meaning:

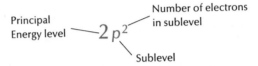

Table 9.1 shows box and spectral notations for the first twenty elements.

		Atomic		Spectral
Symbol	No.	Box Notation		Notation
H	1			$1s^1$
He	2			$1s^2$
Li	3			$1s^2 2s^1$
Be	4			$1s^2 2s^2$
B	5			$1s^2 2s^2 2p^1$
C	6			$1s^2 2s^2 2p^2$
N	7			$1s^2 2s^2 2p^3$
O	8			$1s^2 2s^2 2p^4$
F	9			$1s^2 2s^2 2p^5$
Ne	10			$1s^2 2s^2 2p^6$
Na	11	(Ne-10)		(Ne-10)$3s^1$
Mg	12	(Ne-10)		(Ne-10)$3s^2$
Al	13	(Ne-10)		(Ne-10)$3s^2 3p^1$
Si	14	(Ne-10)		(Ne-10)$3s^2 3p^2$
P	15	(Ne-10)		(Ne-10)$3s^2 3p^3$
S	16	(Ne-10)		(Ne-10)$3s^2 3p^4$
Cl	17	(Ne-10)		(Ne-10)$3s^2 3p^5$
Ar	18	(Ne-10)		(Ne-10)$3s^2 3p^6$
K	19	(Ar-18)		(Ar-18)$4s^1$
Ca	20	(Ar-18)		(Ar-18)$4s^2$

TABLE 9.1
Box and spectral notations for the first twenty elements

We can notice a few things about electronic configurations. First, the total number of arrows in the box notation and also the sum of the superscripts in the spectral notation add up to the element's atomic number. This is not surprising, since an element's atomic number is the number of electrons it has to assign to orbitals.

Second, we see that each element has the same configuration as the one just before it, except for the addition of the last electron. What we're doing is building up configurations, one electron at a time, for the elements in order of increasing atomic number.

Third, we see that writing configurations in both systems becomes redundant, for the reason given in the last paragraph. It's convenient to use *noble gas cores* instead of writing out all the lower electrons each time. Only **noble gas core** the electrons that are being added to outer energy levels are of interest. The core configuration of sodium is $(Ne-10)3s^1$ in spectral notation. This means that sodium has the neon configuration with ten electrons, plus an additional electron in the 3s orbital. Noble gas cores are shown in Table 9.1 for both box and spectral notation for elements following neon. We could also use $(He-2)$ as a noble gas core for elements 3 through 10, but for only two electrons it's a toss-up which way is easiest to write.

Fourth, we see that the box notation shows electrons occupying orbitals singly as long as they can in the *p* sublevel, where there are three orbitals. This is also true of the *d* sublevel, which contains five orbitals.

We see how to write configurations for elements. But how do we know what these configurations are?

ORBITAL ENERGIES.
A very short person putting objects away on shelves prefers to put them on the lowest shelf. If there is no more room on the bottom shelf and there are more objects that have to be put away, then there is no choice but to go to the second and higher shelves. In the same way, electrons prefer to be in the lowest energy orbital. If this orbital is full and there are more electrons to put into orbitals, then there is no choice but to go to the second and higher orbitals.

To decide what an element's electronic configuration is, we first notice what its atomic number is. That's the number of electrons we have to assign. Next, we put electrons into sublevels, starting from the lowest-energy sublevel. When one sublevel is filled, we go on to the next. The number of electrons that each sublevel can hold is as follows: *s*, two electrons; *p*, six electrons; *d*, ten electrons; *f*, fourteen electrons. We don't pair electrons in a sublevel until each orbital has one electron in it.

To put electrons into orbitals we have to know the order of the sublevels' energies. A handy device for finding this order (with a few exceptions) is the Aufbau Diagram in Figure 9.5. In this diagram, arrows give the order of filling. We see that sublevels aren't always filled in order of their principal energy level number. The first case of this is the order *3p4s3d*, instead of *3p3d4s*. After that, there are many other instances.

The reason for this is shown in Figure 9.6. On the left, we see the relative energies of the principal energy levels themselves. As their numbers increase,

**FIGURE 9.5
The Aufbau
diagram**

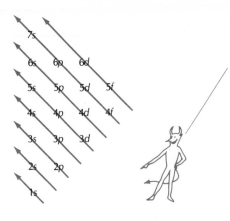

This Aufbau diagram shows the order in which electrons fill sublevels. To use it, start at the bottom of the bottom arrow and read up. Then start at the bottom of the next arrow. And so on. Reading the first four arrows shows this order:

1s 2s 2p 3s 3p 4s

these levels become closer together. When a principal energy level has sublevels, these sublevels arrange themselves around the principal energy level. For instance, at Level 2, the *s* sublevel is below the principal energy level line; the *p* sublevel is above. We say that the principal energy level is split by the presence of sublevels.

The higher the principal energy level, the more sublevels there are and therefore the more splitting. The combination of more splitting and closer principal energy levels causes the overlap shown on the right side of the figure. We see, for instance, that this splitting causes the 3*d* sublevel to have slightly higher energy than the 4*s* sublevel. Since the 4*s* sublevel has lower energy than the 3*d* sublevel, it fills before the 3*d* sublevel. Other overlaps are shown on the figure.

We won't emphasize writing electronic configurations from scratch. In the next section, we'll see that the configurations are the basis for the periodic table. This will make it easy to write outer electronic configurations from the periodic table itself.

9.3 THE PERIODIC TABLE

We've seen that the periodic table is a very important part of studying chemistry. We've already used it a lot without knowing much about it—how it was discovered, why it works, and what it means. Now we'll have a chance to find out some of these things.

DISCOVERY OF THE PERIODIC TABLE. In the last half of the ninteenth century, scientists began to notice that some elements' properties are similar to others', and they began to try arranging the elements according

to their similar properties. (See Box, p. 198.) Using the scientific method, Dmitri Mendeleev concluded that elements' properties were periodic functions of their atomic weights. If so, he said, then the properties of elements missing from his table should be predictable. Three times he was proved correct when the experiments of others uncovered elements he had predicted. However, a few of his predictions were faulty. Iodine, for instance, was predicted to be in the halogen family because of its properties, but its atomic weight dictated that it should be where tellurium is. Clearly, Mendeleev's table wasn't quite correct. Then H. G. J. Moseley demostrated that elements should be arranged by atomic number and not atomic weight. The periodic table that resulted is the one we use today. Together, Mendeleev and Moseley gave us our modern *Periodic Law:* The properties of the elements are periodic functions of their atomic numbers.

Periodic Law

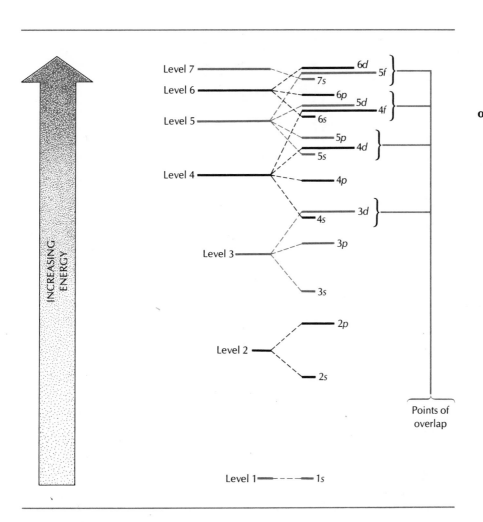

FIGURE 9.6
Splitting
of principal
energy levels
causes
orbital overlap

FIGURE 9.7
Periodic table with electronic configurations

Look at the outer configuration. In Group IA, it's s^1. In Group IIA, it's s^2.

Oof! Over here, we start filling p sublevels. At the end of each row, all the p electrons are in.

I'm jumping across the area where the d electrons go in. This valley is here because there is no d sublevel until the third energy level.

These elements go in here, in the sixth and seventh periods. We usually put them down here instead, because then the table fits better onto a page. If they were put in where they belong, it would make another valley, 14 elements wide.

	IA	IIA	IIIB	IVB	VB	VIB	VIIB	VIIIB	VIIIB	VIIIB	IB	IIB	IIIA	IVA	VA	VIA	VIIA	VIIIA
1	H $1s^1$																	He $1s^1$
2	Li $2s^1$	Be $2s^2$											B $2s^2 2p^1$	C $2s^2 2p^2$	N $2s^2 2p^3$	O $2s^2 2p^4$	F $2s^2 2p^5$	Ne $2s^2 2p^6$
3	Na $3s^1$	Mg $3s^2$											Al $3s^2 3p^1$	Si $3s^2 3p^2$	P $3s^2 3p^3$	S $3s^2 3p^4$	Cl $3s^2 3p^5$	Ar $3s^2 3p^6$
4	K $4s^1$	Ca $4s^2$	Sc $4s^2 3d^1$	Ti $4s^2 3d^2$	V $4s^2 3d^3$	Cr $4s^1 3d^5$	Mn $4s^2 3d^5$	Fe $4s^2 3d^6$	Co $4s^2 3d^7$	Ni $4s^2 3d^8$	Cu $4s^1 3d^{10}$	Zn $4s^2 3d^{10}$	Ga $4s^2 4p^1$	Ge $4s^2 4p^2$	As $4s^2 4p^3$	Se $4s^2 4p^4$	Br $4s^2 4p^5$	Kr $4s^2 4p^6$
5	Rb $5s^1$	Sr $5s^2$	Y $5s^2 4d^1$	Zr $5s^2 4d^2$	Nb $5s^1 4d^4$	Mo $5s^1 4d^5$	Tc $5s^2 4d^5$	Ru $5s^1 4d^7$	Rh $5s^1 4d^8$	Pd $4d^{10}$	Ag $5s^1 4d^{10}$	Cd $5s^2 4d^{10}$	In $5s^2 5p^1$	Sn $5s^2 5p^2$	Sb $5s^2 5p^3$	Te $5s^2 5p^4$	I $5s^2 5p^5$	Xe $5s^2 5p^6$
6	Cs $6s^1$	Ba $6s^2$	La $6s^2 5d^1$	Hf $6s^2 5d^2$	Ta $6s^2 5d^3$	W $6s^2 5d^4$	Re $6s^2 5d^5$	Os $6s^2 5d^6$	Ir $6s^2 5d^7$	Pt $6s^1 5d^9$	Au $6s^1 5d^{10}$	Hg $6s^2 5d^{10}$	Tl $6s^2 6p^1$	Pb $6s^2 6p^2$	Bi $6s^2 6p^3$	Po $6s^2 6p^4$	At $6s^2 6p^5$	Rn $6s^2 6p^6$
7	Fr $7s^1$	Ra $7s^2$	Ac $7s^2 6d^1$	Ku	Ha	106												

$6s^2$ $7s^2$

Ce $4f^2$	Pr $4f^3$	Nd $4f^4$	Pm $4f^5$	Sm $4f^6$	Eu $4f^7$	Gd $5d^1 4f^7$	Tb $4f^9$	Dy $4f^{10}$	Ho $4f^{11}$	Er $4f^{12}$	Tm $4f^{13}$	Yb $4f^{14}$	Lu $5d^1 4f^{14}$
Th $6d^2$	Pa $5f^2 6d^1$	U $5f^3 6d^1$	Np $5f^4 6d^1$	Pu $5f^6$	Am $5f^7$	Cm $6d^1 5f^7$	Bk $5f^8 6d^1$	Cf $5f^{10}$	Es $5f^{11}$	Fm $5f^{12}$	Md $5f^{13}$	No $5f^{14}$	Lr $5f^{14} 6d^1$

▨ Elements whose electronic configurations are not predicted by the Aufbau Diagram.

SPRING

PLOP

ELECTRONS AND THE PERIODIC TABLE.

Figure 9.7 shows the periodic table with all the elements' outer electronic configurations (without noble gas cores). Now we see that elements have similar properties in the same group because they have the same outer configurations. All the elements in Group IA have the outer configuration s^1; all the Group IIA elements have the outer configuration s^2; and so forth. Except for the elements in shaded boxes, we could have written all of these configurations by using the Aufbau Diagram in Figure 9.5 and the atomic numbers.

The part of the periodic table that has elements with outer configurations of s^1 and s^2 is called the *s block*. It's two elements wide because there can be two electrons in the *s* sublevel. The next set of elements, the transition elements, make up the *d block* because they are filling their *d* sublevels. This block is ten elements wide because there can be ten electrons in the *d* sublevel. On the far right is the *p block*, where the *p* sublevel is being filled and the outer configurations go from s^2p^1 to s^2p^6. This block is six elements wide, because the *p* sublevel can contain a total of six electrons. Down at the bottom is the *f block* (the inner transition elements). The *f* block is fourteen elements wide, because there can be fourteen *f* electrons.

s block

d block

p block

f block

Figure 9.8 shows these sublevel blocks. Now we can understand the shape of the periodic table in terms of the numbers of electrons in each sublevel. We can also see that the valence electrons in the Lewis structures of the representative elements are really the two *s* and the six *p* electrons.

The horizontal rows, or periods, of the periodic table are numbered according to the highest principal energy level being filled by the elements in that period. Thus, the first period is for the first energy level. Since the first energy level contains only one sublevel with one orbital, the period contains only two elements, hydrogen and helium. We usually put helium in the *p* sublevel block, even though it's an *s* element, because helium completes the filling of the first energy level and belongs with the rest of the noble gases. Sometimes we find it convenient to put hydrogen over next to helium in the *p* block. In these and other ways, the first period is a little different from all the others.

The second period, lithium through neon (elements 3 through 10) is for the second energy level. The third, sodium through argon, is for the third energy level. In the fourth period, we find we're filling 3*d* after 4*s*, and then we fill 4*p*. As we saw earlier, this is because the 3*d* has higher energy than the 4*s*. Notice, though, that the period number still corresponds to the highest energy level containing electrons. The same is true of the fifth period. In the sixth period, with the inner transition elements, we begin to fill the 4*f* sublevel between 6*s* and 5*d*. The *f* sublevel will always be two energy levels below the period number, and the *d* sublevel will always be one energy level below the period number.

Figure 9.9 shows the periodic table with periods and sublevels.

Now, we can see how to write an element's configuration just from the periodic table—especially one that has the configurations written right on it! Even if we don't have a periodic table with the configurations written on

FIGURE 9.8
Periodic table showing sublevel blocks

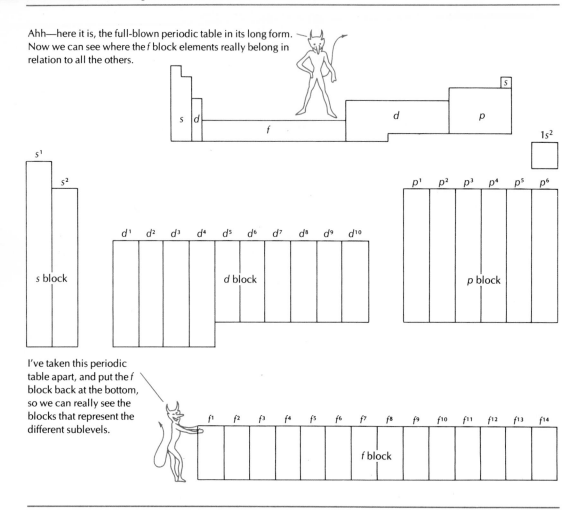

Ahh—here it is, the full-blown periodic table in its long form.
Now we can see where the *f* block elements really belong in
relation to all the others.

I've taken this periodic
table apart, and put the *f*
block back at the bottom,
so we can really see the
blocks that represent the
different sublevels.

it, it's easy now that we understand how the sublevel blocks and the periods
work. This is best illustrated by the example below.

EXAMPLE 9.1: Write the configuration for yttrium. Use spectral notation
with the noble gas core.

Solution: First, locate the element on the periodic table. Second, find the
noble gas in the period above it: this is krypton. Third, decide what
block the element is in: yttrium is in the *d* block. Fourth, count over
from the left of the block to find out how many electrons are in that
sublevel: yttrium is the first element in the *d* block; so it has one electron
in the $4d$ sublevel. Fifth, decide whether there are any filled sublevels:
yes, the $5s$ sublevel is filled since it comes right before the $4d$.

Answer: $(Kr-36)5s^2 4d^1$.

EXAMPLE 9.2: Write the configuration for phosphorus. Use box notation with the noble gas core.

Solution: First, we locate phosphorus. Second, neon is the nearest lower noble gas. Third, phosphorus is in the *p* block. Fourth, three electrons in the *p* block. Fifth, the 3*s* sublevel is filled.

Answer: (Ne-10) [box notation: 3*s* and 3*p* sublevels shown]

WHY THE PERIODIC TABLE WORKS.

We have already seen various trends in the periodic table. We've seen that ionization energy, electron affinity, and electronegativity increase as we go across a period and decrease as we go down a group. We've seen that atomic size and ionic size increase as we go down a group and decrease as we go across a period. We've seen that positive ions are smaller than their atoms, and negative ions are larger than their atoms. Now we can find out the reasons for all these trends.

As we go across a period, each element has one more proton and one more electron than the element to its left. We're staying within the same principal energy level, or shell, but we're increasing the number of electrons

FIGURE 9.9
Periodic table showing periods and sublevels

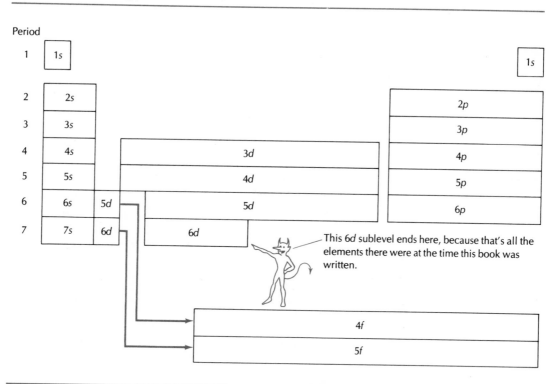

This 6*d* sublevel ends here, because that's all the elements there were at the time this book was written.

A BRIEF HISTORY OF THE PERIODIC TABLE

Time	Persons Involved	Event
1864	John Newlands	Developed the idea that when the elements are arranged in order of increasing atomic weights, every eighth element has recurring chemical and physical properties. Newland's proposal was highly ridiculed by other scientists.
1869	Dmitri Mendeleev	Formulated a law stating that the properties of the elements are periodic functions of their atomic weights. On the basis of holes in his periodic table, predicted undiscovered elements—"eka-aluminum," "eka-silicon," and "eka-boron" ("eka" is Sanskrit for "next to")—and stated what properties they should have.
1870	Lothar Meyer	Independently formulated the same periodic law as Mendeleev's. However, Mendeleev is usually given credit for the discovery, probably because his was more highly publicized and because he was more dramatic in predicting the existence of undiscovered elements.
1875	Lecoq de Boisbaudran	Discovered Mendeleev's "eka-aluminum" and named it gallium. It had all of the properties predicted by Mendeleev.
1876	Clemens Winkler	Discovered Mendeleev's "eka-silicon" and named it germanium. This discovery strengthened Mendeleev's periodic law.
1877	Lars Fredrik Nilson	Discovered Mendeleev's "eka-boron" and named it scandium. With this discovery, the scientific world was convinced that Mendeleev's periodic law was correct.
1914	H. G. J. Moseley	Discovered that each element had a different nuclear charge, which he named the atomic number. Proposed that the elements be ordered by atomic number, not atomic weight. Revised Mendeleev's periodic law to state that the physical and chemical properties of the elements are periodic functions of their atomic numbers. This cleared up a few inconsistencies in the Mendeleev periodic table. Moseley's Periodic Law and table stay with us today.

in that shell and also the number of protons in the nucleus. The more of both kinds of charge there are, the greater the attraction will be between the nucleus and the electron cloud. Electron clouds are squishy, like balloons. The larger the attraction between the nucleus and the electron cloud, the more the electron cloud will be pulled in, and the smaller the atom will be. The stronger the attraction between the nucleus and the electron cloud, the more the nucleus will try to hold onto electrons. This means increased ionization energy and electron affinity as we go across a period from left to right.

As we go down a group, each element further down has one more shell than the one above it, and therefore one more layer of electrons further out. Even though we're also increasing the numbers of protons and electrons as above, a jump from one energy level to another has a much greater effect. Since the size of an atom is the radius from the center of the nucleus to the outside of the electron cloud, adding more energy levels of electrons will clearly make an atom larger. By the same token, the electrons in the outer shell are much further from the nucleus, and therefore the attraction between them and the nucleus is decreased as more shells are added. This makes it easier to remove electrons, which means decreased ionization energy and electron affinity. Electronegativity has the same trends, since it's related to electron affinity and ionization energy. Figure 9.10 illustrates these trends.

We can also see why a positive ion is smaller than the atom from which it was formed. Usually, all of a metal's valence electrons are removed when a positive ion is formed. For instance, Ca^{2+} has its two $4s$ electrons removed. That wipes out the fourth shell completely and exposes the third shell. Since the third shell is closer to the nucleus than the fourth shell was, the ion will be smaller than the atom, just as peeling the skin from a grapefruit results in a smaller object.

When a negative ion is formed from its corresponding atom, electrons are added to the outer shell. The electrons repel each other and make the electron cloud spread out and occupy more volume. This increases the size of the ion beyond that of the neutral atom.

9.4 ELECTRONIC CONFIGURATIONS AND ELEMENTS' BEHAVIOR

Now we can see that the elements react in certain ways because of their electronic configurations.

REPRESENTATIVE ELEMENTS. An element whose s or p sublevel is partially filled can be redefined as a *representative element*. The s or p electrons, we know now, are the elements' valence electrons. The behavior

representative element

**FIGURE 9.10
Trends in size, ionization energy, and electron affinity**

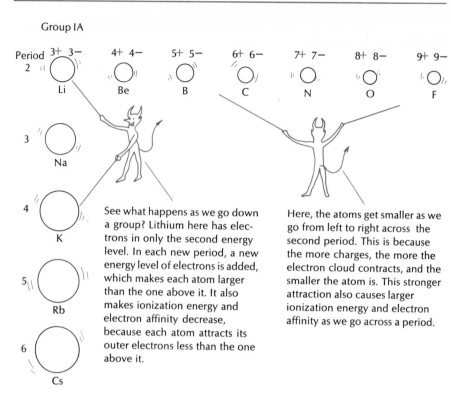

See what happens as we go down a group? Lithium here has electrons in only the second energy level. In each new period, a new energy level of electrons is added, which makes each atom larger than the one above it. It also makes ionization energy and electron affinity decrease, because each atom attracts its outer electrons less than the one above it.

Here, the atoms get smaller as we go from left to right across the second period. This is because the more charges, the more the electron cloud contracts, and the smaller the atom is. This stronger attraction also causes larger ionization energy and electron affinity as we go across a period.

of the representative elements is fairly familiar to us, from earlier chapters. However, there are a few details that can be explained now that we know about orbitals and sublevels.

We saw that some representative metals have variable charge, notably those low down in Groups IVA and VA. Tin and lead have the outer configuration s^2p^2 and the option of forming 2+ or 4+ ions. They have four valence electrons, but two different kinds: s and p. It's easier to remove p electrons than to remove s electrons from the same energy level. This is because the p electrons are further from the nucleus and are less tightly held. (Recall the orbital shapes in Figure 9.4.) The 2+ state of both these metals comes from the removal of the two p electrons only. The 4+ state, of course, comes from the removal of the two s electrons as well. Similarly, bismuth has the outer configuration $6s^26p^3$. We'd expect it to have ionic charges of 3+ and 5+. Thallium, with $6s^26p^1$, has ionic charges of 1+ and 3+.

transition element

TRANSITION ELEMENTS. We haven't said much about transition elements, except that they have variable charge. We can redefine a *transition element* as an element whose d sublevel is being filled. These elements are very interesting.

Look back at the transition elements (the *d* block) in Figure 9.7 (p. 194). First, we can notice some deviations from the electronic configurations we might expect. Chromium and molybdenum don't have the configuration s^2d^4 that we'd predict from the Aufbau Diagram. Instead, their configuration is s^1d^5. By taking an electron out of the *s* sublevel and putting it into the *d* sublevel, these elements can have their *d* sublevel half filled. This is a state of lower energy. Copper, silver, and gold also have configurations we wouldn't have predicted: s^1d^{10} instead of s^2d^9. Here, these elements can have a completely filled *d* sublevel. Half filled and completely filled sublevels are lower energy states, and elements often attempt to achieve these. Since 4*s* and 3*d* sublevels (for copper, silver, and gold) are very close in energy, it's no problem switching electrons back and forth between them.

The transition elements have two kinds of valence electrons: *s* and *d*. The *s* electrons are lost first, because they have higher principal energy levels than the *d* electrons. All transition metals that have two *s* electrons lose them to form ions with 2+ charges, leaving their *d* electrons intact. For higher-charged ions, they then lose varying numbers of *d* electrons. Starting on the left of the *d* block, the maximum ionic charge increases from 3+ for scandium to 7+ for manganese. This maximum corresponds to the metals losing all their unpaired *d* electrons. After manganese, the maximum drops by one per group, with the most common charges being 2+ or 3+ for iron through nickel. Copper, silver, and gold lose their one *s* electron to form the 1+ ionic states. Copper also loses one of its *d* electrons to form the 2+ ion as well as the 1+ ion.

At the end of the series, zinc, cadmium, and mercury have completely filled *d* orbitals. They leave these intact by losing only their two *s* electrons for the 2+ state. We know that zinc and cadmium are fixed-charge ions of 2+. Mercury, in addition, has the 1+ state where it loses one of its *s* electrons and then bonds to itself to form the diatomic ion Hg_2^{2+}.

If we look closely, we can see that groups IB and IIB are numbered according to the number of *s* electrons their elements have. Groups IIIB to VIIB are numbered according to the total of their *s* electrons and unpaired *d* electrons. Group VIIIB contains three vertical columns, because these elements have many similarities.

REVIEW QUESTIONS

The Quantum Mechanical Atom

1. What do we mean by *quantized energy levels?*
2. What are *principal energy levels?* What do we use to describe an atom's principal energy levels?
3. What is a *sublevel?* Name the sublevels in increasing order of energy.
4. What is an *orbital?* Why can we also call it an electron probability volume?
5. Describe the *s, p,* and *d* orbitals in terms of number and shape.

Describing Electronic Configurations

6. What is an element's *electronic configuration?*
7. Give an example of the use of *box notation* and *spectral notation.*
8. Why must the total electrons used in both box notation and spectral notation add up to the element's atomic number?
9. What are *noble gas cores?* Give an example, and state why they are useful.

10. Show, using box notation, how three electrons are distributed among three p orbitals.
11. What is the maximum number of electrons that can be contained in each sublevel?
12. What is the order of filling of sublevels? How can we know this without memorizing the order?
13. Explain why the $4s$ orbital fills before the $3d$, and give another example of this kind of overlap.
14. What do we mean by splitting of principal energy levels?

The Periodic Table

15. What is the *Periodic Law?* What does it mean?
16. How are the elements' outer electronic configurations related to their positions in the periodic table?
17. Describe the various sublevel blocks of the periodic table. What is happening in each block? How wide is each, and why?
18. Describe or sketch the long form of the periodic table, and explain how it is related to the form we usually see.
19. How are the periods related to the principal energy levels?
20. Why does the first period contain only two elements?
21. Why do the d and f sublevels have lower numbers than their period numbers?
22. Explain the steps involved in writing an element's electronic configuration based on its position in the periodic table.

23. Explain the reasons for the trends in ionization energy, electron affinity, and electronegativity with groups and periods in the periodic table.
24. Explain the trends in atomic size in the periodic table.
25. Why are positive ions smaller than the atoms from which they are formed, and negative ions larger than the atoms from which they are formed?

Electronic Configurations and Elements' Behavior
26. What is our new definition of *representative element?*
27. Explain why the representative metals tin and lead have variable charge.
28. What is our new definition of *transition element?*
29. Give the configurations we might predict from the Aufbau Diagram for chromium, molybdenum, copper, silver, and gold. List the elements' actual configurations, and explain the difference.
30. What two kinds of valence electrons do transition elements have? Which ones are lost first when these elements form positive ions?
31. Discuss the ionic charges of the transition metals in the top row.
32. What do the group numbers for the transition elements correspond to?

EXERCISES

1. Which of the following pairs has the lowest energy?
   a. an electron in the first energy level, or an electron in the third energy level
   b. an electron in the s sublevel, or an electron in the d sublevel (same principal energy level)
   c. an electron that occupies an orbital alone, or an electron that shares an orbital with another electron
2. How many electrons can be in each of the following?
   a. s orbital   e. p sublevel
   b. p orbital   f. second energy level
   c. d sublevel   g. $3d$ orbital
   d. first energy level   h. third energy level
3. Explain what each number and letter means in the following.
   a. $3d^3$ c. $5p^4$
   b. $2s^2$ d. $6f^{10}$
4. Write the following spectral notations in box notation.

   a. $1s^2 2s^2 2p^5$ c. $(Ne-10)3s^2 3p^2$
   b. $(Ar-18)4s^2 3d^5$ d. $(Kr-36)5s^1$
5. Write the following box notations in spectral notation.

   a.
      1s   2s   2p
   b. (Ne-10)
             3s   3p
   c. (Kr-36)
              5s   4d
   d. (Ar-18)
              4s
6. Which has higher energy (consult Figure 9.5)?
   a. the $2p$ or the $3p$ sublevel
   b. the $4s$ or the $3d$ sublevel
   c. the $5s$ or the $4f$ sublevel
   d. the $4p$ or the $3d$ sublevel
7. Some of the following spectral notations are wrong. Single out the wrong ones and describe what is wrong with each.

a. $1s^2 2s^2 2p^7$

b. $(Ne-10)3s^2 3p^5$

c. $1s^2 1p^6$

d. $(Ar-18)4s^3$

e. $(Ne-10)2s^1$

f. $(Kr-36)5s^2 4d^2$

g. $(Ne-10)3s^2 3p^6 3d^6$

h. $1s^2 2s^2 2p^2$

i. $1s^2 2s^2 2p^2 3s^2$

j. $1s^2 2s^2 2p^6 2d^1$

8. Some of the following box notations are wrong. Single out the wrong ones and describe what is wrong with each.

   a. ⬚⬚ ⬚⬚⬚
      1s 2s   2p

   b. (Ne-10) ⬚ ⬚⬚⬚
              3s   3p

   c. (Ar-18) ⬚ ⬚⬚⬚⬚⬚
              4s   3d

   d. ⬚ ⬚⬚⬚
      1s   2p

   e. (Kr-36) ⬚ ⬚⬚⬚
              5s   5p

   f. (Ne-10) ⬚ ⬚⬚⬚⬚⬚
              3s   3d

   g. ⬚⬚
      1s 2s

   h. (Ar-18) ⬚⬚
              4s 5s

   i. (Kr-36) ⬚ ⬚⬚⬚⬚⬚⬚⬚
              5s   4f

   j. ⬚⬚ ⬚⬚⬚ ⬚ ⬚⬚⬚
      1s 2s 2p   3s 3p

Consult Figures 9.7, 9.8, and 9.9 for Exercises 9 through 12.

9. What are the symbols for all elements that have the following outer configurations?

   a. $s^2 p^3$ c. $s^2 d^1$ e. $s^2 d^{10} p^6$
   b. $s^2 f^7$ d. $s^1 d^{10}$ f. s^1

10. In what sublevel block are each of the following elements found?

   a. Mg   d. Sn   g. Ar
   b. K   e. Hg   h. W
   c. Ge   f. P   i. U

11. Write symbols for the element or elements that fit(s) these descriptions.

   a. Period 1, s block

b. Period 2, p block

c. Period 3, s block

d. Group VIIA, Period 2

e. Group VB, Period 4

f. Group IB, Period 5

12. Consider the undiscovered element having an atomic number of 114. Assume that it obeys all the rules.

   a. What group would it be in?
   b. What would be its expected core configuration (spectral notation)?
   c. What other elements might it resemble?
   d. What period would it be in?

Do Exercises 13 through 18 without looking at any figures, or any periodic tables.

13. Element number 55 is in Group IA, in the sixth period. Write its outer configuration. Which energy level is being filled?

14. Element 18 is a noble gas. What group is element 17 in?

15. Element 11 has the outer configuration $3s^1$. What is the atomic number of an element having an outer configuration of $3s^2 3p^2$?

16. Element 15 has an outer configuration of $3s^2 3p^3$. What would be the outer configuration of element 20?

17. Element 49 is in Group IIIA, in the fifth period. Write the outer configuration in spectral notation of element 50 and state its group number.

18. Element 35 has the outer configuration of $4s^2 4p^5$. What group and what period is it in?

Consult a periodic table, but not Figure 9.7, for Exercise 19.

19. Write electronic configurations in both spectral and box notations, with noble gas cores, for the following.

   a. Sr   d. Se   g. Tc
   b. Cs   e. Ga   h. Fe
   c. Zr   f. I

20. Would tin and lead be expected to have 3+ ionic charges? Why?

21. What would the expected outer configurations of these ions be?

   a. Cr^{3+} d. Co^{2+} g. Mn^{4+}
   b. Fe^{3+} e. Ag^+ h. Ti^{4+}
   c. Zn^{2+} f. Y^{3+}

10

Changes in States of Matter

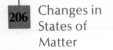
We use changes of state every day. When we boil water, dry clothes, or use a refrigerator, changes of state are working for us. We also make use of the fact that certain things are gases, liquids, and solids at room temperature. If water weren't a liquid, air weren't a gas, and rocks and metals weren't solids at room temperature, our life on earth (if any) would be far different from what it is.

In this chapter, we'll take a closer look at the states of matter themselves and at what happens when a substance changes from one state to another. We'll examine the interactions between the small particles—atoms or molecules or ions—that make up these substances and see what interactions cause their states to be what they are at room temperature.

No matter what state a substance is in at room temperature—gas or liquid or solid—we can change it to one of the others by changing the conditions around it. Two of these conditions are temperature and pressure.

10.1 TEMPERATURE AND HEAT

Figure 10.1 shows what happens to H_2O when we start at temperatures near absolute zero and increasingly add energy. (Throughout these discussions, we'll use the formula "H_2O" to cover all states of the compound water; we'll use the word "water" for the liquid state, "ice" for the solid state, and "steam" or "water vapor" for the gas state.) Three concepts we saw briefly in Chapter 3—specific heat, heat of fusion, and heat of vaporization—are illustrated again here.

At 0 K, or absolute zero, all motion has stopped and everything is a solid. The first sloping portion of the graph indicates the specific heat of ice (0.5 cal/[g × K]). Next, the first flat portion of the graph occurs at the melting point of ice. Here, the temperature remains constant while enough energy is supplied to melt *all* the ice. The energy needed to change H_2O from its solid state to its liquid state at its melting point is the heat of fusion (79.9 cal/g). The next sloping part of the graph indicates the specific heat of water (1 cal/[g × K]). Then we come to the boiling point of water, where the graph flattens out again. The temperature stays constant while enough energy is supplied to boil *all* the water. This energy is the heat of vaporization (540 cal/g). Ater that, the graph slopes up again, indicating the specific heat of steam (about 0.5 cal/[g × K]).

We can easily calculate how much heat is involved in taking H_2O through a series of changes in physical state.

EXAMPLE 10.1: A freezer normally operates at about −15°C (258 K). If 5 kg of ice is removed from a freezer and placed in a picnic cooler, how much heat (in kilocalories) will be absorbed as the ice melts and the water changes to room temperature (295 K)?

Solution: We want to convert 5 kg of ice to kilocalories over a temperature range of 258 K to 295 K. Figure 10.1 shows us that three things happen over this temperature range: the ice warms from 258 to 273, then it melts at 273, then water warms from 273 to 295. We must do this problem in three stages, using three conversion factors: the specific heat of ice (0.5 kcal/[kg × K]), the heat of fusion of ice (79.9 kcal/kg), and the specific heat of water (1 kcal/[kg × K]).

$$\text{To heat ice: } 5 \, \cancel{kg} \times 0.5 \, \frac{kcal}{\cancel{kg} \times \cancel{K}} \times (273 - 258) \cancel{K} \; = \; 37.5 \text{ kcal}$$

$$\text{To melt ice: } 5 \, \cancel{kg} \times 79.9 \, \frac{kcal}{\cancel{kg}} \qquad\qquad = 399.5 \text{ kcal}$$

$$\text{To heat water: } 5 \, \cancel{kg} \times 1 \, \frac{kcal}{\cancel{kg} \times \cancel{K}} \times (295 - 273) \cancel{K} = \underline{110 \quad} \text{ kcal}$$
$$\text{Total} \quad \overline{547} \quad \text{kcal}$$

Answer: 500 kcal.

Most of the heat that's absorbed is taken up in melting the ice. By comparison, heating the ice and the water requires much less heat. That's why ice is a better cooling agent than water at 273 K.

We can reverse this process by starting at the right of the graph and moving to the left. There's no upper limit of temperature, so let's start with

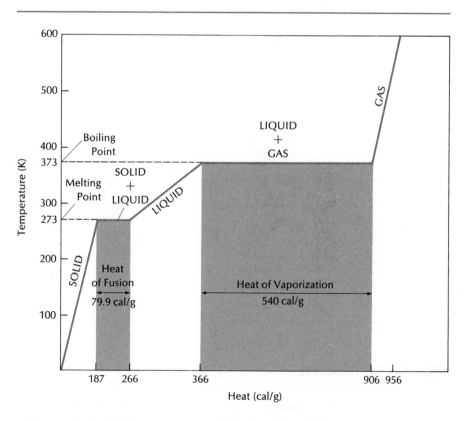

FIGURE 10.1
Temperature-heat curve for water

steam at 600 K. As the steam cools, it gives off energy according to its specific heat until it gets to the condensation point (the same temperature as the boiling point). Then the temperature stays constant while all the steam condenses to liquid water. In this interval, the heat of condensation (the same as the heat of vaporization) is given off. Then as more energy is removed, liquid water cools according to its specific heat. At the freezing point (the same temperature as the melting point), the temperature stays constant until all the water has frozen. The heat of crystallization (the same as the heat of fusion) is given off. Then the ice cools according to its specific heat. We see that the same amount of energy is involved whether we heat or cool a substance. In the first case, the energy is supplied; in the second, it's released.

EXAMPLE 10.2: A heating plant might release steam at 110°C (383 K). Calculate the heat given off when 10 grams of steam at that temperature are condensed on a person's hand and then cooled to body temperature (310 K).

Solution: We want to convert 10 grams of steam to calories. Again, Figure 10.1 shows that three stages occur in the temperature range of 383 K to 310 K. First, the steam cools from 383 K to 373 K. Then the steam condenses at 373 K. Then the water cools from 373 K to 310 K. This gives us three conversion factors: the specific heat of steam (0.5 cal/[g × K]), the heat of condensation of steam (540 cal/g), and the specific heat of water (1 cal/[g × K]).

$$\text{To cool steam: } 10\ g \times 0.5\ \frac{\text{cal}}{g \times K} \times (383 - 373)\ K = \quad 50\ \text{cal}$$

$$\text{To condense steam: } 10\ g \times 540\ \frac{\text{cal}}{g} \qquad\qquad = 5400\ \text{cal}$$

$$\text{To cool water: } 10\ g \times 1\ \frac{\text{cal}}{g \times K} \times (373 - 310)\ K \ = \quad \underline{630\ \text{cal}}$$

$$\text{Total} \qquad 6080\ \text{cal}$$

Answer: 6000 cal, or 6 kcal.

We see why a steam burn is so much worse than a boiling water burn. The heat that the water gave off in cooling from 373 K to 310 K is much less than the heat the steam gave off by condensing to water at 373 K. This high heat of condensation of steam makes it good for heating buildings, though.

Room temperature (about 295 K) occurs on Figure 10.1 where water is in its liquid state. Most substances have temperature-heat curves similar to water's. Of course, the numbers can differ, which is why some things are gases, others liquids, and still others solids at room temperature.

10.2 PRESSURE

Whenever we push on something, we exert a pressure on it. Anything that has weight can exert pressure. The air we live in is a mixture of gases that have volume and mass and weight. Thus air can exert pressure.

ATMOSPHERIC PRESSURE. The earth has air around it because it has enough gravity to hold onto the air. (The moon has gravity, too, but not enough to hold an atmosphere.) Air extends to about 500 miles above the earth, but it becomes less dense the further away it is. This is because the force of gravity grows weaker as the distance from the center of the earth increases. Figure 10.2 shows the various layers of our atmosphere and their relative densities.

In a game called "pig pile," people lie on top of each other in a pile of bodies. The person on the bottom feels more pressure than someone in the middle, who feels more than someone near the top. If we cut an imaginary column of air one meter square from where the atmosphere meets the earth to the top of the atmosphere, we'd be creating a kind of "pig pile" of air molecules. The more molecules that are present, the greater the pres-

**FIGURE 10.2
Density of air
relative to
distance
above sea level**

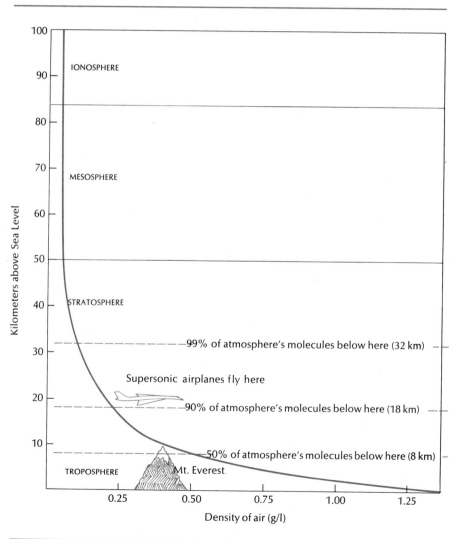

atmospheric pressure

sure. The molecules on the bottom of the column (and the earth itself) feel a lot of pressure from all those molecules above. This is called *atmospheric pressure*. Figure 10.3 shows that atmospheric pressure is greater at sea level than it is on a mountain top, because the column of air extending from sea level contains more molecules than the one extending from a mountain top.

We measure pressure by how much force is exerted on how much surface. This translates as force per unit of area. We fill our tires with air according to the number of pounds per square inch. In the English system, the atmospheric pressure at sea level is 14.7 pounds per square inch, because 14.7 pounds of air push down on a square inch of earth. In chemistry and other sciences, this pressure is called 1 *atmosphere* (*atm*).

atmosphere (atm)

FIGURE 10.3 Pressure varies with altitude, because different amounts of molecules push down

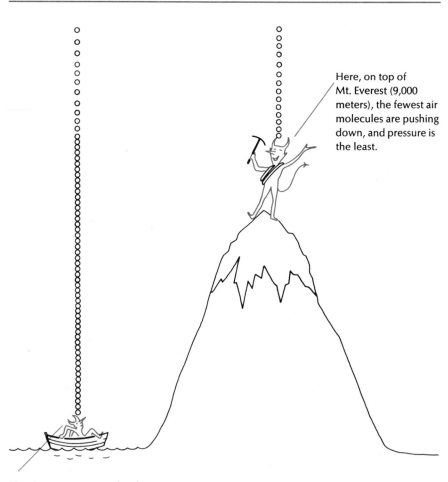

Here, on top of Mt. Everest (9,000 meters), the fewest air molecules are pushing down, and pressure is the least.

Here in New Jersey (sea level), the most air molecules are pushing down, and pressure is the greatest.

Notice that a *pressure of 1 atmosphere* means the atmospheric pressure at sea level. *Atmospheric pressure* means simply the pressure of the atmosphere wherever it's measured. Unless the measurement is taken below sea level, atmospheric pressure is usually less than 1 atmosphere.

Since we live at atmospheric pressure, it might not seem as if any pressure is pushing down on us. After all, we don't feel anything. This is because our bodies are adjusted so that our internal pressure pushes *out* just to equalize the atmospheric pressure that pushes *in*. That is, our bodies are in a state of equilibrium with the atmospheric pressure. *Equilibrium* means a static or dynamic state of balance between opposing forces. ("Static" means "standing still"; "dynamic" means "in motion.") Our bodies and atmospheric pressure are in a state of *static equilibrium* since the equal pressures don't change unless something disturbs the equilibrium. We'll see many examples of dynamic equilibrium a little later, and the contrast will become clear.

equilibrium

static equilibrium

States of equilibrium are often disturbed. Henri Le Chatelier stated a principle to explain what happens when an equilibrium is disturbed. Figure 10.4 illustrates *Le Chatelier's Principle,* which says that an equilibrium system, when disturbed, adjusts itself so as to restore equilibrium.

Le Chatelier's Principle

When we put our bodies into situations where the external pressure is different from the internal pressure, we're placing a stress on the pressure equilibrium between our bodies and their environment. If we climb a 2000-meter mountain, where the atmospheric pressure is lower than at sea level, then the equilibrium will be disturbed. However, given a little time, our bodies will adjust and the equilibrium will shift toward lower pressure. People with high blood pressure, especially, have to take it easy after experiencing large altitude changes, since a sudden release of external pressure can cause blood vessels to rupture. If this happens in the brain, it's a stroke.

A system only succeeds in reestablishing equilibrium if it hasn't been disturbed too much. How much is "too much" depends on the system itself. Although our bodies can adjust to relatively small pressure differences, they would explode in outer space, where the pressure inside our bodies would be pushing out and nothing would be pushing in. Astronauts wear pressurized space suits, which create a human-sized environment of atmospheric pressure. Airplane cabins are also pressurized to compensate for the lower pressure at high altitudes.

We measure pressure with a *barometer*. We can make a barometer with a glass tube, sealed at one end, and a flat-bottomed bowl. We fill the tube with a liquid like mercury and invert the tube carefully in the bowl. The liquid will drop to some level, but it won't all run out. The liquid stops running out when an equilibrium is established between the pressure caused by its weight in the tube and the atmospheric pressure. If the liquid is mercury and the atmospheric pressure is 1 atmosphere, then the mercury will drop to a height of 760 millimeters. A millimeter of mercury in pressure is also called a "torr," after Evangelista Torricelli (1608–1647), who first devised the mercury barometer.

barometer

**FIGURE 10.4
An illustration
of Le Chatelier's
Principle**

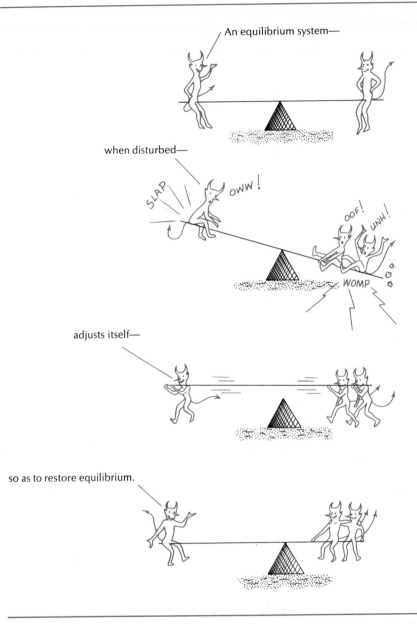

An equilibrium system—

when disturbed—

SLAP

OWW!

OOF!

UNH!

WOMP

adjusts itself—

so as to restore equilibrium.

If we cut off the sealed end of the tube, then the mercury would all run out, because the same atmospheric pressure would be pushing down on the mercury in the tube *and* on the surface of the mercury in the dish. We could make the mercury rise in the tube again by sucking on it with a vacuum pump. The vacuum pump decreases the pressure inside the tube. When the pressure inside the tube is less than atmospheric pressure, the atmospheric pressure pushes the mercury up the tube. But no matter how hard we pump, we can never get the mercury above 760 millimeters, because that's as far as a pressure of 1 atmosphere can push the mercury. Figure 10.5 illustrates how a barometer works.

Mercury is a better barometer liquid than water. Since water is 1/13.6 as dense as mercury, 1 atmosphere would push a column of water up 13.6 times higher than mercury, or 10.3 meters. We'd need a tall ladder to read this barometer. For this reason also, a water well can't be any deeper than 10.3 meters if the air pressure is supposed to push the water out. Pumping water out of a well is like sucking on a straw. Sucking on a straw decreases the pressure inside the straw, and the atmospheric pressure pushes the liquid up the straw. The atmospheric pressure has no trouble pushing liquids up a straw, because the straw is very short. Pumping water out of a well decreases the pressure at the top of the well, and the atmospheric pressure pushes the water up to the top. But if the well were deeper than 10.3 meters, the pump couldn't get the water all the way up, no matter how hard it pumped. In that case, the well would have to be sealed off, and a pressure greater than atmospheric pressure would have to be applied to the water in it.

PRESSURE AND A CONFINED GAS.
Eighteen grams of water occupy only 18 milliliters as a liquid, but 22.4 *liters* as a vapor. This means that less than 0.08 percent of the volume of water vapor is actually occupied by the water molecules. The rest is empty space, which the gas molecules create among themselves by moving fast and bumping into each other frequently.

To measure a solid, it's most convenient to weigh it. We can also weigh a liquid, but since we have to put it in a container, we may as well put it in

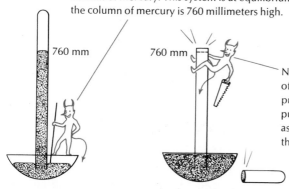

The atmospheric pressure in my lab today happens to be exactly 1 atmosphere. This pressure pushes down on the surface of the mercury in the dish. Since the other end of the tube is sealed off, the only thing that can push back is the weight of the column of mercury. This system is at equilibrium when the column of mercury is 760 millimeters high.

760 mm

760 mm

Now, I've sawed off the sealed end of the tube, to let the atmospheric pressure in. The same pressure is pushing down from inside the tube as outside, so there's no reason for the mercury to rise. It all runs out.

**FIGURE 10.5
A barometer
measures
the height of
a liquid
pushed up
a sealed tube
by atmospheric
pressure**

a marked container and measure its volume instead. Neither weighing nor measuring volume is the best way to measure a gas, because a gas takes up so much space and occupies all of the volume of any container. Instead, we measure the pressure of a gas. A confined gas creates pressure by bumping into the sides of its container. The more molecules there are to bump, the greater the pressure. Thus pressure is a measure of how much of a gas we have.

We can apply pressure to a confined gas, just as we could apply heat to a solid, and change the substance's state. If we start near zero pressure and increase the pressure continuously, we'll push the gas molecules closer together. At some point they will be pushed closely enough to form a liquid or even a solid. So-called bottled gases—like the butane used for cigarette lighters, or the propane used for camping stoves—are liquids when they are in their tanks under pressure. Turning a valve releases the pressure, and they come out as gases.

EFFECTS OF TEMPERATURE AND PRESSURE ON STATE.

From the discussion so far, we can see that both temperature and pressure affect states of matter. The temperature-heat curve for water in Figure 10.1 was really for a pressure of 1 atmosphere. In fact, the boiling point of water is not always 373 K. In the mountains, it is lower than that, as Table 10.1 shows. This is because boiling point decreases as atmospheric pressure decreases.

We see all around us the combined effects of temperature and pressure on states of matter. When bottled propane or butane is released from its tank, the tank nozzle might cool noticeably. In changing from a liquid to a gas, because of released pressure, the substance absorbs its heat of vaporization from the closest thing around. In a refrigerator, substances that are normally gases, such as ammonia, sulfur dioxide, or Freon (CF_2Cl_2), are compressed to liquids and pumped through the refrigerator coils. As the liquid vaporizes, it takes its heat of vaporization from its surroundings (the coils), cooling the coils and the inside of the refrigerator. Then the compressor changes the gas back into a liquid, releasing heat into the room, and the cycle repeats.

Because temperature and pressure affect a substance's state, we can't specify a state without also noting what the temperature and pressure are. A substance at 273 K and a pressure of 1 atmosphere is said to be at *standard temperature and pressure* (STP).

standard temperature and pressure (STP)

10.3 EQUILIBRIA AMONG STATES

Water left in an uncovered glass will eventually evaporate. We can smell mothballs because some of the molecules have escaped into the air and found their way to our noses. Mothballs left out in the open will also eventually disappear.

TABLE 10.1
Variation of water's boiling point with atmospheric pressure

Location	Altitude (meters)	Pressure (atmospheres)	Boiling Point of Water (K)
Death Valley, California	−85	1.04	374
Sea level	0	1.00	373
Mt. Carmel, Israel	550	0.930	371
Mt. Vesuvius, Italy	1200	0.865	369
Mt. Olympus, Greece	3000	0.695	363
Pikes Peak, Colorado	4300	0.593	359
Mt. Kilimanjaro, Tanzania	5900	0.487	354
Mt. K2, Kashmir	8600	0.336	345

Brr! Here on Mt. K2 in Kashmir, it's taking me 24 minutes to cook a 3-minute egg. I wouldn't even be able to cook beans. Water doesn't get hot enough.

Some of a liquid or solid always sneaks into the gas state, even though the substance is below its melting point or boiling point. The molecules that escape from a solid or a liquid make up its *vapor*. The pressure exerted by this vapor is the substance's *vapor pressure*. Everything has a vapor pressure, but some substances have more vapor pressure than others. (Tungsten, which doesn't vaporize much at all, is sometimes described as having a vapor pressure of "one atom per universe.")

vapor

vapor pressure

VAPOR PRESSURE.
Although water in an uncovered glass will evaporate, water in a covered glass will not. Both, however, have vapor pressure. Molecules *are* escaping to the vapor in the covered glass, but molecules are also returning to the liquid state.

Here's our first example of *dynamic equilibrium,* which we run into a lot in chemistry. Two opposing processes are happening at once and at the same rate, so that the net result stays the same. Imagine an old silent film comedy, the action taking place in a grocery store. One of the comedians thinks he is supposed to be stacking cans. The other thinks he is supposed to be taking the cans down and putting them in their boxes. Both scurry around doing their jobs (with the camera going double-speed), oblivious to the other's activities. The result is that the pile of cans stays the same height, even though cans are being moved around at a furious rate. This is an example of dynamic equilibrium: something is being *done* at the same rate it's being *undone.*

dynamic equilibrium

Now, let's look again at the water in the sealed glass. Two processes are going on: (1) molecules are escaping from the liquid and going into the vapor; and (2) molecules are leaving the vapor and going into the liquid. Although the rates of these processes will differ at first, the vapor molecules will soon return to the liquid at the same rate the liquid molecules escape into the vapor. When this happens, the system is at equilibrium. At equilibrium, the net number of molecules in the vapor and the liquid always stays the same, even though both processes are still going on.

Of course, equilibrium is established only if the container is covered. This is one of many examples of Le Chatelier's Principle applied to dynamic equilibrium. We can write the equilibrium between water and water vapor like this:

$$H_2O(l) \rightleftharpoons H_2O(g)$$

Here, the double arrows mean a state of dynamic equilibrium. If the container is uncovered, molecules from the right (the vapor) side will escape to the outside world, disturbing the equilibrium. To attempt to reestablish equilibrium, more molecules from the liquid will go into the vapor. The equilibrium won't be reestablished until either the glass is covered or the liquid is evaporated. We could disturb the equilibrium in the opposite direction, too, by adding more vapor molecules (say, by piping steam into the glass). Then some of the excess vapor would condense.

Disturbing an equilibrium system shifts the equilibrium. Removing water vapor shifts the equilibrium to the vapor side. Adding water vapor shifts the equilibrium to the liquid side. Figure 10.6 shows the position of equilibrium shifting towards water vapor.

The air around us always contains some water vapor. There is a limit, though, to how much water vapor the air can hold at each temperature. In humid weather, our perspiration doesn't evaporate, our clothes don't dry, and crackers and potato chips get soggy. This is another example of Le Chatelier's Principle. If the air has as much, or nearly as much, water vapor as it can hold, then the vapor molecules have nowhere to go but back into the liquid state. The equilibrium shifts toward the liquid. Warm air can hold more water vapor than cold air, so high humidity and hot weather often go together.

The air is much drier in cold climates than in warm climates. If the air is dry, the equilibrium between water and water vapor shifts toward the vapor, and substances lose moisture. Furniture, musical instruments, and our lips and nasal passages are accustomed to a certain amount of water vapor. If that amount drops drastically, they may develop cracks as they dry out. A humidifier can be used to supply the air with water vapor.

VAPOR PRESSURE AND TEMPERATURE.

Why should a liquid or a solid have a vapor pressure? Why don't all of the molecules just stay in their proper states? To answer these questions, we need to think some more about temperature. We said in Chapter 3 that substances are at higher temperatures because their molecules are moving faster. But the temperature of a substance represents only an average of the energies of all the molecules in a substance.

In any group of shoppers, a few will be moving very fast, a few will be moving very slowly, and most will be moving at a speed somewhere in between. When we look at molecules, we see that they behave the same way. Some molecules in a substance move very fast, some move slowly, and most move at a speed somewhere in between. We can plot the percentage

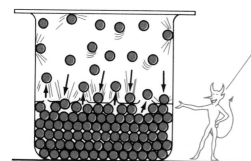

Liquid ⇌ Vapor

See this molecule entering the liquid phase? There are three others doing that in this picture. There are also four molecules going from the liquid to the vapor in this sealed container. We have a state of *equilibrium*.

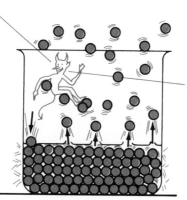

Liquid ⇌ Vapor

Somebody left the cover off this beaker of water! This molecule I'm pointing to is the only one I can see that's going *into* the liquid phase. We still have four molecules leaving, though, just as before.

This system is *not* at equilibrium. It's trying to be, though. It won't succeed until all of the liquid is gone.

of molecules having certain energies against the energies themselves, and we always get a Maxwell-Boltzmann Distribution Curve, shown in Figure 10.7. At a given temperature, some molecules will have enough energy to escape from the liquid or solid and go into the vapor. As the temperature is increased, more molecules will acquire more energy and enter the vapor. Then the vapor pressure increases.

BOILING POINT.
Up to the boiling point, the atmospheric pressure pushes down on the liquid, making most of the molecules stay in the liquid. If we steadily increase the temperature, the vapor pressure increases, too. When we reach a temperature where the vapor pressure of the liquid

FIGURE 10.7
Maxwell-
Boltzmann
distribution
curves

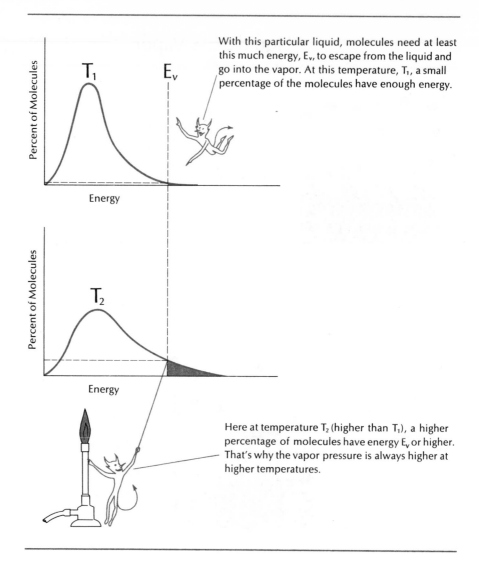

With this particular liquid, molecules need at least this much energy, E_v, to escape from the liquid and go into the vapor. At this temperature, T_1, a small percentage of the molecules have enough energy.

Here at temperature T_2 (higher than T_1), a higher percentage of molecules have energy E_v or higher. That's why the vapor pressure is always higher at higher temperatures.

equals the external pressure that's pushing down on it, then vapor can form anywhere where the liquid is touching the container. The bubbles in a pan of boiling water are water vapor that has formed on the bottom and sides of the pan. Figure 10.8 shows that the temperature at which vapor pressure and external pressure are equal is a liquid's *boiling point*. If the external pressure is less than one atmosphere, then the liquid will boil at a temperature lower than its normal boiling point.

We can cause water to boil at a temperature higher than its normal boiling point by going below sea level or by using a pressure cooker. In a pressure cooker, a valve maintains the inside pressure at 5 pounds per square inch (psi), 10 psi, or 15 psi *more* than atmospheric pressure. (The

boiling point

pressure becomes higher than atmospheric pressure since the steam molecules can't escape.) For water to boil, the vapor pressure of water must also increase, and that means increasing the temperature. At 5 psi (1.3 atm), water boils at 381 K; at 10 psi (1.7 atm), 389 K; and at 15 psi (2 atm), 421 K. For every 10 K increase in temperature, we cut the cooking time about in half. Cooking is a chemical reaction, and we'll see in Chapter 15 that increasing the temperature by 10 K doubles the speed of most chemical reactions. In the same way, we can compute the approximate time it takes to cook things in the mountains. For a 10-K decrease in the boiling point of water, cooking will take twice as long as it would at sea level.

SUBLIMATION. There is an equilibrium between solid and vapor, just as there is between liquid and vapor. Going directly from the solid state to the gas state is called *sublimation*. Almost any solid will sublime if it is subjected to low enough pressures, because the vapor molecules are removed and the equilibrium shifts toward the vapor. Some things sublime at atmospheric pressure. Dry ice (solid CO_2) sublimes instead of melting. So do mothballs.

sublimation

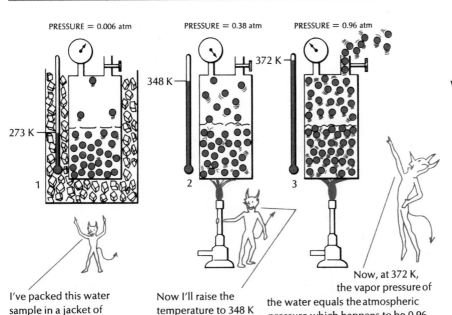

**FIGURE 10.8
The vapor
pressure
of water
increases
with temperature
up to the
boiling point**

PRESSURE = 0.006 atm   PRESSURE = 0.38 atm   PRESSURE = 0.96 atm

348 K   372 K

273 K

1   2   3

I've packed this water sample in a jacket of crushed ice.
It has a very small vapor pressure at this temperature.

Now I'll raise the temperature to 348 K with this burner.

Now, at 372 K, the vapor pressure of the water equals the atmospheric pressure which happens to be 0.96 atmospheres here in my lab today. At this temperature, the water is boiling, so I've opened this safety valve. If I didn't, the pressure inside would build up and maybe explode the container.

Ice has a vapor pressure lower than that of dry ice, but it can sublime because of Le Chatelier's Principle. Frozen clothes on a line will dry, especially if it's windy, because the changing air keeps removing the water vapor and drives the equilibrium toward the vapor. Like evaporation, sublimation works best if the humidity is low rather than high.

Freeze-drying uses Le Chatelier's Principle, too. A substance is frozen, and the water vapor is continually removed with a pump. In a frost-free freezer, the circulating air is kept very dry, either with a drying agent or with a pump. The water molecules escaping from the ice are constantly being removed. As a result, the ice cubes in a frost-free freezer become smaller the longer they sit unused.

FREEZING (MELTING).

The melting point can be defined as the temperature at which the solid is at equilibrium with the liquid. But it's really not quite that simple, because both the solid and the liquid have vapor pressures that we can't ignore. Solid and liquid are at equilibrium with vapor as well as with each other. Figure 10.9 shows that solid and liquid are at equilibrium with the same vapor. Thus *melting point* (*freezing point*) is the temperature at which the solid and liquid have the same vapor pressure. In Chapter 12, we'll see that equal vapor pressure for solid and liquid causes antifreeze to work and salt to melt ice.

melting point

freezing point

**FIGURE 10.9
At the
melting point,
the solid
and liquid
have the same
vapor pressure**

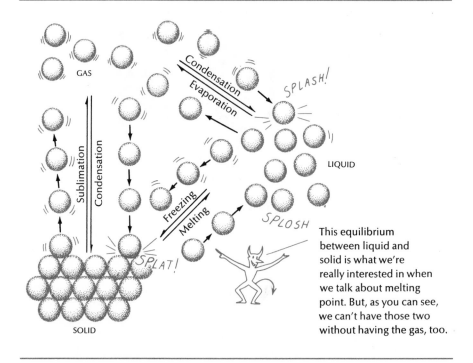

GAS

Condensation

Evaporation

SPLASH!

LIQUID

Sublimation

Condensation

Freezing

Melting

SPLOSH

SPLAT!

SOLID

This equilibrium between liquid and solid is what we're really interested in when we talk about melting point. But, as you can see, we can't have those two without having the gas, too.

At atmospheric pressure, substances melt and boil at different temperatures because the attractions that hold them together have different strengths. In Figure 10.1 we saw that the heat of vaporization of water is much larger than the heat of fusion of ice. This is typical of most substances, because the difference between a liquid and a gas is much greater than that between a solid and a liquid. A liquid is like a rather disorganized solid. The attractions don't hold the particles rigidly together, but they work almost as they do in the solid. In a gas, though, the particles are very far apart and the attractions are slight. It takes much more energy to change a liquid to a gas than it does to change a solid to a liquid.

VAN DER WAALS ATTRACTION. For some substances, melting points and boiling points increase roughly in proportion to formula weight. Figure 10.10 shows graphs of melting points and boiling points versus formula weight for the noble gases and for the halogens. The only attraction between the atoms or molecules in both groups is *van der Waals attraction*. This attraction depends on the number of protons, neutrons, and electrons a substance has, so we can see why it increases with formula weight. All molecules, atoms, and ions have van der Waals attraction for each other. Although it's the weakest of all the attractions we'll consider, it's enough to cause substances with higher formula weight to be liquids (such as Br_2) or solids (such as I_2) at room temperature.

van der Waals attraction

Noble gases form crystals made of single atoms held together by van der Waals attractions. These are *atomic crystals*. We won't encounter them much, because the attraction is so weak that the energy of room temperature is more than enough to change them into gases.

atomic crystal

Halogen crystals are made of molecules held together by van der Waals attraction. These are *molecular crystals*. To melt molecular crystals, we don't break the covalent bonds that hold the atoms together in the molecules. Instead, we overcome only the van der Waals attraction. Some familiar substances that fall into this category are paraffin, mothballs, most petroleum products, graphite, and dry ice. Also included are H_2, N_2, and O_2, which are ordinarily gases because their van der Waals attractions have been overcome by the warmth of room temperature.

molecular crystal

HYDROGEN BONDING. Figure 10.11 shows the graphs of the melting points and boiling points for the hydrogen compounds of the Group VA, VIA, and VIIA elements. The melting points and boiling points for the last three members of each series increase regularly with formula

**FIGURE 10.10
Melting points
and boiling
points increase
with formula
weight for
the halogens
and noble gases**

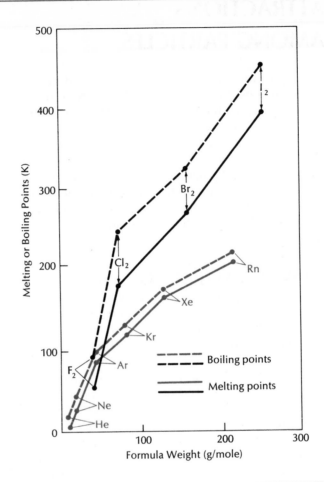

weight, as they did for the noble gases and the halogens. But the first member of each series seems out of place. For these three compounds, HF, H_2O, and NH_3, a stronger attraction —hydrogen bonding—has been added to van der Waals attraction.

We know from Chapter 8 (pp. 169–171) that hydrogen fluoride is a polar molecule, written like this:

$$H \vdash\!\!\longrightarrow F$$

The fluorine has hogged the electron pair so much that the hydrogen is almost a naked proton hanging out on one side. Sometimes we call it an "unshielded proton." Part of its positive charge is exposed and is ready and able to attract something negative. If there are only other HF molecules around, it finds a nonbonding electron pair on another HF molecule and **hydrogen bond** is attracted to it. We define a *hydrogen bond* as an attraction between a hydrogen atom that is bonded to fluorine, oxygen, or nitrogen and the nonbonding electron pair on a fluorine, oxygen, or nitrogen of another molecule. Only these three elements are electronegative enough to cause hydrogen bonding to any great extent. Here's how hydrogen bonding occurs in HF, H_2O, and NH_3:

$$:\!\ddot{F}\!-\!H\cdots:\!\ddot{F}\!-\!H$$

$$:\!\ddot{O}\!-\!H\cdots:\!\ddot{O}\!-\!H$$

$$:\!N\!-\!H\cdots:\!N\!-\!H$$

These are the most common examples, but any compound that contains H—F, H—O, or H—N bonds will form hydrogen bonds. Other examples are hydrogen peroxide (H_2O_2), hydrazine (H_2N—NH_2), and many carbon compounds derived from water and from ammonia. If these compounds are mixed together, they'll hydrogen-bond to one another.

To melt a hydrogen-bonded crystal, we have to break the hydrogen bonds but not the covalent bonds in the molecules. Although a hydrogen

FIGURE 10.11
Hydrogen bonding is stronger than van der Waals Attraction

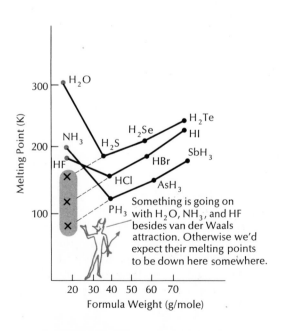

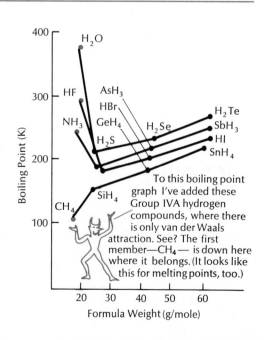

bond is not as strong as a regular covalent bond, it's still strong enough to cause the high melting points and boiling points of HF, H_2O, and NH_3. A hydrogen bond does have some of the restrictions of a regular covalent bond, though. These restrictions are listed here.

1. Only one hydrogen atom can hydrogen-bond to one electron pair.
2. Hydrogen bonding has to occur in a straight line. That is, each hydrogen bond must be in a straight line with the hydrogen nucleus and the nuclei of the two nonhydrogen atoms involved.

Ice is less dense than water because of these two rules. Since H_2O has two unshielded protons and two nonbonding electron pairs, a continuous hydrogen-bonded structure can be formed. When water freezes, this structure is locked in place. To keep the hydrogen bonds in straight lines and to preserve H_2O's bond angle (105°), the molecules have to spread apart. This means that there is a lot of empty space in ice—enough space for a stream of gaseous helium atoms to pass through and come out the other side. (See Figure 10.12.)

If we drop the solid of almost any substance into its liquid, the solid will sink. But ice floats on water, because it's less dense than water. If this weren't true, the ice formed in winter would sink to the bottom of lakes, rivers, and oceans. In spring, the ice would be at the bottom, where it couldn't be warmed and melted. The next winter, more water would freeze, and it still wouldn't melt in the spring. Pretty soon the whole world would be nearly a solid block of ice that would not support life as we know it.

Even though HF and NH_3 can hydrogen-bond, too, their solid states are more dense than their liquid states. HF has three nonbonding electron pairs and only one unshielded proton, so there aren't enough unshielded protons to bond with every electron pair. NH_3 has three unshielded protons and one nonbonding electron pair, so there will always be leftover protons. Thus neither has the possibility of a continuous hydrogen-bonded struc-

ICE-NINE

What if ice had a melting point above room temperature? Kurt Vonnegut, Jr., asked and answered this question in his science fiction novel *Cat's Cradle*. In it, a scientist experimented with crystal structures and created a special crystalline form of ice that he called "ice-nine." Ice-nine "was blue-white. It had a melting point of one-hundred-fourteen-point-four degrees Fahrenheit" (45°C). When ice-nine was added to normal water, the normal water crystallized in the form of ice-nine. The political and environmental results of this situation make for an entertaining story.

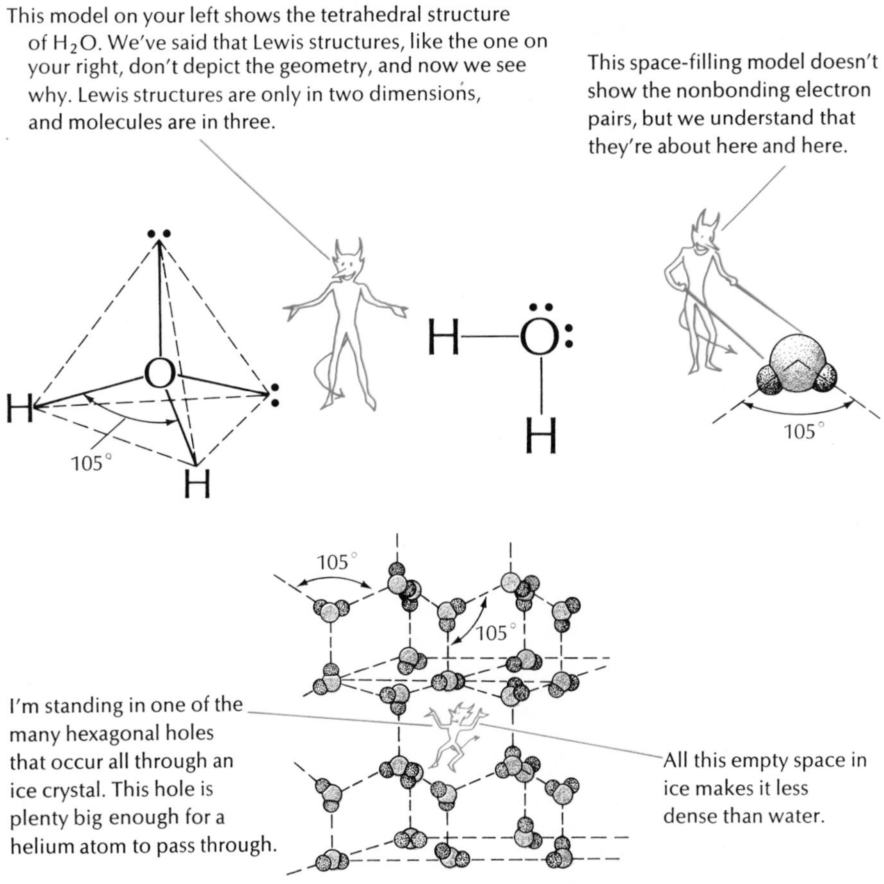

FIGURE 10.12
Structures
of H_2O
and of an
ice crystal

225

This model on your left shows the tetrahedral structure of H_2O. We've said that Lewis structures, like the one on your right, don't depict the geometry, and now we see why. Lewis structures are only in two dimensions, and molecules are in three.

This space-filling model doesn't show the nonbonding electron pairs, but we understand that they're about here and here.

I'm standing in one of the many hexagonal holes that occur all through an ice crystal. This hole is plenty big enough for a helium atom to pass through.

All this empty space in ice makes it less dense than water.

---

ture like that of water, which matches unshielded protons and nonbonding electron pairs exactly.

Hydrogen bonding occurs in liquid water, too, but the bonds are continuously formed and broken as the water molecules move around. However, it is the extensive hydrogen bonding in liquid water that gives water the high specific heat we saw in Chapter 3. Water can absorb a lot of energy, because the energy goes into breaking the many hydrogen bonds.

Ice is an example of a *hydrogen-bonded molecular crystal.* In these crystals, the single units are molecules and the attraction is hydrogen bonding.

hydrogen-bonded molecular crystal

DIPOLE-DIPOLE ATTRACTION.
We saw in Chapter 8 (pp. 172–173) that molecules can be either polar or nonpolar. Polar molecules can be attracted to each other through *dipole-dipole attraction.* This is the

dipole-dipole attraction

attraction of the positive end of one polar molecule for the negative end of another. As we'll see in Chapter 13, a liquid's ability to dissolve other polar substances or to dissolve ionic substances depends on its own polar nature.

Naturally, any molecule that can hydrogen-bond is also polar and participates in dipole-dipole attraction. Where both can occur, the hydrogen bonding is by far the stronger and overpowers the latter. There are molecules, though, that have no hydrogen capable of hydrogen-bonding but are still polar. Examples are NF_3, IF, and CHF_3. Molecules like these form **polar molecular crystal** *polar molecular crystals,* whose units are polar molecules. The interactions are still van der Waals attractions, along with dipole-dipole attractions. These two attractions have about the same strength. To melt a polar molecular crystal, we have to overcome these attractions, but we still don't break the covalent bonds within molecules.

In a liquid, polar molecules can cluster around one another in any direction. The number of molecules that can participate is limited only by the amount of space available, and not by straight lines as in hydrogen bonding.

IONIC BONDING.
From Chapter 7 (pp. 133–135), we know that the units in ionic crystals are positive and negative ions, and the attraction is ionic bonding. Ionic crystals are all solids at room temperature because of the continuity of the crystal and the strength of the ionic bond.

METALLIC BONDING.
metallic crystal
metallic bond
Metallic bonding is a kind of ionic bonding, and that's why many metals behave like ionic compounds. In *metallic crystals,* the particles are positive metal ions and the attraction is a "sea" of electrons composed of the metal atoms' valence electrons. We can think of them as a lattice of metal ions with the sea of electrons poured all through it, holding it together. This is a *metallic bond.*

Electricity is usually caused by moving electrons, and metals are good electrical conductors because of the fluid nature of the electron sea. The malleability and ductility of metals are also caused by the electron sea. Layers of positive ions can slide easily over each other, because the electron sea is squishy and also because the ions in a metal crystal are all alike. When a crystal is struck with a hammer, the layers slide over each other and the metal flattens. In an ionic crystal, sliding the rows of ions past each other places like charges together. When an ionic crystal (like salt) is struck with a hammer, the ions repel each other and the crystal shatters. Figure 10.13 shows the difference between metallic and ionic crystals.

Metallic bonds have varying strengths, depending on how many electrons each metal atom contributes. Sodium and other alkali metals contribute only one electron per atom, so the metallic bond is not terribly strong. These elements form very soft crystals with low melting points. Copper, however, is much harder and has a higher melting point because

FIGURE 10.13
A sea
of electrons
causes
metallic
properties

227

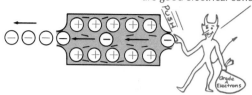

This bar of metal has a sea of electrons that I've represented by this gray gunk. The electrons are very fluid. When I push electrons in this end, they come out the other. That's why metals are good electrical conductors.

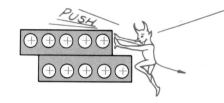

I can slide one layer of this metallic crystal over another. It's easy. Positive ions are still opposite each other, and the sea of electrons that surrounds them keeps them from repelling each other.

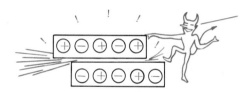

If I slide the layers of an ionic crystal, I push like-charged ions next to each other. The crystal is going to fly apart, because of the repulsion between these like charges!

it can contribute some of its *d* as well as its *s* electrons. All of the transition metals are harder and have higher melting points than the representative metals.

Metals can be made harder still by adding other substances to them. Steel, for instance, contains carbon, which interrupts the metallic crystal of iron at intervals and makes it more difficult for the layers to slide. Steel is thus harder than pure iron.

COVALENT BONDING.

The strongest of all are the attractions in *covalent crystals*. Their individual particles are atoms. They have a continuous structure, like ionic crystals, but the attraction—covalent bonding—is stronger than ionic bonding. We saw the structure of a diamond crystal in Chapter 2 (p. 26). Diamond won't melt. At 3773 K, it will rearrange to the graphite structure.

The atoms in a covalent crystal don't have to be the same. Silicon dioxide

**covalent
crystal**

is made of two kinds of particles: silicon atoms and oxygen atoms. Rocks are hard because they're made mostly of silicon dioxide. To melt or cut a covalent crystal, we actually have to break covalent bonds.

Table 10.2 summarizes the different kinds of crystals and the attractions that hold them together.

TABLE 10.2
Summary of interactions in solids

Kind of Crystal	Units	Attraction	Examples	Comments
Covalent Crystal	Atoms (same or different)	Covalent bonds	Diamond Silicon Boron SiO_2 Carborundum (SiC)	These are all very hard and have high melting points, because a covalent bond is the strongest interaction there is.
Metallic Crystal	Metal ions	"Sea" of electrons (metallic bonds)	All metals	Covers a wide range of melting points, because of different numbers of valence electrons. Most are solids.
Ionic Crystal	Positive and negative ions	Ionic bonds	NaCl KNO_3, and all ionic compounds	Also covers a wide range of melting points, because of differences in lattice energies. Ionic and metallic crystals cover about the same range of melting points. All are solids.
Hydrogen-bonded Molecular Crystal	Hydrogen-bonding molecules	Hydrogen bonds	H_2O (ice) NH_3 HF	Melting points far below those of ionic crystals, because the interactions are much weaker. These substances are liquids or gases at room temperature.
Molecular Crystal	Molecules	Van der Waals attraction	Dry ice N_2, H_2, O_2 Halogens	These melt below hydrogen-bonded crystals. Many are gases at room temperature.
Polar Molecular Crystal	Polar molecules	Dipole-dipole attraction	HCl, CO ICl	
Atomic Crystal	Atoms	Van der Waals attraction	Noble gases	Weakest attraction. All are gases at room temperature.

REVIEW QUESTIONS

Temperature and Heat

1. Without looking at the text explanation, describe what is happening physically during each portion of Figure 10.1.
2. Why is ice a better cooling agent than water, when the two are at the same temperature? Why is steam a better heating agent than water, under the same conditions?
3. How can we tell from Figure 10.1 that water is a liquid at room temperature?

Pressure

4. What is *pressure?* How do we measure it?
5. What is *atmospheric pressure?* What causes it? Why is it greater at sea level than on a mountain top?
6. What is 1 *atmosphere?* How can it be measured?
7. What is *equilibrium?* Give an example of *static equilibrium.*
8. Explain *Le Chatelier's Principle,* and give an example.
9. Explain how a *barometer* works.
10. How does a gas create pressure?
11. Why do we need to measure the pressure of a gas?
12. Explain how pressure can change a substance's physical state.
13. Are bottled gases liquid or gas? Explain.
14. Is the boiling point of water always 373 K? Explain.
15. Explain how a refrigerator works. How is heat of vaporization used?
16. What is *standard temperature and pressure (STP)?*

Equilibria Among States

17. What is *vapor? Vapor pressure?*
18. What is *dynamic equilibrium?* Give an example.
19. Explain how Le Chatelier's Principle is involved in the evaporation of water from an uncovered glass.
20. Why do objects dry out in cold winters?

21. Explain why solids and liquids have vapor pressure. Why does it increase with temperature?
22. What is our new definition of *boiling point?* Explain what happens when a liquid boils.
23. Why do liquids boil at lower temperatures in the mountains?
24. Why does food cook faster in a pressure cooker?
25. What is *sublimation?* Give some familiar examples.
26. How is Le Chatelier's Principle involved in freeze-drying?
27. How do we now define *melting point?*

Attractions Among Particles

28. Why is a substance's heat of vaporization usually larger than its heat of fusion?
29. What is *van der Waals attraction?* What relationship do we find when this is the only attraction between atoms or molecules?
30. What is the difference between an *atomic crystal* and a *molecular crystal?* Give an example of each.
31. What is a *hydrogen bond?* What evidence do we have for its existence?
32. Why is ice less dense than water? How does hydrogen bonding enter in?
33. Why does water have such a high specific heat?
34. What is *dipole-dipole attraction?* How is it different from hydrogen bonding?
35. What is a *metallic bond?* What are *metallic crystals?*
36. How does metallic bonding account for the properties of metals?
37. What is the difference between an *atomic crystal* and a *covalent crystal?*
38. How is a covalent crystal like an ionic crystal? How is it different?
39. List all of the attractions between particles in order of increasing strength.
40. Without looking at Table 10.2, list the different kinds of crystals, their units and attractions, and give an example for each.

EXERCISES

1. An isolated outpost in Siberia wishes to generate its electricity with steam made from snow. How many kilocalories must be supplied to convert 1 kg of snow at −40°C to steam at 100°C?
2. How many grams of steam at 373 K must be condensed to water at 373 K to provide 5 kcal of heat?
3. Ammonia has a heat of vaporization of 327 cal/g at its boiling point, −33°C. If 1 kg of liquid ammonia is allowed to change to a gas at its boiling point, how many kilocalories of heat will it absorb?
4. Imagine an inhabitable planet whose atmospheric pressure is twice that of earth's.

a. What would be the reading on an earth barometer?

b. Would drinking through a straw be easier or more difficult than on earth?

c. Would it take a longer or shorter time to boil an egg in water than it would on earth?

d. Would an individual with high blood pressure be better or worse off than one with normal blood pressure?

5. Here is a temperature-heat graph for an unknown substance.

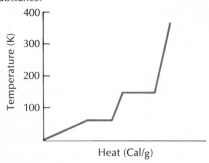

a. What is its physical state at room temperature?

b. Indicate which portions of the graph are its heat of fusion and heat of vaporization.

c. Is the specific heat highest for gas, liquid, or solid?

d. Are the attractions between its particles stronger or weaker than the attractions between particles in H_2O?

6. Alcohol will evaporate faster from an uncovered glass at room temperature than water will. Which has the higher vapor pressure at room temperature?

7. Which of the following would help to keep your house plants from drying out while you went away for a few days? Explain.

a. increasing the temperature of the room

b. decreasing the temperature of the room

c. opening the window

d. closing the window

e. placing a pan of water on the radiator

f. blowing an electric fan on the plants

g. putting the plants in sealed plastic bags

8. Which of the operations in Exercise 7 would help your clothes to dry indoors? Explain. (In f and g, substitute "clothes" for "plants.")

9. Is it possible to cause water to boil at room temperature? How?

10. Dry ice sublimes at atmospheric pressure instead of melting. Yet a puddle of liquid often remains after a piece of dry ice has disappeared. What is the liquid, and where did it come from?

11. At the melting point, the solid and liquid must have the same vapor pressure to coexist. What would happen if a piece of ice were placed into liquid water at a temperature where the vapor pressure of water is greater than that of ice?

12. The following table shows heats of fusion and heats of vaporization for the hydrogen compounds of the Group VIIA elements.

Substance	Heat of Fusion (cal/g)	Heat of Vaporization (cal/g)
H_2O	79.9	540
H_2S	16.7	131
H_2Se	7.4	57
H_2Te	–	42

a. Explain why the heats of vaporization are larger than the heats of fusion for each compound.

b. Explain why both the heats of vaporization and the heats of fusion are largest for H_2O.

13. Explain the following in terms of interactions between particles.

a. Br_2 has a lower melting point than NaCl.

b. N_2 and O_2 are gases at room temperature.

c. Tungsten has a higher melting point than calcium.

d. Br_2 has a higher melting point than Cl_2.

e. H_2O has a higher boiling point than HF.

f. Quartz (SiO_2) has a higher melting point than NaCl.

14. What type of crystal would you expect each of these elements or compounds to form? In each case, what would the units and the attractions be?

a. H_2 e. Cr   i. CO_2

b. P_4 f. $CuCl_2$ j. NO_2

c. NaH   g. HCl   k. Si

d. SO_2 h. NH_3

15. NH_3 and SO_2 were once used as refrigerating gases more than they are today. Both are toxic and corrosive, and therefore unpleasant to work with. Freon-12, CF_2Cl_2, is one substance that has replaced them because it is inert, nontoxic, and nonexplosive. The heats of vaporization of these substances are as follows:

NH_3:   327 cal/g
SO_2:   92.7 cal/g
CF_2Cl_2:   40 cal/g

a. Which is actually the best refrigerant?

b. Explain the differences in heats of vaporization in terms of attractions among particles for each.

11

Gases

Gases are very interesting and useful, because of the huge changes they can undergo. In the last chapter, we saw some of the ways that changes of state can work for us, and that changes involving gases are usually the most significant. In this chapter, we'll look more closely at the gas state itself, starting with air, our most important gas. We'll see some chemical reactions that involve gases, and we'll calculate exactly how changes in pressure, temperature, and volume affect them.

11.1 SOME CHEMISTRY OF AIR

Air is our favorite gas. As we know, though, air isn't just one gas, but a mixture, as shown in Table 11.1. Each of air's major components is important to our life on earth. The gases that are present in smaller amounts affect us very little. Some of these, though, become air pollutants when present in larger amounts. We'll look at some of the important properties of normal air and see how air pollutants are introduced and how they can and should be minimized.

AIR'S IMPORTANT GASES. Of course, oxygen is number one in importance, because without it we couldn't survive. The hemoglobin in our blood combines with the oxygen that we breathe into our lungs and transports it to all parts of our bodies. When oxygen arrives at its various destinations, it combines with hydrogen (which results from other bodily processes) and forms water, liberating energy.

$$O_2 + 4\,H \text{ (in compounds)} \longrightarrow 2\,H_2O + \text{energy}$$

In effect, we use oxygen to "burn" our food, which makes the energy to run our bodies. We also use oxygen to burn fuels like coal and gasoline, which provide us with energy to heat our homes and drive our cars.

Oxygen wasn't always a part of our atmosphere. It didn't exist in any significant amount until about 1.8 billion years ago, when green plants were first evolving. Green plants use carbon dioxide plus the energy from the sun to make sugar, which they then use for energy. This process is called **photosynthesis**, and it produces oxygen.

Living organisms need nitrogen in their bodily structures. Nitrogen gas is very inert, though, so plants and animals can't use it straight from the air. Animals get nitrogen they can use by eating plants and other animals. Plants obtain it by *nitrogen fixation,* which means that nitrogen in the air combines with other elements and enters the soil. The plants then take the compound up in their roots. Natural nitrogen fixation happens when lightning causes the nitrogen and oxygen in the air to react together.

photosynthesis

nitrogen fixation

$$N_2(g) + O_2(g) \xrightarrow{\text{lightning}} 2\,NO(g)$$

NO_2 is formed when NO reacts with oxygen or ozone.

$$2\,NO(g) + O_2(g) \longrightarrow 2\,NO_2(g)$$

$$NO(g) + O_3(g) \longrightarrow NO_2(g) + O_2(g)$$

Rain washes the NO_2 down as nitrites and nitrates.

$$2\,NO_2(g) + H_2O(l) \longrightarrow HNO_2(aq) + HNO_3(aq)$$

Having reached the ground in a compound, the nitrogen can then be absorbed by the plants. Another source of nitrogen for plants is decaying

Name	Formula	Volume Percent	Comments
Nitrogen	N_2	78.09	Rather unreactive gas.
Oxygen	O_2	20.95	Essential for air-breathing animals. Very reactive. Produced by plants.
Argon	Ar	0.93	Very unreactive gas.
Carbon dioxide	CO_2	0.032	Product of burning and breathing. Used by green plants to make sugar.
Neon	Ne	1.8×10^{-3}	Very unreactive gas.
Helium	He	5.2×10^{-4}	Very unreactive gas.
Methane	CH_4	1.5×10^{-4}	Produced by volcanos and some microorganisms.
Krypton	Kr	1.0×10^{-5}	Very unreactive gas.
Hydrogen	H_2	5.0×10^{-6}	Reactive; produced by volcanos and some micro-organisms.
Dinitrogen oxide	N_2O	2.0×10^{-6}	Produced by lightning.
Carbon monoxide	CO	1.0×10^{-6}	Product of burning and of some marine organisms.
Xenon	Xe	8.0×10^{-7}	Very unreactive gas.
Ozone	O_3	2.0×10^{-8}	Formed by ultraviolet light on O_2, and by lightning.
Ammonia	NH_3	6.0×10^{-9}	Product of volcanos and microorganisms.
Nitrogen dioxide	NO_2	1.0×10^{-9}	Formed by lightning and hot fires.
Nitrogen monoxide	NO	6.0×10^{-10}	Formed by lightning and hot fires.
Sulfur dioxide	SO_2	2.0×10^{-10}	Produced by volcanos and burning S.
Hydrogen sulfide	H_2S	2.0×10^{-10}	Produced by volcanos and some microorganisms.

**TABLE 11.1
Composition of
clean dry air
at ground level**

animal waste and dead animal and plant matter. Also, some microorganisms that live in the soil and in the roots of peas, beans, or related plants can fix nitrogen.

With our tremendous agricultural demands on the soil, we can't depend on natural nitrogen fixation. Humans have developed industrial ways of fixing nitrogen. Nitrogen from the air is made to react to form a compound, which is then used as a fertilizer. This is more difficult than it sounds, because nitrogen is very unreactive. Some of these processes need the help **catalyst** of a *catalyst,* a substance that makes a reaction go much faster without itself being changed in the end. A very important nitrogen fixation process is the Haber process.

$$N_2(g) + 3 H_2(g) \xrightarrow[\text{catalyst}]{\text{pressure, } \Delta} 2 NH_3(g)$$

The ammonia is either made into ammonium salts or used directly as a fertilizer.

Still other parts of the air regulate the way we receive and store the sun's **visible light** energy. Sunlight has many components. The part that we see is *visible light*. We don't see ultraviolet and infrared radiation. *Ultraviolet radiation* **ultraviolet radiation** has the highest energy. It gives some people sunburn. We'd burn up if we received all the ultraviolet radiation that the sun sent out. Before the oxygen in our atmosphere was formed, life had been confined to the water for protection from ultraviolet radiation. Then a protective screen of ozone (O_3) was also formed in the upper atmosphere, and life began to exist out of water. Ozone absorbs some ultraviolet radiation.

Ozone is produced by the action of ultraviolet radiation on oxygen. When this high-energy radiation hits an oxygen molecule, it breaks the bond and creates two oxygen atoms.

$$O_2(g) \xrightarrow{\text{uv}} 2 O(g)$$

Single oxygen atoms will react immediately with the first thing they meet. If the first thing is an oxygen molecule, then ozone is formed.

$$O(g) + O_2(g) \longrightarrow O_3(g)$$

Ultraviolet light also destroys the ozone it helps create. When it does, though, energy is absorbed in breaking one of ozone's bonds.

$$O_3(g) \xrightarrow{\text{uv}} O_2(g) + O(g)$$

Of course, the new oxygen atom can react right away with another oxygen molecule and form ozone again. But meanwhile some harmful ultraviolet radiation will be absorbed and prevented from reaching us. The formation and decomposition of ozone are in a state of equilibrium, so that the amount of ozone in the upper atmosphere remains fairly constant. While this is being written, there is controversy over whether some gases we use—such as the Freon in aerosol cans—might be disturbing that equilibrium and reducing the amount of ozone. If this is happening, it could put us in danger of being overexposed to ultraviolet radiation.

Water vapor isn't listed as a component of air in Table 11.1, because its amount varies widely with location. Air can contain as much as 5 percent water vapor in tropical climates, and as little as 0.01 percent at the North Pole or South Pole. Water vapor is an important part of the air, though. Apart from its obvious role in making rain and snow, it and carbon dioxide help maintain a fairly even climate on earth. In what we call the *greenhouse effect,* carbon dioxide and water vapor form a blanket around the earth that keeps in some of the sun's warmth during the night. (See Figure 11.1.) The ultraviolet radiation from the sun changes into *infrared radiation* (which is heat) when it hits the earth. The water vapor and carbon dioxide let the ultraviolet radiation through to the earth during the daytime, but they keep some of the infrared radiation from escaping at night. If the earth couldn't keep some heat this way, we'd be far too cold at night.

Table 11.2 summarizes some of the important reactions that involve gases in the air.

greenhouse effect

infrared radiation

**Figure 11.1
The greenhouse effect**

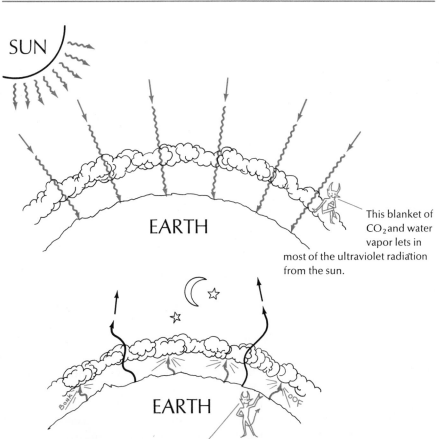

This blanket of CO_2 and water vapor lets in most of the ultraviolet radiation from the sun.

But it doesn't let all of the infrared radiation escape. Earth keeps some of it overnight. This is called the greenhouse effect because the glass of a greenhouse serves the same purpose as the blanket of CO_2 and water vapor.

**TABLE 11.2
Some desirable
reactions
involving gases
in air**

Gas	Reaction	Effect
O_2	$Hb + O_2 \longrightarrow HbO_2$ hemoglobin	Hemoglobin transports oxygen to cells.
	$O_2 \longrightarrow 2\,O^{2-} + energy$ (in cells)	Cells use oxygen to obtain energy.
	$C + O_2 \longrightarrow CO_2 + energy$ (in fuels)	Souce of heat and energy.
O_3	$O_3 \xrightarrow{uv} O_2 + O$	Absorbs some harmful ultraviolet radiation in outer atmosphere.
CO_2	$6\,CO_2 + 6\,H_2O \xrightarrow{light} C_6H_{12}O_6 + 6\,O_2$ (photosynthesis) glucose	Origin of atmospheric oxygen. Vital source of energy for green plants and animals.
N_2	$N_2 + O_2 \xrightarrow{lightning} 2\,NO$	Natural nitrogen fixation.
	$N_2 + 3\,H_2 \xrightarrow[catalyst]{pressure,\,\Delta} 2\,NH_3$	Industrial Haber process for nitrogen fixation.

AIR'S UNDESIRABLE GASES.

We saw some of the major air pollutants in Chapter 4. Now we know from Table 11.1 that traces of some of them are in the lower atmosphere: CO, NO, NO_2, O_3, and SO_2. Although these are pretty harmless in small amounts, our advanced technology is putting far more of them into the atmosphere than it can handle. Carbon monoxide comes from the incomplete burning of fuel, particularly in automobile engines. Nitrogen monoxide is formed whenever air is raised to high temperatures, so that the nitrogen and the oxygen in air react with each other. Automobiles and electric power plants are the primary sources of this pollutant. Nitrogen dioxide is formed from nitrogen monoxide, and ozone is formed from nitrogen dioxide and oxygen. Sulfur oxides form when anything containing sulfur is burned. The primary sources are smelting sulfur ores and burning coal and petroleum that contain sulfur.

**part per
million (ppm)**

We measure air pollutants in *parts per million* (*ppm*). One part per million means one measure (volume, weight, molecule) of something in a million measures of a mixture. One molecule of oxygen in a million molecules of a mixture is one part per million.

Table 11.3 lists some air pollutants and their primary and secondary effects. Sometimes, secondary effects are worse than primary effects. This is especially true of nitrogen monoxide, which leads to nitrogen dioxide and ultimately to the formation of toxic ozone in the lower atmosphere. Although ozone forms a lifesaving screen in the upper atmosphere, it's a dangerous poison to breathe. Ozone, NO_2, and unburned gasoline in

**photochemical
smog**

automobile exhaust produce a great many irritants when acted upon by ultraviolet radiation. We know the mixture as *photochemical smog*.

Nature has some methods for removing air pollutants. Some organisms in the soil use up carbon monoxide. Rain will wash the oxides of nitrogen and sulfur out of the air and into the soil, for plants to use. But natural processes can handle only small amounts of these gases. It's important for us to start at the root of the pollution problem, by controlling the amounts of various gases that we release into our atmosphere. This is much easier said than done, however. Table 11.4 shows the sources of some air pollutants and some of the complex problems involved in trying to remove them.

For instance, to minimize carbon monoxide formation, we supply more oxygen and burn fuel at a higher temperature. But when we do this, we increase the nitrogen monoxide formation. To cut down on the nitrogen monoxide, we supply less oxygen and burn at a lower temperature—but that increases carbon monoxide formation and also causes the release of

TABLE 11.3
Some air pollutants and their effects

Pollutant	Primary Effect[a]	Secondary Effect[a]	Allowed Exposure by Industries
CO_2	None; nontoxic to animals.	Increased amounts may overdo the greenhouse effect, so that climate may become warmer. Eventual effects unknown.	
CO	Poisonous to oxygen-breathing organisms. Reacts with hemoglobin and prevents it from carrying O_2: $Hb + CO \longrightarrow HbCO$		100 ppm (but ill effects noticed at 5 ppm).
NO	Reacts with hemoglobin as CO does. Not as serious as secondary effect.	Reacts with ozone to produce NO_2: $NO + O_3 \longrightarrow NO_2 + O_2$	25 ppm
NO_2	Toxic. Causes respiratory irritation.	Initiator of "smog." Worst effect is as source of atomic oxygen and then ozone: $NO_2 \xrightarrow{uv} NO + O$ $O + O_2 \longrightarrow O_3$	5 ppm
O_3	Toxic. Destroys bronchial passages and prevents breathing. Attacks rubber and other substances.	Reacts with other smog components to form eye and throat irritants.	0.1 ppm
SO_2, SO_3	Suffocating and toxic to animals and plants.	Cause "acid rain," which corrodes statues and buildings.	5 ppm

[a]Primary effects have direct bearing on animals, plants, or the environment. Secondary effects indirectly cause other environmental problems.

TABLE 11.4

Sources of and possible ways to eliminate air pollutants

Pollutant	Source	Way to Eliminate	Comments
CO	Incomplete burning of fuel (automobiles primarily). Some industries.	Burn fuel completely. Supply more oxygen and burn at higher temperature. Or burn CO as it emerges from stack: $2\,CO + O_2 \longrightarrow 2\,CO_2$	This will lead to increased NO formation (see under NO).
O_3	$NO_2 \longrightarrow NO + O$ $O + O_2 \longrightarrow O_3$	Eliminate NO_2.	
NO_2	$NO + O \longrightarrow NO_2$	Eliminate NO.	This will lead to increased CO formation.
NO	Raising air to high temperatures: $N_2 + O_2 \longrightarrow 2\,NO$ Automobiles and electric power plants.	Burn at lower temperatures. Decrease O_2 supply. Remove from smokestack. Some suggested ways: $2\,CO + 2\,NO \longrightarrow N_2 + 2\,CO_2$ $4\,NH_3 + 6\,NO \longrightarrow 5\,N_2 + 6\,H_2O$ $CH_4 + 4\,NO \longrightarrow 2\,N_2 + CO_2 + 2\,H_2O$ Convert to NO_2, then: $4\,NO_2 + Ca(OH)_2 \longrightarrow Ca(NO_3)_2 + 2\,HNO_2$	All substances are gases, which are hard to handle. Temperatures, pressures, and catalysts have to be found which will work and won't produce unwanted side effects. $Ca(NO_3)_2$ could be used as a fertilizer.
SO_2, SO_3	Smelting ore and burning sulfur-containing fuel (coal is the worst). $S + O_2 \longrightarrow SO_2$ (free or combined) $SO_2 + \tfrac{1}{2}O_2 \longrightarrow SO_3$	Don't burn any fuels that contain sulfur. Remove S from fuel before burning. Remove S from ore without burning. One way: $4\,CuFeS_2 + 3\,SO_2 + 12\,HCl \longrightarrow$ $4\,CuCl + 4\,FeCl_2 + 11\,S + 6\,H_2O$ Remove SO_2 from stack gases: $CaCO_3 + SO_2 + \tfrac{1}{2}O_2 \longrightarrow CaSO_4 + CO_2$ $MnO(s) + SO_2(g) \longrightarrow MnSO_3(s)$ $NaOH(aq) + SO_2(g) \longrightarrow NaHSO_3(aq)$ $2\,H_2S(g) + SO_2(g) \longrightarrow 3\,S(s) + 2\,H_2O(g)$ $2\,CO(g) + SO_2(g) \longrightarrow S(s) + 2\,CO_2(g)$	Almost impossible, since all do. This is being attempted. Also would use up SO_2 from another source. Limestone-dolomite process. Solid products must be disposed of or used. Where all reactants are gases, handling is a problem.

unburned gasoline. It's hard to win. Engineers are now struggling with these and other conflicting demands.

Most of our fuel, especially coal, contains sulfur. We must either remove the sulfur before burning the fuel—which is very difficult—or remove the SO_2 from the smokestack as it's formed. There are many ways to do the latter, but most involve large quantities of solid by-products. These by-products have to be removed in some way, and often in themselves pose a pollution problem. If the SO_2 could be used to make sulfuric acid, this would be a practical use; unfortunately, it mostly comes out too dilute to be used for this purpose.

Removal of NO is a very difficult problem. Most of the reactions that would get rid of it involve other gases, which are hard to handle, and special temperatures, pressures, and catalysts must be found to make the reactions go in the desired way. We'll see next exactly how gases are affected by temperature and pressure, and how we measure them.

11.2 MEASURING GASES AT STP

In Chapter 10, we talked about some of the difficulties of measuring gases. The volume of a gas is a useful measurement only if we also measure its temperature and pressure. If we know the temperature and pressure and volume and know what the gas is, we can also know it mass.

MOLAR VOLUME OF A GAS. *Avogadro's Law,* proposed in 1811 by Amedeo Avogadro (1776–1856), states that equal volumes of gases at the same temperature and pressure contain equal numbers of particles. This is true because the gas particles themselves occupy almost no volume compared with the space between them. From Avogadro's Law, we know that equal numbers of gas particles—or equal numbers of moles—occupy the same volume at the same temperature and pressure. In fact, the volume occupied by one mole of any gas at standard temperature and pressure (STP)—called the *molar volume* of a gas—is 22.4 liters (22,400 cm^3). It doesn't matter what the gas is. If we know the volume of a gas at STP, we automatically know how many moles—or molecules, or atoms—it contains. This is a unique property of gases. We can't say the same for liquids or solids.

Avogadro's Law

molar volume

Equal volumes of different gases at STP don't have the same masses, though, as Figure 11.2 demonstrates. This is because the particles themselves have different masses.

We can use the molar volume, 22.4 l/mole, as a conversion factor to find the mass or the volume of a gas at STP.

EXAMPLE 11.1: Burning a certain coal sample yields 455 grams of CO_2. What volume, in liters, would this occupy at STP?

Solution:

Step 1: We want to convert 455 g CO_2 to liters at STP.

Step 2: Our conversion factors are 44.0 g/mole and 22.4 l/mole.

Step 3: Our setup is:

$$455 \, g \, \cancel{CO_2} \times \frac{1 \, \cancel{mole}}{44.0 \, g \, \cancel{CO_2}} \times 22.4 \, \frac{l}{\cancel{mole}} = \underline{\quad} \, l$$

Answer: 232 liters.

We can also calculate a gas's density at STP if we know what the gas is and have an atomic weight table. We don't need any other information. This is another thing we can't do with liquids or solids.

EXAMPLE 11.2: Calculate the density of SO_2 at STP, and compare it with that of air (1.29 g/l).

Solution:

Step 1: Here, we seem to have no given quantity. However, our given quantity is built-in, because we know that the molecular weight of SO_2 is 64.1 g/mole. We want to convert 64.1 g/mole to grams/liter at STP.

Step 2: Our conversion factor is 22.4 l/mole.

Step 3: Our setup is:

$$64.1 \, \frac{g}{\cancel{mole}} \times \frac{1 \, \cancel{mole}}{22.4 \, l} = \underline{\quad} \, \frac{g}{l}$$

Answer: 2.86 g/l, more than twice the density of air. (We see why this air pollutant hangs heavily over a city instead of being dispersed.)

**FIGURE 11.2
One mole
of any gas
occupies
22.4 liters
at STP**

I counted 6.02 x 10²³ particles of each gas into each flask. There are the same number of each, but they have different masses.

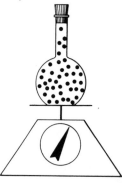

1 mole He
4.00 g
6.02 x 10²³ atoms

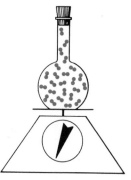

1 mole O_2
32.0 g
6.02 x 10²³ molecules

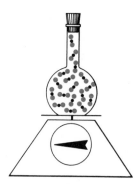

1 mole CO_2
44.0 g
6.02 x 10²³ molecules

Of course, we can also do the reverse of this and calculate the molecular weight if we know the density. We might do this to identify an unknown gas, or to decide what a given substance's molecular formula is.

In Chapter 6, we saw how to determine empirical formulas from percent compositions, and how to determine molecular formulas from a substance's molecular weight. Now we can find out one way these molecular weights are actually determined. If a liquid has a fairly low boiling point, then we can determine its molecular weight by changing it to a gas.

EXAMPLE 11.3: A liquid whose empirical formula is CH is changed to a vapor by heating. Its vapor occupies a volume of 500. cm³ at STP and weighs 1.74 grams. What is its molecular weight?

Solution:

Step 1: We want to convert 1.74 g/500. cm³ to grams/mole. Notice that we could divide this out to get density in grams/cubic centimeter, but we don't need to. The division will be performed in the operation.

Step 2: Our conversion factors are 22.4 l/mole and 10^{-3} l/cm³. We may change 1.74 g/500. cm³ directly to 1.74 g/0.500 l.

Step 3: Our set up is:

$$\frac{1.74 \text{ g}}{0.500 \text{ } l} \times \frac{22.4 \text{ } l}{\text{mole}} = \underline{\quad} \frac{\text{g}}{\text{mole}}$$

Answer: 78.0 g/mole. In example 6.17 (p. 121), we used this molecular weight to decide that the molecular formula of the substance (benzene) is C_6H_6.

In Chapter 6, we also did calculations with chemical equations that involved moles and masses. Now we'll see how to do similar calculations with gas volumes.

MOLE-TO-VOLUME AND VOLUME-TO-MOLE CONVERSIONS

EXAMPLE 11.4: Carbon monoxide can be eliminated from stack gases by burning it as it comes out of the smokestack. How many moles of oxygen will be consumed in burning 1500 liters of CO (measured at STP)? The equation is:

$$2 \text{ CO}(g) + O_2(g) \longrightarrow 2 \text{ CO}_2(g)$$

Solution:

Step 1: We want to convert 1500 l CO to moles of O_2.

Step 2: The equation is balanced.

Step 3: Our conversion factors are 22.4 l CO/mole CO (molar volume of any gas) and 1 mole O_2/2 moles CO (from the equation).

Step 4: Our setup is:

$$1500 \text{ l CO} \times \frac{1 \text{ mole CO}}{22.4 \text{ l CO}} \times \frac{2 \text{ moles O}_2}{1 \text{ mole CO}} = \underline{\quad} \text{ moles O}_2$$

Answer: 130 moles O_2.

Sometimes we can make use of chemical reactions in which solids or liquids react to produce gases. A solid or liquid takes up much less room than a gas and is easier to handle, and the released gas can do work or perform a specific function for us because of its much larger volume. Baking powder, gasoline, jet and rocket fuels, and gunpowder are examples.

EXAMPLE 11.5: Gunpowder is a mixture of powdered carbon, potassium nitrate, and sulfur. When struck, this substance reacts to form a mixture of gases. Because of their much greater volume at STP, the gases create enough pressure to propel a bullet. The equation is:

$$2 C(s) + 2 KNO_3(s) + S(s) \longrightarrow$$
$$CO(g) + CO_2(g) + SO_2(g) + N_2(g) + K_2O(s)$$

If a 0.1-cm³ sample of gunpowder contains 2×10^{-3} moles of KNO_3, and enough C and S to completely react with it, calculate the volume of all the gases produced, at STP, and compare this volume with the volume of the solid gunpowder.

Solution:

Step 1: We want to convert 2×10^{-3} moles of KNO_3 to liters of CO, CO_2, N_2, and SO_2.

Step 2: The equation is balanced.

Step 3: Since there is one mole of each of the four gases produced for every two moles of KNO_3 used, we may use 4 moles gas/2 moles KNO_3 as our conversion factor, as well as 22.4 l gas/mole gas.

Step 4: Our setup is:

$$2 \times 10^{-3} \text{ moles } KNO_3 \times \frac{4 \text{ moles gas}}{2 \text{ moles } KNO_3} \times \frac{22.4 \text{ l gas}}{1 \text{ mole gas}} = \underline{\quad} \text{ l gas}$$

Answer: 0.09 liters, or 90 cm³. Compared with the volume of 0.1 cm³ for solid gunpowder, this represents a volume increase of about 900 times.

VOLUME-TO-VOLUME CONVERSIONS.

In the reactions where both substances of interest are gases, Avogadro's Law allows us to substitute a liter ratio for a mole ratio. For gases, a liter ratio is the same as a mole ratio since equal volumes of gas contain equal numbers of molecules and therefore equal numbers of moles.

EXAMPLE 11.6: In the Haber process for fixing nitrogen, how many liters of NH_3 could be made from 2500 liters of N_2? The equation is:

$$N_2(g) + 3 H_2(g) \longrightarrow 2 NH_3(g)$$

Solution:

Step 1: We want to convert 2500 l N_2 to liters of NH_3.

Step 2: The equation is balanced.

Step 3: Our conversion factor is 2 moles NH_3/mole N_2, which we may change to a liter ratio: 2 l NH_3/l N_2.

Step 4: Our setup is:

$$2500 \text{ l } N_2 \times \frac{2 \text{ l } NH_3}{\text{l } N_2} = \underline{\quad} \text{ l } NH_3$$

Answer: 5000 l NH_3.

Notice that this reaction also causes a change in the total volume occupied by the gases at STP. Whereas the reaction starts with 4 volumes total of gas—1 volume of N_2 and 3 volumes of H_2—it ends with only 2 volumes total of gas (NH_3). The total gas volume has been cut in half. This is another interesting feature of gases. Conservation of mass still prevails, but not conservation of volume.

■ **EXAMPLE 11.7:**   The equation for photosynthesis is as follows:
$$6\,CO_2(g) + 6\,H_2O(l) \longrightarrow C_6H_{12}O_6(aq) + 6\,O_2(g)$$
If a plant were placed in a plastic bag, maintained at STP, with 5.00 liters of CO_2, how many liters of oxygen could it make? Would we notice any change in the volume of the plastic bag?

Solution:
Step 1: We want to convert 5.00 l CO_2 to liters of O_2.
Step 2: The equation is balanced.
Step 3: Although there is a substance in the equation that isn't a gas ($C_6H_{12}O_6$), the two substances we're interested in are gases. Our conversion factor is thus 6 l CO_2/6 l O_2.
Step 4: Our setup is:

$$5.00 \; \cancel{l\,CO_2} \times \frac{6 \; l\,O_2}{6 \; \cancel{l\,CO_2}} = \underline{\hspace{1cm}} l\,O_2$$

Answer: 5.00 l O_2. We wouldn't notice any change in the volume, because there isn't any. (We could have gotten the answer by inspection, too, when we saw that equal numbers of moles of O_2 and CO_2 are involved.)

MASS-TO-VOLUME AND VOLUME-TO-MASS

CONVERSIONS.   Sometimes we might want to convert from grams of a solid to liters of a gas, or vice versa.

■ **EXAMPLE 11.8:**   The burning of charcoal yields mostly carbon monoxide, according to this equation:
$$2\,C(s) + O_2(g) \longrightarrow 2\,CO(g)$$
A. How many liters of CO, measured at STP, would result from burning 1 kg of charcoal in a grill?
B. In a sealed room having a volume of 2×10^5 liters, how many parts per million is that? How does it compare with the maximum tolerance level in Table 11.3?

Solution A:
Step 1: We want to convert 1 kg of carbon to liters of CO.
Step 2: The equation is balanced.
Step 3: Our conversion factors are 12.0 g C/mole C, 1 mole CO/mole C, and 22.4 l CO/mole CO.
Step 4: Our setup is:

$$1000 \; \cancel{g\,C} \times \frac{1 \; \cancel{mole\,C}}{12.0 \; \cancel{g\,C}} \times \frac{1 \; \cancel{mole\,CO}}{\cancel{mole\,C}} \times \frac{22.4 \; l\,CO}{\cancel{mole\,C}} = \underline{\hspace{1cm}} l\,CO$$

Answer A: 2000 l CO.

Solution B: We find the percentage-by-volume and multiply by 10^4 to get parts per million.

$$\frac{2 \times 10^3\ l\ CO}{2 \times 10^5\ l\ total} \times 100 = 1\%\ by\ volume$$

$$1 \times 10^4 = \underline{\quad} ppm$$

Answer B: 10,000 ppm, far above the maximum tolerance level of 100 ppm. We see why charcoal manufacturers tell us not to burn it in the house.

EXAMPLE 11.9: A common way to prepare N_2 in the laboratory is to gently heat ammonium nitrite, according to this equation:

$$NH_4NO_2(s) \xrightarrow{\Delta} N_2(g) + 2\ H_2O(g)$$

How many grams of ammonium nitrite would have to be used to get 50.0 cm³ of nitrogen, measured at STP?

Solution:
Step 1: We want to convert 50.0 cm³ N_2 to grams of NH_4NO_2.
Step 2: The equation is balanced.
Step 3: Our conversion factors are 64.0 g NH_4NO_2/mole NH_4NO_2, 1 mole NH_4NO_2/2 moles N_2, and 22.4 l N_2/mole N_2. We can change 50.0 cm³ to 0.0500 liters.
Step 4: Our setup is:

$$0.0500\ \cancel{l\ N_2} \times \frac{1\ mole\ N_2}{22.4\ \cancel{l\ N_2}} \times \frac{1\ mole\ \cancel{NH_4NO_2}}{2\ \cancel{moles\ N_2}} \times \frac{64.0\ g\ NH_4NO_2}{\cancel{mole\ NH_4NO_2}}$$

$$= \underline{\quad} g\ NH_4NO_2$$

Answer: 0.0714 g NH_4NO_2.

11.3 THE GAS LAWS

All the problems so far have involved gases at STP. In practice, though, gases are seldom—if ever—measured at STP. How do we handle that? We use some laws that let us calculate exactly how the pressure, temperature, and volume of a gas affect one another.

THE EFFECT OF PRESSURE ON VOLUME:

Boyle's Law

BOYLE'S LAW. At constant temperature, the change in volume of a gas is inversely proportional to change in pressure, according to *Boyle's Law*, formulated in 1660 by Robert Boyle (1627–1691). This means that the pressure decreases if the volume increases, and vice versa. Figure 11.3 illustrates Boyle's Law with a sliding piston, which changes the pressure on the gas in the container. At first, 1 liter of gas is at ½ atmosphere. When the pressure is increased to 1 atmosphere, the volume drops to ½ liter. The number of gas molecules remains the same, of course, but the molecules are twice as close together. In the second case, to maintain equilibrium with the increased outside pressure, molecules exert twice as much pressure on the walls of their container. When the pressure is increased even further to 2 atmospheres, the volume is reduced again, to ¼ liter.

Mathematically, this is what Boyle's Law says:

$$V_2 = V_1 \frac{P_1}{P_2}$$

That is, if we start with a gas having initial volume V_1 and initial pressure

FIGURE 11.3

Boyle's Law: At constant temperature, change in gas volume is inversely proportional to change in pressure

Count the molecules in each of these three experiments! Each time I compress the gas, they move closer together and exert more pressure.

Now I'll put twice as much pressure on the gas, compressing it to half its original volume.

Now the pressure is four times what it was, and the volume is one fourth. But all the molecules are still there.

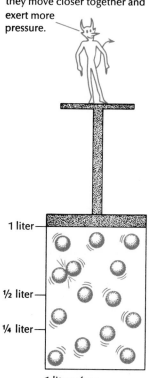

1 liter of gas
½ atmosphere

$V_1 = 1$ liter (l)

$P_1 = \frac{1}{2}$ atmosphere (atm)

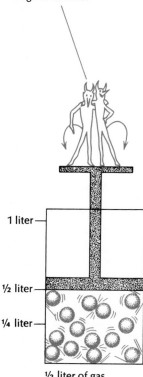

½ liter of gas
1 atmosphere

$V_2 = V_1 \dfrac{P_1}{P_2} = 1\,l \times \dfrac{\frac{1}{2}\ \text{atm}}{1\ \text{atm}}$

$V_2 = \frac{1}{2}\,l$

$P_2 = P_1 \dfrac{V_1}{V_2} = \frac{1}{2}\ \text{atm} \times \dfrac{1\,\cancel{l}}{\frac{1}{2}\,\cancel{l}}$

$P_2 = 1$ atm

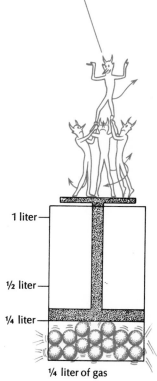

¼ liter of gas
2 atmospheres

$V_3 = V_2 \dfrac{P_2}{P_3} = \frac{1}{2}\,l \times \dfrac{1\ \text{atm}}{2\ \text{atm}}$

$V_3 = \frac{1}{4}\,l$

$P_3 = P_2 \dfrac{V_2}{V_3} = 1\ \text{atm} \times \dfrac{\frac{1}{2}\,\cancel{l}}{\frac{1}{4}\,\cancel{l}}$

$P_3 = 2$ atm

P_1 and change the pressure to P_2, we can calculate the new volume V_2. Boyle's Law can also be stated like this:

$$P_2 = P_1 \frac{V_1}{V_2}$$

That is, if we start with a gas having initial pressure P_1 and initial volume V_1, and change the volume to V_2, we can calculate the new pressure P_2. Calculations with these formulas are shown for the examples in Figure 11.3.

In working problems with these and other gas law formulas, we should always decide first what direction our answer will take. That is, for an increase in pressure, the volume will decrease; for an increase in volume, the pressure will decrease. That's what "inversely proportional" means. If we have some feeling at the beginning for what sort of an answer to expect, we'll avoid the errors that might result from a wrong calculator answer or an upside-down fraction.

EXAMPLE 11.10:   In Example 11.1, we calculated the volume of a sample of CO_2 to be 232 liters at STP. Calculate the volume of this sample if it were collected at standard temperature and 0.876 atm.

Solution: First of all, we see that the pressure is changing from 1 atm (standard pressure) to 0.876 atm: a decrease in pressure. Thus we expect an increase in volume. We're given two pressures and a starting volume ($V_1 = 232$ l). Our setup is:

$$V_2 = V_1 \frac{P_1}{P_2} = 232 \text{ l} \times \frac{1.00 \text{ atm}}{0.876 \text{ atm}} = \underline{\hspace{1cm}} \text{ l}$$

Answer: 265 l. We got the larger volume we expected.

EXAMPLE 11.11:   In Example 11.5, we calculated the volume of a mixture of gases formed by gunpowder to be 90 cm³ at STP. The bullet is propelled by the pressure these gases create when they're confined to the volume of 0.1 cm³. Calculate this pressure, assuming that the temperature remains constant.

Solution: Here, we're given two volumes and a starting pressure ($P_1 = 1$ atm; $V_1 = 90$ cm³; $V_2 = 0.1$ cm³), and we're asked to solve for pressure. Of course, we expect an increase in pressure, since that's the point of the problem, and since the volume is decreasing. Our setup:

$$P_2 = P_1 \frac{V_1}{V_2} = 1.00 \text{ atm} \times \frac{90 \text{ cm}^3}{0.1 \text{ cm}^3} = \underline{\hspace{1cm}} \text{ atm}$$

(Note that we may use cm³ as long as we use it for both volumes.)

Answer: 900 atm, a much larger pressure, as predicted.

THE EFFECT OF TEMPERATURE ON VOLUME:
CHARLES' LAW.   Jacques Charles (1746–1823) noticed that the volume of a gas, at constant pressure, increases in proportion to the Celsius temperature. To show this, blow up a balloon partway, and then put it close to a light bulb that's been on awhile. The heat from the bulb will

cause the balloon to expand visibly, even though it's still subject to the same atmospheric pressure. By the same token, refrigerating a blown-up balloon will cause it to shrink, because a cooled gas contracts (at constant pressure).

Later, Joseph Gay-Lussac (1778–1850) discovered that no matter what its volume, a gas will shrink by $\frac{1}{273}$ of its volume for every degree below zero degrees Celsius it is cooled. In fact, this discovery led Lord Kelvin (William Thomson, 1824–1907) to the development of the Kelvin temperature scale in 1848. We've already seen that zero Kelvin is the temperature at which all motion stops. It's also the temperature at which a gas theoretically would shrink to zero volume, something we know is impossible.

The result of all this is what we now call Charles' Law, even though Gay-Lussac also contributed to it. *Charles' Law* states that the change in volume of a gas at constant pressure is directly proportional to the change in the Kelvin temperature. Or, stated mathematically:

Charles' Law

$$V_2 = V_1 \frac{T_2(K)}{T_1(K)} \quad \text{and} \quad T_2(K) = T_1(K) \frac{V_2}{V_1}$$

Figure 11.4 shows the relationship between volume and temperature.

Hot-air balloons can float in air because the density of hot air is less than the density of the colder air near the earth. However, when the balloon reaches an altitude where the density of its air is equal to the density of the surrounding air, it will stop rising.

EXAMPLE 11.12: Calculate the density of air at 40.°C and standard pressure. (The density of air at STP is 1.29 g/l.) Then, from Figure 10.2 (p. 209), estimate the altitude at which a balloon filled with this 40°C air would stop rising.

Solution: The density of air tells us that 1.29 grams occupy 1.00 liter at STP. To calculate the density at the new temperature ([40. + 273]K = 313 K), we first find the volume that 1.29 grams would occupy at the same pressure and 313 K. Since we're increasing the temperature, we expect a volume greater than 1.00 liter. Thus we're given a starting volume ($V_1 = 1.00$ l) and two temperatures ($T_1 = 273$ K, standard temperature; and $T_2 = 313$ K). Our setup is:

$$V_2 = V_1 \frac{T_2(K)}{T_1(K)} = 1.00 \text{ l} \times \frac{313 \text{ K}}{273 \text{ K}} = 1.15 \text{ l} \text{ (larger, as expected)}$$

Now we can calculate the density:

$$\text{density} = \frac{\text{weight}}{\text{volume}} = \frac{1.29 \text{ g}}{1.15 \text{ l}} = \underline{\quad} \frac{\text{g}}{\text{l}}$$

Answer: 1.12 g/l, less than the density of colder air, as we expected. Figure 10.2 shows the altitude to be about 2 km.

THE EFFECT OF TEMPERATURE ON PRESSURE: GAY-LUSSAC'S LAW.
On a hot day, pressure will build up inside tires as a car is driven. This is an illustration of *Gay-Lussac's Law*, which

Gay-Lussac's Law

states that the pressure of a gas, at constant volume, changes in direct proportion to the change in Kelvin temperature. Or, stated mathematically:

$$P_2 = P_1 \frac{T_2}{T_1} \quad \text{and} \quad T_2 = T_1 \frac{P_2}{P_1}$$

FIGURE 11.4

Charles' Law: At constant pressure, change in gas volume is directly proportional to change in Kelvin temperature

I've just cooled this gas to 100 K, and it occupies ¼ liter. I'll let it warm up. I'm staying on here to provide constant pressure.

Oops! As the gas warms up, the molecules move faster, and the gas expands. Now we're at 200 K.

Here at 400 K, the volume is 4 times what it was at 100 K.

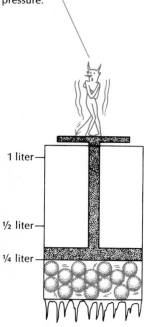

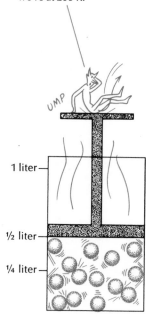

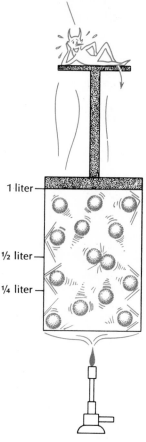

$T_1 = 100\ K$

$V_1 = ¼ \text{ liter (l)}$

$T_2 = 200\ K$

$V_2 = V_1 \dfrac{T_2}{T_1} = ¼ \text{ l} \times \dfrac{200\ K}{100\ K}$

$V_2 = ½ \text{ liter}$

$T = 400\ K$

$V_3 = V_2 \dfrac{T_3}{T_2} = ½ \text{ l} \times \dfrac{400\ K}{200\ K}$

$V_3 = 1 \text{ liter}$

Figure 11.5 illustrates the relationship between temperature and pressure of a gas.

> **EXAMPLE 11.13:** In Example 11.11, we calculated the pressure of a mixture of gases from gunpowder to be 900 atm at standard temperature. Actually,

FIGURE 11.5
Gay-Lussac's Law: At constant volume, change in gas pressure is directly proportional to change in Kelvin temperature

I've cooled another gas to 100 K. This one occupies 1 liter at 1 atmosphere pressure.

Now at 200 K, I have to exert twice as much pressure to keep the gas at this constant volume of 1 liter.

At 400 K, the molecules are moving fast and exerting 4 times as much pressure as they were at 100 K.

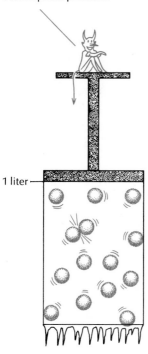

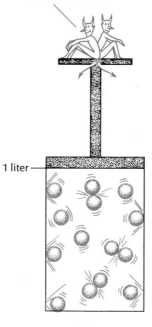

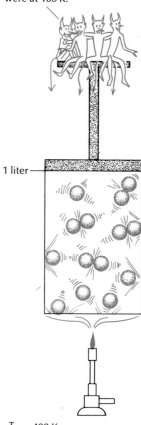

1 liter

1 liter

1 liter

$T_1 = 100$ K

$P_1 = 1$ atm

$T_2 = 200$ K

$P_2 = P_1 \dfrac{T_2}{T_1} = 1 \text{ atm} \times \dfrac{200 \text{ K}}{100 \text{ K}}$

$P_2 = 2$ atm

$T_3 = 400$ K

$P_3 = P_2 \dfrac{T_3}{T_2} = 2 \text{ atm} \times \dfrac{400 \text{ K}}{200 \text{ K}}$

$P_3 = 4$ atm

the temperature rises considerably above standard temperature. Calculate what this pressure would be at a temperature of 1500 K.

Solution: We expect the pressure to be greater at a higher temperature. Here, $P_1 = 900$ atm, $T_1 = 273$ K, and $T_2 = 1500$ K. Our setup is:

$$P_2 = 900 \text{ atm} \times \frac{1500 \cancel{K}}{273 \cancel{K}} = \underline{\hspace{1cm}} \text{ atm}$$

Answer: 5000 atm, greater as we expected.

Gay-Lussac's Law explains why we shouldn't throw aerosol cans into the fire. The can keeps the volume constant, but the increased temperature increases the pressure of the confined gas in the can to the point that the can explodes.

THE COMBINED GAS LAWS.

combined gas laws

We usually measure gases at both temperatures and pressures that aren't STP. In the laboratory, we often generate gases under laboratory conditions of temperature and pressure and then must convert them to STP. To do this, we use the *combined gas laws,* which take into account changes of pressure, temperature, and volume all at once. Since we'll usually want to know how volume changes with temperature and pressure, we'll use the combined gas laws in this form:

$$V_2 = V_1 \left(\frac{T_2}{T_1}\right)\left(\frac{P_1}{P_2}\right)$$

This equation, a combination of all the previous gas laws, says that the new volume of gas (V_2) is going to be the old volume (V_1) times two fractions. One of the fractions represents the temperature change, and one represents the pressure change. We won't always be able to predict the direction of the change when we're using this equation, but we can predict the effect of each fraction on the volume.

EXAMPLE 11.14: In Example 11.9, we calculated that it would take 0.0714 g of NH_4NO_2 to generate 50.0 cm³ of N_2 at STP. What volume would be generated under the laboratory conditions of 23°C and 0.943 atm?

Solution: We're changing our initial volume ($V_1 = 50.0$ cm³) from standard temperature ($T_1 = 273$ K) to a laboratory temperature ($T_2 = [23 + 273]$K $= 296$ K). This is an increase of temperature, so we expect this fraction to cause an increase in volume, and the larger number goes on top: 296 K/273 K. The pressure change is from standard pressure ($P_1 = 1$ atm) to a laboratory pressure ($P_2 = 0.943$ atm). This is a decrease in pressure, and we know that this too will increase the volume: our pressure fraction is 1 atm/0.943 atm. Both fractions increase the volume, so we expect V_2 to be larger than V_1. Our setup is:

$$V_2 = 50.0 \text{ cm}^3 \times \frac{296 \cancel{K}}{273 \cancel{K}} \times \frac{1 \cancel{\text{atm}}}{0.943 \cancel{\text{atm}}} = \underline{\hspace{1cm}} \text{ cm}^3$$

Answer: 57.5 cm³. Larger, as we expected.

EXAMPLE 11.15: The Haber process (see Example 11.6) isn't really performed at STP. If 1500 liters of NH_3 are produced at 30 atm and 450°C, what volume would this be at STP?

Solution: Our initial volume (V_1) is 1500 liters. We're changing temperature from initial ($T_1 = [450 + 273]K = 723$ K) to standard ($T_2 = 273$). Since we're cooling the gas, this fraction will decrease its volume. The pressure change goes from $P_1 = 30$ atm to $P_2 = 1$ atm (standard pressure). A decrease in pressure means an increase in volume. Here, one fraction decreases the volume and one increases it. We can't tell which will win, but we can use our reasoning to make sure the temperature fraction is less than 1, and the pressure fraction is greater than 1. Our setup is:

$$V_2 = 1500 \text{ l} \times \frac{273 \text{ K}}{723 \text{ K}} \times \frac{30 \text{ atm}}{1 \text{ atm}} = \underline{\qquad} \text{ l}$$

Answer: 1.7×10^4 liters. (The pressure fraction wins.)

THE PRESSURE OF A MIXTURE OF GASES:

DALTON'S LAW. Air is a mixture of gases. Sometimes, a gas we collect in the laboratory is a mixture of gases. If two or more gases are mixed in a container, each one will exert its own pressure, without regard for the others. This fact is stated in *Dalton's Law,* named after John Dalton (1766–1844): In a mixture of gases at contant temperature and volume, the total pressure is the sum of the partial pressures. The *partial pressure* means the pressure the gas would exert if it were by itself.

Dalton's Law

partial pressure

Most often, laboratory mixtures contain water vapor as one of the gases. We know that liquids have vapor pressure. Therefore, a gas in a container above water will always have some water vapor in it. When we generate gases in the laboratory and collect them for study, we usually find it convenient to collect them by letting them displace water in a container, such as a bottle or a test tube. When we do this, we always end up with a mixture of the generated gas and water vapor. The pressure of the mixture is the sum of the pressure of the gas and the vapor pressure of water at that temperature. We can write this as an equation.

$$P_{total} = P_{gas} + P_{water\ vapor}$$

The total pressure is the barometric pressure. The vapor pressure of water is usually provided by a table, such as Table 11.5. To find the pressure of a gas we've collected by displacement of water, we read the barometer, take the temperature of the water, and look in Table 11.5 for the vapor pressure of water at that temperature. Then, we use this equation:

$$P_{gas} = P_{total} - P_{water\ vapor}$$

Figure 11.6 illustrates a gas being collected by displacement of water.

EXAMPLE 11.16: In Example 11.14, we calculated that a nitrogen sample would occupy 57.5 cm³ at 23°C and 0.943 atm. If this sample were collected by displacement of water, calculate (A) the pressure of the nitrogen, and (B) the corrected volume occupied by the nitrogen.

Solution A: We use the equation $P_{gas} = P_{total} - P_{water\ vapor}$.
$P_{total} = 0.943$ atm (the barometric pressure). $P_{water\ vapor} = 0.0277$ atm (at 23°C, from Table 11.5). Then:

$$P_{gas} = 0.943\ atm - 0.0277\ atm = \_\_\_\_\ atm$$

Answer A: 0.915 atm.

Solution B: The volume of the nitrogen sample was 57.5 cm³ at 0.915 atm. We want to find the volume at the same temperature but at 0.943 atm. This is an increase in pressure, so we expect the volume to decrease.

$$V_2 = V_1 \frac{P_1}{P_2} = 57.5\ cm^3 \times \frac{0.915\ atm}{0.943\ atm} = \_\_\_\_\ cm^3$$

Answer B: 55.8 cm³. Smaller, as predicted.

TABLE 11.5
Vapor pressure of water

Temperature (°C)	Pressure torr	Pressure atm	Temperature (°C)	Pressure torr	Pressure atm
−15.0	1.44	0.00189	16.0	13.6	0.0179
−14.0	1.56	0.00205	17.0	14.5	0.0191
−13.0	1.69	0.00222	18.0	15.5	0.0204
−12.0	1.83	0.00241	19.0	16.5	0.0217
−11.0	1.99	0.00261	20.0	17.5	0.0231
−10.0	2.15	0.00283	21.0	18.7	0.0245
−9.00	2.36	0.00306	22.0	19.8	0.0261
−8.00	2.51	0.00331	23.0	21.1	0.0277
−7.00	2.72	0.00357	24.0	22.4	0.0294
−6.00	2.93	0.00386	25.0	23.8	0.0313
−5.00	3.16	0.00416	26.0	25.2	0.0332
−4.00	3.41	0.00449	27.0	26.7	0.0352
−3.00	3.67	0.00483	28.0	28.3	0.0373
−2.00	3.96	0.00520	29.0	30.0	0.0395
−1.00	4.26	0.00596	30.0	31.8	0.0419
0.000	4.58	0.00602	35.0	40.2	0.0555
1.00	4.93	0.00648	40.0	55.3	0.0728
2.00	5.29	0.00697	45.0	71.9	0.0946
3.00	5.68	0.00748	50.0	92.5	0.122
4.00	6.10	0.00803	55.0	118.0	0.155
5.00	6.54	0.00861	60.0	149.4	0.197
6.00	7.01	0.00923	65.0	187.5	0.247
7.00	7.51	0.00988	70.0	233.7	0.307
8.00	8.04	0.0106	75.0	289.1	0.380
9.00	8.61	0.0113	80.0	355.1	0.467
10.0	9.21	0.0121	85.0	433.6	0.570
11.0	9.84	0.0130	90.0	525.8	0.692
12.0	10.5	0.0138	95.0	633.9	0.834
13.0	11.2	0.0148	100.	760.0	1.00
14.0	12.0	0.0158	105.	906.1	1.19
15.0	12.8	0.0168	110.	1075	1.41

FIGURE 11.6
A gas
collected
by displacement
of water
always contains
water vapor

253

0.984 atm
pushing down
here

We chemists do this a lot. I'm generating and collecting hydrogen gas. It displaces water in this test tube, which is inverted into this trough of water. The pressure inside the system is 0.984 atm, because it's open to the atmosphere and the atmospheric pressure in my lab today is 0.984 atm.

$$Zn(s) + 2HCl(aq) \longrightarrow H_2(g) + ZnCl_2(aq)$$

metal +
hydrochloric
acid

Now I have a mixture of hydrogen and water vapor at a pressure of 0.984 atm. The vapor pressure of water at $20°C$ is 0.0231 atm. Therefore, the pressure of my hydrogen sample is 0.984 atm − 0.0231 atm = 0.961 atm.

11.4 THE IDEAL GAS EQUATION

The quantities that we've used to calculate with gases can all be tied together into one equation: the ideal gas equation. It contains volume, moles, temperature, and pressure. It's based on the Kinetic-Molecular Theory.

THE KINETIC-MOLECULAR THEORY. To explain the properties of gases, and to develop the ideal gas equation, the *Kinetic-Molecular Theory* makes these assumptions about gases.

Kinetic-
Molecular
Theory

1. *Gases are composed of particles that are very far apart. The particles themselves occupy negligible volume.* This explains gases' ability to expand and contract, and their low density.
2. *Gas molecules are always moving rapidly, and they move more rapidly as the temperature increases. They collide with each other and with the walls of the container.* This explains gases' ability to mix with each

other. It also explains that the pressure exerted by a confined gas is caused by the particles hitting the walls of the container. The pressure increases with temperature because the particles hit the walls more often.

3. *The particles of a gas have no attraction for each other. When they do collide with each other, they bounce right off.*

ideal gas

An *ideal gas* is one that obeys these three assumptions. The energy of an ideal gas at a certain temperature is given by:

$$\text{energy} = nRT$$

Here, n is the number of moles of the gas, R is a conversion factor called the gas constant, and T is the Kelvin temperature. We can see two things right off. First, at 0 K ($T = 0$), there is zero energy, which we already know is true. Also, if there are no moles ($n = 0$), there is no gas, and there can be no energy.

pressure

We can redefine *pressure* as energy per unit of volume, instead of force per unit of area. Pressure is thus a measure of how hard a gas is trying to get out of its container, or how hard an outside pressure is trying to keep the gas in its container. Stated mathematically:

$$P = \frac{\text{energy}}{V}$$

If we substitute nRT for energy, then we have this equation:

$$P = \frac{nRT}{V}$$

ideal gas equation

This gives us the usual form of the *ideal gas equation.*

$$PV = nRT$$

gas constant (R)

In this equation, P is in atmospheres, V is in liters, n is in moles, and T is in Kelvins. To make the units come out right, we use the *gas constant* (R) as a conversion factor. R has the value of:

$$0.0821 \frac{(l \times atm)}{(mole \times K)}$$

which we read, "liter-atmospheres per mole-Kelvin."

WORKING PROBLEMS WITH THE IDEAL GAS EQUATION.

The ideal gas equation is most convenient for solving problems with only one set of conditions. Most commonly, we'll want to solve either for volume or for moles. To solve for volume:

$$V = \frac{nRT}{P}$$

To solve for moles, we must convert the equation to:

$$n = \frac{PV}{RT}$$

EXAMPLE 11.17: In Example 11.4, we calculated that 130 moles of O_2 were needed to burn a certain amount of CO. What volume will this 130 moles of O_2 occupy at 450 K and 2.0 atm?

Solution: We want to solve for volume. We substitute all given quantities into the equation:

$$V = \frac{nRT}{P}$$

$$= \frac{(130 \text{ moles}) \left[0.0821 \frac{(1 \times \text{atm})}{(\text{mole} \times K)} \right] (450 \, K)}{2.0 \text{ atm}} = \underline{\quad} \, l$$

Answer: 2500 liters.

EXAMPLE 11.18: A chemical process has generated 525 liters of NO_2. We want to convert the NO_2 to $Ca(NO_3)_2(s)$, a fertilizer, according to this equation:

$$4 \, NO_2(g) + Ca(OH)_2(s) \longrightarrow Ca(NO_3)_2(s) + 2 \, HNO_2(l)$$

A. If the NO_2 is at 4.2 atm and 350 K, how many moles are there?
B. How many grams of $Ca(OH)_2$ will it take to convert the NO_2?

Solution A: We want to solve for moles. We substitute into this equation:

$$n = \frac{PV}{RT} = \frac{(4.2 \text{ atm}) (525 \, l)}{\left[0.0821 \frac{(l \times \text{atm})}{(\text{mole} \times K)} \right] (350 \, K)} = \underline{\quad} \text{ moles}$$

Note that:

$$\frac{1}{\left(\dfrac{1}{\text{mole}} \right)} = \text{mole}$$

Inverting reciprocals like this is discussed in Appendix B, p. 485.

Answer A: 77 moles.

Solution B: We want to convert moles of NO_2 to grams of $Ca(OH)_2$. The equation is balanced, and our conversion factors are 1 mole $Ca(OH)_2$/4 moles NO_2 and 74.1 g $Ca(OH)_2$/mole $Ca(OH)_2$. Our setup is:

$$77 \text{ moles } NO_2 \times \frac{1 \text{ mole } Ca(OH)_2}{4 \text{ moles } NO_2} \times \frac{74.1 \text{ g } Ca(OH)_2}{\text{mole } Ca(OH)_2} = \underline{\quad} \text{ g } Ca(OH)_2$$

Answer B: 1400 g $Ca(OH)_2$, or 1.4 kg $Ca(OH)_2$

NON-IDEAL BEHAVIOR.
No gas behaves ideally. The noble gases come the closest to ideal behavior, because there is the least attraction between their particles. In general, gases will behave less ideally if we put them under high pressure or at low temperature. When their particles are

close enough together, they will attract each other, and assumption 3 of the Kinetic-Molecular Theory will no longer be true. Water molecules, when they're in the gas state, don't bounce off one another as they're supposed to. Instead, they attract each other, because of hydrogen bonding and dipole-dipole attraction. Molecules with these kinds of attractions usually don't obey the ideal gas equation. We need a table of water vapor pressure at each temperature (Table 11.5), because we have to measure it instead of calculate it.

REVIEW QUESTIONS

Some Chemistry of Air

1. What is *photosynthesis?* How does it explain why our atmosphere contains oxygen?
2. What is *nitrogen fixation?* List some natural and artificial ways of fixing nitrogen.
3. What is a *catalyst?* Why is a catalyst sometimes needed in nitrogen fixation?
4. What part of the sunlight gives us sunburn? How does our ozone layer protect us from this part of sunlight?
5. Explain the *greenhouse effect*. What parts of sunlight are involved, and how?
6. Review the important reactions of gases in air.
7. What are some of the major air pollutants? Where do they come from and why are they hazardous?
8. What are the main ingredients of *photochemical smog?*
9. Why is it dangerous to have ozone in our lower atmosphere?
10. How does nature get rid of some air pollutants? Can we depend on this?
11. Why is it difficult to minimize CO and NO at the same time?
12. What are some of the problems connected with SO_2 removal?

Measuring Gases at STP

13. State *Avogadro's Law*. What is the *molar volume* of a gas? How are these two concepts related?
14. Why do molar volumes of different gases have different masses?
15. How can we use molar volume as a conversion factor to calculate a gas's density at STP?

16. How can we use gas density to determine the molecular weight of a liquid?
17. What are some examples of chemical reactions that produce gases?

The Gas Laws

18. State *Boyle's Law*, and explain it in your own words. What formulas do we use in calculations with Boyle's Law?
19. What law relates temperature and volume of a gas? State the law, and explain how it is related to the Kelvin temperature scale.
20. What is *Gay-Lussac's Law?* How does it explain the behavior of tires on a hot day?
21. How can we predict the direction of an answer when doing gas law calculations?
22. Write the equation for calculating the volume of a gas using the *combined gas laws,* and explain what each fraction means.
23. What is *Dalton's Law?* Why might we need to use it in the laboratory?
24. Explain how we correct the pressure of a gas for the presence of water vapor.

The Ideal Gas Equation

25. State the assumptions of the Kinetic-Molecular Theory. How do these explain all of the previous gas laws?
26. What is an *ideal gas?* What is the energy of an ideal gas?
27. What is the *gas constant?* What are its units?
28. Write the *ideal gas equation* in three forms. How do we tell which one to use in calculations?
29. Do all gases behave ideally? When do they deviate the most from ideal behavior?

EXERCISES

1. An average automobile, without pollution control devices, produces about 5 grams of NO for each mile it is driven. How many liters (measured at STP) would be produced by such an automobile on a 100-mile trip?

2. Carbon monoxide is the air pollutant emitted in the largest quantity in the United States. In 1968, it amounted to 100 million metric tons. How many liters (STP) is this?

3. In 1974, about 2×10^{10} liters (STP) of ammonia were produced. How many metric tons is this?

4. Compute and compare the densities of NO and NO_2 at STP.

5. An unknown air pollutant is analyzed and found to have a density of 1.25 g/l at STP.
   a. Calculate its molecular weight.
   b. Which air pollutant (from Table 11.3) is it likely to be?

6. A sample of an unknown liquid weighing 0.469 grams when converted to its vapor, is found to occupy a volume of 125 cm³ at STP.
   a. Calculate its molecular weight.
   b. If the substance's empirical formula is CH_2, what is its molecular formula?

7. In the natural fixation of nitrogen by lightning (see Table 11.2), how many moles of NO would be produced from 500 liters of nitrogen (measured at STP)?

8. In the process of photosynthesis (Table 11.2), how many liters of O_2 (STP) would be obtained for every 2.5 moles of glucose produced?

9. How many liters (STP) of methane, CH_4, will it take to remove 200,000 liters (STP) of NO emitted from an electric power plant? The equation (from Table 11.4) is:
$$CH_4 + 4\,NO \longrightarrow 2\,N_2 + CO_2 + 2\,H_2O$$

10. How many liters (STP) of nitrogen will be produced by the reaction in Exercise 9?

11. Natural gas contains mostly CH_4, with some sulfur in the form of H_2S. The H_2S can be removed by controlled oxidation, according to this equation:
$$6\,H_2S(g) + 3\,O_2(g) \longrightarrow 6\,S(s) + 6\,H_2O(g)$$
How many grams of sulfur will be obtained by treating 250 liters (at STP) of H_2S in this manner?

12. A power plant that burns 10,000 tons of coal containing 2.5 percent sulfur will emit about 1.8×10^5 liters (STP) of SO_2 each day. If this were all absorbed with calcium carbonate in the limestone-dolomite process (see Table 11.4), how many metric tons of $CaSO_4$ would be produced daily?

13. The Solvay process for making sodium bicarbonate uses this reaction:
$$H_2O(l) + NH_3(g) + CO_2(g) + NaCl(aq) \longrightarrow$$
$$NH_4Cl(aq) + NaHCO_3(aq)$$
How many liters of NH_3 and of CO_2 (both at STP) are needed to make 1.00 kg of sodium bicarbonate, $NaHCO_3$?

14. Each person breathes about 20,000 liters of air (at STP) daily. How many liters would a person have to breathe at 0.72 atmospheres to get the same amount of air? (Assume no change in temperature.)

15. Using the Haber process, 525 liters of NH_3 are produced at 40 atmospheres. What volume would this occupy at standard pressure and the same temperature?

16. A compressor can reduce a gas from 1000 liters at 1 atmosphere to 0.5 liters. What pressure can such a compressor provide?

17. Gas turbines burn liquid fuel to provide high temperatures, producing gases, which then drive the turbine. These gases have a temperature of about 650°C. What volume would 1 liter of such gas have at standard temperature and the same pressure?

18. In a steam turbine, the energy in steam under pressure is used to make mechanical energy, which in turn generates electric power. The steam at about 100 atmospheres is allowed to flow through a nozzle and reach 1 atmosphere, and the resulting expansion turns the turbine. Calculate the volume that 15 liters of high-pressure steam would occupy after such expansion.

19. Compare the density of air on a hot day in Needles, California (43°C), with the density of air on a cold day in Bozeman, Montana (−29°C). Assume a pressure of 1 atmosphere. The density of air at STP is 1.29 g/l.

20. Calculate the pressure inside a spent aerosol can if it is accidentally incinerated at 350°C. Assume that the gas inside the can was originally at 1 atmosphere (why?) and room temperature (25°C).

21. On a cool morning (23°C), you fill your tires with air to a pressure of 2.5 atmospheres. The temperature of the tire later reaches 66°C. Calculate the new pressure inside the tire.

22. In an explosive like blasting gelatin, a solid reacts to form gases. When confined, the gases build up tremendous pressure and explode. If gases are produced at an initial pressure of 713 atm (at 25°C) and finally reach a pressure of 13,000 atm because of the temperature change involved in the reactions, calculate the final temperature.

23. A sample of oxygen gas is collected in the laboratory. It has a volume of 89.2 cm³ at a temperature of 22°C and a pressure of 0.978 atm. Calculate its volume at STP.

24. A chemical equation predicts that 5.40 liters of CO_2 will be obtained at STP. What volume would actually be obtained if the gas were collected under the laboratory conditions of 25°C and 0.902 atmospheres?

25. What is the total pressure of a mixture of 0.234 atm H_2, 0.438 atm N_2, and 0.199 atm He?

26. Using displacement of water, 44.0 cm³ of nitrogen gas is collected at 24.0°C and 0.957 atm.
    a. What is the pressure of the nitrogen?
    b. Calculate the volume of the nitrogen at STP.

27. A chemical reaction predicts 97.2 cm³ of hydrogen gas at STP. What volume would be obtained, if the hydrogen were collected by displacement of water at 22.0°C and 0.954 atm?

28. Baking powders are mostly made of sodium bicarbonate and calcium hydrogen phosphate. When baking powder is wet, this reaction produces carbon dioxide:

    $$NaHCO_3(aq) + CaHPO_4(aq) \longrightarrow$$
    $$NaCaPO_4(aq) + CO_2(g) + H_2O(l)$$

    a. If a teaspoon of baking powder contains 2.00 grams of sodium bicarbonate, how many cubic centimeters of carbon dioxide (at STP) will be obtained from this reaction?
    b. If this were done at a high altitude, where the atmospheric pressure was 0.860 atmospheres, how many cubic centimeters would be obtained?

29. The manufacture of acetylene gas, C_2H_2, involves letting calcium carbide react with water according to this reaction:

    $$CaC_2(s) + 2 H_2O(l) \longrightarrow Ca(OH)_2(aq) + C_2H_2(g)$$

    a. How many liters of C_2H_2 (at STP) would be obtained from 550 kg of CaC_2?

b. How many liters would be obtained at 300°C and 2.00 atm?

30. A person can breathe 0.05 ppm of NO a day without harm. At this level, what volume of NO (at STP) would a person breathe in a daily total of 20,000 l of air?

31. One way to detect very small amounts of ozone is with this reaction:

    $$Hg(l) + O_3(g) \longrightarrow HgO(s) + O_2(g)$$

    The HgO forms a dirty-looking scum on top of the shiny mercury. If 0.012 moles of HgO are obtained, what volume of O_3 at 24°C and 0.989 atm was present?

32. One way to remove SO_2 from the air is to let it react with CO:

    $$SO_2(g) + 2 CO(g) \longrightarrow S(s) + 2 CO_2(g)$$

    Using this formula, compute how many moles of sulfur would be produced if 6×10^5 liters of SO_2 were removed from the air at 0.976 atmospheres and 200°C.

33. SO_2 from ore smelters can be used to make sulfuric acid, according to this equation:

    $$2 SO_2(g) + O_2(g) + 2 H_2O(l) \longrightarrow 2 H_2SO_4(aq)$$

    Using the SO_2 from Exercise 32, (a) how many moles, and (b) how many kilograms of H_2SO_4 could be produced?

34. A supersonic transport plane (SST) releases about 3 metric tons of NO into the atmosphere for every hour it flies. It flies at an altitude of about 20 kilometers; at this altitude the pressure is about 0.13 atmospheres and the temperature is about −56°C.
    a. What volume would 3 metric tons of NO occupy under those conditions?
    b. What volume of O_3 would the NO be capable of destroying, under the same conditions? Here is the equation:

    $$NO + O_3 \longrightarrow NO_2 + O_2$$

12

Solutions

Many familiar substances are solutions. The liquid part of blood is a solution of various salts, gases, and biological molecules in water. Gasoline, vodka, tincture of iodine, and ocean water are also solutions. Even the water we drink is a solution.

We usually think of solutions as being liquids, but they don't have to be. For instance, air is a gaseous solution, and brass is a solid solution. However, most solutions of interest to us here are liquids. Liquid solutions are very useful in chemistry because many chemical reactions take place easily in liquid solutions, which are easy to measure and convenient to handle.

12.1 DESCRIBING SOLUTIONS

solution

homogeneous

solvent

solute

A *solution* is a homogeneous mixture of two or more substances. *Homogenous* means alike throughout. No matter where we take a sample from a solution, or how large the sample is, it will have the same composition and properties as any other sample taken from the same solution. In a solution, the substance present in the largest amount is called the *solvent*. The substances dissolved in the solvent are called *solutes*. Table 12.1 lists some solutions with their solutes and solvents.

**TABLE 12.1
Some common
solutions**

Name	Description	Solute	Solvent
Air	Various gases dissolved in N_2	Gas	Gas
Soda water	CO_2 dissolved in water	Gas	Liquid
Vodka	Alcohol dissolved in water	Liquid	Liquid
Antifreeze	Ethylene glycol dissolved in water	Liquid	Liquid
Dental fillings	Mercury dissolved in silver	Liquid	Solid
Blood plasma	CO_2, O_2, salts, and biological molecules dissolved in water	Gases, solids	Liquid
Tincture of iodine	Iodine dissolved in alcohol	Solid	Liquid
Household ammonia	NH_3 dissolved in water	Gas	Liquid
Gasoline	Various carbon-containing liquids dissolved in each other	Liquids	Liquid
Seawater	Various salts dissolved in water	Solids	Liquid
Syrup	Sugar dissolved in water	Solid	Liquid
Brass	Zinc dissolved in copper	Solid	Solid
Solder	Tin dissolved in lead	Solid	Solid
Vinegar	Acetic acid dissolved in water	Liquid	Liquid

THE CONCENTRATION OF SOLUTIONS.

The amount of solute that is present in a given amount of solution or of solvent is called the *concentration*. We can express concentration in any number of ways, depending on what we want to use the solution for. Right now, we'll introduce the concentration term *grams per liter,* which means the number of grams of solute in one liter of solution. We can express the concentration of any kind of solute this way, even if we don't know what the solute is.

concentration

gram per liter

EXAMPLE 12.1: 100.-cm³ samples of water are taken from the Pacific Ocean and from the Great Salt Lake, and the water is allowed to evaporate from them. The salts that remain (mostly NaCl) are 3.85 grams from the Pacific Ocean and 31.9 grams from the Great Salt Lake. Calculate the original concentration of each in grams per liter.

Solutions: It doesn't matter that we don't know the exact composition of these salt residues. We know how many grams are in 100. cm³, or 0.100 l, so we can easily find the number of grams per liter.

$$\frac{3.85 \text{ g}}{0.100 \text{ l}} = \underline{\quad} \frac{\text{g}}{\text{l}}$$

$$\frac{31.9 \text{ g}}{0.100 \text{ l}} = \underline{\quad} \frac{\text{g}}{\text{l}}$$

Answer: 38.5 g/l for the Pacific Ocean; 319 g/l for the Great Salt Lake. (The Great Salt Lake has a salt concentration nearly ten times that of the Pacific Ocean.)

SOLUBILITY.

If we keep adding salt to a solution of salt in water, we eventually reach a point where no more salt will dissolve, because the water has dissolved all the salt it can. When this happens, we have a *saturated solution.* It means the maximum amount of solute that is *soluble* (will dissolve) to form a given amount of solution at a certain temperature. We define *solubility* as the concentration of a saturated solution. If the concentration of any solution is less than that of a saturated solution, then the solution is *unsaturated.* Solubilities of some common substances are shown in Table 12.2.

saturated solution

soluble

solubility

unsaturated

A diamond is insoluble in water, which means that it doesn't dissolve in water. There is no doubt about diamond, but most things we call "insoluble" in water do dissolve to a small extent. By *insoluble,* then, we usually mean "not very soluble." AgCl is "insoluble" in water. If we stir some around in water, we don't notice any dissolving. Actually, though, some does dissolve: the solubility of AgCl in water is 0.00143 grams/liter at 25°C. This is slight compared with the solubility of NaCl. Sometimes we say that a substance is *sparingly soluble* instead of "insoluble" when it dissolves to a small extent.

insoluble

sparingly soluble

EXAMPLE 12.2: The solubility of oxygen in water is about 4.5×10^{-2} grams/liter. The water portion of an adult's total blood supply is about 5 liters. How many grams of oxygen could dissolve in 5 liters of water?

Solution: We want to convert 5 liters of solution to grams of O_2. Our conversion factor is the solubility. Our setup is:

$$5\,\cancel{l} \times 4.5 \times 10^{-2}\,\frac{g\ O_2}{\cancel{l}} = \underline{\quad}\ g\ O_2$$

Answer: 2×10^{-1} g O_2. Actually, whole blood contains about 7×10^{-1} O_2/l. Because of the low solubility of oxygen in water, most of the oxygen has to be carried by the hemoglobin in the red blood cells. Otherwise, blood couldn't carry enough oxygen from our lungs to our tissues.

12.2 WATER AS A SOLVENT

Water is the single most important chemical on earth. Some organisms can live without oxygen, but none can live without water. All organisms use water to carry salts, sugars, and various biological molecules from one place to another. Human blood is 92 percent water.

But some substances are relatively insoluble in water. We've already

TABLE 12.2 Solubilities of some common substances in water at 20°C

Substance	Solubility (g/l)	Comments
O_2	4.5×10^{-2}	Sparingly soluble.
CO_2	0.145	Soluble enough to be carried mostly by water portion of blood.
N_2	2.4×10^{-2}	Sparingly soluble.
HCl	719	Soluble. Water solutions are hydrochloric acid.
NH_3	320	Soluble. Solutions are aqueous ammonia, or household ammonia.
Cl_2	6.3	Rather soluble. Solutions are chlorine bleaches.
He	2×10^{-3}	Sparingly soluble.
Gasoline	0.4	Sparingly soluble.
Ethyl alcohol	Infinitely soluble	Mixes with water in all proportions.
Ethylene glycol (antifreeze)	Infinitely soluble	Mixes with water in all proportions.
NaCl	35.8	Soluble.
AgCl	1.43×10^{-3}	Sparingly soluble.
Diamond	0	Insoluble.
$CaCO_3$	1.4×10^{-2}	Sparingly soluble.
CuS	3.3×10^{-6}	Rather insoluble.
HgS	1×10^{-6}	Rather insoluble.
NH_4NO_3	118	Soluble.

seen that O_2 is sparingly soluble and must be carried in the blood by hemoglobin. Table 12.2 shows that the gases N_2 and He are also only sparingly soluble. We've seen a solid—diamond—that won't dissolve in water at all, and another solid—AgCl—that is sparingly soluble. Some liquids are insoluble or sparingly soluble in water—oil and grease, for instance, and gasoline. When liquids won't mix with each other, we say they are *immiscible*. (Liquids that *do* mix with each other are *miscible*. Table 12.2 shows that water and ethyl alcohol are miscible.)

immiscible

miscible

Why does water dissolve some things better than others? Why does it dissolve CO_2 better than O_2, and HCl better still? Why does it dissolve ethyl alcohol and not gasoline? Why does it dissolve NaCl much better than AgCl?

For a solute to dissolve in a solvent, the particles in both the pure solute and the pure solvent must separate from each other and mix together. The attractions among particles in the pure state must be replaced by attractions as strong as or stronger than those between solute and solvent particles. If the attractions between solute and solvent particles aren't as strong (or stronger), then the solute won't dissolve well in the solvent. Let's look at some of the ways solutions are formed from different kinds of solutes.

IONIC SOLUTES.

Dissolving an ionic solute is similar to melting it. We have to overcome the crystal's lattice energy to separate the ions. When water (a polar solvent) dissolves an ionic crystal, the polar ends of the water molecules cluster around the ions and pull them off. The interaction of the polar molecules with opposite-charged ions is called *ion-dipole attraction*. It releases energy called *hydration energy* when the solvent is water, and *solvation energy* when the solvent is something else.

ion-dipole attraction

hydration energy

solvation energy

If the hydration (or solvation) energy is enough to pay for the energy needed to break apart the crystal (lattice energy), then the crystal will dissolve. If it isn't enough, the crystal won't dissolve. Figure 12.1 shows the behavior of NaCl and of AgCl in water. The hydration energy of NaCl is 186 kcal/mole—a little more than enough to pay for NaCl's 184-kcal/mole lattice energy—so NaCl does dissolve in water. However, AgCl has too high a lattice energy (216 kcal/mole) to be paid for by the hydration energy, so AgCl doesn't dissolve much in water. In general, ionic compounds with lower lattice energies are more soluble in water than ones with higher lattice energies. If we look back at Figure 7.8 (p. 141), we might predict that the alkali metal halides (the singly charged ions in the figure) would be more soluble than compounds of the Group IIA metals and the Group VIA nonmetals (the doubly charged ions), and this is true.

But why do so-called insoluble ionic compounds like AgCl dissolve at all? For the answer, we should recall from Chapter 10 that some of a substance's molecules always have enough energy to escape to the vapor state, no matter what the temperature, because of the Maxwell-Boltzmann distribution. In the same way, a few ions in a crystal always have more energy than others. The additional hydration energy is enough to dissolve these few ions.

Oceans and lakes without outlets (such as the Great Salt Lake) contain a lot of dissolved salts. The moving water of rivers and streams constantly dissolves parts of the rocks and earth it runs through. These dissolved particles collect in their final destinations—oceans or lakes. We express concentrations in natural water as parts per million (ppm) by weight. This is similar to parts per million by volume, which we used for gases in the last chapter. One part per million by weight means one weight measure of the

FIGURE 12.1
The smaller lattice energy of NaCl makes it more soluble than AgCl

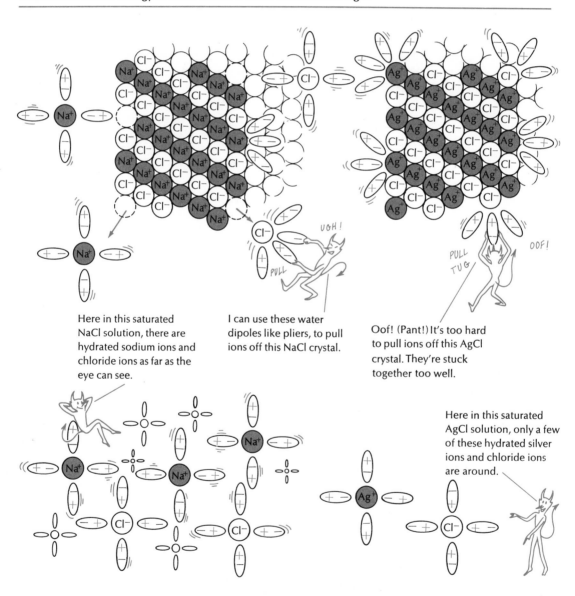

Here in this saturated NaCl solution, there are hydrated sodium ions and chloride ions as far as the eye can see.

I can use these water dipoles like pliers, to pull ions off this NaCl crystal.

Oof! (Pant!) It's too hard to pull ions off this AgCl crystal. They're stuck together too well.

Here in this saturated AgCl solution, only a few of these hydrated silver ions and chloride ions are around.

TABLE 12.3 Main ingredients in seawater[a]

Positive Ions	Ppm (by weight)	Negative Ions	Ppm (by weight)	Gases	Ppm (by weight)
Na^+	10,760	Cl^-	19,353	N_2	10
Mg^{2+}	1,294	SO_4^{2-}	2,712	O_2	7
Ca^{2+}	413	HCO_3^-	142	CO_2	600
K^+	387	Br^-	67		
Sr^{2+}	8	F^-	1.4		
Ba^{2+}	0.05	I^-	0.06		

Elements	Ppm (by weight)	Elements	Ppm (by weight)	Elements	Ppm (by weight)
B	5	Rb	0.12	Fe	0.01
Si	3	P	0.072	Al	0.01
N	0.52	In	0.02	Mo	0.01
Li	0.17	Zn	0.01		

[a]About twenty-nine other elements are present in traces.

solute contained in one million weight measures of total solution. We can get parts per million from weight percent by multiplying the weight percent by 10^4. Table 12.3 shows some of the main ionic solutes in seawater. Na^+ and Cl^- predominate.

Fresh water also contains many ions as impurities. In fact, most of these ions give spring water its flavor. Spring water usually contains calcium, magnesium, and iron(III) ions, as well as sulfate, hydrogen carbonate, and carbonate ions. Water without any ions at all is flat and tasteless. If spring water, or well water, contains quite a bit of Ca^{2+} and Mg^{2+}, it's called "hard water," because it's hard to wash things in it. These ions react with soap and form a precipitate, which is "soap scum." When hard water is boiled away, the CO_3^{2-} that it also contains reacts with the Mg^{2+} and Ca^{2+}. This reaction leaves a residue of $CaCO_3$ and $MgCO_3$, sometimes called "boiler scale." Synthetic detergents work better in hard water than soaps do, because synthetic detergents don't form precipitates with these ions. However, even synthetic detergents don't work as well in hard water as in soft water. The detergent molecules react with Ca^{2+} and Mg^{2+}, and then can't work as detergents any more.

One way of dealing with these ions in hard water is to add a substance to the detergent that will react with the metal ions and get them out of the way. "Phosphate" detergents contain sodium tripolyphosphate (STPP), $Na_5P_3O_{10}$. The tripolyphosphate ion has this Lewis structure:

These ions can surround a metal ion and bond to it, so that the metal ion stays in solution and doesn't react with anything else. Substances that can tie up metal ions in this way are called "complexing agents," or "sequestering agents."

Another way of handling Ca^{2+} and Mg^{2+} in household water is to use a water softener. Most water softeners contain ion-exchange resins, in the form of small brown beads resembling sand. The beads contain sodium ions attached to large resin molecules. When water containing Ca^{2+}, Mg^{2+}, or other positive ions is poured through the water softener, which contains a column of this resin, the sodium ions trade places with the metal ions in the water.

$$2 \, Na(Res) + Ca^{2+} \longrightarrow Ca(Res)_2 + 2 \, Na^+$$

Now the water contains sodium ions, which don't interfere with detergent action. However, people who must limit their sodium intake should not continuously drink water softened by this method.

POLAR HYDROGEN-BONDED SOLUTES.
Dissolving a polar hydrogen-bonded solute presents the same problem as dissolving an ionic solute, but the interactions between solute particles aren't as strong. Also, ionic solutes are only solids, but polar hydrogen-bonded solutes can be solids, liquids, or gases. In Table 12.1, alcohol, ethylene glycol (antifreeze), and ammonia are examples. When these solutes dissolve, their own hydrogen bonds and dipole-dipole attractions are simply replaced by similar attractions with water molecules. Figure 12.2 shows some solutes forming hydrogen bonds with water.

Carbon dioxide is a nonpolar molecule, but it does contain polar bonds. The difference in electronegativity between carbon and oxygen makes the oxygen slightly negative, so that water can hydrogen-bond to it.

$$|\overline{O}{=}\overline{C}{=}\overline{O}| \cdots H{-}\overline{O}{-}H$$

Since CO_2 has no hydrogens, water provides all the hydrogens. This, plus lack of dipole-dipole interactions, makes CO_2 less soluble in water than NH_3 or HCl, both of which do have hydrogens that can hydrogen-bond to water. But the fact that water can hydrogen-bond to it, even one-way, makes CO_2 more soluble than O_2.

All acids dissolve in water because of hydrogen bonding. Except for HCl, HF, HBr, and HI, all acids have O—H groups.

NONPOLAR SOLUTES.
"Oil and water don't mix." This old saying is true. A chemist would put it this way: "Nonpolar solutes don't dissolve well in polar solvents." Some examples of nonpolar solutes, besides oil, are gasoline, oxygen, iodine, wax, and turpentine.

Water doesn't dissolve nonpolar solutes well, because the attractions among water molecules are greater than the van der Waals attractions that the nonpolar solute has to offer. The nonpolar molecules are just squeezed out. Oil is less dense than water, so it floats on water. This lets us clean up oil spills on oceans, with difficulty, by scooping the oil off the top. When a nonpolar liquid is more dense than water, as CCl_4 is, then the water floats on top. In either case, the liquids are immiscible, and two layers are formed.

A little bit of nonpolar solute will dissolve in water, for the same reasons "insoluble" ionic compounds will. We do find O_2 in natural fresh water to the extent of 10 ppm, although it dissolves much better in gasoline

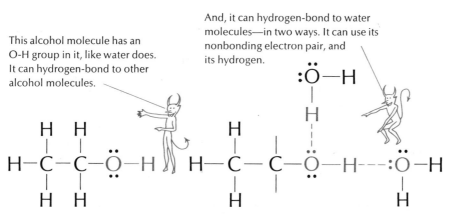

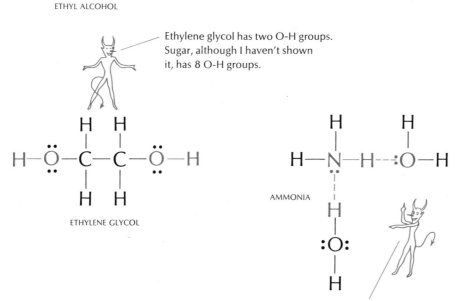

**FIGURE 12.2
Hydrogen bonds
among solute
molecules are
replaced by
hydrogen bonds
between solute
and water**

This alcohol molecule has an O-H group in it, like water does. It can hydrogen-bond to other alcohol molecules.

And, it can hydrogen-bond to water molecules—in two ways. It can use its nonbonding electron pair, and its hydrogen.

ETHYL ALCOHOL

Ethylene glycol has two O-H groups. Sugar, although I haven't shown it, has 8 O-H groups.

ETHYLENE GLYCOL

AMMONIA

Ammonia doesn't have an O-H group, but it does have an N-H group. It can also hydrogen-bond in two ways.

(800 ppm). Water dissolves in gasoline just enough to plug up a car's gas line when it freezes on a cold morning. In general, though, we have to use nonpolar solvents to dissolve large quantities of nonpolar solutes. Turpentine or paint thinner dissolves oil-based paints. Cleaning fluids dissolve grease on clothes. But we can get water to dissolve grease by adding soap or detergent. We'll see how that works next.

12.3 EMULSIONS AND COLLOIDS

colloid

GENERAL PROPERTIES.

Many familiar substances are emulsions or colloids, as shown in Table 12.4. The more general term is *colloid*, a system in which the particles of one substance are dispersed throughout another substance without bonding to solvent molecules. The dispersed particles are usually between 1 nanometer and 100 nanometers in size—too large to be in solution, but too small and light to settle out. Colloids scatter light: that is, a beam of light can be seen going through a colloid because the dispersed particles reflect the light. For the same reasons, sunlight can be seen passing through air that contains dust particles, and car headlights can be seen shining through fog.

emulsion

emulsifying agent

An *emulsion* is a special kind of colloid, where two immiscible liquids are held in suspension by another substance, called an *emulsifying* agent.

FORMING EMULSIONS AND COLLOIDS.

Emulsions or colloids can form by themselves, or we can form them on purpose. We form an emulsion when we use a detergent to help water dissolve grease. A *detergent* is an emulsifying agent that lets oil mix with water.

detergent

A detergent molecule is long and has two ends. One end is ionic and

TABLE 12.4 Some familiar colloidal systems

Substance	Type of Colloid
Shaving foam	Gas dispersed in liquid
Styrofoam	Gas dispersed in solid
Smoke, dust	Solid dispersed in gas
Muddy water	Solid dispersed in liquid
Gelatin	Liquid dispersed in solid
Fog, mist, clouds	Liquid dispersed in gas
Milk	Liquid (butterfat) dispersed in liquid (water) —emulsion
Mayonnaise, butter, cold cream	Liquid dispersed in liquid—emulsion
Latex paint	Solid dispersed in liquid

hydrophilic (water-loving); the other is nonpolar and *hydrophobic* (water-hating). The nonpolar end sticks into a globule of grease to avoid the water. The polar end sticks into the water, which suspends the grease particles in the water so they can be washed away. Figure 12.3 shows how a soap (detergent) works. The suspended grease particles are negatively charged, since the negative ends of the soap molecules stick out into the water. Typically, colloidal particles are electrically charged. They can be

FIGURE 12.3
Detergents can
emulsify grease
with their
hydrophilic and
hydrophobic
ends

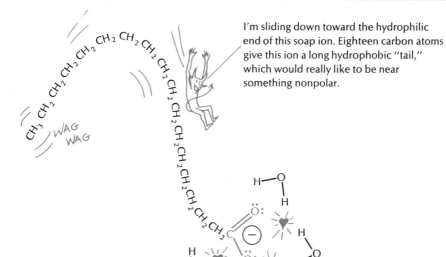
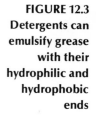

I'm sliding down toward the hydrophilic end of this soap ion. Eighteen carbon atoms give this ion a long hydrophobic "tail," which would really like to be near something nonpolar.

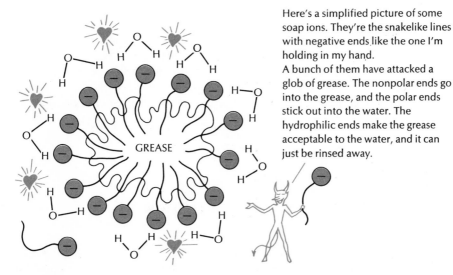

Here's a simplified picture of some soap ions. They're the snakelike lines with negative ends like the one I'm holding in my hand.

A bunch of them have attacked a glob of grease. The nonpolar ends go into the grease, and the polar ends stick out into the water. The hydrophilic ends make the grease acceptable to the water, and it can just be rinsed away.

positively or negatively charged, but they're all the same within a given colloid. The like charges on these particles keep them from coming together and forming bigger particles, which could then settle out and destroy the colloid.

DESTROYING EMULSIONS AND COLLOIDS.   In general, any means that will overcome the repulsion of the charged colloidal particles for each other, and cause them to form larger particles, will break up a colloid. Sometimes a colloid can be destroyed by heat, which gives the particles enough energy to overcome the repulsion and collide with each other. Salt will also destroy a colloid, because the positive and negative ions mask the colloidal particles' electrical repulsion. We see a destroyed colloid in the large sand or silt bars at the mouths of rivers. These are created when suspended dirt particles in a river hit the salt in ocean water.

Rain clouds build up tremendous amounts of electrical charge because of the accumulation of charges on the individual water droplets suspended in air. A rain cloud gets rid of this electrical charge by discharging to the ground or to another cloud. This is lightning. The water droplets can come together when the clouds get rid of this charge. Then it rains.

A colloid can also be destroyed by giving the particles a large surface area to stick onto. A cloudy soup (cloudy because colloidal protein particles are suspended in water) can often be cleared up ("clarified") by adding egg white, boiling, and straining. As the egg white coagulates in the hot water, the colloidal particles stick to it and can be removed with it. In water purification, sediments suspended in water are often removed by forming a precipitate with a large surface area and letting the particles adhere to it. One such reaction is this one:

$$2\,Al_2(SO_4)_3(aq) + 6\,Ca(OH)_2(aq) \longrightarrow 4\,Al(OH)_3(s) + 6\,CaSO_4(s)$$

The aluminum sulfate and calcium hydroxide are added to the cloudy water. The aluminum hydroxide precipitate forms, and the colloidal dirt particles stick to it. Both the aluminum hydroxide and the dirt particles can then be removed. The $CaSO_4$ precipitate helps with this too, but $Al(OH)_3$ is very fluffy and provides a lot of surface for the particles to stick to.

12.4 CONDITIONS AFFECTING SOLUTIONS

The amount of a solute that will dissolve in a given solvent depends on various conditions. These conditions, in turn, depend on the physical state of the solute.

SOLUTIONS OF GASES IN LIQUIDS.

Gases become less soluble in liquids as the temperature increases. An open bottle of soda water will lose its carbonation more rapidly as it warms up. Oxygen is less soluble in warm water than in cold water. The thermal pollution caused by industrial use of water for cooling can decrease the amount of dissolved oxygen in natural water and damage aquatic life.

Pressure is also important to the solubility of gases. A gas is more soluble in a liquid at high pressure than at low pressure. When we uncap a bottle of a carbonated beverage, we release the pressure and the carbon dioxide comes out of solution. Rivers and lakes at high altitudes have less dissolved oxygen in them than those at low altitudes.

Deep-sea divers sometimes experience a painful and dangerous condition called the "bends." Breathing air under the high pressures deep in the ocean causes the nitrogen in the air to be much more soluble in blood than it is at atmospheric pressure. As the divers come up to the surface and the pressure decreases, the nitrogen comes out of solution quickly, with damage to blood vessels. This can be overcome by giving the divers a mixture of helium and oxygen to breathe. Helium isn't very soluble in blood at any pressure.

SOLUTIONS OF SOLIDS IN LIQUIDS.

Pressure doesn't affect the solubility of a solid in any noticeable way. Temperature often does, though. Heating may cause a solid to be more soluble in a liquid. Stirring and decreasing the particle size of a solid will usually help it to dissolve as well.

We can sometimes prepare a *supersaturated solution*—one that contains more solute than a saturated solution at the same temperature. If a solute is more soluble at a higher temperature, we can prepare a saturated solution at a higher temperature and let the solution cool undisturbed. If no solute precipitates out as the solution cools, then we have a supersaturated solution. Such solutions are usually very unstable. They will release their excess solute if we add a small crystal of solute, or if a piece of dust falls into the solution, or if we scratch the sides of the container with a glass rod. All these things provide a surface for the solute to crystallize on.

**supersaturated
solution**

DISSOLVED OXYGEN IN NATURAL WATER.

Oxygen dissolves in rivers and streams when the water's constant tumbling over rocks brings it in contact with air. Once the water feeds into a lake or ocean, though, it can obtain oxygen only at the surface. Thus it's difficult to replenish dissolved oxygen in lakes or oceans if the amount is decreased in any way.

Natural fresh water at sea level contains only 10 ppm of oxygen. Seawater contains even less (7 ppm), because oxygen is less soluble in salt water.

These small quantities of dissolved oxygen are easily removed by water pollutants in various ways.

All living organisms need phosphate. The small amount of phosphate in water usually limits the amount of algae that can grow. But as our sewers carry phosphate detergents to water bodies, large amounts of algae form. As the algae grow and die, they use oxygen. They also clog the water surface, which prevents more oxygen from replenishing what's used up. Eventually, fish and plants die because of lack of oxygen. This process— **eutrophication** called *eutrophication* (overnourishment)—can occur naturally over many years. It would have taken nature 15,000 years to accomplish the eutrophication of Lake Erie. Humans managed to do it in 50 years. Clearly, it's important to keep excess phosphates out of our natural waters.

Although oxygen-forming water plants can help replenish the oxygen in water, excess sediment will shut out the sunlight these plants need for photosynthesis. Excessive amounts of organic matter in natural water also decrease the oxygen supply, because decaying animal matter and plant matter use oxygen.

12.5 THE BEHAVIOR OF SOLUTIONS

Solutions behave differently from the pure solvents they contain in a number of interesting ways.

VAPOR PRESSURE. The vapor pressure of a solution is always lower than the vapor pressure of the pure solvent at the same temperature. To escape into the vapor state, solvent molecules have to be at the surface of the liquid. If a solute is dissolved in the liquid, some solute particles take up space at the surface. Fewer solvent particles can escape, and the rate of escape is slower. The solvent vapor, though, deposits particles into the liquid at the same rate it would if no solute were there. Thus when equilibrium is reached, fewer molecules are in the vapor than would be there if the solvent were pure, as Figure 12.4 shows.

BOILING POINT. Since the vapor pressure of a solvent is lowered by the addition of solute, we have to raise the temperature so that the vapor pressure will equal the atmospheric pressure. This results in an elevation of the boiling point. A solvent's boiling point will be raised a certain amount by the addition of a given amount of solute. For water, the boiling point will be raised 0.512°C for every mole of solute that's dissolved in 1000. grams of water. Salt water takes longer to boil than pure water, because the salt raises the boiling point of water.

When a solution containing a solid solute like salt evaporates, only the pure solvent enters the vapor; the solid solute is left behind. This explains why the oceans are salty and keep getting saltier. In the "water cycle" of

FIGURE 12.4
A solute lowers
the vapor
pressure of
a solvent

273

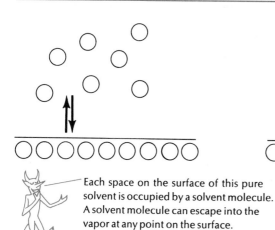

Each space on the surface of this pure solvent is occupied by a solvent molecule. A solvent molecule can escape into the vapor at any point on the surface.

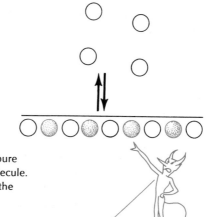

These solute particles take up room at the surface of this solution. The solvent molecules have less surface area to escape from. The vapor molecules still deposit in the solution, though. They don't care what's on the surface. The result is that fewer solvent molecules end up in the vapor.

natural waters, rain falls on land and finds its way to rivers and streams. They dissolve parts of rocks and ground as they move toward the oceans. Water evaporates from the oceans, leaving behind the dissolved salts. The water vapor becomes rain, and the cycle starts over. More salts are washed into the ocean as the water is recycled, but the total amount of water stays the same. This natural "water cycle" is an example of *distillation,* a process by which a liquid is converted to vapor and then the vapor is condensed to a liquid.

distillation

We can use distillation to obtain pure water or any pure liquid. We boil water that contains a solute that doesn't evaporate itself, let the steam condense on something cold, and collect the condensed water (called "distilled water"). The impurities will be left behind. Figure 12.5 shows a setup for chemical distillation.

When a mixture of liquids is distilled, the liquid with the lower boiling point will usually boil off first. Distillation is used to make alcoholic beverages stronger, because alcohol has a lower boiling point than water.

FREEZING POINT.
Adding a solute to a solvent lowers the solvent's freezing point, because it lowers its vapor pressure. When a solution freezes, the pure solid solvent freezes out at first. At the freezing point, then, we

have pure solid solvent, solution, and solvent vapor—all at equilibrium. As we saw before, the vapor pressures of the liquid and the solid have to be the same at the freezing point. Since the vapor pressure of the solvent in the solution is now lower, the temperature at which the pure solid solvent has this same vapor pressure will also have to be lower. This is the new freezing point, lower than the freezing point of the pure solvent.

Adding antifreeze to the water in a car radiator lowers the freezing point of water by lowering its vapor pressure. One mole of any solute added to 1 kilogram of water will lower the freezing point of water by 1.84°C. Any solute can act as an antifreeze as long as it's soluble enough. Ethylene glycol is used because it's very soluble, doesn't damage the cooling system, doesn't boil off when the radiator gets hot, and is itself a fairly good coolant.

molality

In experiments that involve changes in temperature and changes of state, the concentration term is not grams per liter. We use *molality* (*m*), which is moles of solute per kilogram of solvent. We use moles instead of grams because the lowering of the freezing point depends on moles and not grams. We use 1 kilogram of solvent instead of 1 liter of solution because mass doesn't change with temperature, whereas volume does. If we prepared a molar solution at 25°C and used it at 0°C, we'd introduce some error into our experiment.

**FIGURE 12.5
A simple
distillation
experiment**

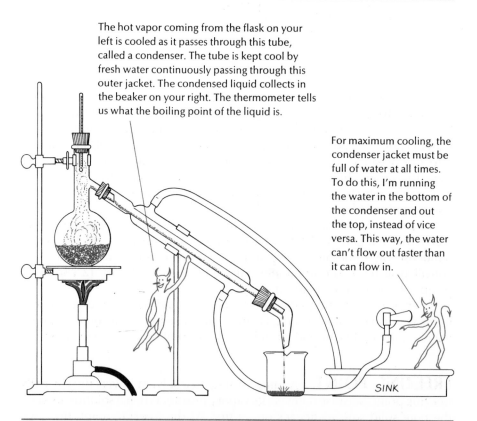

The hot vapor coming from the flask on your left is cooled as it passes through this tube, called a condenser. The tube is kept cool by fresh water continuously passing through this outer jacket. The condensed liquid collects in the beaker on your right. The thermometer tells us what the boiling point of the liquid is.

For maximum cooling, the condenser jacket must be full of water at all times. To do this, I'm running the water in the bottom of the condenser and out the top, instead of vice versa. This way, the water can't flow out faster than it can flow in.

SINK

EXAMPLE 12.3: Calculate the molality of a radiator solution that is prepared by dissolving 3.5 kg of ethylene glycol (molecular weight 62.0 g/mole) in 6.5 kg of water.

Solution: We want to convert 3.5 kg of ethylene glycol per 6.5 kg of water to moles of ethylene glycol per kilogram of water. Our conversion factor is 62.0 g/mole, the formula weight of ethylene glycol. We may convert 3.5 kg directly to 3500 g.

$$\frac{3500 \text{ g solute}}{6.5 \text{ kg solvent}} \times \frac{1 \text{ mole solute}}{62.0 \text{ g solute}} = \underline{\quad} m$$

Answer: 8.7 *m* (8.7 moles solute/kg solvent).

To calculate what the freezing point of a water solution will be, we use this formula:

$$T_f = 0.00°C - \left(1.84\frac{°C}{m}\right)m$$

Here, T_f is the freezing point of the solution (the *Temperature* at which ice freezes from the solution); 0.00°C is the freezing point of pure water; 1.84°C/m (degrees Celsius per molal) is the *freezing-point constant* of water; and *m* is the molality of the solution.

freezing-point constant

EXAMPLE 12.4: Calculate the freezing point of the antifreeze solution in Example 12.3.

Solution: The molality of the solution is 8.7 *m*. Thus:

$$T_f = 0.00°C - \left(1.84\frac{°C}{m}\right)(8.7\,m)$$

$$= 0.00°C - 16.0°C$$

Answer: −16°C. (The radiator would be protected from freezing down to this temperature.)

We use the lowered freezing point of solutions to make ice cream and to melt the ice on streets and sidewalks. We've seen that any solute will lower water's freezing point. Salt is especially useful for this because it's plentiful and dissolves well in water. To make ice cream, we pack the outer jacket of the ice cream freezer with a mixture of ice and salt. The ice will melt somewhat, and the temperature will go down. The ice cream in the middle container freezes when the temperature is low enough (about −10°C). The same thing happens when we throw rock salt on a frozen sidewalk: the ice melts, and the temperature goes down. The salt on the ice makes a solution. The ice−now trying to be at equilibrium with a solution of lower freezing point−melts. As it melts, it takes its heat of fusion from its surroundings, lowering the temperature.

Selective freezing, like distillation, can be used to separate some mixtures. Figure 12.6 shows that when a mixture of liquids is cooled, the liquid having the highest freezing point will freeze out of the solution first, leaving the other one behind.

**FIGURE 12.6
Separating
a mixture
by selective
freezing**

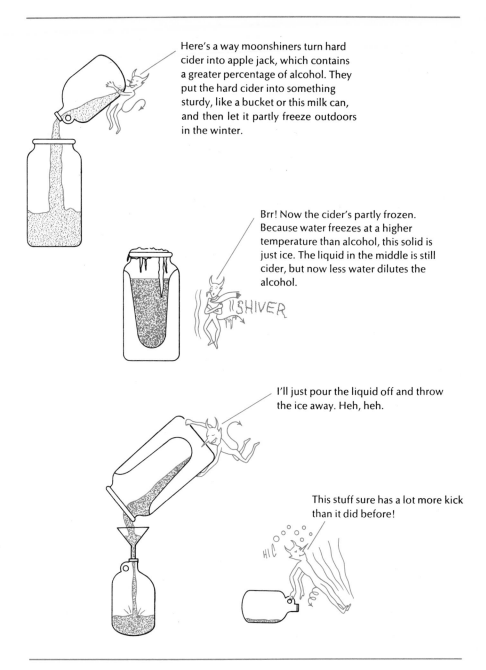

Here's a way moonshiners turn hard cider into apple jack, which contains a greater percentage of alcohol. They put the hard cider into something sturdy, like a bucket or this milk can, and then let it partly freeze outdoors in the winter.

Brr! Now the cider's partly frozen. Because water freezes at a higher temperature than alcohol, this solid is just ice. The liquid in the middle is still cider, but now less water dilutes the alcohol.

SHIVER

I'll just pour the liquid off and throw the ice away. Heh, heh.

This stuff sure has a lot more kick than it did before!

HIC

OSMOTIC PRESSURE. When placed in water, a dried prune will swell and become plump. A cucumber placed in brine will wrinkle and become smaller. Our skin becomes wrinkled after a time in soapy water. Salt and sugar solutions can be used to preserve food. All these things happen because of a solution behavior called osmosis. *Osmosis* means the flow of pure solvent through a semipermeable membrane from a dilute solution to a more concentrated solution. A *semipermeable membrane* lets solvent but not solute particles pass through its pores. In any living organism, the solvent is always water, and the water has many solutes dissolved in it. Skin and cell membranes are semipermeable. When a prune is placed in water, the water goes through the membrane (the skin) from the more dilute solution (pure water) to the more concentrated solution (the juice inside the prune). A brine solution has more solute in it than the juice inside a cucumber, so the water will pass from the inside of the cucumber into the brine solution, and the cucumber will shrink. Sugar and salt solutions can be used as preservatives because bacteria that cause spoilage lose water by osmosis through their cell walls, and die.

Osmosis causes a pressure to be exerted, as we can tell when the prune's skin is pushed outward. *Osmotic pressure* is what would have to be applied to prevent osmosis from happening, as shown in Figure 12.7. If we apply more than osmotic pressure to a solution, the solvent molecules will go in the opposite direction. This is called *reverse osmosis*. It's used to remove salt from water and to help industries recycle their waste products. An industrial waste solution might contain small concentrations of a usable substance, formerly too small to bother trying to recover. Reverse osmosis lets the industries concentrate their waste solutions and recover the materials instead of throwing them away. This cuts down on water pollution and also saves money.

Organisms are very sensitive to changes in the osmotic pressure of their environment or their bodily fluids. For this reason, many saltwater fish can't survive in fresh water, and vice versa. When a hospital patient receives a solution intravenously, the solution must have the same osmotic pressure as blood plasma. This is because red blood cells will expand or even burst in solutions more dilute than their internal solutions, and they will shrink in more concentrated solutions. In either case, the red blood cell won't function properly.

12.6 REACTIONS THAT FORM PRECIPITATES

We've already seen that an unwanted substance, such as a phosphate ion, can be removed from water by precipitating it as part of an insoluble compound. Wanted substances can be removed from solution by precipitation, too. Table 12.3 showed that the ocean contains many ions, which makes it a potential source of chemicals. Magnesium, for example, can be recovered from seawater by precipitating Mg^{2+} as insoluble $Mg(OH)_2$. But how do we know what substances are insoluble and what to add to get them to precipitate?

**FIGURE 12.7
Osmosis occurs
when solvent
molecules pass
through a
semipermeable
membrane into
a more
concentrated
solution**

(Blub!) This beaker is separated by a semipermeable mebrane. I can hear those solute particles trying to get over here on the pure water side, but the holes in the membrane are too small. This pure water will pass through the membrane into the more concentrated solution.

When this system has reached equilibrium, there is a difference in height between the two sides. Osmotic pressure is created by the weight of the higher column. The osmotic pressure is proportional to this difference in height.

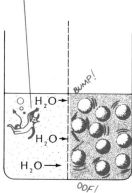

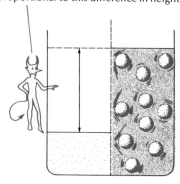

We can make water diffuse back through the membrane until the system is just the way it was at first. To do so, we apply the osmotic pressure.

This is a way to remove salt from water. Applying pressure to the saltwater side forces water molecules to pass back to the less concentrated side.

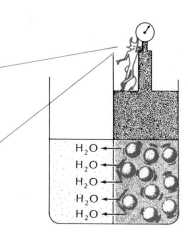

WRITING IONIC EQUATIONS.

Table 12.5 shows which ionic compounds are soluble and which are insoluble. (Of course, we've already said that few substances are entirely "insoluble." Here, though, we draw the line at a solubility of roughly 0.5 g/l.)

In Figure 12.1, we saw what happens when a soluble ionic compound dissolves. We can write an equation for this.

$$NaCl(s) \longrightarrow Na^+ + Cl^-$$

**net ionic
equation**

This equation shows ions going into solution. An equation that shows ions going into or out of solution is a *net ionic equation*. We don't write "(aq)" after the ions, because we understand that they're in aqueous solution. We can write the net ionic equation for any soluble ionic compound in the same way. Such compounds can be sources of ions in solution, which might be needed for other reactions, as we'll soon see.

EXAMPLE 12.5: Write a net ionic equation for what happens when $Al_2(SO_4)_3$ is added to water.

Solution: From Table 12.5, we see that $Al_2(SO_4)_3$ is classified as soluble.

Answer: $Al_2(SO_4)_3(s) \longrightarrow 2\,Al^{3+} + 3\,SO_4^{2-}$

For insoluble substances, we don't write an equation that shows ions going into solution.

EXAMPLE 12.6: Write a net ionic equation for what happens when $PbSO_4$ is added to water.

Solution: From Table 12.5, we see that $PbSO_4$ is classified as insoluble.

Answer: $PbSO_4(s) \longrightarrow PbSO_4(s)$. (This is not very interesting.)

A more interesting and useful net ionic equation shows the formation of an insoluble compound from its ions. We can write this kind of equation for any substance that is insoluble according to Table 12.5. Some examples:

$$Hg_2^{2+} + 2\,Cl^- \longrightarrow Hg_2Cl_2(s)$$
$$3\,Ca^{2+} + 2\,PO_4^{3-} \longrightarrow Ca_3(PO_4)_2(s)$$
$$Ag^+ + I^- \longrightarrow AgI(s)$$

But where do we get the ions to form these insoluble compounds? Obviously not from their parent compounds, because they don't dissolve. We get these ions from other compounds that do dissolve. To form Hg_2Cl_2, we need a source of Hg_2^{2+} and a source of Cl^-. The source of Hg_2^{2+} can be any soluble compound of mercury(I) ion; a convenient compound is $Hg_2(NO_3)_2$. There are many soluble chlorides we could choose from, including KCl. If we started with solid $Hg_2(NO_3)_2$ and solid KCl and put them into water, here's what would happen.

$$Hg_2(NO_3)_2(s) + 2\,KCl(s) \longrightarrow Hg_2^{2+} + 2\,NO_3^- + 2\,K^+ + 2\,Cl^- \longrightarrow$$
$$Hg_2Cl_2(s) + 2\,K^+ + 2\,NO_3^-$$

The potassium and nitrate ions, which we needed originally to provide the soluble sources of mercury(I) ions and chloride ions, don't react. For this reason, they're called *spectator ions*. The above reaction could be used to get rid of mercury in mercury-polluted water, if the mercury were in the form of Hg_2^{2+}.

spectator ions

In practice, we don't start with soluble ionic compounds in the solid form. Instead, we use solutions where the compounds already exist as separate ions. For the reaction above, we'd use a solution of $Hg_2(NO_3)_2$ ($Hg_2^+ + 2\,NO_3^-$) and a solution of KCl ($K^+ + Cl^-$). Then, our ionic equation becomes:

$$Hg_2^{2+} + 2\,NO_3^- + 2\,K^+ + 2\,Cl^- \longrightarrow Hg_2Cl_2(s) + 2\,K^+\,2\,NO_3^-$$

TABLE 12.5 Solubilities of some common ionic compounds

	F^-	Cl^-	Br^-	I^-	S^{2-}	OH^-
Ag^+	$Ag^+ + F^-$	AgCl (white)	AgBr (yellow)	AgI (yellow)	Ag_2S (black)	–
Pb^{2+}	PbF_2 (white)	$PbCl_2$ (white)	$PbBr_2$ (white)	PbI_2 (yellow)	PbS (black)	$Pb(OH)_2$ (white)
Hg_2^{2+}	–	Hg_2Cl_2 (white)	Hg_2Br_2 (yellow)	Hg_2I_2 (yellow)	Hg_2S (black)	–
Hg^{2+}	–	$Hg^{2+} + 2 Cl^-$	$Hg^{2+} + 2 Br^-$	HgI_2 (red)	HgS (black)	–
Mg^{2+}	MgF_2 (white)	$Mg^{2+} + 2 Cl^-$	$Mg^{2+} + 2 Br^-$	$Mg^{2+} + 2 I^-$	–	$Mg(OH)_2$ (white)
Cu^{2+}	CuF_2 (white)	$Cu^{2+} + 2 Cl^-$	$Cu^{2+} + 2 Br^-$	$Cu^{2+} + 2 I^-$	CuS (black)	$Cu(OH)_2$ (blue)
Zn^{2+}	ZnF_2 (white)	$Zn^{2+} + 2 Cl^-$	$Zn^{2+} + 2 Br^-$	$Zn^{2+} + 2 I^-$	ZnS (white)	$Zn(OH)_2$ (white)
Fe^{2+}	FeF_2 (white)	$Fe^{2+} + 2 Cl^-$	$Fe^{2+} + 2 Br^-$	$Fe^{2+} + 2 I^-$	FeS (black)	$Fe(OH)_2$ (green)
Ca^{2+}	CaF_2 (white)	$Ca^{2+} + 2 Cl^-$	$Ca^{2+} + 2 Br^-$	$Ca^{2+} + 2 I^-$	–	$Ca^{2+} + 2 OH^-$
Ba^{2+}	BaF_2 (white)	$Ba^{2+} + 2 Cl^-$	$Ba^{2+} + 2 Br^-$	$Ba^{2+} + 2 I^-$	–	$Ba^{2+} + 2 OH^-$
Sr^{2+}	SrF_2 (white)	$Sr^{2+} + 2 Cl^-$	$Sr^{2+} + 2 Br^-$	$Sr^{2+} + 2 I^-$	–	$Sr^{2+} + 2 OH^-$
Co^{2+}	$Co^{2+} + 2 F^-$	$Co^{2+} + 2 Cl^-$	$Co^{2+} + 2 Br^-$	$Co^{2+} + 2 I^-$	CoS (black)	$Co(OH)_2$ (pink)
Ni^{2+}	$Ni^{2+} + 2F^-$	$Ni^{2+} + 2 Cl^-$	$Ni^{2+} + 2 Br^-$	$Ni^{2+} + 2 I^-$	NiS (black)	$Ni(OH)_2$ (green)
Fe^{3+}	FeF_3 (green)	$Fe^{3+} + 3 Cl^-$	$Fe^{3+} + 3 Br^-$	$Fe^{3+} + 3 I^-$	–	$Fe(OH)_3$ (brown)
Al^{3+}	$Al^{3+} + 3 F^-$	$Al^{3+} + 3 Cl^-$	$Al^{3+} + 3 Br^-$	$Al^{3+} + 3 I^-$	–	$Al(OH)_3$ (white)
Cr^{3+}	CrF_3 (green)	$Cr^{3+} + 3 Cl^-$	$Cr^{3+} + 3 Br^-$	$Cr^{3+} + 3 I^-$	–	$Cr(OH)_3$ (green)

(All compounds containing Na^+, K^+, NH_4^+, and NO_3^- are soluble.)

Insoluble compounds are shown in color. Soluble compounds are written as separate ions.

complete ionic equation

This is a *complete ionic equation,* which shows all the ions in the solution, not just the ones that react. If we remove the spectator ions from the equation, then we're back to our original net ionic equation, which shows only the ions that have changed.

To form a precipitate, we look for a source of positive or negative ions. These sources will be soluble compounds, and they must contain the ions that we want.

N−	SO_4^{2-}	CO_3^{2-}	PO_4^{3-}	CrO_4^{2-}	
₃CN (white)	Ag_2SO_4 (white)	Ag_2CO_3 (yellow)	Ag_3PO_4 (yellow)	Ag_2CrO_4 (red)	Ag^+
₂(CN)₂ (yellow)	$PbSO_4$ (white)	$PbCO_3$ (white)	$Pb_3(PO_4)_2$ (white)	$PbCrO_4$ (yellow)	Pb^{2+}
	Hg_2SO_4 (white)	Hg_2CO_3 (yellow)	—	Hg_2CrO_4 (red)	Hg_2^{2+}
$g^{2+} + 2\,CN^-$	—	$HgCO_3$ (red)	—	—	Hg^{2-}
$g^{2+} + 2\,CN^-$	$Mg^{2+} + SO_4^{2-}$	$MgCO_3$ (white)	$Mg_3(PO_4)_2$ (white)	$Mg^{2+} + CrO_4^{2-}$	Mg^{2+}
₂u(CN)₂ (yellow green)	$Cu^{2+} + SO_4^{2-}$	$CuCO_3$ (blue)	$Cu_3(PO_4)_2$ (blue)	$CuCrO_4$ (yellow)	Cu^{2+}
₂n(CN)₂ (white)	$Zn^{2+} + SO_4^{2-}$	$ZnCO_3$ (white)	$Zn_3(PO_4)_2$ (white)	$ZnCrO_4$ (yellow)	Zn^{2+}
	$Fe^{2+} + SO_4^{2-}$	$FeCO_3$ (gray)	$Fe_3(PO_4)_2$ (white)	—	Fe^{2+}
	$CaSO_4$ (white)	$CaCO_3$ (white)	$Ca_3(PO_4)_2$ (white)	$Ca^{2+} + CrO_4^{2-}$	Ca^{2+}
₂a²+ + 2 CN⁻	$BaSO_4$ (white)	$BaCO_3$ (white)	$Ba_3(PO_4)_2$ (white)	$BaCrO_4$ (yellow)	Ba^{2+}
·²+ + 2 CN⁻	$SrSO_4$ (white)	$SrCO_3$ (white)	$Sr_3(PO_4)_2$ (white)	$SrCrO_4$ (yellow)	Sr^{2+}
₂o(CN)₂ (violet)	$Co^{2+} + SO_4^{2-}$	$CoCO_3$ (red)	$Co_3(PO_4)_2$ (red)	$CoCrO_4$ (gray black)	Co^{2+}
₂Ni(CN)₂ (yellow brown)	$Ni^{2+} + SO_4^{2-}$	$NiCO_3$ (dark green)	$Ni_3(PO_4)_2$ (light green)	—	Ni^{2+}
	$2\,Fe^{3+} + 3\,SO_4^{2-}$	—	$FePO_4$ (pink)	—	Fe^{3+}
	$2\,Al^{3+} + 3\,SO_4^{2-}$	—	$AlPO_4$ (white)	—	Al^{3+}
	$2\,Cr^{3+} + 3\,SO_4^{2-}$	—	$CrPO_4$ (violet)	—	Cr^{3+}

Dashes indicate either that the compound decomposes in water or that no data are available.

EXAMPLE 12.7: Suggest a solution of an ionic compound that could be used to remove Hg^{2+} from mercury-polluted water. Write the complete and net ionic equations.

Solution: Here, we have mercury(II) ion instead of mercury(I) ion. In the Hg^{2+} row of Table 12.5, the first insoluble mercury(II) compound is HgI_2. The polluted water provides the Hg^{2+}, but we need a source of iodide ions. Let's choose KI from Table 12.5.

Answer: A KI solution. Complete ionic equation:
$$Hg^{2+} + 2\,K^+ + 2\,I^- \longrightarrow HgI_2(s) + 2\,K^+$$

Net ionic equation:
$$Hg^{2+} + 2\,I^- \longrightarrow HgI_2(s)$$

In this example, there's no negative ion to go with the Hg^{2+} in the polluted water. There had to be negative ions there, but we didn't care about them or even know what they were. This will often be true.

EXAMPLE 12.8: List six ionic compounds whose solutions could be used to precipitate phosphate ion from phosphate-polluted water. Choose one such compound and write complete and net ionic equations.

Solution: Table 12.5 shows that every phosphate compound is insoluble except sodium, potassium, and ammonium phosphates. Let's choose to form precipitates of $Mg_3(PO_4)_2$, $Ca_3(PO_4)_2$, $Cu_3(PO_4)_2$, $AlPO_4$, $Sr_3(PO_4)_2$, and $FePO_4$. For each, we need a compound that will supply the metal ion.

Answer: $Mg(NO_3)_2$, $CaCl_2$, $CuSO_4$, $AlBr_3$, SrI_2, and $Fe(NO_3)_3$, among others. Complete ionic equation for the formation of $Ca_3(PO_4)_2$:
$$3\,Ca^{2+} + 6\,Cl^- + 2\,PO_4^{3-} \longrightarrow Ca_3(PO_4)_2(s) + 6\,Cl^-$$

Net ionic equation:
$$3\,Ca^{2+} + 2\,PO_4^{3-} \longrightarrow Ca_3(PO_4)_2(s)$$

In cases like the one above, we can choose one of many compounds to precipitate a given ion. In the laboratory, the choice might be simplified by what compounds are available or what solutions are already prepared. It's best to avoid cyanides, if possible, because they're all so poisonous. We'd want to make sure that the ions left in solution wouldn't interfere with our plans for the solution. When chemists want a negative ion, they use sodium, potassium, and sometimes ammonium compounds of the desired negative ion most often (Example 12.7). When they want a positive ion, chemists use a nitrate or sometimes a chloride compound of the desired positive ion (Example 12.8). In industry, cost is the primary reason for choosing a particular compound, followed by convenience. $Ca(OH)_2$ is used to remove phosphate from large amounts of polluted water because it's easily obtained from limestone and therefore cheaper than other sources of calcium ions.

EXAMPLE 12.9: Mine drainage usually contains large amounts of the pollutants Fe^{3+} and SO_4^{2-}. Choose a compound that will (a) remove only Fe^{3+}; (b) remove only SO_4^{2-}; and (c) remove both at once. Write net ionic equations for each.

Solution: To solve (a), we choose an insoluble Fe^{3+} compound from Table 12.5, and put a sodium or potassium ion with the negative ion. (b) We choose an insoluble SO_4^{2-} compound, and put a nitrate ion with the positive ion. (c) We can try to combine the negative ion from (a) with the positive ion from (b), or we can choose an entirely different soluble compound that will precipitate both.

Answer: (a) NaOH; (b) $Pb(NO_3)_2$; (c) $Ba(OH)_2$, because $Pb(OH)_2$ is insoluble.

$$Fe^{3+} + 3\,OH^- \longrightarrow Fe(OH)_3(s)$$
$$Pb^{2+} + SO_4^{2-} \longrightarrow PbSO_4(s)$$
$$2\,Fe^{3+} + 2\,SO_4^{2-} + 2\,Ba^{2+} + 6\,OH^- \longrightarrow 2\,Fe(OH)_3(s) + 2\,BaSO_4(s)$$

(The last net ionic equation is the same as the complete ionic equation, because all ions are removed.) $Ca(OH)_2$ is actually used in the mining industry, again because it's cheaper.

When we form a precipitate, the solution becomes cloudy. To remove the precipitate, we have to separate it from the liquid part of the solution. There are two ways to do this in the laboratory. One is *filtration*. We pour the liquid into a funnel that contains a piece of filter paper. The solution goes through the paper, and the precipitate is trapped on it. Another way is *centrifugation*. A test tube containing the cloudy solution is whirled around and around very fast in a centrifuge, which packs the small solid particles together at the bottom of the tube. Then the liquid part can be poured off. In industry, where large amounts of precipitate have to be removed, different methods are used. Sometimes, the solution is allowed to stand for a time in large tanks, and the precipitate simply settles out.

filtration

centrifugation

Sometimes a cloudy solution, meaning a precipitate is forming, can be used to test whether a given ion is present. Most precipitates are white, but some are colored, and many sulfides are even black. (Colors of precipitates are shown in Table 12.5.) If we added chloride ion to an unknown solution and got a precipitate, we'd know that our original solution contained either Ag^+, Pb^{2+}, or Hg_2^{2+}, because Table 12.5 gives these as the only ions that form insoluble chlorides.

EXAMPLE 12.10: An industrial effluent is suspected to contain sulfide ion. A few drops of $Cu(NO_3)_2$ solution is added to a small sample, and a black precipitate is obtained. Is this a positive test for sulfide ion? Would any other ions interfere with this test? Write the net ionic equation.

Solution: We look at Table 12.5 and see what insoluble compounds of copper(II) there are. In addition to sulfide, we find fluoride, hydroxide, chromate, carbonate, and phosphate. CuS is the only black one, though, so this is a positive test. The others wouldn't interfere unless there were so much of them that they masked the black CuS.

Answer: Yes, test is positive. The other ions probably wouldn't interfere.

$$Cu^{2+} + S^{2-} \longrightarrow CuS(s)$$

EXAMPLE 12.11: Would anything happen if solutions of $PbCl_2$ and K_2CrO_4 were mixed? Write the net ionic equation, if any.

Solution: First, we see that both compounds are soluble, so we can write their separate ions: $Pb^{2+} + 2\,Cl^- + K^+ + CrO_4^{2-}$. Table 12.5 shows one insoluble combination of these ions.

Answer: Yes, $PbCrO_4$ would precipitate.

$$Pb^{2+} + CrO_4{}^{2-} \longrightarrow PbCrO_4(s)$$

This reaction is sometimes used as a test for lead(II) ion in the absence of interfering ions. A yellow precipitate is obtained.

EXAMPLE 12.12: Would anything happen if solutions of $Zn(NO_3)_2$ and $BaBr_2$ were mixed? Write the net ionic equation, if any.

Solution: We write these separate ions: $Zn^{2+} + 2 NO_3{}^- + Ba^{2+} + 2 Br^-$. Table 12.5 shows no insoluble combination of these ions.

Answer: No. Nothing would happen.

CALCULATIONS.

molarity (M)

One way to perform a reaction in solution is to weigh out calculated amounts of the reactants, add them to water, and mix them together. But it's easier and quicker to use a prepared solution. As long as we know the solution's concentration, we can simply use a measured amount of it. For this application, we want to know how many moles of solute are in our solution. *Molarity* (M), another way of expressing concentration, means the number of moles of solute per 1 liter of solution (moles/liter). To find molarity, we have to know what the solute is so we can find its formula weight. A 1.00 M (molar) solution of NaCl would be a solution of 58.5 grams (1 mole) of NaCl in 1 liter of solution.

Solutions expressed in molarity are prepared by putting the correct amount of solid solute into a special flask, and then adding water, with occasional shaking, up to a mark on the flask. The flask measures the total volume of solution. If we wanted 1 liter of solution, it wouldn't do to add 1 liter of water to the solute, because then the total volume of the solution would be more than a liter.

EXAMPLE 12.13: How many grams of NaCl must be used to prepare 1.00 liter of 0.500 M solution?

Solution: We want to change 1.00 liter of solution to grams of NaCl. Our conversion factors are the molarity (0.500 moles/l) and the formula weight of NaCl (58.5 g/mole). Our setup:

$$1.00 \text{ l solution} \times \frac{0.500 \text{ moles NaCl}}{\text{l solution}} \times \frac{58.5 \text{ g}}{\text{mole NaCl}} = \underline{\qquad} \text{ g NaCl}$$

Answer: 29.2 g NaCl.

Now that we've prepared our NaCl solution, we can use it to find the concentration of a mercury-polluted solution. This problem is like the problems of Chapter 6. We have a new conversion factor: the molarity of solutions.

EXAMPLE 12.14: If 31.6 cm³ of our 0.500 M NaCl solution are needed to completely precipitate all the $Hg_2{}^{2+}$ as Hg_2Cl_2 from 25.0 cm³ of the polluted water, what is the concentration of $Hg_2{}^{2+}$ in the water?

Solution: Write the net ionic equation:

$$Hg_2^{2+} + 2\,Cl^- \longrightarrow Hg_2Cl_2(s)$$

We want to convert 31.6 cm³ (0.0316 l) of NaCl solution to moles/liter of Hg_2^{2+} solution. First, we must find the number of moles of Hg_2^{2+}. Our conversion factors are 0.500 moles Cl^-/l and 1 mole Hg_2^{2+}/2 moles Cl^-. Our setup:

$$0.0316\,\cancel{l\,Cl^-} \times \frac{0.500\,\cancel{moles\,Cl^-}}{\cancel{l\,Cl^-}} \times \frac{1\,mole\,Hg_2^{2+}}{2\,\cancel{moles\,Cl^-}} = 0.00790\,moles\,Hg_2^{2+}$$

We know now that this much Hg_2^{2+} is contained in the 25.0-cm³ sample, so we can easily find the molarity, or the number of moles per liter.

$$\frac{0.00790\,moles\,Hg_2^{2+}}{0.0250\,l} = \underline{\quad}\,M\,Hg_2^{2+}$$

Answer: 0.316 M Hg_2^{2+}.

Now, suppose that this mercury solution is a small sample of a huge 20,000-liter vat of the same solution. We want to remove the mercury from the water before the water is released into the sewer, both to avoid polluting and also to recover valuable mercury. In the previous problem, we found the concentration of mercury in the solution so we'd know the amount of NaCl needed to remove the mercury.

■ **EXAMPLE 12.15:** How many kilograms of NaCl must be added to the 20,000-liter vat of solution to remove all the mercury?

Solution: We want to convert 20,000 liters of Hg_2^{2+} solution to grams of NaCl. Our conversion factors are 0.316 moles Hg_2^{2+}/l Hg_2^{2+}; 2 moles NaCl/mole Hg_2^{2+} (the mole ratio from the equation); and 58.5 g/mole (the formula weight of NaCl). Our setup:

$$20{,}000\,\cancel{l\,Hg_2^{2+}\,sol.} \times 0.316\frac{moles\,\cancel{Hg_2^{2+}}}{\cancel{l\,Hg_2^{2+}\,sol.}} \times \frac{2\,moles\,\cancel{NaCl}}{\cancel{mole\,Hg_2^{2+}}} \times \frac{58.5\,\cancel{g}}{\cancel{mole\,NaCl}}$$

$$\times \frac{1\,kg}{10^3\,\cancel{g}} = \underline{\quad}\,kg\,NaCl$$

Answer: 700 kg NaCl.

When we prepare a solution of an ionic compound, we're usually interested in only one of the ions. When we prepared the NaCl solution, what we really wanted was a source of chloride ions. We could have used KCl, NH_4Cl, $CaCl_2$, or any soluble chloride. For this reason, we sometimes refer to a solution in terms of the ion we're interested in. We might call our NaCl solution a "chloride solution," even though there are also sodium ions in it. Similarly, a "solution of silver ions" means a solution of any soluble silver salt (there aren't many!), such as $AgNO_3$.

REVIEW QUESTIONS

Describing Solutions

1. What is a *solution?* What is a *solvent,* and what is a *solute?*
2. Give some examples of solutions. For each, state which is the solvent and which is the solute.
3. What do we mean by the *concentration* of a solution? How can we express the concentration of a solution even if we don't know what the solute is?
4. What is a *saturated solution?* How do we express its concentration?
5. What do the words *soluble* and *insoluble* mean? What does *sparingly soluble* mean?

Water as a Solvent

6. List some substances that are soluble and insoluble in water.
7. Name two liquids that are *miscible,* and two that are *immiscible.*
8. What energy must be overcome in dissolving an ionic solute? How does water overcome this energy? Why are some ionic solutes insoluble in water?
9. Explain why some ions are always present in solution, even when the compound is insoluble.
10. How do we express the concentration of natural water? What are some of the chief ions present in seawater?
11. What is hard water? Why does it make washing difficult? What are some ways of dealing with it?
12. What are some hydrogen-bonded solutes? Explain how water can dissolve these.
13. Given an example of a nonpolar solute to which water can hydrogen-bond.
14. Why doesn't water dissolve nonpolar solutes? What solvents do we use to dissolve nonpolar solutes?

Emulsions and Colloids

15. Explain the relationship between *colloids, emulsions,* and *emulsifying agents.* List some familiar colloids.
16. How do *detergents* work?
17. What keeps colloidal particles from coming together and settling out?
18. How can we destroy a colloid? Why might we want to?

Conditions Affecting Solutions

19. How do temperature and pressure affect the solubility of a gas in a liquid?
20. What is a *supersaturated solution?* How can we prepare one?

21. How does natural water get its dissolved oxygen? How much is there?
22. Why is phosphate a water pollutant? What is *eutrophication?*

The Behavior of Solutions

23. Why is the vapor pressure of a solution lower than the vapor pressure of the pure solvent?
24. How does the lower vapor pressure of the solvent in a solution affect the solvent's boiling point in that solution?
25. What is *distillation?* Give an example.
26. How does the lower vapor pressure of a solution affect its freezing point?
27. Why does antifreeze work?
28. What is *molality?* Why must we use it in experiments with freezing point?
29. How can we calculate the freezing point of a water solution?
30. What is the *freezing-point constant* of water? What does it mean?
31. How does salt melt ice and help make ice cream?
32. What happens when the temperature of a mixture of liquids gradually decreases?
33. What is *osmosis?* What is a *semipermeable membrane?* Give some examples.
34. What is *osmotic pressure?* What causes it? How do we measure it?
35. Explain how *reverse osmosis* can desalinate water and concentrate solutions.

Reactions That Form Precipitates

36. Explain how precipitation is used to remove ions from solutions.
37. What happens when a soluble ionic compound dissolves? Write an equation.
38. What is a *net ionic equation?* Write a net ionic equation that shows ions forming an insoluble compound.
39. What are *spectator ions?* Write a *complete ionic equation* and indicate the spectator ions.
40. How can we decide which of several possible precipitate-forming ions to use in the laboratory?
41. Can a complete ionic equation be the same as its net ionic equation? Explain.
42. How can we remove a precipitate from solution after it's formed?
43. How can we predict whether a precipitate will be formed if solutions of two compounds are mixed?
44. What concentration term do we use in precipitation reactions? How can it be used as a conversion factor?

45. How can we find the concentration of an unknown solution? Why might we want to do this?

46. Why is a NaCl solution sometimes called a "chloride solution"? Could we also call it a "solution of sodium ions"? Explain.

EXERCISES

1. A 50.0-cm³ sample of water from the Colorado River is found to contain 0.352 grams of dissolved solids. Calculate the concentration in grams per liter.

2. A certain preparation of corn syrup contains 1.1 kg of corn sugar per liter of corn syrup. A recipe calls for 150 g of corn sugar, to be dissolved in water. How many cubic centimeters of corn syrup must be used to get 150 g of corn sugar?

3. It has been suggested that gold might be recovered from seawater. If seawater contains about 4×10^{-9} g/l of dissolved gold, how many liters of seawater would have to be processed to get 1 gram of gold? Does it seem feasible to process this much sea water?

4. A 20.0-liter saturated solution of iodine in water contains 5.80 grams of iodine. A 10.0-cubic-centimeter saturated solution of iodine in alcohol contains 2.05 grams of iodine. Calculate the solubility of iodine in each solvent. In which is it more soluble? Why do you think alcohol is used as the solvent for tincture of iodine? (See Table 12.1.)

5. It is desirable to separate the much more valuable AgCl from the NaCl in a solid mixture of the two. Explain how this might be done.

6. Which compound in each of the following pairs would probably be the more soluble in water? Explain for each.
   a. HF or F_2
   b. LiF or BeO
   c. N_2 or NO_2
   d. H_2S or H_2SO_4
   e. CH_4 or CH_3OH
   f. $CHCl_3$ or HCl
   g. NH_3 or NCl_3
   h. CCl_4 or $CaCl_2$
   i. SO_3 or O_3

7. An old saying is, "Don't try to make mayonnaise during an electrical storm." Does this have any basis in fact? Explain.

8. Would a detergent work better or worse in salt water than it does in fresh water? Explain.

9. When opened, a refrigerated bottle of soda water will fizz more at 10,000 feet than at sea level. Explain.

10. Why does honey often contain sugar crystals after it has been standing for some time?

11. In 1974, oxygen gas was the third most important chemical produced. It is obtained from air by distillation: air is liquified, and its components are allowed to boil off. The three chief components of air have these boiling points: O_2, $-183°C$; N_2, $-196°C$; Ar, $-186°C$. List these in the order they would boil off.

12. Propylene glycol (molecular weight 76.1g/mole) can be used as antifreeze. How many kilograms of propylene glycol would be needed to make a solution of 9.0 m, using 6.5 kilograms of water?

13. Methyl alcohol (molecular weight 32.0) has been used as an antifreeze. What would be the freezing point of a solution containing 27.0 grams of methyl alcohol and 73.0 grams of water?
$$(m = [-T_f]/[1.84°C/m])$$

14. Maple syrup is mostly a solution of sucruose in water. Calculate the molality of the syrup if a sample freezes at $-0.50°C$. Assume that the syrup contains no solutes other than sucrose.

15. Could antifreeze (ethylene glycol) be used instead of salt to freeze ice cream? Why, or why not?

16. A little water dissolved in gasoline can plug a gas line as it freezes in cold weather. If a mixture of alcohols called "dry gas" is added directly to the gasoline, the water will not freeze. Explain how this works.

17. Explain the following, on the basis of osmosis or osmotic pressure.
   a. When sprinkled with sugar, a dish of sliced fruit will form its own juice.
   b. Meat that is salted before cooking tends to dry out.
   c. Although trees have no pump (heart) to circulate their fluids, water is drawn from the soil up into the branches and leaves.
   d. An effective way to kill a snail or slug in your garden is to sprinkle it with salt.
   e. Drinking salt water actually dehydrates (removes water from) our tissues.

18. A leading candy maker uses reverse osmosis to concentrate its waste sugar solutions so that the sugar can be recovered and used again. Explain how this could be done.

19. Solutions of $Al_2(SO_4)_3$ and $Fe_2(SO_4)_3$ are used to remove phosphate from water. Write complete and net ionic equations.

20. Suggest a compound whose solution could be

used to remove each of the following ions from solution. Write complete and net ionic equations for each.

a. Pb^{2+} d. F^- g. Co^{2+}
b. CO_3^{2-} e. Cr^{3+} h. Cl^-
c. Cu^{2+} f. CN^- i. Al^{3+}

21. Would a precipitate form if water solutions of the following pairs were mixed? If so, write the complete and net ionic equations.

a. K_2CO_3 and $MgCl_2$ d. CoF_2 and $Ca(OH)_2$
b. $Pb(NO_3)_2$ and SrI_2 e. NaOH and KCl
c. $ZnBr_2$ and $NiSO_4$ f. $HgCl_2$ and $(NH_4)_2S$

22. Suggest a compound whose water solution could be used to tell whether you had one or the other solution in each of the following pairs. Write net ionic equations for the reactions, and tell your reasoning.

a. NaOH or Na_2SO_4
b. $CoCl_2$ or $CuCl_2$
c. KCN or K_2CrO_4
d. $Mg(NO_3)_2$ or $Ca(NO_3)_2$
e. $(NH_4)_2S$ or $(NH_4)_2CO_3$
f. $ZnBr_2$ or $NiBr_2$

23. Solubility may be expressed in moles per liter (M) as well as in grams per liter. Ag_2S has a solubility of about 2×10^{-17} M. How many grams of Ag_2S are present in 500. cm^3 of a saturated solution?

24. The U.S. Department of Public Health limit on the amount of cyanide ion allowed in drinking water is 8×10^{-6} M. An industrial waste solution containing CN^- is allowed to react with 0.10-M $AgNO_3$ solution. It is found that 45.2 cm^3 of silver nitrate solution will precipitate all the cyanide ion in 10.0 liters of waste.

a. Write the complete and net ionic equations.
b. What is the concentration of the cyanide ion in the waste?
c. Will the government allow the waste to be used for drinking water?

25. A silver-plating company wants to recover silver from its waste solution, which is found to contain 0.0023 M Ag^+. How many kilograms of KCl must be added to precipitate all of the Ag^+ from 2500 liters of solution?

26. A solution of a rat poison containing F^- is allowed to react with $CaCl_2$. It is found that all the F^- in 10.0 cm^3 of rat poison solution can be precipitated as CaF_2 when 28.2 cm^3 of 1.0 M $CaCl_2$ are added. What is the concentration of F^- in the rat poison?

27. How many kilograms of $Ca(OH)_2$ are needed to precipitate all the magnesium from 1500 liters of seawater? Mg^{2+} is present in seawater at a concentration of 5×10^{-2} M.

13

Acids and Bases

As early as the seventeenth century, a class of compounds was recognized whose water solutions tasted sour, turned litmus (a vegetable dye) red, and could dissolve many things. These substances were named acids. Another class of compounds was known whose water solutions were slippery or soapy to the touch, turned litmus blue, and could cut grease. These were called alkalis, or bases. It was observed that acids react with bases, or neutralize them, to form salts.

Many familiar substances are acids or bases. Vinegar and citrus juices are acids. Stomach acid helps begin the digestive process and kills many microorganisms that we ingest. Household ammonia, lye, and drain or oven cleaner are common bases, as are most laundry or dishwasher detergents. Some of these, like household ammonia, are solutions.

Maintaining just the right amount of acid or base in a solution is often extremely important. For instance, if blood isn't kept at just the right acidity, the hemoglobin can't take on oxygen and release carbon dioxide when it's supposed to. We'll learn how to measure acidity or basicity with pH, and what the term means. We'll see what buffers are and how they're used to maintain a constant acidity or basicity in the blood and elsewhere. But first, we need to find out what acids and bases are and what they do.

13.1 STRONG ACIDS AND STRONG BASES

We learned the names of acids and bases, and saw some of their reactions, in Chapters 4 and 5. Now we'll see that there's a difference between strong and weak acids and bases. This difference shows up in their water solutions, which are the convenient substances to work with.

WATER SOLUTIONS OF STRONG ACIDS. A solution of hydrochloric acid can be prepared by bubbling hydrogen chloride gas through water. What happens is shown by this equation:

$$HCl(g) + H_2O(l) \longrightarrow Cl^-(aq) + H_3O^+(aq)$$

hydronium ion

strong acid

The substance H_3O^+ is called *hydronium ion,* and it is always formed when a strong acid is dissolved in water. In fact, a *strong acid* is defined as one that forms as many hydronium ions when dissolved in water as there were acid molecules at the start. According to one theory, an acid contains a "loose" hydrogen, which breaks away from its bonding electron pair and fastens itself onto one of water's available electron pairs to form H_3O^+, as illustrated in Figure 13.1.

The acids H_2SO_4, HNO_3, $HClO_4$, HBr, and HI are also strong acids that convert completely to hydronium ions when they dissolve in water. Table

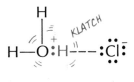

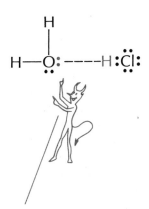

Water has two available electron pairs. One of them wants HCl's hydrogen, which HCl is holding very loosely.

When the hydrogen breaks away, it leaves behind the whole bonding electron pair. This makes a negatively charged chloride ion.

After the encounter, there are as many of these hydronium ions and chloride ions as there were HCl molecules to begin with.

13.1 shows equations for these conversions. These strong acids are all covalent compounds, but they ionize (form ions) in water.

The strong acids commonly used in the chemistry laboratory are sulfuric, nitric, and hydrochloric. Concentrated sulfuric acid is 98 percent H_2SO_4 by weight and about 18 molar. It can cause serious damage to human tissues if spilled on the skin and should always be handled with care. Concentrated nitric acid is about 70 percent HNO_3 by weight and about 16 molar, and it is also hazardous. Concentrated hydrochloric acid is about 36 percent HCl by weight and about 12 molar. It's not quite as dangerous as the other two, but it should still be used with caution. Solutions of these acids that are labeled "dilute" are usually 6 molar for hydrochloric and nitric acids and 3 molar for sulfuric acid.

WATER SOLUTIONS OF STRONG BASES.
Whereas the strong acids are covalent compounds, the common strong bases are all

$$HCl(g) + H_2O(l) \longrightarrow Cl^-(aq) + H_3O^+(aq)$$
$$H_2SO_4(l) + H_2O(l) \longrightarrow HSO_4^-(aq) + H_3O^+(aq)$$
$$HNO_3(l) + H_2O(l) \longrightarrow NO_3^-(aq) + H_3O^+(aq)$$
$$HClO_4(l) + H_2O(l) \longrightarrow ClO_4^-(aq) + H_3O^+(aq)$$
$$HBr(g) + H_2O(l) \longrightarrow Br^-(aq) + H_3O^+(aq)$$
$$HI(g) + H_2O(l) \longrightarrow I^-(aq) + H_3O^+(aq)$$

TABLE 13.1
Equations showing the strong acids dissolving in water

ionic compounds. We already know from Chapter 12 how an ionic compound dissolves in water. Metal hydroxides are the most common strong bases. Here's how one dissolves in water.

$$NaOH(s) \longrightarrow Na^+(aq) + OH^-(aq)$$

strong base

Here, as with the salts of Chapter 12, ions are not being created but only separated and mixed through the solution. Hydroxide ions are responsible for the properties of a base solution. When a *strong base* dissolves in water, the amount that dissolves yields exactly as many hydroxide ions in solution as its formula would predict. For instance, every mole of dissolved NaOH produces a mole of hydroxide ions; and every mole of dissolved $Ba(OH)_2$ produces two moles of hydroxide ions. But Table 12.5 (pp. 280–281) shows that few hydroxides are very soluble. Table 13.2 shows some soluble strong bases and how they form hydroxide ions in solution. These and other soluble bases are the only ones useful in making base solutions. NaOH and KOH are more soluble than the other three.

The strong base used most often in the chemistry laboratory is sodium hydroxide (lye), although potassium hydroxide is sometimes used, too. Concentrated solutions of these bases are usually 12 molar; dilute solutions are 6 molar. Both of these bases will burn the skin and dissolve wool and other fabrics, and they should be handled carefully. They also etch glass slowly and are usually kept in plastic or wax-lined bottles for this reason.

REACTIONS BETWEEN STRONG BASES AND STRONG ACIDS.

A strong acid solution contains hydronium ions; a strong base solution contains hydroxide ions. When these solutions are mixed, this reaction takes place:

$$H_3O^+ + OH^- \longrightarrow 2 H_2O$$

(Here, as in Chapter 12, we'll leave out the expressions (*aq*) and (*l*), since we assume all reactions to be in aqueous solution.) This is the net ionic equation for the reaction of any strong acid solution with any strong base solution. The reaction of any acid and base in Tables 13.1 and 13.2 could be expressed with this net ionic equation. The complete ionic equation would depend on which acid and which base were being used. Table 13.3 shows complete and net ionic equations for some strong acid-base reactions.

**TABLE 13.2
Some common
soluble
strong bases**

$$NaOH(s) \longrightarrow Na^+(aq) + OH^-(aq)$$
$$KOH(s) \longrightarrow K^+(aq) + OH^-(aq)$$
$$Ba(OH)_2(s) \longrightarrow Ba^{2+}(aq) + 2 OH^-(aq)$$
$$Ca(OH)_2(s) \longrightarrow Ca^{2+}(aq) + 2 OH^-(aq)$$
$$Sr(OH)_2(s) \longrightarrow Sr^{2+}(aq) + 2 OH^-(aq)$$

TABLE 13.3
Complete and net ionic equations for some strong acid-base reactions

Complete Ionic Equation	Net Ionic Equation
$HSO_4^- + H_3O^+ + Na^+ + OH^- \longrightarrow 2\,H_2O + Na^+ + HSO_4^-$	$H_3O^+ + OH^- \longrightarrow 2\,H_2O$
$H_3O^+ + NO_3^- + K^+ + OH^- \longrightarrow 2\,H_2O + K^+ + NO_3^-$	$H_3O^+ + OH^- \longrightarrow 2\,H_2O$
$2\,H_3O^+ + 2\,ClO_4^- + Ba^{2+} + 2\,OH^- \longrightarrow 4\,H_2O + Ba^{2+} + 2\,ClO_4^-$	$2\,H_3O^+ + 2\,OH^- \longrightarrow 4\,H_2O$
$2\,H_3O^+ + 2\,NO_3^- + Ca^{2+} + 2\,OH^- \longrightarrow 4\,H_2O + Ca^{2+} + 2\,NO_3^-$	$2\,H_3O^+ + 2\,OH^- \longrightarrow 4\,H_2O$

It's not as easy to see the reaction of strong acids and bases as it is to see a precipitate forming. However, if we mixed 6-molar hydrochloric acid and 6-molar sodium hydroxide together, we'd be able to feel the beaker getting warm. Acid-base reactions are exothermic. Mixing concentrated acids and bases together is dangerous, because so much heat is generated that the solution usually spatters and can splash out of its container.

13.2 WEAK ACIDS AND WEAK BASES

Weak acids and *bases* don't ionize much in water, and that's why they're considered weak. Their water solutions don't contain very many hydronium or hydroxide ions.

weak acid

weak base

WEAK ACIDS IN WATER.
For a moment let's consider a solution of water in water. This reaction happens to a very small extent:

$$H_2O + H_2O \longrightarrow H_3O^+ + OH^-$$

Both hydronium ions and hydroxide ions are produced, which means that water is both a weak acid and a weak base. In a 1 liter sample of normal water, we'd find only 10^{-7} moles each of hydronium and hydroxide ions.

Other weak acids dissolved in water form some hydronium ions—more than water alone does. For instance, a 1 liter solution containing one mole of acetic acid ($HC_2H_3O_2$) will have about 4×10^{-3} moles of hydronium ions, as shown in Figure 13.2. When we're writing ionic equations with weak acids, we write them in their original forms even though a few ions are present. (We did the same thing in Chapter 12, when we wrote insoluble ionic compounds as complete formulas even though a few ions are always present.) Weak acids include all acids that we haven't specified previously as strong.

Acetic acid is the most common weak acid used in the chemistry laboratory. We already know that vinegar is a dilute solution of acetic acid in water. Pure acetic acid, without any water in it, is a clear, colorless liquid, like water. Its melting point is slightly below room temperature (16.7°C), so at room temperature there are usually some solid crystals in it. Because

**FIGURE 13.2
Weak acids
give only a
few hydronium
ions in water**

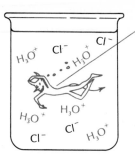

Swimming around in this beaker of hydrochloric acid, I can't find *any* HCl molecules. *None!* That's because HCl is a strong acid that is 100 percent ionized in water.

$$HCl + H_2O \rightarrow Cl^- + H_3O^+$$
$$100\%$$

Now here in this beaker of acetic acid, it's a different story! I have a hard time finding any hydronium ions and acetate ions, although there are a few here. Acetic acid is a weak acid and is only about 1 to 2 percent ionized.

$$HC_2H_3O_2 + H_2O \rightarrow C_2H_3O_2^- + H_3O^+$$
$$1\%-2\%$$

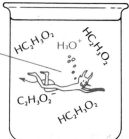

these crystals look like ice, pure acetic acid is also called "glacial" acetic acid. It has an overpowering vinegar smell and, like any concentrated acid, can burn skin. Dilute acetic acid is usually 6 molar. Vinegar is about 5 percent acetic acid and about 0.8 molar.

WEAK BASES IN WATER.

As we saw in the previous section, water itself is a weak base. When dissolved in water, other weak bases also form a few hydroxide ions—more than plain water does but fewer than a strong base does.

Ammonia is the weak base used most often in the chemistry laboratory. When ammonia gas is bubbled through water to make aqueous ammonia, this reaction happens to a small extent.

$$NH_3(g) + H_2O(l) \longrightarrow NH_4^+(aq) + OH^-(aq)$$

Ammonia is a covalent compound that ionizes in solution—in contrast with the strong bases, which are ionic compounds. In a 1-liter solution containing one mole of ammonia, we'd find only about 4×10^{-3} moles of hydroxide ions. Concentrated aqueous ammonia (sometimes incorrectly labeled "ammonium hydroxide, NH_4OH") is about 27 percent NH_3, and about 16 molar. Dilute aqueous ammonia is about 10 percent and 6 molar.

Another weak base sometimes used in solution is the carbonate ion (CO_3^{2-}). As we know from Chapter 12, any soluble carbonate, such as Na_2CO_3, is a source of carbonate ions. Carbonate produces some hydroxide ions in water, according to this reaction:

$$CO_3{}^{2-} + H_2O \longrightarrow HCO_3{}^- + OH^-$$

Other negative ions can also be weak bases, as we'll see later.

When we're writing ionic equations with weak bases, we write the bases as if they don't form hydroxide ions, just as we write weak acids in their original forms.

REACTIONS OF WEAK ACIDS AND WEAK BASES.

When strong acids and bases react, water is always a product. This isn't true of reactions between weak acids and bases. Here's the equation for the reaction between ammonia and acetic acid:

$$NH_3 + HC_2H_3O_2 \longrightarrow NH_4{}^+ + C_2H_3O_2{}^-$$

The hydrogen has moved from the acetic acid to the ammonia. The product, ammonium acetate, is written as separate ions because it's a soluble salt. Table 13.4 shows some reactions between weak acids and weak bases, weak acids and strong bases, and strong acids and weak bases. In the latter cases, we write the strong acids or bases in the ionic form. Here are two examples.

$$H_3O^+ + Cl^- + NH_3 \longrightarrow NH_4{}^+ + Cl^- + H_2O$$
$$\text{strong acid} \quad \text{weak base}$$

Net:
$$H_3O^+ + NH_3 \longrightarrow NH_4{}^+ + H_2O$$

$$HC_2H_3O_2 + Na^+ + OH^- \longrightarrow H_2O + Na^+ + C_2H_3O_2{}^-$$
$$\text{weak acid} \qquad \text{strong base}$$

Net:
$$HC_2H_3O_2 + OH^- \longrightarrow C_2H_3O_2{}^- + H_2O$$

Table 13.4 points out some interesting things. First, no water is formed when weak acids and bases react with each other, but water is formed when the acid, base, or both are strong. In the case of a strong acid, the hydronium ion is reacting, and there will always be a water molecule left. In the case of a strong base, the hydroxide ion is reacting, and a water molecule will always result when it gains a hydrogen.

Second, we see that some substances can react twice. Carbonate ion, for instance, can gain two hydrogens, either one at a time or both at once. If there is enough acid, both can happen, and we get carbonic acid.

$$2\,H_3O^+ + CO_3{}^{2-} \longrightarrow 2\,H_2O + H_2CO_3$$
$$(CO_2 + H_2O)$$

We write "$(CO_2 + H_2O)$" under carbonic acid, because it always decomposes to carbon dioxide and water when it's formed.

Acids that have more than one hydrogen, such as sulfuric and phosphoric, lose them one at a time or, if there is enough hydroxide around, all at once. H_2SO_4 acts as a strong acid when it loses its first hydrogen, and as a weak acid when it loses the second. H_3PO_4 acts as a weak acid for each

Table 13.4
Ionic equations showing reactions of weak acids and weak bases

Complete Ionic Equation	Net Ionic Equation
Weak Acids and Weak Bases	
$HF + 2\,Na^+ + CO_3^{2-} \longrightarrow HCO_3^- + 2\,Na^+ + F^-$	$HF + CO_3^{2-} \longrightarrow HCO_3^- + F^-$
$H_3PO_4 + NH_3 \longrightarrow NH_4^+ + H_2PO_4^-$	Same as complete ionic equation
$HC_2H_3O_2 + 3\,Na^+ + PO_4^{3-} \longrightarrow C_2H_3O_2^- + 3\,Na^+ + HPO_4^{2-}$	$HC_2H_3O_2 + PO_4^{3-} \longrightarrow C_2H_3O_2^- + HPO_4^{2-}$
$HC_2H_3O_2 + 2\,Na^+ + CO_3^{2-} \longrightarrow C_2H_3O_2^- + 2\,Na^+ + HCO_3^-$	$HC_2H_3O_2 + CO_3^{2-} \longrightarrow C_2H_3O_2^- + HCO_3^-$
$HC_2H_3O_2 + Na^+\,HCO_3^- \longrightarrow C_2H_3O_2^- + Na^+ + H_2CO_3$ $(CO_2 + H_2O)$	$HC_2H_3O_2 + HCO_3^- \longrightarrow C_2H_3O_2^- + H_2CO_3$ $(CO_2 + H_2O)$
Strong Acids and Weak Bases	
$H_3O^+ + Cl^- + 2\,Na^+ + CO_3^{2-} \longrightarrow H_2O + Cl^- + 2\,Na^+ + HCO_3^-$	$H_3O^+ + CO_3^{2-} \longrightarrow H_2O + HCO_3^-$
$H_3O^+ + Cl^- + Na^+ + HCO_3^- \longrightarrow H_2O + Cl^- + Na^+ + H_2CO_3$ $(CO_2 + H_2O)$	$H_3O^+ + HCO_3^- \longrightarrow H_2O + H_2CO_3$ $(CO_2 + H_2O)$
$H_3O^+ + HSO_4^- + NH_3 \longrightarrow H_2O + HSO_4^- + NH_4^+$	$H_3O^+ + NH_3 \longrightarrow H_2O + NH_4^+$
$H_3O^+ + NO_3^- + PO_4^{3-} \longrightarrow H_2O + NO_3^- + HPO_4^{2-}$	$H_3O^+ + PO_4^{3-} \longrightarrow H_2O + HPO_4^{2-}$
Weak Acids and Strong Bases	
$Na^+ + HSO_4^- + Na^+ + OH^- \longrightarrow 2\,Na^+ + SO_4^{2-} + H_2O$	$HSO_4^- + OH^- \longrightarrow SO_4^{2-} + H_2O$
$HC_2H_3O_2 + K^+ + OH^- \longrightarrow C_2H_3O_2^- + K^+ + H_2O$	$HC_2H_3O_2 + OH^- \longrightarrow C_2H_3O_2^- + H_2O$
$Na^+ + HCO_3^- + Na^+ + OH^- \longrightarrow 2\,Na^+ + CO_3^{2-} + H_2O$	$HCO_3^- + OH^- \longrightarrow CO_3^{2-} + H_2O$
$2\,HF + Ba^{2+} + 2\,OH^- \longrightarrow 2\,F^- + Ba^{2+} + 2\,H_2O$	$2\,HF + 2\,OH^- \longrightarrow 2\,F^- + 2\,H_2O$

of its three hydrogens. We'd write these equations to show how H_2SO_4 and H_3PO_4 react with excess hydroxide ions:

$$H_3O^+ \;+\;\; OH^- \longrightarrow 2\,H_2O$$
$$HSO_4^- \;+\;\; OH^- \longrightarrow \;\; H_2O + SO_4^{2-}$$
$$\overline{H_3O^+ + HSO_4^- + 2\,OH^- \longrightarrow 3\,H_2O + SO_4^{2-}} \qquad \text{Total}$$

$$H_3PO_4 \;\;+\;\;\; OH^- \longrightarrow H_2PO_4^- \;+\;\; H_2O$$
$$H_2PO_4^- \;+\;\;\; OH^- \longrightarrow HPO_4^{2-} \;+\;\; H_2O$$
$$HPO_4^{2-} \;+\;\;\; OH^- \longrightarrow PO_4^{3-} \;\;\;+\;\; H_2O$$
$$\overline{H_3PO_4 \;\;+ 3\,OH^- \longrightarrow PO_4^{3-} \;\;\;+ 3\,H_2O} \qquad \text{Total}$$

13.3 MEASURING ACIDS AND BASES

We know that acids and bases have different strengths. Spilling vinegar on the skin does no harm, but we'd feel it if we spilled sulfuric acid of the same concentration. Our stomachs contain about 0.02 molar HCl, but if we drank 6 molar HCl we'd be very sick. Milk of magnesia, $Mg(OH)_2$, is a base that we take for an upset stomach, but NaOH in the same concentration would burn our insides. The difference in these reactions is in how many hydronium or hydroxide ions are present.

HYDRONIUM-ION AND HYDROXIDE-ION
CONCENTRATION.
We can easily predict the hydronium-ion concentration of a strong acid and the hydroxide-ion concentration of a strong base. Each comes from its molarity. A 0.01-molar HCl solution has a hydronium-ion concentration of 0.01 M, because HCl ionizes completely. A 0.05 M NaOH solution has a hydroxide-ion concentration of 0.05 M. We write square brackets to mean "concentration." For example, "$[H_3O^+]$ = 0.01 M" means "a hydronium-ion concentration of 0.01 molar." Similarly, "$[OH^-]$ = 0.05 M" means "a hydroxide-ion concentration of 0.05 M."

As we saw earlier, pure water contains 10^{-7} moles per liter each of H_3O^+ and OH^-. Or, for pure water:

$$[H_3O^+] = 1.0 \times 10^{-7}\ M$$
$$[OH^-] = 1.0 \times 10^{-7}\ M$$

In pure water at 25°C, multiplying the hydronium-ion concentration by the hydroxide-ion concentration gives us a value of 1.0×10^{-14}.

$$[H_3O^+][OH^-] = (1.0 \times 10^{-7})(1.0 \times 10^{-7}) = 1.0 \times 10^{-14}$$

Adding an acid to water will increase the hydronium-ion concentration and decrease the hydroxide-ion concentration. Adding a base will do the opposite. Thus in acid or base solutions, the concentrations of hydronium ions and hydroxide ions aren't 1.0×10^{-7}, but their product is still 1.0×10^{-14}. That is:

$$[H_3O^+][OH^-] = 1.0 \times 10^{-14}$$

The hydronium-ion concentration of a strong acid and the hydroxide-ion concentration of a strong base depend only on how much acid or base is present in solution. But the concentrations can't be predicted that easily for weak acids and bases, because they depend on the relative strengths of the weak acids or bases. We won't go into the ways hydronium- and hydroxide-ion concentrations can be calculated for weak acids and bases. An easier and more accurate way of finding out these concentrations is just to measure them. We'll soon see how this is done.

THE pH OF SOLUTIONS.

The term "pH" is a familiar one in the advertising and the environmental vocabularies. An antiblemish soap or a shampoo is supposed to be "pH-adjusted." By law, a laundry detergent that gives a pH greater than 11 when dissolved in a washerful of water must be so labeled. pH is a simple and widely used way of expressing hydronium-ion concentration.

As a kind of shorthand notation, pH makes it easier to express acidity and basicity since it does not use exponential numbers. For instance, a pH of 7.00 means a hydronium-ion concentration of 1.0×10^{-7} M—the pH of pure water at 25°C. The lower the pH (below 7, down to zero), the more acidic the solution; the higher the pH (above 7, up to 14), the more basic. A pH of 7.00 is neutral and is the dividing line between acids and bases. Table 13.5 lists pH values for some common solutions.

If we know either the hydronium-ion concentration, the hydroxide-ion concentration, or the pH of a solution, we can find the other two by using the scales in Figure 13.3. The scale on the left is a coarse scale. The hydronium-ion concentration on the left reads from bottom to top; pH and hydroxide-ion concentration read from top to bottom. To use the coarse scale, we draw an imaginary line through the value we know and read straight across to find the other values. This is easy for whole-numbered pH values. We see that a pH of 3 means a hydronium-ion concentration of 10^{-3} and a hydroxide-ion concentration of 10^{-11}. On this scale, multiplying the two concentrations together (that is, adding their exponents) always gives 10^{-14}.

It's not quite as easy for values that fall between the whole-number lines. For instance, a sample of normal gastric juice (stomach acid) might have a pH of 1.43. We'd have trouble finding exactly where 1.43 is on the coarse scale, because the whole numbers are so close together. To make this easier, a section between whole numbers has been magnified and set to the right in Figure 13.3. This is the fine scale, and it lets us read the decimal part of the pH and the concentrations that go with it. The coarse scale is for getting the exponents, and the fine scale is for getting the rest. The values on the fine scale are set up so that when they're multiplied together

TABLE 13.5 299
pH values of
some common
solutions

Solution	pH	
Battery acid	0	
Stomach acid	1.4–1.8	
Lemon juice	2.1	
Vinegar	2.9	
Soda water	3	INCREASING ACIDITY
Wine	3.5	
Tomato juice	4	
Black coffee	5	
Urine, sour milk	6	
Rainwater	6.5	
Pure water, 25°C	7.00	Neutral
Blood	7.35–7.45	
Seawater	8	
Soaps, shampoos	8–9	
Detergents	9–10	INCREASING BASICITY
Milk of magnesia	10	
Household ammonia	11.9	
Liquid bleach	12	
Household lye	14	

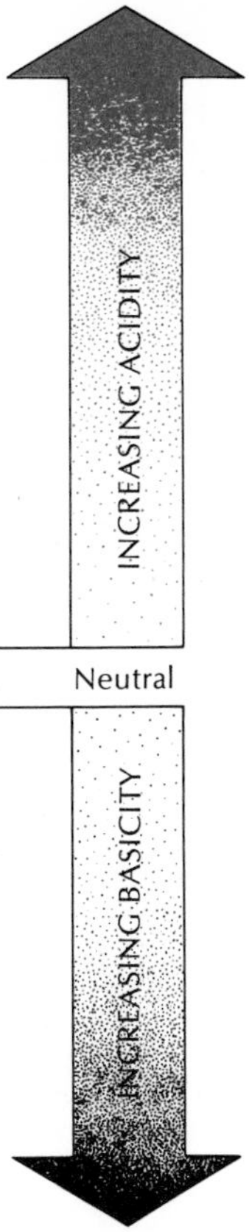

the answer comes out as close to 10 as possible. When we've finished using both the coarse and fine scales, the exponents of the two concentrations should add up to −15. (1×10^{-14} is the same as 10×10^{-15}.)

To find hydronium-ion and hydroxide-ion concentrations from a fractional pH, we use these steps.

Step 1: *Find the exponentials on the coarse scale.*
To do this, locate the pH value on that scale as closely as possible; it will fall between two whole-number lines. Our pH of 1.43 falls between 1 and 2. Since the $[H_3O^+]$ scale reads from bottom to top, its value is between 10^{-1} and 10^{-2}. We choose the smaller exponential; 10^{-2}. Similarly, on the $[OH^-]$ scale, the value falls between 10^{-12} and 10^{-13}. Again, we choose the smaller, 10^{-13}.

Step 2: *Find the rest of the numbers on the fine scale.*
To do this, locate the decimal part of the pH—in this case, 0.43. Reading

**FIGURE 13.3
Scales
for conversions
between pH
and
concentrations**

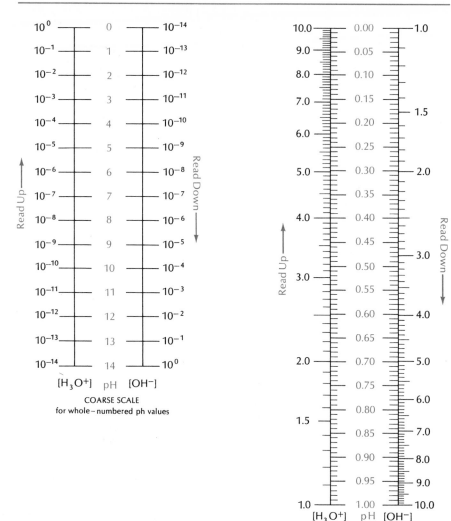

COARSE SCALE
for whole–numbered ph values

FINE SCALE
for fractional ph values

from bottom to top on the $[H_3O^+]$ scale, we see that this value corresponds to 3.7. On the $[OH^-]$ scale (top to bottom), this is 2.7.

Step 3: *Combine the two parts of both concentrations.*

$$[H_3O^+] = 3.7 \times 10^{-2} \ M$$
$$[OH^-] = 2.7 \times 10^{-13} \ M$$

Step 4: *Check the answer by multiplying the two concentrations together.*

$$(3.7 \times 10^{-2})(2.7 \times 10^{-13}) = 10 \times 10^{-15}$$

Our answer checks. This product should be close to 10×10^{-15}; sometimes it may be slightly higher or lower because of the degree of accuracy of the scales. Often, it's enough just to add the exponents to -15.

EXAMPLE 13.1: A blood sample has a pH of 7.51. Is it acidic or basic? Find $[H_3O^+]$ and $[OH^-]$.

Solution: First, the blood is slightly basic since its pH is greater than 7.00.
Step 1: The exponential for $[H_3O^+]$ is 10^{-8}; for $[OH^-]$, it's 10^{-7}.
Step 2: On the fine scale, 0.51 corresponds to 3.1 for $[H_3O^+]$ and 3.2 for $[OH^-]$.
Step 3: $[H_3O^+] = 3.1 \times 10^{-8}$ M; $[OH^-] = 3.2 \times 10^{-7}$ M.
Step 4: $(3.1 \times 10^{-8})(3.2 \times 10^{-7}) = 9.9 \times 10^{-15}$ (close enough). Our answer checks.

Answer: The blood is basic. $[H_3O^+] = 3.1 \times 10^{-8}$ M; $[OH^-] = 3.2 \times 10^{-7}$ M.

Suppose we want to know the pH of a solution of HCl that is 0.0045 M. Since HCl is a strong acid, this means that $[H_3O^+]$ is 0.0045 M, or 4.5×10^{-3} M. To find pH when we know $[H_3O^+]$ or $[OH^-]$, we follow these steps.

Step 1: *Find the whole number by using the coarse scale.*
To do this, locate the concentration on the appropriate scale: 4.5×10^{-3} falls between 10^{-3} and 10^{-2}, reading from bottom to top on the $[H_3O^+]$ scale. This means a pH between 2 and 3, and we choose the smaller number, 2.
Step 2: *Find the rest of the number on the fine scale.*
To do this, locate the coefficient of the concentration—in this case, 4.5—on the appropriate scale. This corresponds to 0.35 on the pH scale.
Step 3: *Put the two parts of the pH together.*
pH = 2.35. There is no quick way to check the answer in this conversion. A not-so-quick way is to convert the pH back to $[H_3O^+]$ and see whether it agrees with the starting concentration.

EXAMPLE 13.2: Find the pH of a 0.0055 M $Ca(OH)_2$ solution.

Solution: First, since $Ca(OH)_2$ is a strong base, its $[OH^-]$ is what we'd expect from its concentration. Every mole of $Ca(OH)_2$ gives us two moles of OH^-, so $[OH^-] = 0.0110$, or 1.1×10^{-2} M.
Step 1: This value falls between 10^{-2} and 10^{-3} on the $[OH^-]$ scale, meaning a pH between 11 and 12. We choose 11 for the whole number.
Step 2: On the fine scale, 1.1 for $[OH^-]$ corresponds to 0.04 on the pH scale.
Step 3: 11.04.

Answer: pH = 11.04.

We'll know whether our answer is in the right ball park or not by remembering that a basic solution should have a pH greater than 7, which this one does.

Suppose we want to know what $[H_3O^+]$ is for the preceding example. To convert between $[OH^-]$ and $[H_3O^+]$, we follow these steps.

Step 1: *Find the exponent on the coarse scale.*

Since $[OH^-]$ is between 10^{-2} and 10^{-1}, this means that $[H_3O^+]$ is between 10^{-13} and 10^{-12}. We choose 10^{-13}.

Step 2: *Find the rest of the number on the fine scale.*

The reading 1.1 on the $[OH^-]$ scale corresponds to 9.1 on the $[H_3O^+]$ scale.

Step 3: *Put the two parts together.*

$$[H_3O^+] = 9.1 \times 10^{-13}\ M$$

Step 4: *Check the answer by multiplying the two concentrations together.*

$$(1.1 \times 10^{-2})(9.1 \times 10^{-13}) = 10 \times 10^{-15}$$

Our results check.

APPLICATIONS AND MEASUREMENT OF pH. Maintaining a certain pH value or range is often important, especially in biological systems. For example, our blood maintains itself at a pH of between 7.35 and 7.45. If the pH falls slightly below 7.35, the condition is called acidosis; if it rises slightly above 7.45, the condition is called alkalosis. (In Example 13.1, the donor of the blood with pH 7.51 has alkalosis.) Both conditions must be treated. If the blood changes more than a few tenths of a pH unit from the normal range, the results are usually fatal. Hemoglobin itself is a weak acid, and too much acid or base interferes with its function of picking up, carrying, and releasing oxygen.

Most plants grow best in soil with a pH between 6 and 7. Higher or lower values prevent them from absorbing nutrients from the soil. For instance, a too-acidic soil can prevent plants from absorbing phosphate. Most plants absorb this nutrient as $H_2PO_4^-$. A too-acidic soil would convert it to H_3PO_4, and a too-basic soil would convert it to HPO_4^{2-} or PO_4^{3-}. In either case, plants would not be able to absorb as much phosphate.

Bacteria have an optimum pH range, too. Pickling foods in vinegar is an effective way to preserve them, because most bacteria that cause food spoilage won't grow in solutions having the low pH of vinegar.

Shampoos normally have a pH of about 8. Scalp, on the other hand, is on the acid side, with a pH of around 6. Rinsing the hair with vinegar after shampooing neutralizes the base left by the shampoo and restores the acid condition of the scalp. "Alkaline scalp" is a dry, flaky condition resembling dandruff. A shampoo advertised as "pH-adjusted" has a pH of around 6. Its makers have added various acids to lower the pH.

Rainwater is naturally slightly acidic (pH of 6.5), as we saw in Table 13.5. This is because some atmospheric carbon dioxide is always dissolved in it, which makes carbonic acid. The air pollutants NO_2, SO_2, and SO_3 increase the acidity of rainwater even further. In 1966 in Europe, the pH of rainwater was measured to be about 4. That's frightening when we remember that a pH decrease of 2.5 means that acid concentrations increases over 100 times. We saw in Chapter 5 that such acid rain can dissolve buildings and statues.

Mine drainage also adds to the "pH pollution" of our environment. Any kind of mining exposes buried sulfur compounds to the oxygen of the air. The oxygen attacks the sulfur and converts it to sulfuric acid, which then washes into streams, rivers, and lakes. Salmon, trout, and other kinds of fish can't live in water with a pH below 5.5.

Maintaining a certain pH, or correcting a too-high or a too-low pH, is thus very important. To do it, we have to be able to measure pH in the first place. One way to measure pH is with a pH meter. This instrument has a glass probe that is inserted into the solution to be measured. The pH can be read on a scale or digital display.

Another way of measuring pH is with indicators or pH paper. *Indicators* are dyes that change color at a certain pH value. The first indicators were vegetable dyes and we still use some of these, such as litmus. Impregnating this dye onto absorbent paper and cutting it into strips gives us litmus paper, commonly used in the chemistry laboratory. Litmus paper turns red in acid and blue in base, but it doesn't tell what the pH is. We can use vegetable dyes to observe the behavior of acids and bases in a simple kitchen experiment (see Box below).

indicator

THE EFFECT OF pH ON A VEGETABLE DYE

This interesting and colorful kitchen experiment will demonstrate the effects of varying pH on vegetable dyes. Grind up part of a red cabbage in about two cups of water (use a blender if you have one). Strain the pulp out with a sieve or some cheesecloth. Divide the purple liquid into a number of portions. Test foods and household substances like vinegar, lemon juice, detergent, ammonia, drain cleaner (dangerous, so use a small amount), wine, and coffee by adding them to separate portions of the purple liquid. The dye goes through a number of delightful color changes, as shown below. This is one way you can estimate the pH values of some of these substances. If enough things are tried, the set of samples will show very gradual color changes. The dye in red cabbage has these colors for approximate pH values:

pH	2	3	4	5	6	7	8 9	10 11	12	13	14
Color	Red	Red- purple	Purple	Blue- purple	Blue	Blue-green	Green	Yellow

Now a great variety of synthetic dyes exist which change color over a wide range of pH values. A mixture of these dyes, covering a desired pH range, impregnated onto paper and cut in strips gives us pH paper. A strip of the paper is dipped into the test solution and compared with a color chart provided with the pH paper. pH paper is less accurate but sometimes more convenient—and certainly less expensive—than a pH meter.

Soil can be tested with pH paper. Acidity is a more common problem than basicity; if a soil is found to be too acidic, lime (CaO) or ground limestone ($CaCO_3$) is usually added to neutralize the acid. A pH meter would be used for more critical measurements, such as blood pH. Chemistry laboratories use both methods, depending on the nature of the experiment.

13.4 THE STRUCTURES OF ACIDS AND BASES

We've seen how acids and bases react with each other, and we've seen how to measure them. Now we'll find out what makes an acid an acid and a base a base.

BRØNSTED-LOWRY ACIDS AND BASES.

Up to now, we've seen acids as substances that release H_3O^+ in water, and bases as substances that release OH^- in water. This is formally called the Arrhenius concept of acids and bases. A more recent and more general description of acids and bases was proposed independently by J. N. Brønsted and T. M. Lowry in 1923. This description is as follows: An *acid* is a proton donor, and a *base* is a proton acceptor. A *proton* is a hydrogen atom without its electron, or a hydrogen ion. (Since a hydrogen atom consists only of a proton and an electron, removing the electron leaves the hydrogen nucleus, which is a proton.) When a proton is removed from its electron pair on an acid and bonded to an available electron pair on a base, this process is called *proton transfer*. All the acid-base reactions we've seen so far have been proton transfer reactions. The process is shown in Figure 13.4. Looking back at Figure 13.1, we see that the ionization of HCl in water is proton transfer, with the HCl as the acid and water as the base.

At the very least, an acid must contain a hydrogen, and a base must have an available electron pair. However, the converse isn't always true: containing a hydrogen or an available electron pair doesn't guarantee that a substance will act as an acid or base.

We see from Figure 13.4 that proton transfer is like a game of "musical protons," with electron pairs on an acid and base competing for a single proton. The "winner" that holds the proton more strongly is the base in that relationship. When the reaction is over, a new acid and base have been created: HB^+ now has a hydrogen, and A^- has an available electron

acid

base

proton

proton transfer

FIGURE 13.4
Illustration
of proton
transfer

305

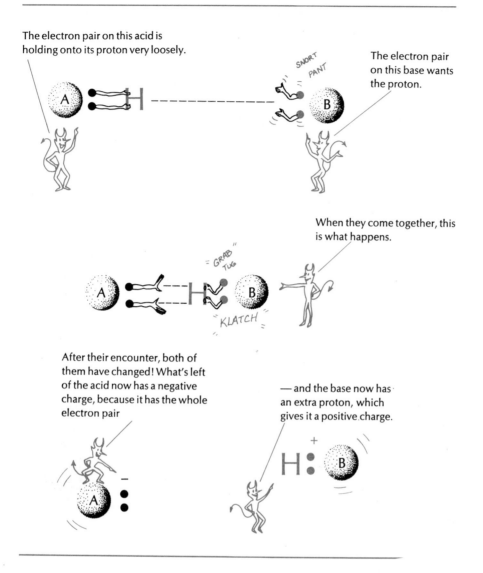

The electron pair on this acid is
holding onto its proton very loosely.

The electron pair
on this base wants
the proton.

When they come together, this
is what happens.

After their encounter, both of
them have changed! What's left
of the acid now has a negative
charge, because it has the whole
electron pair

— and the base now has
an extra proton, which
gives it a positive charge.

pair. This is an example of what we call *conjugate pairs*. Every acid forms
its *conjugate base* by donating a proton. Every base forms its *conjugate
acid* by accepting a proton. Table 13.6 shows some common conjugate
pairs of acids and bases, arranged in order of strength. The stronger the
acid, the weaker its conjugate base, and vice versa.

conjugate pair

conjugate base

conjugate acid

We can use Table 13.6 to predict how or whether certain acid-base reactions will take place. First, we see that some substances are only acids;
others are only bases. A few, such as HCO_3^-, can be either one. An acid
will react only with bases that are below it on the table. HCO_3^- reacts as
an acid with OH^-, but as a base with H_3O^+.

TABLE 13.6
Some common conjugate acid-base pairs

	Acids	Bases	
Form H_3O^+ in water	$HClO_4$	ClO_4^-	These do not act as bases
	HCl	Cl^-	
	HNO_3	NO_3^-	
	H_2SO_4	HSO_4^-	
Acids only	H_3O^+	H_2O	Acid or base
	H_2SO_3	HSO_3^-	Acid or base
	HSO_4^-	SO_4^{2-}	Base only
	H_3PO_4	$H_2PO_4^{2-}$	Acid or base
	HF	F^-	Base only
	$HC_2H_3O_2$	$C_2H_3O_2^-$	Base only
	H_2CO_3	HCO_3^-	Acid or base
	H_2S	HS^-	Acid or base
Acid or base	$H_2PO_4^{2-}$	HPO_4^{2-}	Acid or base
Acid or base	HSO_3^-	SO_3^{2-}	Bases only
Acid only	$HClO$	ClO^-	
Acid only	NH_4^+	NH_3	
Acid or base	HCO_3^-	CO_3^{2-}	
Acid or base	HPO_4^{2-}	PO_4^{3-}	
Acid or base	HS^-	S^{2-}	
Acid or base	H_2O	OH^-	

INCREASING ACIDITY

INCREASING BASICITY

Substances appearing in both columns are connected by colored lines.

EXAMPLE 13.3: Write the net ionic equation for the reaction, if any, that takes place when solutions of NaOH and NH_4Cl are mixed. Label conjugate pairs.

Solution: First, write all substances that are mixed, in their ionic forms: $Na^+ + OH^- + NH_4^+ + Cl^-$. Next, decide from Table 13.6 if any of these are acids or bases, and which is which. Na^+ is neither; Cl^- doesn't act as a base or an acid. NH_4^+ is in the acid column above OH^-, so NH_4^+ reacts with OH^-, and Na^+ and Cl^- are spectator ions.

Answer: $NH_4^+ + OH^- \longrightarrow NH_3(g) + H_2O$

  acid   base

(The colored lines connect conjugate pairs.)

In fact, adding a strong base to an ammonium salt is a common laboratory preparation of ammonia gas.

> **EXAMPLE 13.4:**   Write the net ionic equation for the reaction, if any, that takes place when solutions of $NaNO_3$ and $HC_2H_3O_2$ are mixed. Label conjugate pairs.
>
> **Solution:** First, we write, "$Na^+ + NO_3^- + HC_2H_3O_2$." Table 13.6 shows that $HC_2H_3O_2$ is an acid, but NO_3^- is neither an acid nor a base.
>
> **Answer:** No reaction will occur, because there is no base.

> **EXAMPLE 13.5:**   Write the net ionic equation for the reaction, if any, that takes place when solutions of $NaHCO_3$ and KH_2PO_4 are mixed.
>
> **Solution:** First, we write, "$Na^+ + HCO_3^- + K^+ + H_2PO_4^-$." Both HCO_3^- and $H_2PO_4^-$ are in both the acid and base columns of Table 13.6, so we have to decide which way they will react. In the acid column, we find $H_2PO_4^-$ above HCO_3^-, meaning that $H_2PO_4^-$ is the stronger acid. These roles are reversed in the base column.
>
> **Answer:** $H_2PO_4^- + HCO_3^- \longrightarrow HPO_4^{2-} + H_2CO_3$
>
>   acid   base   ($H_2O + CO_2$)

The answer here is the reaction that occurs in baking powder when water is added. The CO_2 that's formed makes baked goods rise. $NaHCO_3$ and KH_2PO_4 are examples of acids and bases that are also salts and thus occur as solid compounds. This is often convenient, since we can mix them in the solid form and they won't react. Baking powder contains a drying agent so that it won't react on the shelf. When we want it to react, we add water, and that lets the ions move around and come in contact with each other.

LEWIS ACIDS AND BASES.   An even more general description of acids and bases is that proposed by G. N. Lewis, of Lewis-structure fame. According to the Lewis concept, an *acid* is an electron-pair acceptor, and a *base* is an electron-pair donor. All acids and bases covered by the Brønsted-Lowry theory are also covered by the Lewis theory. A proton can certainly accept an electron pair, so a proton donor is also an electron-pair acceptor. By the same token, a proton acceptor must have an available electron pair and therefore is also an electron-pair donor.

acid

base

There are many substances that are defined as acids in the Lewis sense but not in the Brønsted-Lowry sense. One of the most common of these is boric acid, often written H_3BO_3. Its Lewis structure is:

$$
\begin{array}{c}
H \\
| \\
|\overline{O}| \\
| \\
H-\overline{\underline{O}}-B-\overline{\underline{O}}-H
\end{array}
$$

The structure of this acid is better described with the formula $B(OH)_3$.

We saw in Chapter 8 that boron and other members of Group IIIA can participate in coordinate covalent bonds, because they have room to accept a whole electron pair. Boric acid reacts with a base, such as hydroxide ion, not by donating a proton, but by accepting an electron pair to form $B(OH)_4^-$.

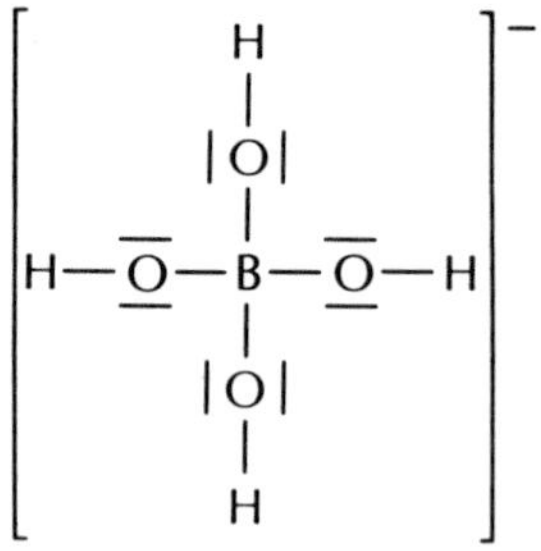

$$
\left[
\begin{array}{c}
\text{H} \\
| \\
|\overline{\text{O}}| \\
| \\
\text{H}-\overline{\text{O}}-\text{B}-\overline{\text{O}}-\text{H} \\
| \\
|\overline{\text{O}}| \\
| \\
\text{H}
\end{array}
\right]^-
$$

The equation for this reaction is:

$$B(OH)_3 \ + \ OH^- \longrightarrow \ B(OH)_4^-$$

Lewis acid Lewis base   borate ion

As we might expect, $Al(OH)_3$ also reacts as a Lewis acid. We already know that it acts as a Brønsted-Lowry base. Substances that react as either acids or bases are said to be *amphoteric*. Another amphoteric hydroxide is $Zn(OH)_2$. These two hydroxides react with base as follows:

amphoteric

$$Al(OH)_3(s) + OH^-(aq) \longrightarrow Al(OH)_4^-(aq)$$
aluminate ion

$$Zn(OH)_2(s) + 2\ OH^-(aq) \longrightarrow Zn(OH)_4^{2-}(aq)$$
zincate ion

Although the Lewis acid-base theory is more general than the Brønsted-Lowry theory, we'll find the latter more convenient to use in this chapter.

BUFFER SYSTEMS.

Blood maintains a pH between 7.35 and 7.45 even though various bodily processes are always adding acids and bases to it. It maintains pH with two important buffer systems. A *buffer system* is a mixture of a weak acid and its conjugate base that resists changes in pH. The base takes care of excess acid; the acid takes care of excess base.

buffer system

One of blood's buffer systems is the conjugate pair $H_2PO_4^-/HPO_4^{2-}$. Here's how this conjugate pair takes care of excess acid or base:

Excess acid: $H_3O^+ + HPO_4^{2-} \longrightarrow H_2O + H_2PO_4^-$

Excess base: $OH^- \ + H_2PO_4^- \longrightarrow H_2O + HPO_4^{2-}$

Since these reactions are happening all the time, a constant ratio of the conjugate acid to the conjugate base is maintained.

The second important buffer system is the H_2CO_3/HCO_3^- system. This system also plays the equally important role of picking up CO_2 from the tissues and carrying it, as HCO_3^-, in the blood to the lungs. At the lungs, hemoglobin (which we'll write HHb instead of Hb to show that it's an acid) picks up oxygen to form $HHbO_2$. When it does, it becomes more acidic and reacts with HCO_3^-, like this:

$$HHbO_2 + HCO_3^- \longrightarrow HbO_2^- + H_2CO_3$$

The H_2CO_3 decomposes, and CO_2 is released at the lungs and exhaled.

"Buffered" aspirin contains the systems HCO_3^-/CO_3^{2-} and glycine (a biological acid)-glycinate. These buffer systems work the same way. We'll be taking a closer look at buffers in Chapter 15.

RELATIVE STRENGTHS OF ACIDS AND BASES.

HCl is an acid; H_2O is a weaker acid; NH_3 is a base; and CH_4 is neither an acid nor a base. To be an acid, a compound's hydrogen must be "loose." Again, energies determine strengths of acids. Figure 13.5 shows the slow-motion ionization of an acid in water. When HCl gas ionizes in water, these things must happen: (1) The acid molecules must be in the gas state (HCl already is); (2) the bond to hydrogen must be broken (for HCl, this means the molecule is simply broken down into separate atoms); (3) the gaseous atoms must be changed into gaseous ions; and (4) the resulting gaseous ions must then be added to water and hydrated.

We've already had access to some of the information we need to add up these energies. Bond energies are given in Table 8.1 (p. 161), and ionization energies and electron affinities are given in Figure 7.9 (p. 143). All we need is the hydration energy for the ions, given below in the summary of energies.

Dissociation energy:	$HCl(g) + 102.0\,kcal \longrightarrow H(g)$	$+ Cl(g)$
Ionization energy:	$H(g) + 312.0\,kcal \longrightarrow H^+(g)$	$+ e^-(g)$
Electron affinity:	$Cl(g) + e^-(g) \longrightarrow Cl^-(g)$	$+ 85.1\,kcal$
Hydration energy:	$H^+(g) + H_2O(l) \longrightarrow H_3O^+(aq)$	$+ 264.0\,kcal$
Hydration energy:	$Cl^-(g) \longrightarrow Cl^-(aq)$	$+ 84.0\,kcal$
Heat of solution:	$HCl(g) + H_2O(l) \longrightarrow H_3O^+(aq)$	$+ 19.1\,kcal$

hydration energy

heat of solution

We'll expand our definition of *hydration energy* from Chapter 12 to mean the energy released when a mole of gaseous ions is dissolved in water. The *heat of solution* is the net amount of energy released when a mole of any substance dissolves in water. For HCl there is an overall release of energy, and the processes that require energy are paid for by processes that release energy. The two largest energies are the ionization energy of hydrogen and the hydration energy of the gaseous hydrogen ions. These two numbers stay the same no matter what the acid is. The hydration energy isn't quite enough to pay for the ionization energy, but it helps enough so that relatively small excesses of energies can tip the balance in the direction of ionization. If a substance isn't an acid (doesn't ionize in water), all or some of these is the reason: (1) The bond energy is too high; (2) the electron affinity isn't high enough; or (3) the hydration energy of the negative ion isn't high enough. We can look at structures of acids and see why their strengths vary.

FIGURE 13.5
The ionization of an acid in water, in slow motion

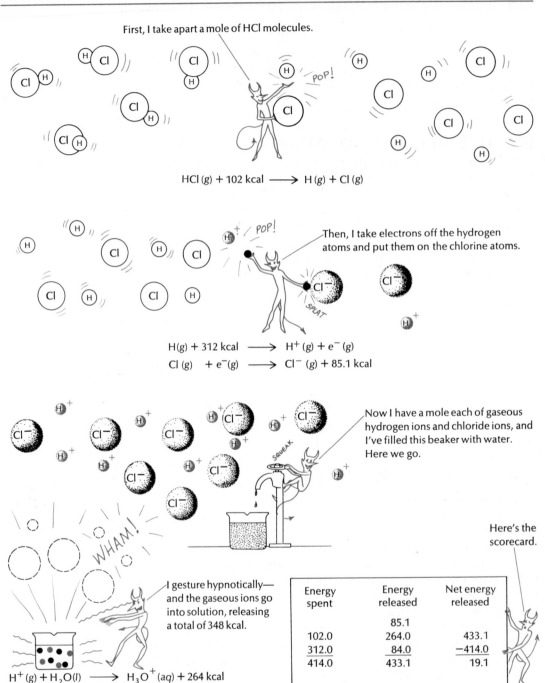

First, I take apart a mole of HCl molecules.

POP!

$$HCl\,(g) + 102\text{ kcal} \longrightarrow H\,(g) + Cl\,(g)$$

Then, I take electrons off the hydrogen atoms and put them on the chlorine atoms.

POP!

SPLAT

$$H(g) + 312\text{ kcal} \longrightarrow H^+\,(g) + e^-\,(g)$$
$$Cl\,(g) + e^-(g) \longrightarrow Cl^-\,(g) + 85.1\text{ kcal}$$

Now I have a mole each of gaseous hydrogen ions and chloride ions, and I've filled this beaker with water. Here we go.

SQUEAK

Here's the scorecard.

WHAM!

I gesture hypnotically—and the gaseous ions go into solution, releasing a total of 348 kcal.

$$H^+\,(g) + H_2O(l) \longrightarrow H_3O^+\,(aq) + 264\text{ kcal}$$
$$Cl^-\,(g) \longrightarrow Cl^-\,(aq) + 84\text{ kcal}$$

Energy spent	Energy released	Net energy released
	85.1	
102.0	264.0	433.1
312.0	84.0	−414.0
414.0	433.1	19.1

ACID STRUCTURE RELATED TO STRENGTH.

The acidity of the halogen acids increases in the order HF, HCl, HBr, HI. This is the order of decreasing bond energy given in Table 8.1. For oxyacids, where the acidic hydrogen is always bonded to oxygen, anything that will weaken the O—H bond will make the acid stronger. Let's consider the series of chlorine oxyacids.

$$H-\overline{\underline{O}}-\overline{\underline{Cl}}| \qquad H-\overline{\underline{O}}-\overline{\underline{Cl}}-\overline{\underline{O}}|$$

hypochlorous   chlorous

$$H-\overline{\underline{O}}-\overline{\underline{Cl}}-\overline{\underline{O}}| \qquad H-\overline{\underline{O}}-\underline{Cl}-\overline{\underline{O}}|$$
$$\qquad\ \ |\underline{\overline{O}}| \qquad\qquad\qquad |\underline{\overline{O}}|$$

chloric   perchloric

The acid strength increases from left to right. HClO is the weakest and HClO$_4$ is the strongest. The acid strength increases with the number of oxygens (in color) that aren't also bonded to hydrogen. HClO$_4$ has three such oxygens; HClO has none. Now we can see why H$_2$SO$_4$ is strong, whereas H$_2$SO$_3$ and H$_3$PO$_4$ are weak.

$$H-\overline{\underline{O}}-S-\overline{\underline{O}}-H \qquad H-\overline{\underline{O}}-S-\overline{\underline{O}}-H \qquad H-\overline{\underline{O}}-P-\overline{\underline{O}}-H$$

Sulfuric acid has two oxygens that aren't bonded to hydrogen; sulfurous and phosphoric acids each have only one. Extremely strong oxyacids have three; strong oxyacids have two; weak oxyacids have one; and extremely weak oxyacids have none.

It might seem as if we're neglecting the structure of bases and their strengths in this discussion. This isn't so if we remember that the stronger the acid, the weaker its conjugate base. Using this reasoning, we see that the base strength of polyatomic ions *decreases* with the number of oxygens that aren't bonded to hydrogen in their conjugate acids. That is, the base strength decreases in the series ClO$^-$, ClO$_2^-$, ClO$_3^-$, ClO$_4^-$. By the same token, HSO$_3^-$ and H$_2$PO$_4^-$ are stronger bases than HSO$_4^-$.

Oxygen is the second most electronegative element, which makes it more electronegative than the central atom in any oxyacid. The more oxygens that are attached to the central atom, the more polar bonds there are. The more polar bonds there are, the more positive the central atom becomes. The more positive the central atom becomes, the more it tends to repel the proton, and therefore the stronger the acid.

If an acid has more than one proton to lose, the first is always much stronger than the second. H_2SO_4 is a strong acid, but HSO_4^- is weak. H_2SO_3 is weak, but HSO_3^- is weaker still. This is because it takes more energy to remove a proton from a negatively charged ion, as we'd expect.

Organic acids—that is, carbon-based acids—have this characteristic grouping:

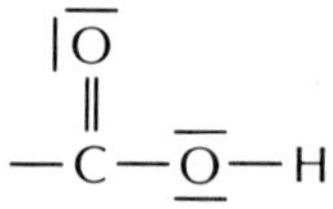

$$-\overset{\overset{\displaystyle |\overline{O}}{\|}}{C}-\overline{O}-H$$

(This is often abbreviated —COOH.) Most organic acids are weak, because they have only one oxygen that isn't bonded to hydrogen. Here are the structures of three common acids with the —COOH grouping.

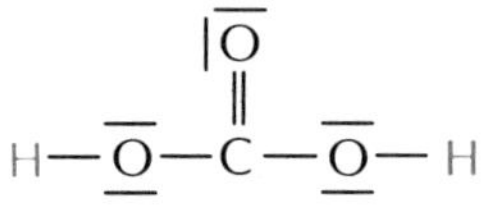

carbonic acid
(the simplest)

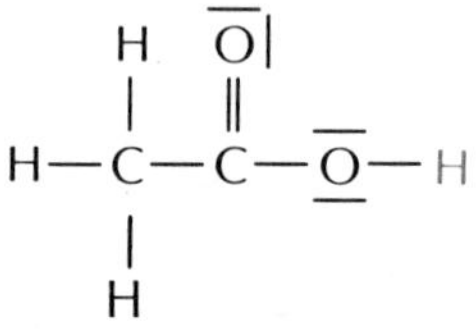

acetic acid

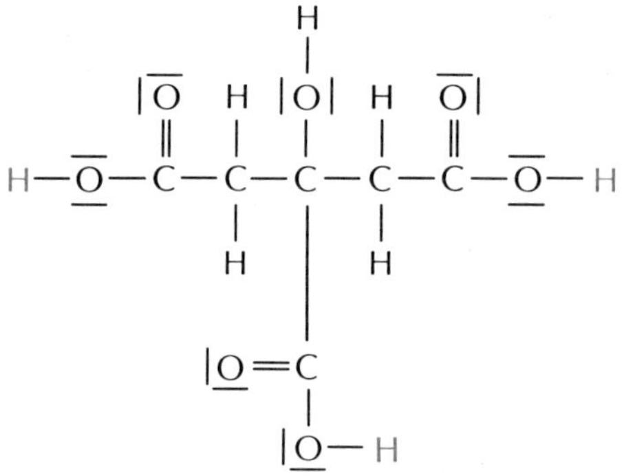

citric acid

In these, the acidic hydrogens are marked in color. The —OH group where carbon is not bonded to another oxygen isn't appreciably acidic, as we'd expect. Although organic acids may have seemingly complicated structures, the important part is the —COOH group.

13.5 REACTIONS OF ACIDS AND BASES IN SOLUTION

In Chapter 12, we looked at the formation of precipitates and how to remove ions from solution. Now we'll see that acids and bases can be used to dissolve many things and to put ions *into* solution.

HOW ACIDS DISSOLVE INSOLUBLE SUBSTANCES. If an

insoluble substance contains a negative ion that's a base, we can often dissolve it by treating it with a strong acid. In Chapter 12, we saw that many sulfides, carbonate, hydroxides, and phosphates are insoluble. According to Table 13.6, these ions are bases. Many oxides are also insoluble. But since the oxide ion is also a base, many oxides can be dissolved by acids. Dissolving the FeO coating on steel with H_2SO_4 (called "pickling")—a reaction we saw in Example 5.38 (p. 98)—is an acid-base reaction. The ionic equation is:

$$H_3O^+ + HSO_4^- + FeO(s) \longrightarrow Fe^{2+} + SO_4^{2-} + 2\,H_2O$$

$$\underset{acid}{} \quad \underset{acid}{} \quad \underset{base}{}$$

■ **EXAMPLE 13.6:** Could H_2SO_4 be used to dissolve CuS? Write the ionic equation for the reaction, if any.

Solution: We find the sulfide ion on the list of bases in Table 13.6, so this reaction is possible. The ionic equation is written in the usual way.

Answer: H_2SO_4 can be used to dissolve CuS.

$$H_3O^+ + HSO_4^- + CuS(s) \longrightarrow H_2O + SO_4^{2-} + Cu^{2+} + H_2S(g)$$

(The sulfide ion, when treated with strong acid, will always go all the way to H_2S by accepting two protons.)

We actually had this reaction in Example 5.39 (p. 98), where sulfuric acid is used to dissolve copper from ores containing CuS.

■ **EXAMPLE 13.7:** Could a strong acid be used to dissolve AgCl? Choose any strong acid and write the ionic equation for the reaction, if any.

Solution: The chloride ion is at the top of the list of bases in Table 13.6, and it's labeled as not acting as a base. AgCl is neither acidic nor basic.

Answer: A strong acid would be no help in dissolving AgCl. Insoluble substances whose negative ions aren't bases can't be dissolved by acids.

Acids can dissolve metals, too, as we saw in Examples 5.33 and 5.34 (p. 97). Hydrochloric acid dissolves zinc metal to produce hydrogen gas. We'd write the complete and net ionic equations like this:

Complete: $\quad 2\,H_3O^+ + 2\,Cl^- + Zn(s) \longrightarrow$
$$Zn^{2+} + 2\,Cl^- + 2\,H_2O + H_2(g)$$

Net: $\qquad 2\,H_3O^+ + Zn(s) \longrightarrow Zn^{2+} + 2\,H_2O + H_2(g)$

Since Cl^- is a spectator ion, it doesn't matter which strong acid we use. It's the hydronium ion that dissolves metal. This class of reactions isn't proton transfer; it's electron transfer. We'll reserve the discussion of electron transfer reactions for the next chapter.

Acids can also dissolve gases, if the gases are basic. The only common basic gas is ammonia. Ammonia dissolves very well in solutions of strong acids, because of this reaction:

$$H_3O^+ + NH_3(g) \longrightarrow H_2O + NH_4^+$$

If ammonia is an unwanted product of a reaction, it can be kept out of the air by passing it through an acid solution.

HOW BASES DISSOLVE INSOLUBLE SUBSTANCES.

If an insoluble substance is an acid, it can be dissolved with a base. Many greases contain heavy organic acids. We can write —COOH for any organic acid, since it's the —COOH part that's the acid.

$$-COOH + OH^- \longrightarrow -COO^- + H_2O$$

This is one reason that detergents have to be basic: to help dissolve the grease. Another reason is that detergents are sodium salts of organic acids. The negative ion part is necessary to provide the water soluble end of the detergent molecule, as we saw in Chapter 12. If we add acid to a detergent solution, this reaction will happen:

$$H_3O^+ + -COO^- \longrightarrow H_2O + -COOH$$

The detergent will be converted to its conjugate acid, and it won't work any more. The water-softening agents will also be converted to their conjugate acids, and they won't work either.

Drain and oven cleaners contain NaOH because of its ability to dissolve grease. But bases, like acids, will also dissolve some metals. For this reason, makers of drain and oven cleaners warn us not to use their products on aluminum pans. Strong bases dissolve aluminum in this way:

$$Al(s) + 2\,OH^- + 2\,H_2O \longrightarrow Al(OH)_4^- + H_2(g)$$
$$\text{aluminate ion}$$

(This is an electron transfer reaction, so we won't discuss it further here.)

Some gases—SO_2, SO_3, CO_2, and NO_2—form acids when they're added to water. These gases are acidic, and will dissolve in base solutions.

$$OH^- + CO_2(g) \longrightarrow HCO_3^-$$

Basic solutions are most useful for dissolving gases, since most common gases are acidic. Acidic solutions are most useful for dissolving solids, since most insoluble solids have negative ions that are bases.

CALCULATIONS IN ACID-BASE REACTIONS.

We've seen how to calculate the molarity of an acid or base or any solute. When working with acids or bases, we often want to dilute a solution that's too concentrated for our purposes. To do so, we take a known amount of the concentrated solution and, adding more solvent, bring it up to a known new volume. Only the amount of solvent changes; the amount of solute remains the same. But this means the concentration changes.

To find out how much concentrated solution to dilute to a certain final volume, we use this equation:

$$V_c = \frac{M_d}{M_c} V_d$$

V_c and M_c are the volume and molarity of the concentrated solution; V_d and M_d are the volume and molarity of the dilute solution.

EXAMPLE 13.8: A laboratory experiment calls for 0.5 M HCl, but the only solution in the lab is 12 M (concentrated) HCl. What volume of 12 M HCl must be diluted to make 0.5 liters of 0.5 M HCl?

Solution: The volume of the concentrated solution is our unknown here. The volume of the dilute solution is 0.5 liters, and the concentrations of the concentrated and dilute solutions are 12 M and 0.5 M.

$$V_c = \frac{M_d}{M_c} V_d = \frac{0.5\,M}{12\,M} (0.5\ l) = \underline{\quad} l$$

Answer: 0.02 l, or 20 ml.

A concentrated acid is always diluted by adding it slowly, with stirring, to some of the water. Then the rest of the water is added to make the desired final volume. This is a safety procedure. A large heat of solution is given off when concentrated acids are diluted. If water is poured into a concentrated acid, the heat will be given off locally, where the water hits the acid. This can cause the hot acid to spatter. It's all right to add the water directly to less concentrated acids. The dilution of a concentrated acid, using the data of Example 13.8, is demonstrated in Figure 13.6. Of course, the formula for dilution can be used for any solution, not just acids and bases.

When all the base in one solution has reacted with all the acid from another solution, the process is called *neutralization*. Sometimes we use neutralization to find the concentration of an acid or base solution. We do this by titrating the solution of unknown concentration against a solution of known concentration. *Titration* is the process of gradually adding a strong acid or a strong base solution to a strong or weak base or acid solution until neutralization takes place. If we want to determine the concentration of an acid solution, we place a known volume of it in an Erlenmeyer flask. Then we add a few drops of an indicator called phenolphthalein, which is colorless in acid and pink in base. We add a base solution of known concentration from a buret, as shown in Figure 13.7. When the mixture shows the slightest visible tinge of pink, we know there is a very slight excess of base present and that our acid has been neutralized. The buret tells us the amount of base solution we added. Knowing the volumes of the acid and base, and the concentration of the base, we can calculate the concentration of the acid. (These problems are like the ones with precipitation in Chapter 12.)

neutralization

titration

**FIGURE 13.6
Diluting a
concentrated
acid**

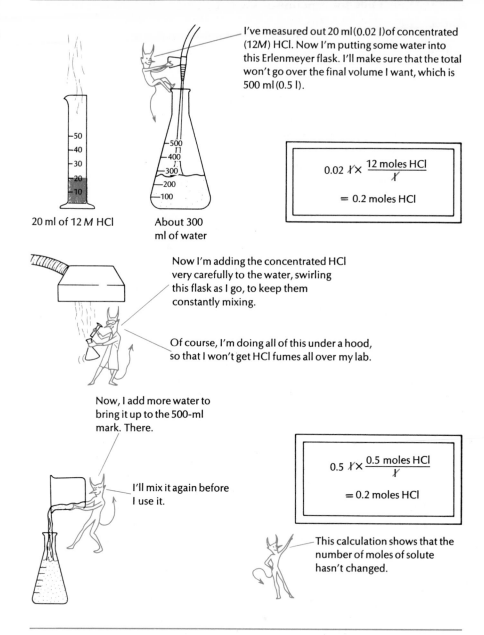

I've measured out 20 ml (0.02 l) of concentrated (12M) HCl. Now I'm putting some water into this Erlenmeyer flask. I'll make sure that the total won't go over the final volume I want, which is 500 ml (0.5 l).

20 ml of 12 M HCl

About 300 ml of water

$$0.02 \cancel{l} \times \frac{12 \text{ moles HCl}}{\cancel{l}}$$
$$= 0.2 \text{ moles HCl}$$

Now I'm adding the concentrated HCl very carefully to the water, swirling this flask as I go, to keep them constantly mixing.

Of course, I'm doing all of this under a hood, so that I won't get HCl fumes all over my lab.

Now, I add more water to bring it up to the 500-ml mark. There.

I'll mix it again before I use it.

$$0.5 \cancel{l} \times \frac{0.5 \text{ moles HCl}}{\cancel{l}}$$
$$= 0.2 \text{ moles HCl}$$

This calculation shows that the number of moles of solute hasn't changed.

EXAMPLE 13.9: The acetic acid in a 25.0-milliliter vinegar sample is neutralized with 35.2 milliliters of 0.512 M NaOH solution. What is the molarity of the acetic acid in the vinegar sample?

Solution: First, we write the equation for the reaction:

$$\text{NaOH}(aq) + \text{HC}_2\text{H}_3\text{O}_2(aq) \longrightarrow \text{NaC}_2\text{H}_3\text{O}_2(aq) + \text{H}_2\text{O}(l)$$

Next, we want to convert 35.2 milliliters (0.0352 liters) of NaOH to moles of $HC_2H_3O_2$. Our conversion factors are 0.512 moles NaOH/liter (the molarity of the NaOH) and the mole ratio from the equation, 1 mole $HC_2H_3O_2$/mole NaOH.

$$0.0352 \text{ l NaOH} \times \frac{0.512 \text{ moles NaOH}}{\text{l NaOH}} \times \frac{1 \text{ mole } HC_2H_3O_2}{\text{mole NaOH}}$$

$$= 0.0180 \text{ moles } HC_2H_3O_2$$

I've put 25.0 milliliters of vinegar into this flask. It contains a certain number of moles of acetic acid, but I don't know how many yet.

Now, I'll add a drop of phenolphthalein indicator. I can't see it, because it's colorless in acid.

TINK

And, I've filled this buret with 50 milliliters of 0.512 M NaOH. The buret has markings on it so that I know how much base I've added.

This stopcock lets me add the base to the acid solution as fast or as slowly as I want to.

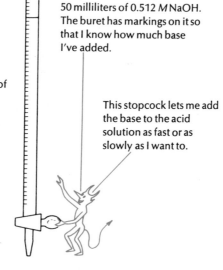

FIGURE 13.7
Titration
of an acid
against a base

Now, I'm titrating the acid against the base. When the solution stays just a little pink, I'll stop adding base.

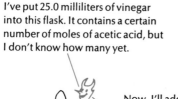

DRIP
DRIP

SWIRL

$$NaOH \, (aq) + HC_2H_3O_2 \, (aq) \longrightarrow$$
$$NaC_2H_3O_2(aq) + H_2O(l)$$

Now the solution is slightly pink, and it took 35.2 ml (0.0352 l) of base solution to do it. According to these calculations, I used 0.0180 moles of base to neutralize the acid, so there must have been 0.0180 moles of acid there in the first place—right?

$$0.0352 \text{ l NaOH} \times \frac{0.512 \text{ moles NaOH}}{\text{l NaOH}}$$

$$= 0.0180 \text{ moles NaOH}$$

Now we know that 0.0180 moles of acetic acid are contained in 25.0 ml, and we can easily calculate molarity.

$$\text{molarity} = \frac{\text{moles}}{\text{liter}} = \frac{0.0180 \text{ moles}}{0.0250 \text{ l}} = \underline{\qquad} M \text{ HC}_2\text{H}_3\text{O}_2$$

Answer: 0.720 M $HC_2H_3O_2$.

EXAMPLE 13.10: A sample of water from mine drainage contains H_2SO_4. A 25.0-milliliter sample of the water requires 45.0 milliliters of 0.112 M NaOH to be neutralized (both protons). What is the molarity of H_2SO_4 in the mine drainage sample?

Solution:

$$H_2SO_4(aq) + 2\,NaOH(aq) \longrightarrow Na_2SO_4(aq) + 2\,H_2O(l)$$

We want to convert 0.0450 l NaOH to moles of H_2SO_4. Our setup:

$$0.0450 \text{ l NaOH} \times \frac{0.112 \text{ moles NaOH}}{\text{l NaOH}} \times \frac{1 \text{ mole } H_2SO_4}{2 \text{ moles NaOH}}$$
$$= 2.52 \times 10^{-3} \text{ moles } H_2SO_4$$

$$\text{molarity} = \frac{\text{moles}}{\text{liter}} = \frac{2.52 \times 10^{-3} \text{ moles}}{2.50 \times 10^{-2} \text{ liters}} = \underline{\qquad} M \text{ H}_2\text{SO}_4$$

Answer: 0.101 M H_2SO_4.

EXAMPLE 13.11: The mining company that produces the acid drainage wants to neutralize the acid by adding solid lime, CaO. How many kilograms of lime must be added to 25,000 liters of the 0.101-M mine drainage?

Solution:

$$CaO(s) + H_2SO_4(aq) \longrightarrow CaSO_4(aq) + H_2O(l)$$

We want to convert 2.5×10^4 liters of H_2SO_4 to kilograms of CaO. Our conversion factors are 0.101 moles H_2SO_4/liter; 1 mole CaO/mole H_2SO_4; and 56.0 grams CaO/mole CaO. Our setup:

$$2.5 \times 10^4 \text{ l } H_2SO_4 \times \frac{0.101 \text{ moles } H_2SO_4}{\text{l } H_2SO_4} \times$$
$$\frac{1 \text{ mole CaO}}{\text{mole } H_2SO_4} \times \frac{56.1 \text{ g CaO}}{\text{mole CaO}} \times \frac{1 \text{ kg}}{10^3 \text{ g}} = \underline{\qquad} \text{ kg CaO}$$

Answer: 142 kg.

REVIEW QUESTIONS

Strong Acids and Strong Bases

1. What is *hydronium ion?* When does it form?
2. What are the *strong acids?* Write equations for their ionizations in water.
3. What are some *strong bases?* What do they have in common?
4. Besides the fact that they are bases, how are the strong bases different from the strong acids?

5. What reaction occurs between any strong acid and any strong base? Write the net ionic equation.
6. Write a complete ionic equation for the reaction of a strong acid with a strong base. Label the spectator ions.
7. Why is it dangerous to mix concentrated acids and bases together?

Weak Acids and Weak Bases

8. Write the equation for water dissolving in water.
9. How much hydronium ion and hydroxide ion are present in normal water?
10. What is a weak acid? How do we write one in ionic equations?
11. What is a weak base? Give a common example.
12. Write an equation that shows the carbonate ion acting as a weak base.
13. Write ionic equations that show (a) a weak acid reacting with a weak base; (b) a strong acid reacting with a weak base; and (c) a weak acid reacting with a strong base.
14. Give examples of (a) a base that can gain two hydrogens; and (b) an acid that can lose two hydrogens. Write equations for each step.

Measuring Acids and Bases

15. How can we find $[H_3O^+]$ for a strong acid and $[OH^-]$ for a strong base?
16. What is the relationship between $[H_3O^+]$ and $[OH^-]$ for any acid or base solution?
17. What is pH? What does a pH of 7.00 mean? How does pH tell us whether a solution is acidic or basic?
18. How do we use the coarse pH scale of Figure 13.3 to convert between whole-number pH and concentrations? What does a pH of 3 mean?
19. Explain how to use Figure 13.3 (a) to find $[H_3O^+]$ and $[OH^-]$ from pH; (b) to find pH from $[H_3O^+]$ or $[OH^-]$; and (c) to convert between $[H_3O^+]$ and $[OH^-]$.
20. How can we tell if our $[H_3O^+]$ and $[OH^-]$ are correct?
21. What happens if blood falls outside the pH range of 7.35 to 7.45?
22. Why do we need to measure pH? What are two ways of measuring pH?
23. What is an *indicator*? Give an example.
24. How can a too-acidic soil be corrected?

The Structures of Acids and Bases

25. Give the Brønsted-Lowry definitions of acids and bases, and illustrate.
26. What is meant by *proton* in the Brønsted-Lowry concept? What is *proton transfer*? Give an example.
27. What is a *conjugate pair*? Give an example, and label each half.
28. How are the strengths of acids and their conjugate bases related? Give examples of this from Table 13.6.
29. How can we use Table 13.6 to predict acid-base reactions?
30. Name a substance that is (a) an acid only; (b) a base only; (c) neither an acid nor a base; (d) both an acid and a base.
31. What is a *buffer system*? Give an example.
32. List the energies involved when an acid ionizes in water, and describe the processes that occur. What energies may be involved if a substance isn't an acid?
33. How does the Lewis structure of an oxyacid give us a rough idea of how strong it is?
34. Which is the stronger base, ClO_4^- or ClO^-? How do we know?
35. When an acid has two or more protons to lose, what are the relative acidities of each successive proton? Why?
36. Why are most organic acids weak?

Reactions of Acids and Bases in Solution

37. What kind of insoluble substances can strong acids dissolve? Give an example, and write the equation.
38. Why does ammonia gas dissolve well in strong acid? Write the equation.
39. What kind of solids do bases dissolve well? Write an equation.
40. Why do detergents work poorly in acid solution?
41. Why are bases better at dissolving gases than acids are? Write an equation as an example.
42. How do we calculate the volume of concentrated solution that must be diluted to obtain a certain volume and concentration of dilute solution?
43. What is *neutralization*? How do we know when neutralization has happened?
44. What is *titration*? How is it used to find the concentration of an acid or base solution?

EXERCISES

1. Write complete and net ionic equations for reactions between the following acids and bases in water solution. Classify each acid and base as weak or strong.
   a. $HClO_4$ and KOH
   b. $HC_2H_3O_2$ and $Ca(OH)_2$
   c. NH_3 and $HC_2H_3O_2$
   d. HCl and Na_3PO_4
   e. HNO_3 and $Sr(OH)_2$
   f. $NaHCO_3$ and HF
2. Potash, K_2CO_3, is present in wood ashes. Caustic potash, KOH, can be made by adding water to potash. Write the complete and net ionic equations that show this conversion.
3. One type of fire extinguisher contains sulfuric acid and sodium hydrogen carbonate in separate

containers. When the tank is tipped upside down, these mix and form carbon dioxide, which puts out the fire. Write complete and net ionic equations for this reaction, and identify the acid and the base.

4. Give the ion concentration requested for each of the following.
   a. 0.035 M HNO_3:[H_3O^+]
   b. 0.15 M KOH:[OH^-]
   c. 0.0021 M HCl:[H_3O^+]
   d. 6.8 $\times$ 10^{-4} M $Ca(OH)_2$:[OH^-]

5. From pH values given in Table 13.5, give [H_3O^+] for each of the following.
   a. battery acid   d. pure water, 25°C
   b. soda water   e. seawater
   c. black coffee   f. liquid bleach

6. From pH values given in Table 13.5, give [H_3O^+] and [OH^-] for each of the following.
   a. lemon juice   d. household ammonia
   b. wine   e. vinegar
   c. rainwater

7. Find the pH of the following, and classify each as acidic or basic.
   a. 0.036 M $HClO_4$
   b. 0.15 M KOH
   c. a solution whose [H_3O^+] is 7.5 $\times$ 10^{-5} M
   d. a solution whose [OH^-] is 4.3 $\times$ 10^{-8} M
   e. a solution whose [H_3O^+] is 8.7 $\times$ 10^{-9} M
   f. a solution whose [OH^-] is 0.20 M

8. Fill in the following table.

[H_3O^+]	[OH^-]	[H_3O^+]	[OH^-]
10^{-7}	___	2.3 $\times$ 10^{-4}	___
___	10^{-1}	___	9 $\times$ 10^{-8}
___	0.045	0.12	___

9. Write net ionic equations for two reactions that show water acting as a proton donor and as a proton acceptor.

10. Fill in the following table without looking at Table 13.6.

Conjugate Acid	Conjugate Base	Conjugate Acid	Conjugate Base
$HC_2H_3O_2$	___	___	SO_4^{2-}
___	H_2O	HCO_3^-	___
NH_4^+	___	___	OH^-
___	F^-	HPO_4^{2-}	___
H_3O^+	___	HNO_3	___
___	CO_3^{2-}	___	NH_3

11. Use Table 13.6 to predict whether or not a reaction would occur if water solutions of the following pairs were mixed. Write net ionic equations for each reaction that would occur.

a. NaF and HCl   e. $NaHSO_4$ and NH_3
b. $HC_2H_3O_2$ and $KHSO_3$ f. HCl and HClO
c. Na_2S and H_3PO_4 g. NaOH and K_2CO_3
d. NH_4Cl and Na_3PO_4 h. $KHCO_3$ and H_2SO_4

12. Sodium bicarbonate and solid citric acid ($H_3C_6H_5O_7$) are the ingredients in Alka Seltzer that cause it to fizz in water. Write the net ionic equation for the reaction.

13. Making acetylene by treating calcium carbide with water is an acid-base reaction in the Brønsted-Lowry sense. Write an ionic equation for this reaction and label the acid and base.

$$CaC_2(s) + 2\,H_2O(l) \longrightarrow Ca(OH)_2(aq) + C_2H_2(g)$$
$$\text{acetylene}$$

14. Write equations that illustrate the conjugate pair H_2CO_3/HCO_3^- acting as a buffer system. Do the same for the system HCO_3^-/CO_3^{2-}.

15. The bond energy of HBr is 86.5 kcal/mole. The electron affinity of Br is 79.5 kcal/mole. The hydration energy of $Br^-(g)$ is 76.4 kcal/mole. Using these figures and others given in the chapter, write a series of equations and calculate the heat of solution of HBr.

16. On the basis of Lewis structures, predict which acid in the following pairs is the stronger acid.
   a. HClO or $HClO_3$ d. $HClO_2$ or H_2SO_4
   b. H_3PO_4 or H_3PO_3 e. $HBrO_2$ or $HBrO_4$
   c. HNO_2 or HNO_3 f. H_2SO_3 or HClO

17. A commercial source of phosphoric acid is the treatment of phosphate rock, $Ca_3(PO_4)_2$, with sulfuric acid. In this case, a strong acid is used to dissolve a solid. Write the complete ionic equation, and explain why sulfuric acid will dissolve phosphate rock.

18. We saw in Chapter 12 that the first step in recovering magnesium from the ocean is to precipitate $Mg(OH)_2$. The second step is to dissolve the precipitate in HCl. This is another example of a strong acid dissolving a solid. Write the complete ionic equation, and explain why HCl dissolves $Mg(OH)_2$.

19. Write net ionic equations for dissolving the following substances in strong acid. If a substance cannot be dissolved in strong acid, explain why.
   a. zinc ore, ZnS
   b. Chile saltpeter, KNO_3
   c. boiler scale, $CaCO_3$
   d. calomel, Hg_2Cl_2
   e. lime, CaO
   f. $Al(OH)_3$

20. Write net ionic equations for dissolving the following substances in strong base. If a substance cannot be dissolved in strong base, explain why.

a. copper ore,
CuS

c. SO_3
d. SO_2

b. butyric acid
(rancid butter),
C_3H_7COOH

e. phosphate rock,
$Ca_3(PO_4)_2$
f. HCl gas

21. Sometimes, people whose stomachs don't manufacture enough HCl must take synthetic HCl as medicine. How many milliliters of 12 M HCl would be needed to make 1.00 liter of HCl in the same concentration as stomach acid (0.016 M)?

22. How many milliliters of 6 molar acetic acid must be diluted to get 0.50 liters of acetic acid having about the same concentration as vinegar (0.8M)?

23. A student is analyzing a sample of household ammonia by titrating it against 0.0500 M HCl. A 10.0-milliliter sample of the ammonia requires 24.1 milliliters of the HCl. Calculate the molarity of the ammonia.

24. What is the molarity of a 25.0-milliliter vinegar solution that is neutralized by 28.1 milliliters of 0.122 M NaOH?

25. Palmitic acid, an ingredient in palm oil, is used in making soap:

$$C_{15}H_{31}-COOH(s) + NaOH(aq) \longrightarrow$$
$$C_{15}H_{31}-COONa(aq) + H_2O$$
soap

How many milliliters of 1.00 M NaOH would it take to neutralize 50.0 grams of palmitic acid? The molecular weight of palmitic acid is 256 g/mole.

26. Lactic acid, C_2H_5OCOOH, is the sour ingredient in sour milk and buttermilk. A recipe that calls for sour milk or buttermilk usually also calls for baking soda ($NaHCO_3$). Write the equation for the reaction between lactic acid and baking soda, and calculate the number of grams of baking soda needed to neutralize 0.0510 M lactic acid in 1 cup (about 250 cm^3) of sour milk.

27. A sample of rainwater collected near a copper smelter is analyzed for acid content. It turns out that a 100.-milliliter sample of the rainwater is neutralized by 22.4 milliliters of 0.0122 M NaOH. Assuming that the acid present is sulfurous acid, which resulted from the reaction of SO_2 with water, what is the molarity of acid in the rainwater?

14

Electro-chemistry

So far, the energy we've seen in chemical reactions has been only in the form of heat. But heat isn't the only form of energy. Electricity is another one, and it can take part in chemical reactions just as heat can. Electrochemistry covers a class of chemical reactions that involve electrical energy. When we turn on a flashlight or start a car, we're using electrochemistry. The chemical activity in a battery is like an exothermic reaction: the battery releases energy in the form of electricity. A car bumper's chromium plating comes from the equivalent of an endothermic reaction: electricity must be supplied. Electrochemical processes that extract metals and nonmetals from their ores or from seawater are also like endothermic reactions.

We've seen precipitation reactions in which positive and negative ions are traded (Chapter 12), and we've seen acid-base reactions involving proton transfer (Chapter 13). In this chapter, we'll look at electrochemical reactions, where electrons are transferred.

14.1 ELECTRONS IN CHEMICAL REACTIONS

Electrons are involved in all chemical reactions, but in electron transfer reactions they're involved as actual reactants and products.

SPONTANEOUS ELECTRON TRANSFER REACTIONS.

Many familiar reactions and applications involve electron transfer. Table 14.1 lists some typical spontaneous electron transfer reactions. Whereas precipitation and acid-base reactions involve only double replacement, electron transfer reactions can be combination of elements to form compounds, decomposition where elements are formed, or single replacement, as well as other more complex types.

electron donor In electron transfer, the substance that gives up electrons is the *electron donor,* and the substance that receives electrons is the *electron acceptor.* Another term for electron transfer is "oxidation-reduction." *Oxidation* means loss of electrons, and *reduction* means gain of electrons. ("Oxidation" used to mean only combining with oxygen. Combining with oxygen does cause a substance to lose electrons, so now oxidation means more generally any process in which electrons are lost.) The electron donor, since it causes another substance to gain electrons, is called the *reducing agent.* The electron acceptor, since it causes another substance to lose electrons, is called the *oxidizing agent.* In oxidation-reduction reactions, also called *redox (reduction + oxidation) reactions,* the reducing agent is oxidized and the oxidizing agent is reduced. Figure 14.1 illustrates these relationships.

electron acceptor

oxidation

reduction

reducing agent

redox reaction

The substances on Table 14.1 that are reacting as oxidizing agents are shown in color. These equations don't show any electrons being reactants or products. To show this, we break each reaction into two parts.

TABLE 14.1
Some spontaneous electron transfer reactions

Reaction	Type	Comments
$2 Na(s) + Cl_2(g) \longrightarrow 2 NaCl(s)$	Combination (elements)	When an ionic compound forms, electrons are transferred from the metal to the nonmetal.
$CuSO_4(aq) + Zn(s) \longrightarrow ZnSO_4(aq) + Cu(s)$ Net ionic: $Cu^{2+} + Zn(s) \rightarrow Zn^{2+} + Cu(s)$ This is the reaction that happens in one kind of galvanic cell.	Single replacement	When a metal reacts with a metal ion, electrons are transferred from the metal atom to the metal ion.
$6 H_3O^+ + Al(s) \longrightarrow Al^{3+} + 3 H_2(g) + 6 H_2O(l)$ Strong acids dissolve many metals.	Single replacement	When a metal reacts with a strong acid, electrons are transferred from the metal atoms to the acid's protons.
$2 Al(s) + 6 H_2O(l) + 2 OH^-(aq) \longrightarrow$ $\quad\quad\quad\quad\quad\quad 2 Al(OH)_4^- + 3 H_2(g)$ Strong bases dissolve many metals.	Single replacement	When a metal reacts with a strong base, electrons are transferred from the metal atoms to hydroxide ion's hydrogens.
$2 I^- + Cl_2(g) \longrightarrow I_2(s) + 2 Cl^-$ Extracting iodine from seawater with chlorine.	Single replacement	When a nonmetal reacts with a nonmetal ion, electrons are transferred from the nonmetal ion to the nonmetal atom.
$4 Fe(s) + 3 O_2(g) + H_2O(l) \longrightarrow 2 Fe_2O_3(s) + H_2O$ Iron rusting in moist air.	Combination	Electrons are transferred from the iron to the oxygen.
$(NH_4)_2Cr_2O_7 \longrightarrow Cr_2O_3(s) + N_2(g) + 4 H_2O(l)$ Volcano reaction.	Decomposition	Some electron transfer reactions are very complex.

ELECTRON TRANSFER HALF-REACTIONS.

We can see that electron transfer is happening in this net ionic equation taken from Table 14.1:

$$Cu^{2+}(aq) + Zn(s) \longrightarrow Cu(s) + Zn^{2+}(aq)$$

Clearly, the zinc atom is giving its electrons to the copper(II) ion. Copper(II) ion is the oxidizing agent and zinc atom is the reducing agent. At the end of the reaction, copper(II) ion has been reduced and zinc has been oxidized. As we've done with several other processes before, we can break this down into partial reactions.

$$Zn(s) \longrightarrow Zn^{2+}(aq) + 2e^- \quad\quad\quad Oxidation$$
$$Cu^{2+} + 2e^- \longrightarrow Cu(s) \quad\quad\quad Reduction$$

FIGURE 14.1
Reducing agents are electron donors, and oxidizing agents are electron acceptors

REDUCING AGENT
(Electron Donor)

OXIDIZING AGENT
(Electron Acceptor)

Reducing Agents hold their electrons very loosely. This particular reducing agent will donate only one electron, but many can donate more than one.

Oxidizing agents are hungry for electrons. This guy has room for only one, but many oxidizing agents can accept more than one.

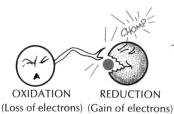

OXIDATION   REDUCTION
(Loss of electrons) (Gain of electrons)

It helps me to remember which is the oxidizing agent and which is the reducing agent if I say that the reducing agent relinquishes its electrons. Then the oxidizing agent is the one that's left.

Now the redox reaction is over, and the oxidizing agent has the electron.

OXIDIZED REDUCING AGENT
(electrons lost)

REDUCED OXIDIZING AGENT
(electrons gained)

half-reaction

Each of these represents a *half-reaction*. Adding the half-reactions gives the total reaction. In electron transfer reactions, one half-reaction must always show electrons being given up and one must show electrons being accepted. As with chemical substances, electrons can be neither destroyed nor created, so the number of electrons lost is always the same as the number gained. Although electrons don't appear anywhere in the complete equation, they do appear as either reactants or products in the half-reactions. Like the other partial reactions we've seen, these happen simultaneously, and not one at a time.

If we put a piece of zinc metal into a solution containing copper(II) ions, we'd see something happen. The solution, originally blue because of the presence of the blue copper(II) ion, becomes colorless as the copper(II) ions are replaced by colorless zinc ions. The surface of the zinc metal changes from shiny silver grey to dark as copper metal is deposited (plated) on it. The solution warms up as energy is released in the form of heat.

Because this reaction releases energy, we can use it in a battery. But we can't let the zinc and copper(II) ions come in direct contact with each other, because then the released energy doesn't do any useful work. To make it do useful work, and to get the energy as electricity instead of heat, we have to make the electron transfer happen through an external circuit and not directly. This means separating the zinc from the copper(II) ions.

Figure 14.2 shows zinc and copper(II) ions connected in a galvanic cell. A *galvanic cell,* named after Luigi Galvani, is any cell in which a spontaneous redox reaction is harnessed to produce electricity. *Batteries* contain various types of galvanic cells. In this particular one, a bar of zinc metal is sticking into the zinc solution and a bar of copper metal is sticking into the copper solution. These bars are *electrodes,* where each half-reaction will take place. The partition is there to keep the copper(II) ion from coming into contact with the zinc electrode and taking the zinc's electrons directly.

galvanic cell

battery

electrode

When the electrodes aren't connected, nothing happens. But when we connect them through an external circuit, something like a relay race begins. A zinc atom on the zinc electrode donates two electrons, and goes into solution as a zinc ion. The electrons that zinc donates whiz around the circuit to the copper electrode, causing the light bulb to light on the way. As the electrons reach the copper electrode, they are accepted by waiting copper(II) ions. As soon as a copper(II) ion accepts two electrons, it becomes a copper atom and part of the metal electrode. The stream of electrons flowing around the circuit is an electric current.

In this cell, positive zinc ions are constantly formed on one side, and positive copper(II) ions are constantly lost on the other side. But a solution, like a chemical formula, must be electrically neutral. The reaction would stop as soon as there was a slight excess of either positive or negative ions in either compartment. To keep the reaction going, we make the partition porous. Negative sulfate ions and positive zinc ions can move through the partition, which equalizes the charge balance in each compartment. The copper(II) ions don't move through the partition because they would be moving into a compartment that already had too many positive ions in it.

In any cell, the electrode where reduction takes place is called the *cathode,* and the electrode where oxidation takes place is called the *anode.* In this cell, the copper electrode is the cathode, where the reduction half-reaction takes place. The zinc ions won't be reduced, even though they can come in contact with the cathode, because they are much worse electron acceptors than copper(II) ions.

cathode

anode

The zinc electrode is the anode, where the oxidation half-reaction takes place. The sulfate ions can come in contact with the anode, but nothing happens to them. They are neither oxidizing nor reducing agents, but spectator ions. If a copper(II) ion touched the zinc electrode, though, it would take electrons directly from the zinc atoms and stop the current

**FIGURE 14.2
A galvanic cell harnesses spontaneous electron transfer by passing electrons around a circuit**

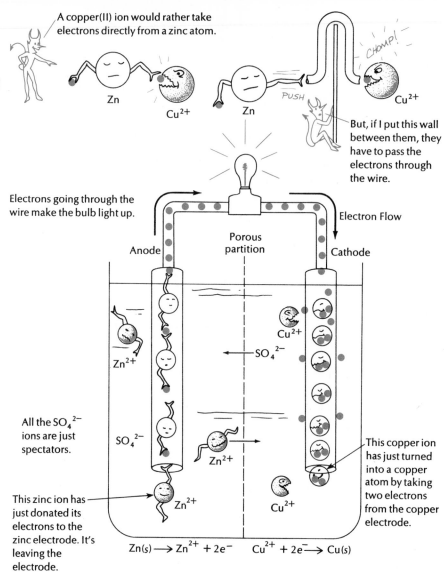

A copper(II) ion would rather take electrons directly from a zinc atom.

Zn   Cu²⁺   Zn   CHOMP!   Cu²⁺

PUSH

But, if I put this wall between them, they have to pass the electrons through the wire.

Electrons going through the wire make the bulb light up.

Electron Flow

Anode   Porous partition   Cathode

Zn^{2+}

All the SO₄²⁻ ions are just spectators.

SO_4^{2-}

Zn^{2+}

This zinc ion has just donated its electrons to the zinc electrode. It's leaving the electrode.

Zn^{2+}

Cu^{2+}

SO_4^{2-}

Cu^{2+}

Cu^{2+}

This copper ion has just turned into a copper atom by taking two electrons from the copper electrode.

$$Zn(s) \longrightarrow Zn^{2+} + 2e^- \qquad Cu^{2+} + 2e^- \longrightarrow Cu(s)$$

flow through the circuit. But the porous partition helps keep the copper(II) ions on their own side.

When the zinc has all been oxidized, or when the copper(II) ions have all been reduced, the battery is dead.

This particular battery is only one of many possible ones. We see, though, that a battery is an electron pump. When we connect it, it pumps electrons around a circuit. We use the following general symbol to mean a battery.

The short vertical line next to the minus sign indicates the electron source (where the electrons come out). The long vertical line next to the plus sign indicates the electron sink (where the electrons go in). The minus sign at the electron source shows that it is repelling the negatively charged electrons. The plus sign at the electron sink shows that it is attracting electrons. The same number of electrons must go in as go out. For this to happen, there has to be a complete circuit. A disconnected battery delivers no current.

14.2 ELECTROLYTIC REACTIONS

Electrons from an electron pump, such as a battery or direct current, can be used to drive an electron transfer reaction that normally wouldn't proceed spontaneously. This kind of reaction is called an *electrolytic reaction*. It occurs only if the reactants conduct electricity.

electrolytic reaction

CONDUCTIVITY. We saw in Chapter 10 that metals conduct electricity because electrons can move easily through them. Although we've mostly talked about electrons so far, electricity is any kind of moving charge. Positive and negative ions are charged particles too, as electrons are. Any substance that contains ions that can move will conduct electricity.

Ions in a solid crystal can't conduct electricity because they can't move. But if we melt the crystal or dissolve it in water, the ions can move and the substance will conduct electricity. Figure 14.3 illustrates the conductivity of sodium chloride, melted and in solution.

A substance whose solution can conduct electricity is called an *electrolyte*. If its solution will conduct electricity well, a substance is a *strong electrolyte*. Solutions of strong electrolytes contain a lot of ions, either because the substance ionizes completely or because it is a soluble ionic compound. A *weak electrolyte's* solution will also conduct electricity, but not nearly as well; this is because it doesn't contain many ions. Weak electrolytes either don't ionize completely — like weak acids and bases — or are relatively insoluble ionic compounds. A *nonelectrolyte* is a substance whose solution won't conduct electricity at all, because it contains no ions. Table 14.2 gives examples of each kind of electrolyte.

electrolyte

strong electrolyte

weak electrolyte

nonelectrolyte

Water itself is listed as a nonelectrolyte, even though it does form a few ions. The concentration of hydronium and hydroxide ions in water — 10^{-7} M for each — isn't enough for water to conduct electricity. Even so, we shouldn't be in contact with water when we're using electricity. Dissolved ions in tap water, plus salt that's on our skin, can make water conduct enough to be dangerous.

Cars that spend a lot of time around oceans or where winter roads must be salted tend to rust rapidly. The rusting of iron is an electrochemical process, as we saw in Table 14.1. The salt makes an electrolytic solution that speeds up the rusting reaction.

ELECTROLYSIS. Conductivity and electrolysis go together. A battery or direct current source conducts electricity when connected to a solution or a melted ionic compound; electrolysis happens then, too. *Electrolysis* is the use of electrical energy to drive a chemical reaction.

electrolysis

We know this reaction occurs spontaneously:

$$2\,Na(s) + Cl_2(g) \longrightarrow 2\,NaCl(s) + energy$$

FIGURE 14.3 Moving ions conduct electricity

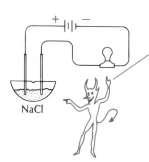

When I put these electrodes into a dish of salt crystals, nothing happens. The light doesn't light. No conductivity. The ions in sodium chloride are fastened tightly in their crystal structure.

NaCl

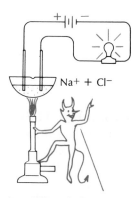

If I melt the salt, though, the light lights up! There is conductivity. The ions can move and conduct current.

$Na^+ + Cl^-$

Water by itself doesn't conduct electricity. The light is unlit.

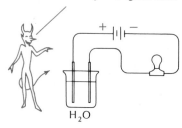

H_2O

But now watch what happens when I shake some salt into the water. When the ions are dissolved, they can move and conduct current. The light lights up.

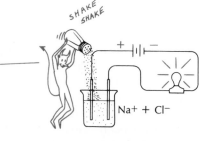

SHAKE SHAKE

$Na^+ + Cl^-$

TABLE 14.2 331

Strong Electrolytes	Weak Electrolytes	Nonelectrolytes	
Strong acids, such as:	Weak acids, such as:	Any covalent compound	TABLE 14.2 Examples of strong, weak, and nonelectrolytes
$H_3O^+ + HSO_4^-$	$HC_2H_3O_2$	that isn't an acid or base,	
$H_3O^+ + Cl^-$	H_3PO_4	such as:	
$H_3O^+ + NO_3^-$	HF	ethyl alcohol	
$H_3O^+ + ClO_4^-$	H_2SO_3	sugar	
Strong bases, such as:	Weak bases, such as:	glycerin	
$Na^+ + OH^-$	NH_3	antifreeze	
$Ca^{2+} + 2OH^-$	Insoluble salts, such as:	water	
Soluble salts, such as:	AgCl		
$Na^+ + Cl^-$	$BaSO_4$		
$K^+ + NO_3^-$	CuO		
$2NH_4^+ + SO_4^{2-}$			

Sodium chloride won't decompose spontaneously to form sodium and chlorine. But we can force it to decompose by supplying electrical energy. This is the reaction that takes place in the electrolysis of melted NaCl:

$$2\,NaCl(l) + energy \longrightarrow 2\,Na(l) + Cl_2(g)$$

This reaction isn't quite the reverse of the formation of sodium chloride, because it happens at a higher temperature, where both sodium chloride and sodium are liquids. This difference, plus some other distinctions, cause the two energies to have slightly different values.

Electrolysis is a way to recover sodium and chlorine from seawater. First, the water is evaporated, leaving the solid salt. Then the salt is melted and electrolyzed. Chlorine gas comes off at the anode and liquid sodium drips from the cathode.

An *electrolytic cell* is a cell in which electrical energy is pumped in to **electrolytic cell** cause a chemical reaction. An electrolytic cell is the opposite of a galvanic cell, where a chemical reaction is used to provide electrical energy. Figure 14.4 gives us a detailed look at the sodium chloride electrolytic cell. The circuit must be complete for electrical conductivity to occur. The circuit is completed by the movement of the ions, which pick up and deposit electrons. The positive ions move to the cathode, where they accept electrons pumped in by the battery.

Cathode: $\qquad Na^+(l) + e^- \longrightarrow Na(l) \qquad$ *Reduction*

At the same time, negative ions move to the anode and donate their electrons to the battery's sink.

Anode: $\qquad 2\,Cl^-(l) \longrightarrow Cl_2(g) + 2e^- \qquad$ *Oxidation*

Because they move toward the cathode, positive ions are also called **cation** *cations* (read, "cat-ions"). Negative ions are called *anions* (read, "an-ions"), **anion** because they move toward the anode.

We said that the number of electrons going in and out of a battery must

FIGURE 14.4
The electrolysis of melted NaCl

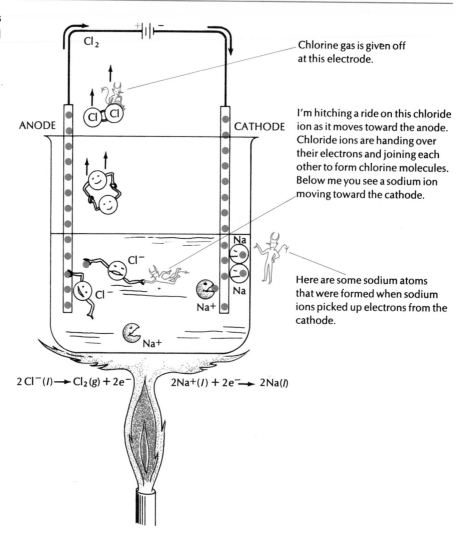

Chlorine gas is given off at this electrode.

I'm hitching a ride on this chloride ion as it moves toward the anode. Chloride ions are handing over their electrons and joining each other to form chlorine molecules. Below me you see a sodium ion moving toward the cathode.

Here are some sodium atoms that were formed when sodium ions picked up electrons from the cathode.

$$2\,Cl^-(l) \longrightarrow Cl_2(g) + 2e^- \qquad 2\,Na^+(l) + 2e^- \longrightarrow 2\,Na(l)$$

be the same. To show this, we make sure that the electrons are balanced by multiplying one or both of the half-reactions by appropriate numbers. In this case, we multiply the cathode half-reaction by 2. Then we can add the half-reactions to get the overall reaction, and the electrons will cancel.

Cathode:	$2\,Na^+(l) + 2e^- \longrightarrow 2\,Na(l)$
Anode:	$2\,Cl^-(l) \longrightarrow Cl_2(g) + 2e^-$
Overall:	$2\,Na^+(l) + 2\,Cl^-(l) \longrightarrow 2\,Na(l) + Cl_2(g)$

Seawater can be electrolyzed directly. In that case, hydrogen is produced at the cathode, instead of sodium, according to these half-reactions:

Anode:	$2\,Cl^-(aq) \longrightarrow Cl_2(g) + 2e^-$
Cathode:	$2\,H_2O(l) + 2e^- \longrightarrow H_2(g) + 2\,OH^-(aq)$
Overall:	$2\,Cl^-(aq) + 2\,H_2O(l) \longrightarrow Cl_2(g) + H_2(g) + 2\,OH^-(aq)$

Sodium ions are spectators in this reaction. With the chlorine and hydrogen going off as gases, what we have left is a solution of sodium hydroxide (lye). The electrolysis of seawater thus produces three useful substances: hydrogen, chlorine, and lye.

Another electrolytic process uses a mercury cathode and gets sodium metal directly from seawater. Mercury is able to dissolve sodium metal. As soon as it forms, sodium dissolves in the mercury. The mercury is kept flowing through so the sodium is always being removed. Then the mercury-sodium mixture is taken to another chamber where the sodium is allowed to react with water to form sodium hydroxide and hydrogen. The mercury can be used over and over again, but a lot of it can escape in the waste water. This particular process, called the mercury cell process, has been a major source of mercury pollution.

When a more dilute solution of NaCl or any ionic compound in water is electrolyzed, water itself is decomposed, according to these half-reactions:

Anode:	$6\,H_2O(l) \longrightarrow O_2(g) + 4\,H_3O^+(aq) + 4e^-$
Cathode:	$2[2\,H_2O + 2e^- \longrightarrow H_2(g) + 2\,OH^-(aq)]$
Overall:	$10\,H_2O(l) \longrightarrow$
	$\quad O_2(g) + 4\,H_3O^+(aq) + 2\,H_2(g) + 4\,OH^-(aq)$

(Notice that we multiplied the cathode reaction by 2, so the electrons would cancel out of both equations.) If we added some phenolphthalein indicator to water that was being electrolyzed, we'd see the water turning pink around the cathode, where hydroxide ions were being formed. Eventually, though, the four hydronium ions would react with the four hydroxide ions to produce eight water molecules. When we subtract these from the ten on the left, our net reaction is:

$$2\,H_2O(l) \longrightarrow 2\,H_2(g) + O_2(g)$$

Here, both the sodium and chloride ions are spectators. They serve only to carry the current and to make the solution electrically neutral. This is another way that hydrogen is produced commercially, with oxygen as a by-product.

Many metals are produced by electrolysis of their compounds. Magnesium is prepared this way. At last we can finish the process of obtaining magnesium metal from seawater that we started two chapters ago. In Chapter 12, we saw seawater being treated with slaked lime, $Ca(OH)_2$, to precipitate the magnesium as $Mg(OH)_2$.

$$Mg^{2+}(aq) + 2\,OH^-(aq) \longrightarrow Mg(OH)_2(s)$$

Then, in Chapter 13, we saw the magnesium hydroxide being filtered out and dissolved in HCl.

$Mg(OH)_2(s) + 2 H_3O^+(aq) + 2 Cl^-(aq) \longrightarrow$
$$Mg^{2+}(aq) + 2 Cl^-(aq) + 4 H_2O(l)$$

Now the water is removed by evaporation, leaving solid $MgCl_2$, which is then melted and electrolyzed.

$$Mg^{2+}(l) + 2 Cl^-(l) \longrightarrow Mg(s) + Cl_2(g)$$

ELECTROPLATING. "Plating" means depositing a thin coating of one metal over another metal. When this is done in an electrolytic cell, it's called *electroplating*. Silver plate, a thin layer of silver over an object made of another metal (usually nickel), is an example of electroplating.

electroplating

In silver-plating an object like a nickel spoon, the spoon itself is used as the cathode in a solution of silver nitrate. The silver ions move to the cathode, accept electrons, and plate out on the spoon.

Cathode: $\qquad\qquad\qquad Ag^+(aq) + e^- \longrightarrow Ag(s)$

To replace the silver ions, a bar of silver metal is used for the anode.

Anode: $\qquad\qquad\qquad Ag(s) \longrightarrow Ag^+(aq) + e^-$

The silver atoms, giving up their electrons to the anode, dissolve into the solution as silver ions. The nitrate ions are spectators. There is no net reaction here, but silver has been moved from the anode to the spoon.

Copper and chromium plating are also done this way. "Tin" cans are actually steel cans that have been tin-plated because steel rusts and tin doesn't. In plating, the object to be plated is the cathode, the solution contains ions of the metal to be plated out, and the anode is a bar of the solid metal that is being plated out.

14.3 OXIDIZING
AND REDUCING AGENTS

We've seen that some redox reactions proceed spontaneously and others require energy. Now we'll see how to tell which is which.

STANDARD ELECTRODE POTENTIALS. Table 14.3 shows oxidizing and reducing agents, with their half-reactions, arranged in order of strength. We can use this table to decide whether a given oxidizing agent will react with a given reducing agent or not. Every oxidizing agent has a reduced form, and every reducing agent has an oxidized form, just as every acid has a conjugate base and every base has a conjugate acid. The stronger an oxidizing agent, the weaker its reduced form is as a reducing agent, and vice versa. Like proton transfer and protons, electron transfer is a contest between two substances for one or more electrons.

Unlike acid-base reactions, redox reactions are usually visible: a gas or solid is formed, a solid is dissolved, or there is a color change. Heat is usually involved, too. We see in the table that changes between ions in solution, and solids or gases out of solution, are frequent. For example, when iron metal is oxidized, it goes into solution as Fe^{2+}; when H_3O^+ is reduced, H_2 goes out of solution as a gas. Also, many half-reactions contain substances other than the oxidizing or reducing agent, such as H_2O, OH^-, H_3O^+, and others. These are present to provide atom balance for the half-reactions. And finally, the number of electrons being transferred is often more than one, while in proton transfer reactions one was the usual number.

Accompanying each half-reaction is a number called the *standard electrode potential* (E^0). This potential describes the tendency of a given half-reaction to proceed in the direction it's written. The more positive the potential, the more the half-reaction would tend to proceed. The more negative the potential, the less it would tend to proceed. These potentials provide the basis for the order of oxidizing and reducing agents in the table. The hydrogen/hydronium-ion electrode—with a potential of zero—is the dividing line between positive and negative. We'll be explaining and working with these potentials in more detail. Right now, though, we'll see how to use the table to predict reactions.

**standard elec-
trode potential
(E^0)**

PREDICTING REDOX REACTIONS.

An oxidizing agent will react only with reducing agents that are below it in the table. Generally speaking, alkali metal ions and alkaline earth metal ions in solution will not be oxidizing agents, but they usually will be spectator ions. Similarly, the negative ions sulfate and phosphate are usually neither oxidizing nor reducing agents but spectator ions. This information, plus the table, can be used to predict reactions. Let's see how by finding out if a reaction will take place when aluminum metal is placed in a solution of nickel(II) sulfate. Our goal is to write the net ionic equation for the reaction, if there is one.

Step 1: Write all substances in their correct forms.
In our example, they are $Al(s)$, $Ni^{2+}(aq)$, and $SO_4^{2-}(aq)$.

Step 2: Decide whether any of these are oxidizing or reducing agents.
We've been told that SO_4^{2-} is neither, but we do find Ni^{2+} in the oxidation column above $Al(s)$ in the reduction column. Thus $Ni^{2+}(aq)$ will oxidize $Al(s)$.

Step 3: Write the two half-reactions, balance the electrons, and add the two equations.

$$Al(s) \longrightarrow Al^{3+}(aq) + 3e^-$$
$$Ni^{2+}(aq) + 2e^- \longrightarrow Ni(s)$$

Here, we have a loss of three electrons but a gain of only two. To balance the electrons, we multiply the top equation by 2 and the bottom equation by 3.

$$2\,Al(s) \longrightarrow 2\,Al^{3+}(aq) + 6e^-$$
$$\underline{3\,Ni^{2+}(aq) + 6e^- \longrightarrow 3\,Ni(s)}$$
$$2\,Al(s) + 3\,Ni^{2+}(aq) \longrightarrow 2\,Al^{3+}(aq) + 3\,Ni(s)$$

TABLE 14.3
Oxidizing and reducing agents

Reduction Half-Reaction	Reducing Agents	Electrode Potential, E^0 (volts)
$2 F^-(aq) \longrightarrow F_2(g) + 2e^-$	F^-	-2.65
$4 H_2O(l) \longrightarrow H_2O_2(aq) + 2 H_3O^+(aq) + 2e^-$	H_2O	-1.77
$PbSO_4(s) + 6 H_2O(l) \longrightarrow$ $PbO_2(s) + SO_4{}^{2-}(aq) + 4 H_3O^+(aq) + 2e^-$	$PbSO_4$	-1.68
$Au(s) \longrightarrow Au^{3+}(aq) + 3e^-$	Au	-1.50
$Mn^{2+}(aq) + 12 H_2O(l) \longrightarrow MnO_4{}^-(aq) + 8 H_3O^+(aq) + 5e^-$	Mn^{2+}	-1.50
$2 Cl^-(aq) \longrightarrow Cl_2(g) + 2e^-$	Cl^-	-1.36
$2 Cr^{3+}(aq) + 21 H_2O(l) \longrightarrow Cr_2O_7{}^{2-}(aq) + 14 H_3O^+ + 6e^-$	Cr^{3+}	-1.33
$Mn^{2+}(aq) + 6 H_2O(l) \longrightarrow MnO_2(s) + 4 H_3O^+(aq) + 2e^-$	Mn^{2+}	-1.23
$6 H_2O(l) \longrightarrow O_2(g) + 4 H_3O^+(aq) + 4e^-$	H_2O	-1.23
$2 Br^-(aq) \longrightarrow Br_2(l) + 2e^-$	Br^-	-1.06
$NO(g) + 6 H_2O(l) \longrightarrow NO_3{}^-(aq) + 4 H_3O^+(aq) + 3e^-$	NO	-0.96
$Ag(s) \longrightarrow Ag^+(aq) + e^-$	Ag	-0.80
$Fe^{2+}(aq) \longrightarrow Fe^{3+}(aq) + e^-$	Fe^{2+}	-0.77
$Mn(OH)_3(s) + NH_3(aq) \longrightarrow MnO_2(s) + H_2O(l) + NH_4{}^+(aq) + e^-$	$Mn(OH)_3$	-0.74
$H_2O_2(aq) + 2 H_2O(l) \longrightarrow O_2(g) + 2 H_3O^+(aq) + 2e^-$	H_2O_2	-0.68
$2 I^-(aq) \longrightarrow I_2(s) + 2e^-$	I^-	-0.54
$Ni(OH)_2(s) + 2 OH^-(aq) \longrightarrow NiO_2(s) + 2 H_2O(l) + 2e^-$	$Ni(OH)_2$	-0.49
$Cu(s) \longrightarrow Cu^{2+}(aq) + 2e^-$	Cu	-0.34
$H_2S(aq) + 2 H_2O(l) \longrightarrow S(s) + 2 H_3O^+(aq) + 2e^-$	H_2S	-0.14
$Hg(l) + 2 OH^-(aq) \longrightarrow HgO(s) + H_2O(l) + 2e^-$	Hg	-0.10
$H_2(g) - 2 H_2O(l) \longrightarrow 2 H_3O^+(aq) + 2e^-$	H_2	0.00
$Pb(s) \longrightarrow Pb^{2+}(aq) + 2e^-$	Pb	$+0.13$
$Sn(s) \longrightarrow Sn^{2+}(aq) + 2e^-$	Sn	$+0.14$
$Ni(s) \longrightarrow Ni^{2+}(aq) + 2e^-$	Ni	$+0.25$
$Pb(s) + SO_4{}^{2-}(aq) \longrightarrow PbSO_4(s) + 2e^-$	Pb	$+0.36$
$Fe(s) \longrightarrow Fe^{2+}(aq) + 2e^-$	Fe	$+0.44$
$Zn(s) \longrightarrow Zn^{2+}(aq) + 2e^-$	Zn	$+0.76$
$Cd(s) + 2 OH^-(aq) \longrightarrow Cd(OH)_2(s) + 2e^-$	Cd	$+0.81$
$H_2(g) - 2 OH^-(aq) \longrightarrow 2 H_2O(l) + 2e^-$	H_2	$+0.83$
$Cr(s) \longrightarrow Cr^{2+}(aq) + 2e^-$	Cr	$+0.91$
$Zn(s) + 2 OH^-(aq) \longrightarrow Zn(OH)_2(s) + 2e^-$	Zn	$+1.25$
$Al(s) \longrightarrow Al^{3+}(aq) + 3e^-$	Al	$+1.66$
$Mg(s) \longrightarrow Mg^{2+}(aq) + 2e^-$	Mg	$+2.37$
$Na(s) \longrightarrow Na^+(aq) + e^-$	Na	$+2.71$
$Li(s) \longrightarrow Li^+(aq) + e^-$	Li	$+3.01$

INCREASING STRENGTH OF REDUCING AGENTS

Electrode Potential, E^0 (volts)	Oxidizing Agents	Oxidation Half-Reaction
+2.65	F_2	$F_2(g) + 2e^- \longrightarrow 2\,F^-(aq)$
+1.77	H_2O_2	$H_2O_2(aq) + 2\,H_3O^+(aq) + 2e^- \longrightarrow 4\,H_2O(l)$
+1.68	PbO_2	$PbO_2(s) + SO_4^{2-}(aq) + 4\,H_3O^+ + 2e^- \longrightarrow$ $PbSO_4(s) + 6\,H_2O(l)$
+1.50	Au^{3+}	$Au^{3+}(aq) + 3e^- \longrightarrow Au(s)$
+1.50	MnO_4^-	$MnO_4^-(aq) + 8\,H_3O^+(aq) + 5e^- \longrightarrow Mn^{2+}(aq) + 12\,H_2O(l)$
+1.36	Cl_2	$Cl_2(g) + 2e^- \longrightarrow 2\,Cl^-(aq)$
+1.33	$Cr_2O_7^{2-}$	$Cr_2O_7^{2-}(aq) + 14\,H_3O^+(aq) + 6e^- \longrightarrow 2\,Cr^{3+}(aq) + 21\,H_2O(l)$
+1.23	MnO_2	$MnO_2(s) + 4\,H_3O^+(aq) + 2e^- \longrightarrow Mn^{2+}(aq) + 6\,H_2O(l)$
+1.23	O_2	$O_2(g) + 4\,H_3O^+(aq) + 4e^- \longrightarrow 6\,H_2O(l)$
+1.06	Br_2	$Br_2(l) + 2e^- \longrightarrow 2\,Br^-(aq)$
+0.96	NO_3^-	$NO_3^-(aq) + 4\,H_3O^+(aq) + 3e^- \longrightarrow NO(g) + 6\,H_2O(l)$
+0.80	Ag^+	$Ag^+(aq) + e^- \longrightarrow Ag(s)$
+0.77	Fe^{3+}	$Fe^{3+}(aq) + e^- \longrightarrow Fe^{2+}(aq)$
+0.74	MnO_2	$MnO_2(s) + H_2O(l) + NH_4^+(aq) + e^- \longrightarrow Mn(OH)_3(s) + NH_3(aq)$
+0.68	O_2	$O_2(g) + 2\,H_3O^+(aq) + 2e^- \longrightarrow H_2O_2(aq) + 2\,H_2O(l)$
+0.54	I_2	$I_2(s) + 2e^- \longrightarrow 2\,I^-(aq)$
+0.49	NiO_2	$NiO_2(s) + 2\,H_2O(l) + 2e^- \longrightarrow Ni(OH)_2(s) + 2\,OH^-(aq)$
+0.34	Cu^{2+}	$Cu^{2+}(aq) + 2e^- \longrightarrow Cu(s)$
+0.14	S	$S(s) + 2\,H_3O^+(aq) + 2e^- \longrightarrow H_2S(aq) + 2\,H_2O(l)$
+0.10	HgO	$HgO(s) + H_2O(l) + 2e^- \longrightarrow Hg(l) + 2\,OH^-(aq)$
0.00	H_3O^+	$2\,H_3O^+(aq) + 2e^- \longrightarrow H_2(g) + 2\,H_2O(l)$
−0.13	Pb^{2+}	$Pb^{2+}(aq) + 2e^- \longrightarrow Pb(s)$
−0.14	Sn^{2+}	$Sn^{2+}(aq) + 2e^- \longrightarrow Sn(s)$
−0.25	Ni^{2+}	$Ni^{2+}(aq) + 2e^- \longrightarrow Ni(s)$
−0.36	$PbSO_4$	$PbSO_4(s) + 2e^- \longrightarrow Pb(s) + SO_4^{2-}$
−0.44	Fe^{2+}	$Fe^{2+}(aq) + 2e^- \longrightarrow Fe(s)$
−0.76	Zn^{2+}	$Zn^{2+}(aq) + 2e^- \longrightarrow Zn(s)$
−0.81	$Cd(OH)_2$	$Cd(OH)_2(s) + 2e^- \longrightarrow Cd(s) + 2\,OH^-(aq)$
−0.83	H_2O	$2\,H_2O(l) + 2e^- \longrightarrow H_2(g) + 2\,OH^-(aq)$
−0.91	Cr^{2+}	$Cr^{2+}(aq) + 2e^- \longrightarrow Cr(s)$
−1.25	$Zn(OH)_2$	$Zn(OH)_2(s) + 2e^- \longrightarrow Zn(s) + 2\,OH^-(aq)$
−1.66	Al^{3+}	$Al^{3+}(aq) + 3e^- \longrightarrow Al(s)$
−2.37	Mg^{2+}	$Mg^{2+}(aq) + 2e^- \longrightarrow Mg(s)$
−2.71	Na^+	$Na^+(aq) + e^- \longrightarrow Na(s)$
−3.01	Li^+	$Li^+(aq) + e^- \longrightarrow Li(s)$

INCREASING STRENGTH OF OXIDIZING AGENTS

Step 4: *Check the atom and charge balance.*

The atoms balance, and the charges are 6+ on each side. Yes, a reaction will occur, and the equation we've written is correct.

This reaction would allow us to nickel-plate an aluminum object without supplying any energy, because the reaction proceeds spontaneously. While it was happening, we'd see the mixture bubbling, and the green $Ni^{2+}(aq)$ would be replaced by the colorless $Al^{3+}(aq)$. A thin layer of nickel would coat the aluminum object.

EXAMPLE 14.1: Write the net ionic equation for the reaction, if any, that would occur if a piece of iodine were placed in a solution of NaCl.

Solution:
Step 1: The substances are $I_2(s)$, $Na^+(aq)$, and $Cl^-(aq)$.
Step 2: We find I_2 as an oxidizing agent *below* Cl^- as a reducing agent.

Answer: No reaction would occur.

In fact, if we look back at Table 14.1, we can see that the reverse of this reaction is used to remove iodine from seawater. If we bubbled chlorine gas through a solution containing iodide ions, we'd see fine dark crystals of iodine precipitating. Water solutions of chlorine are often used to test for the presence of iodide ion in an unknown solution.

EXAMPLE 14.2: Could $KMnO_4$ be used to remove H_2S from waste water? (That is, will $KMnO_4$ react with H_2S?) Write the equation for the reaction, if any.

Solution:
Step 1: $K^+(aq)$, $MnO_4^-(aq)$, and $H_2S(aq)$.
Step 2: We find MnO_4^- as an oxidizing agent above H_2S as a reducing agent, so a reaction will take place.
Step 3: The half-reactions are:

$$2[MnO_4^-(aq) + 8\,H_3O^+(aq) + 5e^- \longrightarrow Mn^{2+}(aq) + 12\,H_2O(l)]$$
$$5[H_2S(aq) + 2\,H_2O(l) \longrightarrow S(s) + 2\,H_3O^+(aq) + 2e^-]$$

$$2\,MnO_4^-(aq) + 5\,H_2S(aq) + 6\,H_3O^+(aq) \longrightarrow 2\,Mn^{2+}(aq) + 5\,S(s) + 14\,H_2O(l)$$

(Notice that some H_2O and H_3O^+ canceled on each side.)
Step 4: Atom balance checks. The charge on the left is $2(1-) + 6(1+) = 4+$; the charge on the right is $2(2+) = 4+$. The equation is correct.

Answer: Yes, $KMnO_4$ could be used to remove H_2S. The equation is given above.

Permanganate ion is a good oxidizing agent, as we see from its position in the table. It also provides its own built-in indicator for seeing when the reaction is complete. MnO_4^- is a deep purple, which changes to the almost colorless Mn^{2+} as the reaction proceeds.

EXAMPLE 14.3: Will a copper penny dissolve in nitric acid? Write the net ionic equation for the reaction, if any.

Solution: Here, we're asked not only whether a reaction will take place, but also to interpret the question. The only way a metal can dissolve in an aqueous solution is if it's converted to its positive ion. Therefore, if a metal is to dissolve, it must be oxidized. Thus our task is to find out if nitric acid will oxidize copper metal.

Step 1: $Cu(s)$, $H_3O^+(aq)$, and $NO_3^-(aq)$.

Step 2: H_3O^+ is below Cu, but NO_3^- is above Cu. Cu can be oxidized by NO_3^-.

Step 3: The half-reactions are:

$$3[Cu(s) \longrightarrow Cu^{2+}(aq) + 2e^-]$$
$$\underline{2[NO_3^-(aq) + 4 H_3O^+(aq) + 3e^- \longrightarrow NO(g) + 6 H_2O(l)]}$$
$$3\,Cu(s) + 2\,NO_3^-(aq) + 8\,H_3O^+(aq) \longrightarrow 3\,Cu^{2+}(aq) + 2\,NO(g) + 12\,H_2O(l)$$

Step 4: Atom balance checks. The charge on the left is $2(1-) + 8(1+) = 6+$; on the right, $3(2+) = 6+$. The equation is correct.

Answer: A penny will dissolve in nitric acid. The equation is above.

This reaction is often demonstrated in chemistry classes. As the solution turns blue from the blue Cu^{2+}, a brown gas bubbles out of it. This gas is NO_2, which forms as the NO reacts with the oxygen of the air.

EXAMPLE 14.4: Would there be any reaction if hydrogen and oxygen gas were bubbled through water at the same time? Write the net ionic equation for the reaction, if any.

Solution:

Step 1: $H_2(g)$, $O_2(g)$, and $H_2O(l)$.

Step 2: O_2 is in the column of oxidizing agents. Both H_2 and H_2O are in the column of reducing agents, but only H_2 is below O_2.

Step 3:

$$2[H_2(g) + 2 H_2O(l) \longrightarrow 2 H_3O^+(aq) + 2e^-]$$
$$\underline{O_2(g) + 4 H_3O^+(aq) + 4e^- \longrightarrow 6 H_2O(l)}$$
$$2 H_2(g) + O_2(g) \longrightarrow 2 H_2O(l)$$

Step 4: Atoms and charges balance.

Answer: A reaction will occur, as in the equation above.

This answer shouldn't surprise us, because we know that hydrogen and oxygen react spontaneously to form water. Our bodies use this reaction indirectly to provide us with energy. And the reaction is also used in *fuel cells*, which are batteries that use substances normally burned as fuel. When we make electricity by burning hydrogen, we have to convert the heat energy to mechanical energy by making steam turn a turbine. Then we convert mechanical energy to electricity. Every time one kind of energy is changed to another kind, some of the energy is lost. If we can go directly from the chemical reaction to electrical energy, we won't waste as much. A hydrogen-oxygen fuel cell does that, at a high temperature and with catalysts. At the same time, it produces water that is suitable for drinking. Fuel cells are efficient, but they are expensive. The fuels have to be very pure, and expensive catalysts must be used. So far, fuel cells have been used extensively only in space missions.

fuel cell

Where more than one reaction is possible, the reaction involving the oxidizing and reducing agents furthest apart will be preferred in exothermic reactions, because the most energy can be released. For endothermic reactions, the oxidizing and reducing agents closest together will be preferred, because less energy input is required. We see now why, in the electrolysis of a moderately concentrated NaCl solution, hydrogen is obtained at the anode instead of sodium. Chloride ion, in the column of reducing agents, is closer to H_2O as an oxidizing agent than it is to sodium.

14.4 CALCULATIONS WITH ELECTRODE POTENTIALS

Combinations of standard electrode potentials determine how much voltage can be obtained from a certain reaction, or what voltage will have to be supplied to make a nonspontaneous reaction proceed. We'll take a look at voltage itself and how it's related to the energy of reaction.

VOLTAGE CALCULATIONS. A river is flowing water. We saw in Chapter 7 that we can make it do work for us by damming it up and then letting it fall from higher potential energy to lower potential energy. The dam is a barrier—a potential barrier. The water on top of the barrier will fall spontaneously to the bottom and release energy. The water at the bottom of the barrier will not rise spontaneously to the top. If we want the water at the bottom to go to the top, we have to supply energy and pump it up there.

voltage
Electricity is flowing charge. To do work for us, it too must fall from higher potential to lower potential. Here, *voltage* is the potential barrier. A positive electrode potential means that the electrons are on top of the barrier and will fall spontaneously to the bottom. A negative electrode potential means that the electrons are at the bottom of the barrier and won't rise spontaneously to the top. If we want electrons to go from the bottom to the top, we have to supply energy and pump them up there with a battery or some other voltage source.

To find the voltage of any reaction, we combine the individual electrode potentials of its two half-reactions by adding them algebraically. (In electrolysis of melted salts, we'll use the electrode potentials of Table 14.3 even though these are for ions in aqueous solution and not for melted salts. Although this usage is not strictly correct, the values are close enough for our purposes.) We find that the standard electrode potential is -2.71 volts for the reduction of sodium ion, and -1.36 volts for the oxidation of chloride ion. The fact that the oxidation of the chloride ion involves two electrons and the reduction of the sodium ion involves only one makes no difference to the potential. The potential barrier is the same height no

TABLE 14.4 341
Voltage
calculations for
some reactions

| | E^0 and |
Reaction with Half-Reactions	Total Potential
$2\,I^-(aq) + Cl_2(g) \longrightarrow I_2(s) + 2\,Cl^-(aq)$	
$\quad\quad 2\,I^- \longrightarrow I_2(s) + 2e^-$	-0.54 V
$Cl_2(g) + 2e^- \longrightarrow 2\,Cl^-(aq)$	$+1.36$ V
Extraction of iodine from seawater with chlorine.	$+0.83$ V
$Cu^{2+}(aq) + Zn(s) \longrightarrow Cu(s) + Zn^{2+}(aq)$	
$\quad Cu^{2+}(aq) + 2e^- \longrightarrow Cu(s)$	$+0.34$ V
$\quad\quad\quad Zn(s) \longrightarrow Zn^{2+}(aq) + 2e^-$	$+0.76$ V
A simple galvanic cell.	$+1.10$ V
$Mg^{2+}(l) + 2\,Cl^-(l) \longrightarrow Mg(s) + Cl_2(g)$	
$\quad Mg^{2+}(aq) + 2e^- \longrightarrow Mg(s)$	-2.37 V
$\quad\quad 2\,Cl^-(aq) \longrightarrow Cl_2(g) + 2e^-$	-1.36 V
Electrolysis of $MgCl_2$.	-3.73 V

matter how many electrons go over it, just as a dam stays the same height no matter how much water goes over it. The number of electrons does affect the energy, though, as we'll see a little later.

The total potential for the electrolysis of sodium chloride is thus $(-2.71) + (-1.36) = -4.07$ volts. This means that we'd have to provide at least 4.07 volts to make the reaction go, as illustrated in Figure 14.5. A positive total potential for a reaction means that the reaction will go spontaneously and provide as much voltage as the value of the potential. To make a battery, a reaction must have a positive voltage. Table 14.4 shows voltage calculations for some of the reactions we've already discussed.

Standard electrode potentials are measured relative to one another. We couldn't measure an oxidation or a reduction potential by itself, because these half-reactions don't go by themselves. There has to be one of each. The values of the electrode potentials were arrived at by assigning the hydronium-ion/hydrogen electrode a value of 0.00 and then measuring the others relative to that one.

EXAMPLE 14.5: Calculate the voltage provided by a flashlight battery. The total reaction is:

$$Zn(s) + 6\,NH_4^+(aq) + 2\,MnO_2(s) \longrightarrow$$
$$Zn^{2+}(aq) + 2\,Mn(OH)_3(s) + 6\,NH_3(aq)$$

Solution: First, select the appropriate half-reactions from Table 14.3. We find $Zn(s)$ in the column of reducing agents but MnO_2 appears twice in the column of oxidizing agents. We choose the equation that contains NH_4^+. Next, add up the half-reactions to make sure that they give the correct overall equation.

E^0

$Zn(s) \longrightarrow Zn^{2+}(aq) + 2e^-$	$+\ 0.76$ V
$2[MnO_2(s) + H_2O(l) + NH_4^+(aq) + e^- \longrightarrow Mn(OH)_3(s) + NH_3(aq)]$	$+\ 0.74$ V
$Zn(s) + 2\,MnO_2(s) + 2\,H_2O(l) + 2\,NH_4(aq) \longrightarrow$	$+\ 1.50$ V

$$Zn^{2+}(aq) + 2\,Mn(OH)_3(s) + 2\,NH_3(aq)$$

The half-reactions are correct, so we can go ahead and combine their electrode potentials: $(+0.76 \text{ V}) + (+0.74 \text{ V}) = \underline{\quad}$ V.

Answer: 1.50 volts.

FIGURE 14.5 Electrolysis proceeds only when the driving voltage exceeds the negative potential

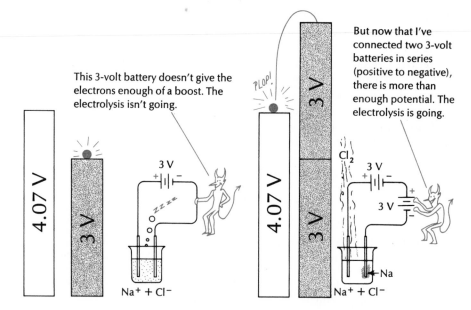

These barriers represent the potentials of the two half-reactions. The electrons are at the bottom, because the potentials are negative.

2.71 V

1.36 V

$Na^+ + e^- \longrightarrow Na$
$E^0 = -2.71$ volts

$2 Cl^- \longrightarrow Cl_2(g) + 2e^-$
$E^0 = -1.36$ volts

Putting those two half-reactions together means stacking their negative potentials one on top of the other.

1.36 V

2.71 V

$2 Na^+ + 2 Cl^- \longrightarrow 2 Na(l) + Cl_2(g)$
$E^0 = (-2.71) + (-1.36) = -4.07$ volts

This 3-volt battery doesn't give the electrons enough of a boost. The electrolysis isn't going.

4.07 V

3 V

3 V

$Na^+ + Cl^-$

But now that I've connected two 3-volt batteries in series (positive to negative), there is more than enough potential. The electrolysis is going.

PLOP!

3 V

4.07 V

3 V

3 V

Cl_2

3 V

3 V

Na

$Na^+ + Cl^-$

Connecting batteries in series means stacking up their potentials.

ENERGY CALCULATIONS. The amount of energy released when water falls over a dam depends on two things: the height of the dam, and the amount of water falling over it. Ten thousand liters of water falling over a 50-meter dam gives us twice as much energy as 5,000 liters of water falling over the same dam. Doubling the height of the dam also gives us twice as much energy with the same amount of water.

The amount of energy released when electrons fall from a potential barrier also depends on two things: the height of the potential barrier, and the number of moles of electrons falling over it. One mole of electrons falling through 1 volt will provide 23.1 kilocalories of energy. Two moles falling through 1 volt will provide twice as much energy: 46.2 kilocalories. One mole falling through 2 volts also provides 46.2 kilocalories. Figure 14.6 illustrates these concepts.

We've introduced a new conversion factor. If 23.1 kilocalories of energy

FIGURE 14.6
Energy depends on quantity and potential

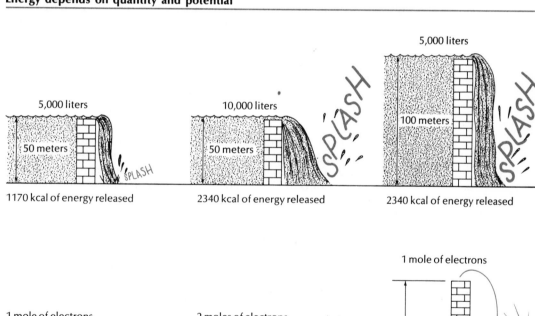

1170 kcal of energy released   2340 kcal of energy released   2340 kcal of energy released

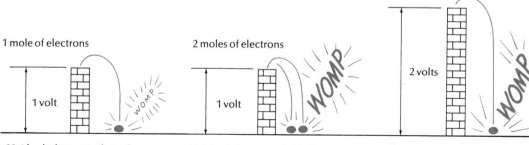

23.1 kcal of energy released   46.2 kcal of energy released   46.2 kcal of energy released

are released when 1 mole of electrons falls through 1 volt, then we have 23.1 kilocalories per volt-mole of electrons, or:

$$23.1 \frac{\text{kilocalories}}{(\text{volt})(\text{mole e}^-)}$$

This is also the energy that it would take to push 1 mole of electrons through a potential of 1 volt. In either case, we can calculate the energy for any reaction if we know its voltage and how many moles of electrons are being transferred. This is the equation:

Energy in kilocalories

$$= (\text{potential in volts})(\text{moles of electrons})\left[23.1 \frac{\text{kilocalories}}{(\text{volt})(\text{mole e}^-)}\right]$$

or

$$E = (\text{volts})(\text{moles e}^-)\left[23.1 \frac{\text{kilocalories}}{(\text{volt})(\text{mole e}^-)}\right]$$

To calculate the energy for a total reaction, we use the total number of moles of electrons that are transferred, as shown in Table 14.5 for a few examples. If, on the other hand, we want to know the energy based on a specific reactant or product, we use the mole ratio of substance to electrons.

EXAMPLE 14.6: How much energy would be provided if 250 grams of lead were used up in a lead storage (car) battery? The two half-reactions are:

$$Pb(s) + SO_4{}^{2-} \longrightarrow PbSO_4(s) + 2e^- \qquad +0.36 \text{ V}$$
$$PbO_2(s) + 4 H_3O^+(aq) + SO_4{}^{2-}(aq) + 2e^- \longrightarrow PbSO_4(s) + 6 H_2O(l) \quad +1.68 \text{ V}$$

Solution: First, let's make sure we have all the quantities needed to solve the energy equation. Adding the voltages of the half-reactions gives us the volts: $(+1.68) + (+0.36) = 2.04$ volts. We get the moles of electrons from the grams of lead given, by using these two conversion factors: the atomic weight of lead (207 g/mole); and the mole ratio of electrons to lead, using the total number of electrons transferred (2 moles e$^-$/1 mole Pb). Our setup is:

$$250 \text{ g Pb} \times \frac{1 \text{ mole Pb}}{207 \text{ g Pb}} \times \frac{2 \text{ moles e}^-}{\text{mole Pb}} = 2.4 \text{ moles e}^-$$

Next, we put all the values into the energy equation and solve.

$$E = (+2.04 \text{ volts})(2.4 \text{ moles e}^-)\left[23.1 \frac{\text{kilocalories}}{(\text{volts})(\text{moles e}^-)}\right] = \underline{\qquad} \text{ kilocalories}$$

Answer: 110 kilocalories.

Figure 14.7 shows a diagram of a lead storage battery. The anode is coated with lead and the cathode is coated with lead(IV) oxide. The electrodes are held apart with plastic spacers, and the space inside is filled with 3-M sulfuric acid. As we just saw, this cell provides about 2 volts. For a 6- or a 12-volt battery, three or six of these cells are connected in series.

Some of the water in a lead storage battery evaporates, and some is lost by electrolysis. If a battery's water weren't replenished now and then, the

TABLE 14.5
Total energy calculations for some electrochemical reactions

Reaction	Potential	Moles e^-	Calculation	Energy for Total Reaction
$2\,Na^+(l) + 2\,Cl^-(l) \longrightarrow 2\,Na(l) + Cl_2(g)$ Electrolysis of NaCl.	-4.07 V	2 moles e^-	$(-4.07\ V)(2\ \text{moles } e^-)\left[23.1\ \dfrac{\text{kcal}}{(V)(\text{mole } e^-)}\right]$	-188 kcal
$Mg^{2+}(l) + 2\,Cl^-(l) \longrightarrow Mg(l) + Cl_2$ Electrolysis of $MgCl_2$.	-3.73 V	2 moles e^-	$(-3.73\ V)(2\ \text{moles } e^-)\left[23.1\ \dfrac{\text{kcal}}{(V)(\text{mole } e^-)}\right]$	-172 kcal
$2\,I^-(aq) + Cl_2(g) \longrightarrow I_2(s) + 2\,Cl^-(aq)$ Iodine from seawater.	$+0.83$ V	2 moles e^-	$(+0.83\ V)(2\ \text{moles } e^-)\left[23.1\ \dfrac{\text{kcal}}{(V)(\text{mole } e^-)}\right]$	$+38.3$ kcal
$3\,Cu(s) + 2\,NO_3^-(aq) + 3\,H_3O^+(aq) \longrightarrow$ $3\,Cu^{2+}(aq) + 2\,NO(g) + 12\,H_2O(l)$ Copper penny dissolving in HNO_3.	$+0.62$ V	6 moles e^-	$(+0.62\ V)(6\ \text{moles } e^-)\left[23.1\ \dfrac{\text{kcal}}{(V)(\text{mole } e^-)}\right]$	$+85.9$ kcal

**FIGURE 14.7
One cell of a
lead storage
battery**

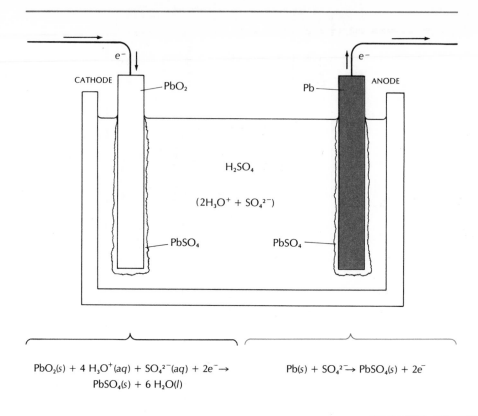

$$PbO_2(s) + 4\ H_3O^+(aq) + SO_4{}^{2-}(aq) + 2e^- \rightarrow$$
$$PbSO_4(s) + 6\ H_2O(l)$$

$$Pb(s) + SO_4{}^{2-} \rightarrow PbSO_4(s) + 2e^-$$

$$PbO_2(s) + Pb(s) + 4\ H_3O\ (aq) + 2\ SO_4{}^{2-}(aq) \rightarrow 2\ PbSO_4(s) + 6\ H_2O(l)$$
$PbSO_4(s)$ coats both anode and cathode as reaction proceeds

battery would dry out and the ions could no longer conduct current. The lead(II) sulfate produced in both half-reactions sticks to the electrode where it's formed. When all the lead and lead(IV) oxide have been changed to lead(II) sulfate, the battery is dead. But it can be recharged, by pumping electrons into the battery in the opposite direction. This reverses the reactions, and turns the lead(II) sulfate on the electrodes back into lead and lead(IV) oxide. Since a car recharges its battery while it runs, a battery should last forever. But after a while the plastic spacers begin to loosen, and some of the lead(II) sulfate falls to the bottom of the battery and isn't available for recharging. Eventually, the battery has to be traded in.

14.5 OXIDATION NUMBERS

**oxidation
number**

The number of electrons lost or gained in any half-reaction is determined by changes in the oxidizing and reducing agents' oxidation numbers. The *oxidation number* of an element tells how many more or fewer electrons it has than it would have as the free element. For an example, let's look at this half-reaction:

$$Zn^{2+} + 2e^- \longrightarrow Zn(s)$$

The reactant Zn^{2+} has an oxidation number of $2+$, which means that the element has two fewer electrons than it would have as a free element. The product Zn is the free element and has an oxidation number of zero. Two electrons are transferred, because zinc's oxidation number goes from $2+$ to zero. If an oxidation number is negative (as it is with Cl^-, whose oxidation number is $1-$), then the element has more electrons than it would have as a free element.

In oxidation, the oxidizing agent's oxidation number is decreased (the element gains electrons). In reduction, the reducing agent's oxidation number is increased (the element loses electrons). Once we learn how to determine oxidation numbers, we can use them to decide how many electrons are being transferred and finally to write complete half-reactions.

DETERMINING OXIDATION NUMBERS.
For monatomic ions, the oxidation number is the same as the ionic charge. Zinc ion, whose ionic charge is $2+$, has an oxidation number of $2+$. And chloride ion, whose ionic charge is $1-$, has an oxidation number of $1-$. For covalent compounds and polyatomic ions, the oxidation numbers of the atoms involved are based on electronegativity differences. For these, oxidation number is an electron bookkeeping device. Each electron pair shared between two atoms is assigned to the more electronegative atom, and then the electrons are counted for each element. For example:

$$|\overline{Cl}{-}\overline{Cl}| \qquad H{-}\overline{Cl}| \qquad \left[|\overline{O}{-}\overline{Cl}{-}\overline{O}|\right]^-$$

In Cl_2, there is no electronegativity difference. Neither owns the pair, and the oxidation number is 0. In HCl, Cl is more negative than H, so the bonding electron pair is assigned to Cl. This gives Cl eight electrons, one more than it would have as a free element, so its oxidation number is $1-$. H has no electrons, one fewer than it would have as a free element, so its oxidation number is $1+$. In ClO_2^-, O is more electronegative than Cl, so each O gets a bonding electron pair. This gives each O eight electrons— two more than it would have as a free element—so its oxidation number is $2-$. Cl now only has four electrons—three less than it would have as a free element—so its oxidation number is $3+$. All oxidation numbers in a compound must total zero, and in a polyatomic ion, they must add up to the ion's total charge.

EXAMPLE 14.7: Find the oxidation number of each element in $PbSO_4$ and PbO_2.

Solution: In $PbSO_4$, the oxidation number of Pb^{2+} is $2+$. In the sulfate ion, O is more electronegative than S, so the four O's get all four electron pairs. Each O then has eight electrons—two more than it has as the free element—so its oxidation number is $2-$. S has no electrons—six less than it has as the free element—so its oxidation number is 6+. Then the charge of the sulfate ion is $(6+) + (8-) = 2-$. In PbO_2, the oxidation numbers are the ionic charges.

Answer: $PbSO_4$: $Pb = 2+$, $S = 6+$, $O = 2-$. $(2+) + (6+) + 4(2-) = 0$
PbO_2: $Pb = 4+$, $O = 2-$. $(4+) + 2(2-) = 0$

Determining oxidation numbers for elements in many compounds would lead us to see that the oxidation numbers of O and H usually remain the same in most of their compounds. We can use their oxidation numbers as references to find other oxidation numbers, according to the rules in Table 14.6.

EXAMPLE 14.8: What are the oxidation numbers of Mn in $KMnO_4$ and in MnO_2?

Solution: In $KMnO_4$, we use K (1+) and O (2−) as references. Then we must balance Mn with their total: $(1+) + (4 \times -2) = 7-$. For MnO_2, Mn must balance oxygen's total of 4−.

Answer: 7+ in $KMnO_4$; 4+ in MnO_2.

EXAMPLE 14.9: What are the oxidation numbers of N in NO_3^- and in NH_4^+?

Solution: In NO_3^-, oxygen totals 6−. For a total charge of 1−, N must be 5+. In NH_4^+, hydrogen totals 4+. For a total charge of 1+, N must be 3−.

Answer: 5+ in NO_3^-; 3− in NH_4^+.

USING OXIDATION NUMBERS.

Sometimes we might need to balance an oxidation-reduction reaction when we don't have access to the necessary half-reactions. Redox reactions are often complex, and attempting to balance them by the trial-and-error method of Chapter 6 frequently leads only to frustration. Also, to be balanced properly, a redox equation must have its electrons balanced. It's possible to have an equation whose atoms balance correctly but whose electrons don't.

The first problem in balancing a redox equation is deciding what elements have changed oxidation numbers. One approach is to check every single atom's oxidation number on both sides. But we can narrow the choice a little with these guidelines: (1) If possible, write the equation in net ionic form (this will eliminate the spectator ions); and (2) if hydrogen and oxygen do not appear as H_2, O_2, or a peroxide, hydrogen and oxygen have not changed.

Now, let's use a step approach to balancing a redox equation. A test for sulfurous acid in rainwater is to add a solution of $K_2Cr_2O_7$. If sulfurous acid is present, the yellow color of the dichromate ion changes to the green color of the chromium(III) ion, according to this unbalanced equation:

$$K_2Cr_2O_7(aq) + H_2SO_3(aq) \longrightarrow\!\!\!\!| Cr_2(SO_4)_3(aq) + K_2SO_4(aq) + H_2O(l)$$

TABLE 14.6
Rules for determining oxidation numbers, with examples

Rules	Examples		
	Compound	Element	Oxidation Number
1. The oxidation number of a monatomic ion is equal to its charge. Metals always have zero or positive oxidation numbers.	FeO	Fe O	2+ 2−
2. The oxidation number of a free element is zero.		H_2 Cu	0 0
3. The usual oxidation number of hydrogen in a compound is 1+, except in metal hydrides, where it is 1−.	HCl NaH	H Cl Na H	1+ 1− 1+ 1−
4. The usual oxidation number of oxygen in a compound is 2−, except in peroxides, where it's 1−.	H_2O H_2O_2	H O H O	1+ 2− 1+ 1−
5. All other oxidation numbers are assigned to produce the total charge on the substance. Rules 1 through 4 take precedence. The total of the oxidation numbers in a covalent compound must add up to zero; the total for a positive or negative polyatomic ion must add up to the ion's total change. Usually the central atom in a polyatomic ion or covalent compound is the one whose oxidation number is in question.	CO_2 SO_4^{2-} HCO_3^-	O C O S H O C	2− (Rule 4) 4+ (needed for total of zero) 2− (Rule 4) 6+ (needed for total of 2−) 1+ (Rule 3) 2− (Rule 4) 4+ (needed for total of 1−)

Our goal is to balance the equation.

Step 1: *Write the equation in net ionic form.*

$$Cr_2O_7^{2-} + H_2SO_3 \longrightarrow 2\,Cr^{3+} + 3\,SO_4^{2-} + SO_4^{2-} + H_2O$$

Step 2: *Decide which substances have changed oxidation numbers.*
Since the equation contains no H_2, O_2, or peroxides, we know hydrogen and oxygen haven't changed. That leaves only Cr and S. It's a good bet that both have changed, since one substance must lose and one must gain electrons. A check of the oxidation numbers verifies this. Cr is 6+ on the left and 3+ on the right. S is 4+ on the left and 6+ on the right.

Step 3: *Determine how many electrons have been lost and gained, and write incomplete half-reactions.*

In our example, Cr went from 6+ to 3+, so each Cr gained 3 electrons. However, there are two Cr in $Cr_2O_7^{2-}$, so that makes 6 electrons gained altogether.

$$Cr_2O_7^{2-} + 6e^- \nrightarrow 2\,Cr^{3+}$$

S went from 4+ on the left to 6+ on the right, so each S lost 2 electrons.

$$H_2SO_3 \nrightarrow SO_4^{2-} + 2e^-$$

Step 4: *Balance the oxygens and hydrogens in the half-reactions by adding H_2O, OH^-, or H_3O^+.*
What combinations of these to add depends on whether the reaction occurs in acidic or basic solution, and on which side of the half-reaction lacks oxygen or hydrogen. We use these guidelines:

	To side where O needed, add, for each O needed:	To other side, add for each O:
Acidic solution	$3\,H_2O$	$2\,H_3O^+$
Basic solution	$2\,OH^-$	$1\,H_2O$

	To side where H needed, add, for each H needed:	To other side, add for each H:
Acidic solution	$1\,H_3O^+$	$1\,H_2O$
Basic solution	$1\,H_2O$	$1\,OH^-$

(When it's not apparent whether the solution is acidic or basic, this information would be given.) Now let's balance the hydrogens and oxygens in our example. We know the solution is acidic because of H_2SO_3. In the first half-reaction, we need to balance $Cr_2O_7^{2-}$ by adding seven oxygen atoms on the right. We add 21 H_2O to the right and 14 H_3O^+ to the left. We check our atom and charge balances and find that they're correct.

$$Cr_2O_7^{2-} + 6e^- + 14\,H_3O^+ \longrightarrow 2\,Cr^{3+} + 21\,H_2O$$

In the second half-reaction, SO_4^{2-} on the right has one more oxygen than H_2SO_3 on the left, so we need one oxygen on the left. We add 3 H_2O to the left and 2 H_3O^+ to the right. We also need two hydrogens on the right, so we add 2 H_3O^+ to the right and 2 H_2O to the left. We write all of this down so that we can simplify it.

$$H_2SO_3 + 3\,H_2O + 2\,H_2O \longrightarrow SO_4^{2-} + 2\,H_3O^+ + 2\,H_3O^+ + 2e^-$$

Then we combine the waters and hydronium ions, and check the atom and charge balances, which are correct.

$$H_2SO_3 + 5\,H_2O \longrightarrow SO_4^{2-} + 4\,H_3O^+ + 2e^-$$

Step 5: *Balance the electrons and add the half-reactions.*
To balance the electrons in our example, we must multiply the second half-reaction by 3.

$$3(H_2SO_3 + 5\,H_2O \longrightarrow SO_4{}^{2-} + 4\,H_3O^+ + 2e^-)$$

Then we can add the half-reactions.

$$Cr_2O_7{}^{2-} + 14\,H_3O^+ + 6e^- \longrightarrow 2\,Cr^{3+} + 21\,H_2O$$
$$3\,H_2SO_3 + 15\,H_2O \longrightarrow 3\,SO_4{}^{2-} + 12\,H_3O^+ + 6e^-$$
$$\overline{Cr_2O_7{}^{2-} + 3\,H_2SO_3 + 15\,H_2O + 14\,H_3O^+ \longrightarrow}$$
$$2\,Cr^{3+} + 3\,SO_4{}^{2-} + 21\,H_2O + 12\,H_3O^+$$

Step 6: *Consolidate the equation and check the atom and charge balances.*
In our example we consolidate the waters and hydronium ions. The balanced equation is:

$$Cr_2O_7{}^{2-} + 3\,H_2SO_3 + 2\,H_3O^+ \longrightarrow 2\,Cr^{3+} + 3\,SO_4{}^{2-} + 6\,H_2O$$

EXAMPLE 14.10: Nitric acid dissolves many substances more effectively than hydrochloric or sulfuric acid does. This is because nitric acid contains nitrate ion, a powerful oxidizing agent, in addition to the oxidizing agent H_3O^+. The other two strong acids have only H_3O^+. CuS dissolves with difficulty in HCl but easily in HNO_3, according to this unbalanced equation:

$$CuS(s) + HNO_3(aq) \not\longrightarrow Cu(NO_3)_2(aq) + S(s) + NO(g) + H_2O(l)$$

Balance the equation.

Solution:
Step 1:

$$CuS(s) + H_3O^+ + NO_3{}^- \not\longrightarrow Cu^{2+} + S(s) + NO(g) + H_2O(l)$$

Step 2: S has changed from $2-$ in CuS to zero in S. N has changed from $5+$ in $NO_3{}^-$ to $2+$ in NO.
Step 3:

$$CuS(s) \longrightarrow Cu^{2+}(aq) + S(s) + 2e^-$$
$$NO_3{}^-(aq) + 3e^- \not\longrightarrow NO(g)$$

Step 4: The first half-reaction is balanced. Now for the second.

$$4\,H_3O^+(aq) + NO_3{}^-(aq) + 3e^- \longrightarrow NO(g) + 6\,H_2O(l)$$

Step 5:

$$3\,CuS(s) \longrightarrow 3\,Cu^{2+}(aq) + 3\,S(s) + 6e^-$$
$$\underline{8\,H_3O^+(aq) + 2\,NO_3{}^-(aq) + 6e^- \longrightarrow 2\,NO(g) + 12\,H_2O(l)}$$
$$3\,CuS(s) + 8\,H_3O^+(aq) + 2\,NO_3{}^-(aq) \longrightarrow$$
$$3\,Cu^{2+}(aq) + 3\,S(s) + 2\,NO(g) + 12\,H_2O(l)$$

Step 6: The equation is consolidated. Atoms and charges balance.

Answer:

$$3\,CuS(s) + 8\,H_3O^+(aq) + 2\,NO_3{}^-(aq) \longrightarrow$$
$$3\,Cu^{2+}(aq) + 3\,S(s) + 2\,NO(g) + 12\,H_2O(l)$$

In this example, we see that sulfur undergoes a change in oxidation number different from that of the previous example ($2-$ to zero, instead of $4+$ to $6+$). We also see from the initial unbalanced equation that some of the nitrate ions remained intact at the end of the reaction; they provide a negative ion to balance the Cu^{2+} in solution. Thus some of the nitrate ions acted as oxidizing agents and some acted as spectator ions.

REVIEW QUESTIONS

Electrons in Chemical Reactions

1. What reaction types are usually electron transfer? Give examples.
2. Define the following words, and explain how they relate to one another: *oxidation, reduction, oxidizing agent, reducing agent, redox.*
3. What is a *half-reaction?* Write two examples, one showing electrons as reactants and one showing electrons as products.
4. Describe what happens when a piece of zinc metal is placed into a solution of copper(II) sulfate.
5. What is a *galvanic cell?* Sketch the zinc-copper galvanic cell, and describe what happens when it is connected.
6. Define *anode* and *cathode.* Write the half-reactions that occur at each electrode in the zinc-copper galvanic cell.
7. What is the symbol for a battery? Where do the electrons come out, and where do they go in?

Electrolytic Reactions

8. What is an *electrolytic reaction?*
9. Explain how ions can conduct electricity. Define *strong electrolyte, weak electrolyte,* and *non-electrolyte,* and give examples of each.
10. Why is it dangerous to use electricity when in contact with water?
11. Describe the *electrolysis* of sodium chloride. What are *cations* and *anions,* and how did they get their names?
12. How do we add half-reactions to get a total reaction?
13. How is electrolysis of seawater different from electrolysis of melted NaCl? What are the products of each?
14. What are the products of electrolysis of a very dilute NaCl solution?

15. Explain how magnesium metal is extracted from seawater.
16. What is *electroplating?* How does it work?

Oxidizing and Reducing Agents

17. How do we use Table 14.3 to decide whether a redox reaction will occur spontaneously?
18. What is a *standard electrode potential?* What is the significance of its sign?
19. List the steps involved in predicting a redox reaction. Illustrate each with an example.
20. What happens to a metal when it dissolves in an aqueous solution?
21. If more than one oxidizing or reducing agent is present, how do we know which will be preferred?

Calculations with Electrode Potentials

22. What is *voltage?* What does its sign mean? How do we find the voltage of a redox reaction?
23. What determines the amount of energy involved in a redox reaction?
24. How many kilocalories of energy do we get when one mole of electrons falls through one volt?

Oxidation Numbers

25. What is the *oxidation number* of an element? What happens to the oxidation number during oxidation? During reduction?
26. Explain how oxidation numbers are determined, and give an example.
27. In balancing redox equations, how do we use oxidation numbers to decide which substances have been oxidized and which reduced?
28. How do we balance hydrogen and oxygen in half-reactions?
29. Summarize the steps involved in balancing a redox equation when the half-reactions are not given.

EXERCISES

1. Identify the oxidizing agent and the reducing agent in each of these electron transfer reactions.
   a. $Cu(s) + S(s) \longrightarrow CuS(s)$
   b. $N_2(g) + O_2(g) \longrightarrow 2\,NO(g)$
   c. $4\,H_3O^+(aq) + Fe(s) \longrightarrow$
   $$2\,H_2(g) + 4\,H_2O(l) + Fe^{2+}(aq)$$
   d. $2\,Cl^-(aq) + F_2(g) \longrightarrow Cl_2(g) + 2\,F^-(aq)$
   e. $Zn(s) + 2\,OH^-(aq) + 2\,H_2O(l) \longrightarrow$
   $$Zn(OH)_4{}^{2-}(aq) + H_2(g)$$

   f. $2\,AgNO_3(aq) + Mg(s) \longrightarrow$
   $$2\,Ag(s) + Mg(NO_3)_2(aq)$$
2. In Exercise 1, identify the oxidized substances and the reduced substances.
3. In a galvanic cell that consists of a lead electrode and an aluminum electrode, these half-reactions take place:
   $$Al(s) \longrightarrow Al^{3+}(aq) + 3e^-$$
   $$Pb^{2+}(aq) + 2e^- \longrightarrow Pb(s)$$

a. Which is the anode, and which is the cathode? How do you know?

b. Sketch such a cell and indicate the direction of electron flow.

4. Classify each of the following as a weak electrolyte, a strong electrolyte, or a nonelectrolyte (assume aqueous solution).

a. $MgCl_2$ e. $PbCl_2$ i. H_2O
b. H_2CO_3 f. $BaSO_4$ j. KOH
c. HNO_3 g. NH_3 k. $Mg(OH)_2$
d. $NaHCO_3$ h. H_3PO_4

5. Aluminum is prepared commercially by electrolyzing melted Al_2O_3.

a. Write half-reactions for this electrolysis, balance the electrons, and add the half-reactions to obtain a balanced equation.

b. Sketch this electrolytic cell. Indicate the cathode and anode and battery terminals, and show the direction of electron flow.

c. Describe what happens at each electrode.

6. Impure copper metal is refined by an electrolytic process similar to electroplating. A bar of impure copper is used as the anode, and a bar of pure copper is used as the cathode. Dilute sulfuric acid is used as the electrolyte. Sketch such a cell and describe each electrode reaction.

7. Use Table 14.3 to predict whether a reaction would occur spontaneously when each of the following pairs were mixed. If a reaction would occur, write the balanced ionic equation.

a. $Pb(s) + Cr(NO_3)_2(aq)$
b. $KMnO_4(aq) + KI(aq)$
c. $Ag(s) + HCl(aq)$
d. $Ag(s) + HNO_3(aq)$
e. $FeSO_4(aq) + MnO_2(s)$
f. $CuSO_4(aq) + HNO_3(aq)$
g. $Na_2Cr_2O_7(aq) + H_2O_2(aq)$
h. $PbO_2(s) + KBr(aq) + H_2SO_4(aq)$

8. A student used an aluminum weighing cup to weigh out some solid copper(II) sulfate. Afterward, he found that the weighing cup had holes in it where individual copper(II) sulfate crystals had come in contact with it. Explain what happened and write a balanced equation for the reaction.

9. Should HCl be used to remove an oxide coating from aluminum? Why?

10. In Table 12.3, we saw that the amount of fluoride ion in seawater is between that of bromide and iodide ions. Could the method used to extract Br_2 and I_2 from seawater (addition of chlorine) also be used to extract F_2? Explain, with reference to appropriate electrode potentials.

11. Could H_2SO_4 clean a gold ring without damaging it? How do you know?

12. Calculate the voltage produced by a hydrogen-oxygen fuel cell (see Example 14.4). How many fuel cells would be needed to electrolyze NaCl?

13. Alkaline storage batteries contain hydroxide ions. One kind is a nickel-cadmium (Nicad) battery, used in calculators and in other portable electronic equipment. The overall reaction is as follows:

$$Cd(s) + NiO_2(s) + 2 H_2O(l) \longrightarrow$$
$$Cd(OH)_2(s) + Ni(OH)_2$$

Write the two half-reactions, chosen from Table 14.3, and calculate the voltage of this cell. (Notice the unusual oxidation number of nickel.)

14. If a tin can is scratched, the iron underneath the tin will corrode much faster than it would have if the tin hadn't been there at all. This is because the iron acts as the anode and the tin acts as the cathode. These half-reactions take place:

Cathode:
$$Sn^{2+}(aq) + 2 e^- \longrightarrow Sn(s)$$

Anode:
$$Fe(s) \longrightarrow Fe^{2+}(aq) + 2e^-$$

The tin acts as the cathode because iron is a better reducing agent than tin.

a. Calculate the voltage of this cell.

b. Would the iron corrode as quickly if zinc were used as a coating instead? Explain.

15. If a mixture of NaCl and LiBr is melted and electrolyzed, what product will first be obtained at each electrode? Explain.

16. A student wishes to identify the terminals of a battery whose markings have been removed. She uses the battery to electrolyze water containing a little Na_2SO_4. What would be observed, and what conclusions could be drawn?

17. Aluminum metal is added to a solution containing $Fe(NO_3)_2$ and $Pb(NO_3)_2$.

a. Two redox reactions are possible. Write their net ionic equations.

b. Which reaction would be preferred? Explain.

18. Iron pipes can be prevented from corroding by connecting them to a block of magnesium and burying the "mixture." The magnesium, called a "sacrificial metal," eventually disappears and must be replaced. Explain how this works.

19. FeI_3 does not exist. After referring to Table 14.3, give a possible reason why.

20. Calculate the energy, in kilocalories, provided by the total reaction that takes place in a flashlight battery. (See Example 14.5.)

21. Which takes more energy to produce by electrolysis, sodium metal or magnesium metal? (Answer this question by calculating the energy required to produce a mole of each one.)

22. For the copper-zinc galvanic cell, (a) calculate the energy provided by the total reaction, and (b) find

how many of these cells would provide enough voltage and energy to electrolyze one mole of NaCl.

23. How much energy would be required to electrolyze a box (454 grams) of table salt?

24. An alkaline storage battery used in artificial heart pacemakers uses this overall equation:

$$HgO(s) + Zn(s) + H_2O(l) \longrightarrow Zn(OH)_2(s) + Hg(l)$$

Calculate the energy provided by the total reaction.

25. Determine the oxidation number of each element in these compounds.

a. H_2O_2 d. Hg_2Cl_2 f. $MnSO_3$

b. $K_2Cr_2O_7$ e. SO_2 g. NiO_2

c. $NaClO_3$

26. Silver-zinc batteries are efficient but expensive. They use an unusual oxidation number of silver. The total reaction is:

$$Zn(s) + AgO(s) + H_2O(l) \nrightarrow$$
$$Zn(OH)_2(s) + Ag_2O(s)$$

Use oxidation numbers to write balanced half-reactions, and write the balanced ionic equation.

27. Write balanced ionic equations for the following reactions by writing balanced half-reactions and combining them.

a. $MnO_2(s) + HCl(aq) \nrightarrow$
$$MnCl_2(aq) + Cl_2(g) + H_2O(l)$$

b. $I_2 + Cl_2 + H_2O \longrightarrow HIO_3 + HCl$

c. $BaO_2(s) + HCl(aq) \nrightarrow$
$$BaCl_2(aq) + H_2O(l) + Cl_2(g)$$

Rates and Equilibria of Chemical Reactions

When we put food into a refrigerator, boil an egg, or plunge a burned finger into ice-cold water, we're using temperature to change the rates of chemical reactions. Putting food into the refrigerator slows down the chemical reactions that can cause food spoilage. Cooking an egg or anything else involves chemical reactions that are speeded up at higher temperatures. Ice-cold water will slow down the chemical reactions that damage tissue right after a burn. From this we see that chemical reactions can take place at different rates, or speeds. We'll look at some other ways besides temperature that we can use to slow down a reaction we don't want to happen or to speed up one we do want to happen.

Besides reaction rates, we'll also consider how far reactions go to completion. Some reactions go all the way; in Chapter 6, we assumed they all did. But in some reactions, the products react with each other to form reactants and reverse the reaction. When we inhale and exhale, our bodies are using just such reversible reactions. Hemoglobin reacts to bind oxygen, but what if it didn't let go of the oxygen when it got to the tissues? And what if our blood dissolved carbon dioxide but didn't release it at the lungs? Here, concentration changes are being used to drive a chemical reaction in a desired direction. We'll see some other ways to drive a reaction in the direction we want it to go.

15.1 RATES OF CHEMICAL REACTIONS

When we take sodium bicarbonate for an upset stomach, we should feel better right away. Acid-base reactions happen as soon as their solutions are mixed, and are over before you can say "phenolphthalein." Precipitation reactions happen just about as fast. If we were trying to remove phosphate from polluted water, we wouldn't have to wait for the precipitate of calcium phosphate after we'd added the calcium hydroxide. Both acid-base and precipitation reactions depend only on how fast the reacting ions or molecules can combine. Once they meet, it's all over.

Some kinds of reactions—mostly redox and some biological or organic reactions—take longer to happen. Iron takes a while to rust, fortunately. Many reactions between gases are quite slow. We'll look next at explanations of why some reactions go faster than others.

THE COLLISION THEORY OF REACTION RATES.   When

reaction rate   we define *reaction rate* as how fast the reaction goes, we're really talking about how many molecules, ions, or atoms react in a certain amount of time. We can measure the rate of a reaction by removing samples at various times to find out how much reactant (or how much product) there is. If we did this, we'd find that the rate depends on the number (or concentration) of reactant atoms, ions, or molecules. As the reaction progresses, the concentration of reactants decreases, because they're being used up in the reaction. Figure 15.1 illustrates the decrease of rate as concentration decreases.

If we did further experiments, we'd find that the rate of a reaction increases with temperature as well as with concentration. An explanation of these observations lies in the *collision theory:* For molecules (or atoms or ions) to react, they have to bump into each other (collide), and they have to have enough energy to react. The reason the particles must bump each other is pretty obvious: How else can they react? But how much energy is "enough" for a reaction?

collision theory

Every reaction has an energy barrier that its reactants must overcome to become products. This energy barrier is like the potential barrier in Chapter 14; to push electrons over the potential barrier, we had to give them a boost of at least as much voltage as the barrier. To push reactants over the energy barrier, we have to give them a boost of at least as many kilocalories

FIGURE 15.1
Rate of reaction decreases as reactants disappear

Yawn! 13, 14, 15—I counted 15 sheep going over the fence in the last minute. That's a rate of 15 sheep per minute. This corral is really jammed full of sheep and they're all pushing and shoving and jostling each other. I don't blame them for wanting to get out of there.

Now most of the sheep have gone, and the rate has decreased a lot. Only one sheep escapes every minute. A chemical reaction is like this. The rate is fast at first, and grows slower and slower as more and more of the reactants are used up.

358 activation
energy

effective
collision

per mole as the energy barrier. This amount of energy is the *activation energy,* and it's different for every reaction.

To cross the energy barrier, the reactants have to hit each other *and* they have to have the required activation energy after they've hit. When they do, an *effective collision* occurs, and the particles react. The rate of a reaction depends on the number of effective collisions that occur in a given amount of time. But where do the reactants get the energy?

To answer that, we recall the Maxwell-Boltzmann Distribution Curve of Chapter 10 (p. 218): Some molecules always have enough energy to escape from the liquid and enter the vapor state. This can be applied to reactants, too: Some reactant molecules always have enough energy to fall over the barrier. If the energy barrier is high, then only a few will have enough energy; if it's low, then a lot will. The number of molecules that have enough energy to fall over the energy barrier determines the rate of a reaction, as shown in Figure 15.2.

When a reaction starts, the first particles to react are the ones with enough energy to fall over the barrier. The reaction keeps on going, though, even when these have reacted. The remaining particles hit each other and exchange energy, so that some of them are always getting more. The Maxwell-Boltzmann curve keeps redistributing itself, so that there are always particles that have high energy, as illustrated in Figure 15.3.

FACTORS AFFECTING REACTION RATE. If we want a reaction to go faster, we can increase the number of effective collisions (and thus the reaction rate) in these ways.

1.   We can increase the concentrations of the reactants.
2.   If one or more of the reactants is a gas, we can increase the pressure. Increasing the pressure of a gas is the same as increasing its concentration, as we learned in Chapter 11.
3.   We can increase the temperature. A temperature increase of 10 K will make a reaction go roughly twice as fast.
4.   We can use a catalyst, if we can find one that works. A catalyst speeds up a reaction by lowering the energy barrier, so that more particles can get across it. The catalyst usually remains unchanged at the end of the reaction. By using a catalyst, it is often possible to avoid the high temperatures that might otherwise be needed to make a reaction with high activation energy proceed. (See Box.)

15.2 CHEMICAL EQUILIBRIUM

chemical
equilibrium

Chemical equilibrium is a state in which two opposing chemical reactions are taking place at the same rate. This is another example of the dynamic equilibrium we saw in Chapter 10, where a process is being done as fast as it's being undone. Here, the process being done and undone is a reversible chemical reaction.

FIGURE 15.2
**Reactions having
low activation
energies go fast**

359

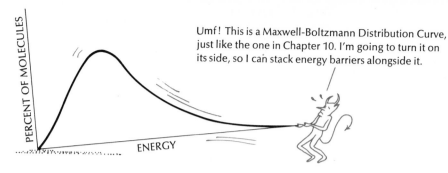

Umf! This is a Maxwell-Boltzmann Distribution Curve, just like the one in Chapter 10. I'm going to turn it on its side, so I can stack energy barriers alongside it.

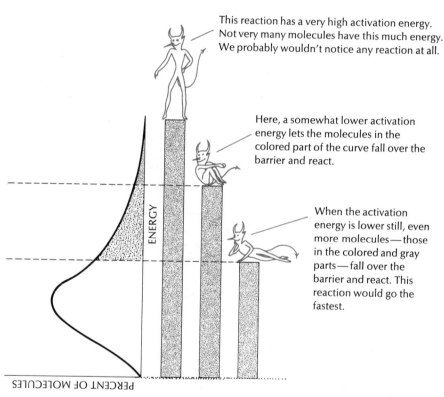

This reaction has a very high activation energy. Not very many molecules have this much energy. We probably wouldn't notice any reaction at all.

Here, a somewhat lower activation energy lets the molecules in the colored part of the curve fall over the barrier and react.

When the activation energy is lower still, even more molecules—those in the colored and gray parts—fall over the barrier and react. This reaction would go the fastest.

REVERSIBLE CHEMICAL REACTIONS.

The reaction of oxygen with sulfur dioxide to make sulfur trioxide, an important industrial reaction, is an example of a *reversible chemical reaction*, one that can take place in either of two directions. To show that a reaction is reversible, we write it with double arrows, like this:

**reversible
chemical
reaction**

$$2\,SO_2(g) + O_2(g) \rightleftharpoons 2\,SO_3(g)$$

In this reaction, we might start with a mixture of sulfur dioxide and oxygen.

FIGURE 15.3
**As high-energy
molecules react,
others take
their places**

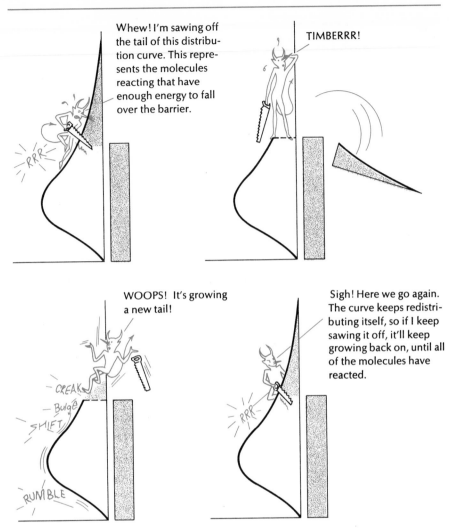

The rate would be high at first, because the concentration of the reactants would be high. As the reactants disappeared, the rate of the forward reaction would decrease. Meanwhile, as sulfur trioxide was formed, it would become the reactant in the reverse reaction. At first, the rate would be low because there wouldn't be very much sulfur trioxide. As the forward reaction progressed, more sulfur trioxide would be available and the reverse rate would increase. The forward rate would decrease and the reverse rate would increase, until eventually the two rates would be the same. Then the system would be at equilibrium.

We can always approach an equilibrium from either side. We could start with SO_3 and let it decompose to SO_2 and O_2. In that case, we'd write:

$$2\,SO_3(g) \rightleftharpoons 2\,SO_2(g) + O_2(g)$$

THE CATALYTIC CONVERTER

Up to now, the three biggest problems with automobile emissions have been carbon monoxide, unburned gasoline, and nitrogen monoxide. The CO and unburned gasoline are from incomplete combustion. One way to avoid them is to increase the amount of air and the temperature in the engine. But this also increases the amount of NO formed.

The reaction between N_2 and O_2 to form NO has a high energy barrier—too high for much NO to form at ordinary temperatures. This is lucky, because air is mostly N_2 and O_2, which mix freely, but which don't react to produce poisonous NO in the air. In a gasoline engine, though, the heat produced by the burning of gasoline gives some of the N_2 and O_2 enough energy to get over the barrier and form NO.

A relatively new device, called a "catalytic converter," takes the exhaust from the engine and allows the gasoline and CO to burn as completely as they would at a much higher temperature. The catalyst, a mixture of platinum and palladium, does this by lowering the energy barrier for the burning of CO and gasoline. The catalyst has no effect on the NO energy barrier and so does not cause more NO to form.

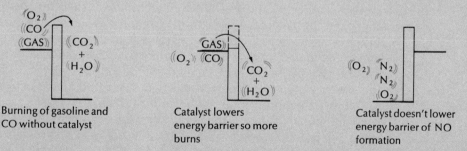

Burning of gasoline and CO without catalyst

Catalyst lowers energy barrier so more burns

Catalyst doesn't lower energy barrier of NO formation

Leaded gasoline can't be used in an automobile that has a catalytic converter. Lead "poisons" the catalyst so that it doesn't work.

An undesirable side effect of the catalytic converter is increased emissions of SO_3, formerly not a big problem in car exhaust. Small amounts of SO_2 are always produced by combustion of gasoline. But the catalytic converter lowers the energy barrier for SO_3 formation. Whereas a car without a converter releases about 1 milligram of SO_3 per mile, a car with a converter releases 10 milligrams to 30 milligrams per mile. And that's not all. H_2O—another product of combustion—can combine with SO_3 to produce sulfuric acid and, in time, destroy the converter.

The two ways of writing the same reversible reaction mean exactly the same thing. At equilibrium, we can no longer tell the products from the reactants, because all substances are both. However, the way a reaction is written usually determines which we call the reactants and which we call the products. Often, the way we write the equation reflects what the equation is used for. The first of the above reactions is important industrially to make sulfur trioxide, so it would more commonly be written that way.

$$2\, SO_2(g) + O_2(g) \rightleftharpoons 2\, SO_3(g)$$

When we write the equation this way, SO_2 and O_2 are the reactants and the reaction between them is the forward reaction. SO_3 is the product and its decomposition is the reverse reaction.

FACTORS AFFECTING THE POSITION OF EQUILIBRIUM.

In a reversible reaction, the energy of the products can be—and usually is—different from the energy of the reactants. The energy barrier is approached from two different directions, and from different starting energies. The activation energies of the two reactions are different, so each reaction has a different distance to travel up the energy barrier. The difference between the activation energies of the reactants and the products is the heat of reaction. The reaction between sulfur dioxide and oxygen is exothermic.

$$2\, SO_2(g) + O_2(g) \rightleftharpoons 2\, SO_3(g) + 41.2 \text{ kcal}$$

The energy barrier for the forward reaction is lower than for the reverse reaction, and this favors the formation of product, as shown in Figure 15.4. In this case, we say that the position of the equilibrium lies to the right. As we see in the figure, though, an equilibrium doesn't necessarily lie all the way to the right or left. If we calculated the theoretical yield of SO_3 based on the reaction going completely to the right, we'd find that at equilibrium at 1000 K, we'd get only about 60 percent of that.

For endothermic reactions, the energy of the reactants is lower than the energy of the products, and the position of the equilibrium lies on the side of the reactants. We'd get less than 50 percent of the theoretical yield in that case. Figure 15.5 shows various possibilities of equilibrium positions.

In Chapter 10 (p. 211), we introduced Le Chatelier's Principle which says that an equilibrium system, when disturbed, adjusts itself so as to restore equilibrium. This principle applies to chemical equilibrium, too—very much so. Disturbing a chemical equilibrium by changing its conditions causes the position to shift as equilibrium is reestablished. Which way the position is shifted depends on how the change affects the rates of the forward and reverse reactions. We'll look at these condition changes one by one, as we did for the reaction rate.

Increasing the temperature will increase the rates of both the forward and reverse reactions. Whichever reaction has the higher activation energy

FIGURE 15.4

363

The position of
equilibrium lies
to the side of
lower energy

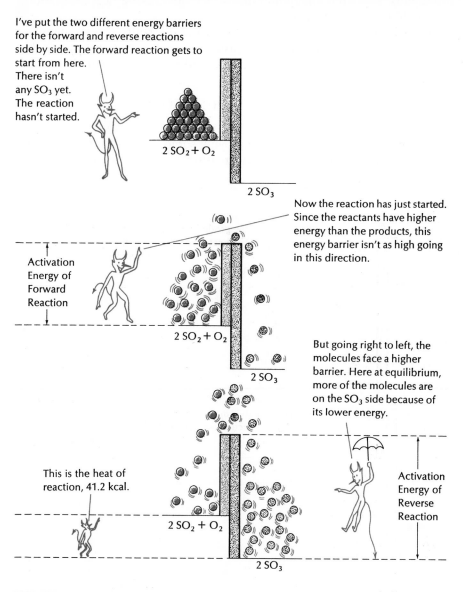

I've put the two different energy barriers for the forward and reverse reactions side by side. The forward reaction gets to start from here. There isn't any SO$_3$ yet. The reaction hasn't started.

2 SO$_2$ + O$_2$

2 SO$_3$

Now the reaction has just started. Since the reactants have higher energy than the products, this energy barrier isn't as high going in this direction.

Activation Energy of Forward Reaction

2 SO$_2$ + O$_2$

2 SO$_3$

But going right to left, the molecules face a higher barrier. Here at equilibrium, more of the molecules are on the SO$_3$ side because of its lower energy.

This is the heat of reaction, 41.2 kcal.

Activation Energy of Reverse Reaction

2 SO$_2$ + O$_2$

2 SO$_3$

will be affected more by temperature. If we know what the relative activation energies are, we can predict the direction of shift; if not, we can still predict that equilibrium will be established faster. Increasing the temperature also means supplying heat. If heat is a reactant or a product (which it always is), then this will increase the rate of the reaction in which heat appears as a reactant. The equilibrium will shift away from the side that contains heat. For example, in this reaction:

$$2\,SO_2(g) + O_2(g) \rightleftharpoons 2\,SO_3(g) + 41.2\ kcal$$

adding heat shifts the equilibrium to the left, and taking heat away shifts the equilibrium to the right.

Increasing the concentration of any substance shifts the equilibrium away from that substance, and decreasing the concentration of any substance shifts the equilibrium toward that substance. For example, in the reaction:

$$H_2CO_3(aq) \rightleftharpoons H_2O(l) + CO_2(g)$$

increasing the concentration of H_2CO_3 shifts the equilibrium to the right. Decreasing the concentration (by removing some H_2CO_3) shifts the equilibrium to the left. Increasing or decreasing the concentration of H_2O

FIGURE 15.5
Equilibrium can lie to the right, to the left, or in between

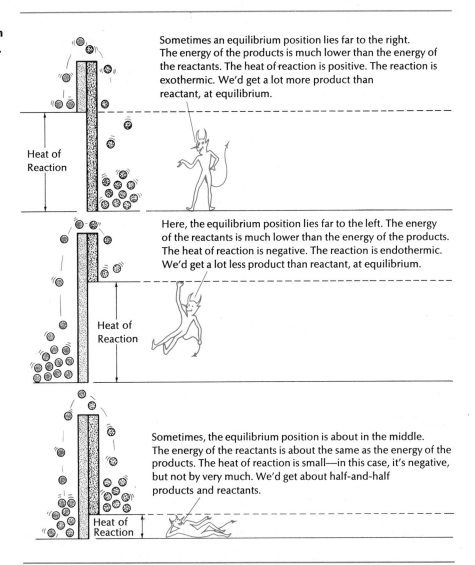

Sometimes an equilibrium position lies far to the right. The energy of the products is much lower than the energy of the reactants. The heat of reaction is positive. The reaction is exothermic. We'd get a lot more product than reactant, at equilibrium.

Heat of Reaction

Here, the equilibrium position lies far to the left. The energy of the reactants is much lower than the energy of the products. The heat of reaction is negative. The reaction is endothermic. We'd get a lot less product than reactant, at equilibrium.

Heat of Reaction

Sometimes, the equilibrium position is about in the middle. The energy of the reactants is about the same as the energy of the products. The heat of reaction is small—in this case, it's negative, but not by very much. We'd get about half-and-half products and reactants.

Heat of Reaction

won't have any effect. (Where a reaction happens in water solution and water is a reactant, there is always so much water that a change in concentration makes no difference.)

Increasing or decreasing the pressure of a gas is the same as increasing or decreasing its concentration. Increasing the pressure shifts the equilibrium away from a gas, and decreasing the pressure shifts the equilibrium toward a gas. In the above reaction, CO_2 is the only gas involved. Increasing the pressure shifts the equilibrium to the left, and decreasing the pressure shifts the equilibrium to the right.

Where more than one gas is involved, increasing the pressure shifts the equilibrium toward the side containing fewer moles of gas. For example, in the reaction:

$$2\,SO_2(g) + O_2(g) \rightleftharpoons 2\,SO_3(g) + 42.1\ \text{kcal}$$

the left side has three moles of gas—two of SO_2 and one of O_2—and the right side has only two moles of gas. Increasing the pressure will shift the equilibrium to the right, and decreasing the pressure will shift the equilibrium to the left.

A catalyst will not affect the position of equilibrium, but it will speed a reaction up and help equilibrium be established faster.

DRIVING CHEMICAL REACTIONS. Now that we know how conditions affect equilibrium, we can use this information to make an equilibrium shift in the direction we want.

EXAMPLE 15.1: We've seen that the equilibrium position of the reaction for the formation of SO_3 is such that we get only 60 percent of the theoretical yield at 1000 K. What conditions could we change to help us get more product?

Answer: Getting more product means shifting the equilibrium to the right. We can increase the pressure, add more SO_2 or O_2, or remove SO_3 or heat as they are formed.

Figure 15.6 shows how some of these conditions are actually used in the industrial preparation of SO_3.

We see that removing a product is a good way to shift an equilibrium to the right, and removing a reactant is a good way to shift it to the left. Sometimes another chemical reaction can be used to remove a product or a reactant. Some important reversible reactions that happen in blood are:

$$Hb + O_2(g) \rightleftharpoons HHbO_2(aq) \quad \textit{(hemoglobin bound to } O_2 \textit{ is more acidic)}$$
$$HHbO_2(aq) + HCO_3{}^-(aq) \rightleftharpoons H_2CO_3(aq) + HbO_2{}^-(aq)$$
$$H_2CO_3(aq) \rightleftharpoons CO_2(g) + H_2O(l)$$

At the lungs, there is a high pressure (concentration) of O_2, which pushes the equilibrium of the first reaction to the right, forming more $HHbO_2$.

FIGURE 15.6
Industrial
preparation
of SO₃

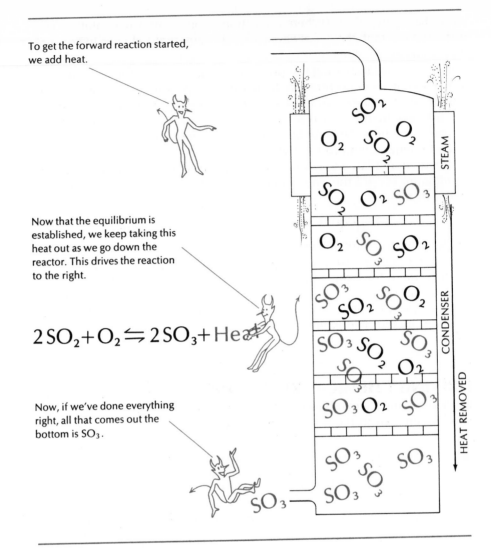

To get the forward reaction started, we add heat.

Now that the equilibrium is established, we keep taking this heat out as we go down the reactor. This drives the reaction to the right.

$$2\,SO_2 + O_2 \rightleftharpoons 2\,SO_3 + Heat$$

Now, if we've done everything right, all that comes out the bottom is SO₃.

The increased HHbO₂ pushes the equilibrium of the second reaction to the right, forming more H_2CO_3. And the increased H_2CO_3 pushes the equilibrium of the third reaction to the right, releasing from the blood the CO_2 we exhale.

At the tissues, there is a high pressure of CO_2 because it is a waste product of metabolism. The high pressure of CO_2 pushes the equilibrium of the third reaction to the left, forming more H_2CO_3, which pushes the second reaction's equilibrium to the left. The increased HHbO₂ that's formed pushes the equilibrium of the first reaction to the left, releasing to the tissues the O_2 they need.

A reversible reaction that can ruin this whole sequence is this one, in which inhaled carbon monoxide binds to hemoglobin:

$$HHb(aq) + CO(g) \rightleftharpoons HHbCO(aq)$$

This removes HHb from the first reaction above, which shifts the equilibrium to the left. The rest of the sequence is then forced in the wrong direction. This means that HHb won't bind O_2, and CO_2 won't be removed from the tissues. We can't last long under either condition. If the amount of carbon monoxide inhaled isn't too high, the problem can be solved by using this reversible reaction (breathing oxygen):

$$HHbCO(aq) + O_2(g) \rightleftharpoons HHbO_2(aq) + CO(g)$$

This equilibrium lies to the left. About two hundred molecules of O_2 have to be supplied to free one hemoglobin molecule from HHbCO.

If the CO_2 content of blood becomes too high, our biological response is to pant, thereby increasing the intake of O_2. When we exercise strenuously, our bodies metabolize faster and more CO_2 is produced. That's why we pant after or during exercise. We need this reflex to control the CO_2 level. Too much CO_2 in blood makes it too acidic, because of this reaction:

$$H_2CO_3(aq) + H_2O(l) \rightleftharpoons HCO_3^-(aq) + H_3O^+(aq)$$

The H_3O^+ can then react with the HbO_2^- in the second of our three reactions. This would produce more $HHbO_2$, which would force the equilibrium of the first reaction to the left, and interfere with hemoglobin's ability to bind oxygen. This is one reason the pH of blood must be carefully controlled, as we saw in Chapter 13.

Using one reaction to drive another is helpful in the chemistry laboratory, too. When we dissolve a precipitate, such as $Mg(OH)_2$, in strong acid, we're using these reversible reactions:

$$Mg(OH)_2(s) \rightleftharpoons Mg^{2+}(aq) + 2\,OH^-(aq)$$
$$2\,H_3O^+(aq) + 2\,OH^-(aq) \rightleftharpoons 4\,H_2O(l)$$

The hydronium ion reacts with the hydroxide ion, removing hydroxide ion from the first reaction. The first equilibrium shifts to the right, and $Mg(OH)_2$ dissolves.

15.3 EQUILIBRIUM CALCULATIONS

So far we've seen what causes an equilibrium to shift and how to predict the direction of the shift. Now we'll see how to describe the positions of equilibria with numbers, which we can then use for more exact predictions.

THE EQUILIBRIUM CONSTANT. We could investigate an equilibrium system by analyzing samples of it to find out the concentration of each substance. If we took three samples from the reaction between SO_2 and O_2 to produce SO_3, at a constant temperature of 1000 K, we might

TABLE 15.1 Possible concentrations for a reaction at equilibrium

$2 SO_2(g) + O_2(g) \rightleftharpoons 2 SO_3(g)$				
Concentration				Equilibrium Constant (K)
SO_2	O_2	SO_3	Calculations	
0.100	0.225	0.800	$\dfrac{(0.800)(0.800)}{(0.100)(0.100)(0.225)} =$	284
1.00	0.352	10.0	$\dfrac{(10.0)(10.0)}{(1.00)(1.00)(0.352)} =$	284
0.400	0.507	4.80	$\dfrac{(4.80)(4.80)}{(0.400)(0.400)(0.507)} =$	284

obtain the three sets of data in Table 15.1. The concentrations themselves are different in each sample, but if we substitute them into this formula:

$$\frac{[SO_3][SO_3]}{[O_2][SO_2][SO_2]}$$

equilibrium constant (K)

we come out with the same value for each sample: 284. This value is the *equilibrium constant (K)* for this reaction. It stays constant as long as the temperature stays the same, even though the individual concentrations may change.

Every reversible reaction has such an equilibrium constant. Its value has to be determined experimentally, but we can write the equilibrium constant expression for any reversible reaction from its equation. The products are in the numerator, and the reactants are in the denominator. Each substance appears the same number of times that it appears in the chemical equation.

EXAMPLE 15.2: Write the equilibrium constant expression for this reaction:

$$N_2(g) + 3 H_2(g) \rightleftharpoons 2 NH_3(g)$$

Answer:

$$\frac{[NH_3][NH_3]}{[N_2][H_2][H_2][H_2]} = K$$

The value of the equilibrium constant tells us the position of an equilibrium. If the constant is greater than 1, as it is with 284, then the equilibrium lies to the right. If it's less than 1, then the equilibrium lies to the left. If it's around 1, then the equilibrium is about in the middle. The larger the equilibrium constant for a reaction, the smaller it is for the reaction written in the opposite direction. When we write a reaction in the opposite direction, the new equilibrium constant is the reciprocal of the old one. For instance, when the SO_2/SO_3 reaction is written this way:

$$43.2 \text{ kcal} + 2 SO_3(g) \rightleftharpoons 2 SO_2(g) + O_2(g)$$

the equilibrium constant is 1/284, or 3.52×10^{-3}. This constant tells us that the equilibrium lies to the left.

Equilibrium constants change with temperature. For an exothermic reaction, such as the formation of SO_3, the equilibrium constant decreases as the temperature increases. For an endothermic reaction, such as the decomposition of SO_3, the equilibrium constant increases as the temperature increases. Table 15.2 shows equilibrium constants for both the formation and decomposition of SO_3 at various temperatures. At room temperature (300 K), the equilibrium constant for the formation of SO_3 is extremely large, meaning that the equilibrium lies far on the SO_3 side. However, if we mix SO_2 and O_2 at room temperature, nothing happens. This is because the energy barrier is high. Heat must be supplied to push the reactants over the energy barrier, but heat must be removed after equilibrium is established, so the equilibrium will shift in favor of SO_3. We already saw this happening in Figure 15.6.

At around 1400 K, the equilibrium constant for the formation of SO_3 drops below 1. At temperatures above this, the equilibrium lies further and further toward the SO_2 side.

SPECIAL KINDS OF EQUILIBRIUM CONSTANTS. Many
equilibrium constant expressions aren't as complicated as those we've just seen. We introduced one simplified equilibrium constant in Chapter 13:

$$[H_3O^+][OH^-] = 10^{-14}$$

This really states the value of the equilibrium constant for the ionization of water, which is a reversible reaction.

$$H_2O(l) + H_2O(l) \rightleftharpoons H_3O^+(aq) + OH^-(aq)$$

For reversible reactions that happen in water solution, the concentration of water stays pretty much the same even though small amounts of water might be appearing or disappearing. The water concentration doesn't appear in the denominator of the equilibrium constant expression. The value of the water concentration need not be known, and is automatically

K for Formation of SO_3 $2\,SO_2(g) + O_2(g) \rightleftharpoons 2\,SO_3(g)$	Temperature (K)	K for Decomposition of SO_3 $2\,SO_3(g) \rightleftharpoons 2\,SO_2(g) + O_2(g)$	
1.1×10^{22}	300	9.1×10^{-23}	**TABLE 15.2**
3.2×10^{6}	700	3.12×10^{-7}	**Equilibrium**
8.1×10^{4}	800	1.2×10^{-5}	**constants vary**
3.2×10^{3}	900	3.1×10^{-4}	**with**
2.8×10^{2}	1000	3.6×10^{-3}	**temperature**
3.9×10^{1}	1100	2.6×10^{-2}	
7.5	1200	1.3×10^{-1}	
1.8	1300	5.6×10^{-1}	
5.6×10^{-1}	1400	1.8	

ion product K_w　included in the equilibrium constant. This particular equilibrium constant is called K_w, the *ion product* of water (10^{-14}).

　Another equilibrium constant whose expression doesn't have a denominator is the *solubility product*, K_{sp}. In a saturated solution of a relatively insoluble compound, dissolving and crystal formation are reversible processes at equilibrium.

solubility product K_{sp}

$$AgCl(s) \rightleftharpoons Ag^+(aq) + Cl^-(aq)$$
$$K_{sp} = [Ag^+][Cl^-] = 1.8 \times 10^{-10}$$

The value of K_{sp} tells us that the equilibrium lies far to the left, which we know because silver chloride doesn't dissolve much. Sometimes we might want to decrease its solubility even further, to avoid losing too much expensive silver ion. By adding a large amount of chloride ion, we can shift the equilibrium even further to the left, removing more Ag^+ from solution. This is the *common ion effect*: adding one of the ions of an insoluble substance decreases the solubility of that substance. We can use K_{sp} to illustrate the common ion effect.

common ion effect

EXAMPLE 15.3: A precipitate of AgCl has been prepared in the laboratory and is about to be washed free of impurities. The concentration of Ag^+ in a saturated solution of AgCl is 1.35×10^{-5} M. To avoid losing this much Ag^+ in the washing, the experimenter washes the precipitate with 1 M NaCl. How many moles per liter of Ag^+ will be lost in this case?

Solution: Since:

$$[Ag^+][Cl^-] = 1.8 \times 10^{-10}$$

then

$$[Ag^+] = \frac{1.8 \times 10^{-10}}{[Cl^-]}$$

The NaCl solution is the source of the common ion, Cl^-. Therefore:

$$[Cl^-] = 1\ M$$
$$[Ag^+] = \frac{1.8 \times 10^{-10}}{1} = \underline{\quad}\ M\ Ag^+$$

Answer: 1.8×10^{-10} moles Ag^+ per liter. The Ag^+ loss has been cut by 10^5.

EXAMPLE 15.4: Silver acetate is quite a bit more soluble than silver chloride. The K_{sp} of silver acetate is 2.3×10^{-3}. What should be the concentration of a $NaC_2H_3O_2$ solution to keep the silver ion concentration down to 1.0×10^{-3}?

Solution: From the K_{sp} expression:

$$[Ag^+][C_2H_3O_2^-] = 2.3 \times 10^{-3}$$

we may write:

$$[C_2H_3O_2^-] = \frac{2.3 \times 10^{-3}}{[Ag^+]} = \frac{2.3 \times 10^{-3}}{1.0 \times 10^{-3}} = \underline{\quad}\ M\ NaC_2H_3O_2$$

Answer: $2.3\ M\ NaC_2H_3O_2$. Since silver acetate is so much more soluble than silver chloride, a lot more Ag^+ would be lost.

Another kind of equilibrium expression is K_a, which is the *acid dissociation constant,* or an equilibrium constant for the ionization of an acid. For example:

$$H_2CO_3(aq) + H_2O(l) \rightleftharpoons HCO_3^-(aq) + H_3O^+(aq)$$

$$K_a = \frac{[HCO_3^-][H_3O^+]}{[H_2CO_3]} = 4.4 \times 10^{-7}$$

The equilibrium lies to the left, as we know because carbonic acid is a weak acid. The ordering of acid strengths in Table 13.6 (p. 306) was based on decreasing K_a values for the acids. The larger the K_a, the stronger the acid.

BUFFERS. We've looked at some cases where equilibrium positions have been changed by large amounts. In biological systems like blood, though, very small changes are constantly taking place. We saw in Chapter 13 that the blood must maintain a pH of between 7.35 and 7.45 (hydronium-ion concentration between 4.5×10^{-8} and 3.6×10^{-8}), even as small amounts of acid and base are constantly being added to it. Two buffer systems especially help the blood maintain its pH. These buffer systems are H_2CO_3/HCO_3^- and $H_2PO_4^-/HPO_4^{2-}$. To see how a buffer really works, let's look first at a simple analogy.

The five members of a neighborhood club take a vote. Three vote no and two vote yes, which is a 60 percent vote against. If one of the no voters switches to a yes, then the yeses have 60 percent of the vote. In such a small club, one person is enough to tip the scale, because one person is a large percentage of the total. But what if the club were much larger, with 5000 members? In a vote of 3000 noes and 2000 yeses, the noes still have it with 60 percent. If one no voter switches to yes, the totals become 2999 to 2001 and the no percentage becomes 59.98. Not much of a change. That one vote makes almost no difference at all, because the one voter is buffered by the large total number of participants.

Essentially, this is how a mixture of a weak acid and its conjugate base works as a buffer. To see how a buffer works, we'll first rearrange the K_a expression.

$$[H_3O^+] = K_a \times \frac{[acid]}{[conjugate\ base]}$$

We see that the hydronium-ion concentration, and therefore the pH, depends on two things: the K_a of the particular acid, and the ratio of acid to conjugate base, called the *buffer ratio.* To keep a pH constant, a K_a should be fairly close (within about one power of ten) to the desired hydronium-ion concentration. Thus the H_2CO_3/HCO_3^- system, with K_a of 4.4×10^{-7}, qualifies to maintain a hydronium-ion concentration between 4.5×10^{-8} and 3.6×10^{-8}. If the hydronium-ion concentration we want to maintain happens to be exactly the same as the K_a, then the buffer ratio has to be

buffer ratio

exactly 1. If the desired hydronium-ion concentration is slightly different from the K_a, as it is in blood, then the buffer ratio will be some number other than 1.

EXAMPLE 15.5: A sample of blood contains 1.1×10^{-3} M HCO_3^- and 1.0×10^{-4} M H_2CO_3. Calculate the buffer ratio and the resulting pH.

Solution: First, the buffer ratio:

$$\frac{[H_2CO_3]}{[HCO_3^-]} = \frac{1.0 \times 10^{-4}}{1.1 \times 10^{-3}} = 9.1 \times 10^{-2}$$

Now for the hydronium-ion concentration:

$$[H_3O^+] = (4.4 \times 10^{-7})(9.1 \times 10^{-2}) = 4.0 \times 10^{-8}$$

We convert it to pH using Figure 13.3 (p. 300).

Answer: Buffer ratio $= 9.1 \times 10^{-2}$, pH $= 7.40$.

We see that to achieve the hydronium-ion concentration we need, we must multiply the K_a of carbonic acid by 9.1×10^{-2}. If this buffer ratio changes, then the hydronium-ion concentration changes too. A good buffer is one that keeps its buffer ratio from changing very much, even though hydronium ion or hydroxide ion is added.

When hydronium ion is added to the buffer system, it reacts with HCO_3^- like this:

$$HCO_3^-(aq) + H_3O^+(aq) \rightleftharpoons H_2CO_3(aq) + H_2O(l)$$

This is the reverse of the ionization of carbonic acid, so its equilibrium constant is the reciprocal of the K_a for carbonic acid: $K = 1/(4.4 \times 10^{-7})$ $= 2.3 \times 10^6$. The equilibrium lies far to the right. Essentially all the hydronium ion will react completely with HCO_3^- to form H_2CO_3. If we start with more HCO_3^- than H_3O^+, there will be no H_3O^+ at the end of the reaction; the number of moles of H_2CO_3 formed will exactly equal the number of moles of H_3O^+ added; and the amount of HCO_3^- destroyed will exactly equal the amount of H_3O^+ added.

EXAMPLE 15.6: For the blood sample of Example 15.5, calculate the concentrations of HCO_3^- and H_2CO_3 that would remain after adding H_3O^+ equivalent to a concentration of 1.0×10^{-5} M.

Solution: The concentration of hydronium ion added is less than the concentration of HCO_3^-. For the 1.0×10^{-5} M H_3O^+ that reacts, 1.0×10^{-5} M HCO_3^- will be destroyed. The concentration of HCO_3^- is then $(1.1 \times 10^{-3}) - (1.0 \times 10^{-5}) = 1.1 \times 10^{-3}$—no change, within the limits of our accuracy. The H_2CO_3 concentration becomes $(1.0 \times 10^{-4}) + (1.0 \times 10^{-5}) = 1.1 \times 10^{-4}$—a very small change.

Answer: $[HCO_3^-] = 1.1 \times 10^{-3}$ M; $[H_2CO_3] = 1.1 \times 10^{-4}$ M.

Now let's see how these concentration changes affect the buffer ratio and the pH.

EXAMPLE 15.7: Calculate the new buffer ratio and pH for the concentrations of Example 15.6.

Solution:

$$\text{buffer ratio} = \frac{1.1 \times 10^{-4}}{1.1 \times 10^{-3}} = 1.0 \times 10^{-1}$$

$$[H_3O^+] = (4.4 \times 10^{-7})(1.0 \times 10^{-1}) = 4.4 \times 10^{-8}$$

Answer: Buffer ratio $= 1.0 \times 10^{-1}$; pH $= 7.36$.

The pH is still within the allowed range. The buffer ratio can maintain the pH because its individual concentrations are very high compared with the added amounts of acid or base. The buffered H_2CO_3/HCO_3^- solution is like the club with many members. The 1.0×10^{-5} M H_3O^+ makes hardly any difference to the large (by comparison) 1.1×10^{-3} M HCO_3^-. The buffer system in blood works because the changes in acidity are small. But if the amounts of added acid or base were as large or larger than the amount of buffer acid or conjugate base, then the buffer wouldn't work any more.

To show just how important this buffering system is, let's see what would happen if we added the same amount of acid to an unbuffered solution. A hydronium-ion concentration of 4.0×10^{-8} M means a hydroxide-ion concentration of 2.5×10^{-7} M. We can prepare a solution having the same pH as blood by making a 2.5×10^{-7} M NaOH solution.

EXAMPLE 15.8: Calculate the pH resulting when the equivalent of 1.0×10^{-5} M H_3O^+ is added to a solution of 2.5×10^{-7} M NaOH.

Solution: We know that hydronium and hydroxide ions react with each other completely. Since there is more acid than base, all of the base will be used up, and there will be some acid left.

$$[H_3O^+] = (1.0 \times 10^{-5}) - (2.5 \times 10^{-7}) = 1.0 \times 10^{-5}$$

The H_3O^+ has completely overwhelmed the OH^-.

Answer: pH $= 5.00$.

The pH has changed by nearly 2. The unbuffered solution is like the club with only a few members. The amount of hydronium ion added was very large compared with the amount of hydroxide ion already there, and the addition was enough to change the solution from basic to acidic.

We could do the same kind of calculations for the addition of base instead of acid. When base is added to the buffer system, this reaction takes place:

$$H_2CO_3(aq) + OH^-(aq) \rightleftharpoons HCO_3^-(aq) + H_2O(l)$$

In the reactions of a weak acid with a strong base, the equilibrium lies far to the right. As with the addition of acid, we assume that a given amount of base produces the same amount of HCO_3^- and destroys the same amount of H_2CO_3.

REVIEW QUESTIONS

Rates of Chemical Reactions

1. What do we mean by *reaction rate?* How does it change as a reaction proceeds?
2. How does the *collision theory* explain changes in reaction rates?
3. What is *activation energy?* How is it like voltage?
4. What is an *effective collision?* How does the number of effective collisions influence the reaction rate?
5. When a chemical reaction starts, what determines which particles react first? What determines how many will react at a time?
6. What are the ways we can make a reaction go faster?
7. How does a catalyst increase the rate of a reaction?

Chemical Equilibrium

8. What is *chemical equilibrium?*
9. Give an example of a *reversible chemical reaction.* Tell what happens to the forward and reverse rates as the system approaches equilibrium.
10. How do we know which is the forward reaction and which the reverse reaction?
11. Sketch energy barriers for an endothermic reaction and for an exothermic reaction. Label the activation energies and the heat of reaction.
12. Explain how the position of equilibrium is affected by (a) temperature; (b) concentration; (c) pressure; and (d) a catalyst.

13. Under what conditions would changing the water concentration make no difference to the position of equilibrium? Explain.
14. Explain how a reaction can be driven in a desired direction by changing the conditions.
15. What are some reversible reactions that happen in blood? How do they depend on each other?
16. Why do we pant? Why is this an important biological response?

Equilibrium Calculations

17. What is an *equilibrium constant?* Give an example of an equilibrium constant and its expression.
18. What happens to an equilibrium constant when its reaction is written in reverse?
19. How does an equilibrium constant change with temperature?
20. Write the expression for K_w. Why doesn't it contain water concentration?
21. Write the expression for a *solubility product.*
22. What is the *common ion effect?* Explain how it can be used to decrease a salt's solubility.
23. Write the expression for the ionization of an acid.
24. What two quantities determine the pH of a buffer solution?
25. Explain how a buffer can resist changes in pH.
26. Under what conditions would the H_2CO_3/HCO_3^- buffer system in blood no longer be effective? Why?

EXERCISES

1. Some energy barriers are shown below. In each pair, which reaction would go faster, 1 or 2?

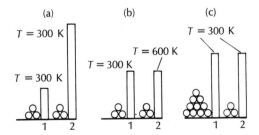

(a)   (b)   (c)

2. State whether each of the following is endothermic or exothermic. Which has the higher activation energy, the forward reaction or the reverse reaction?

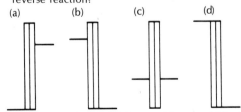

(a)   (b)   (c)   (d)

3. State where the equilibrium position would lie for each part of Exercise 2.
4. For each part of Exercise 2, state whether the forward reaction or the reverse reaction would be more affected by changes in temperature.

5. TiO_2, a white paint pigment, is prepared industrially according to this reversible reaction:

$$TiCl_4(g) + O_2(g) \rightleftharpoons$$
$$TiO_2(s) + 2\,Cl_2(g) + 17\,kcal$$

State what effect each of the following would have on the position of equilibrium.
   a. increasing the pressure
   b. decreasing the pressure
   c. removing solid TiO_2 as it is formed
   d. supplying heat
   e. removing heat
   f. adding a catalyst

6. Sketch an energy barrier diagram for the reversible reaction in Exercise 5. Label the heat of reaction and the activation energies for the forward and reverse reactions.

7. In each of the following industrial processes, state what conditions should be used to obtain the maximum amount of product.
   a. preparation of lime from limestone:
      $$CaCO_3(s) + 44\,kcal \rightleftharpoons CaO(s) + CO_2(g)$$
   b. first step in acetylene preparation (preparation of calcium carbide):
      $$CaO(s) + 3\,C(s) + 111\,kcal \rightleftharpoons$$
      $$CaC_2(s) + CO(g)$$
   c. second step in acetylene preparation:
      $$CaC_2(s) + 2\,H_2O(l) \rightleftharpoons$$
      $$Ca(OH)_2(s) + C_2H_2(g) + 149\,kcal$$
      $$\text{acetylene}$$
   d. Haber process for nitrogen fixation:
      $$N_2(g) + 3\,H_2(g) \rightleftharpoons 2\,NH_3(g) + 22\,kcal$$
   e. first step in Solvay process for making sodium bicarbonate:
      $$NH_3(g) + CO_2(g) + H_2O(l) \rightleftharpoons NH_4HCO_3(aq)$$

8. Sketch energy barrier diagrams for parts a, b, c, and d of Exercise 7. Label each activation energy and the heat of reaction.

9. Sketch energy barrier diagrams for each of the following cases, and state whether the position of equilibrium would lie to the left or to the right.
   a. energy of products greater than energy of reactants; large activation energy
   b. energy of products greater than energy of reactants; no activation energy
   c. energy of products less than energy of reactants; small activation energy

10. With reference to the blood equilibria on pages 365–367, state whether each of the following would cause slower or more rapid breathing.
   a. breathing CO_2
   b. breathing a basic gas, such as NH_3
   c. breathing pure oxygen instead of air

11. Write an equilibrium constant expression for each of the following.
   a. $2\,NO(g) + O_2(g) \rightleftharpoons 2\,NO_2(g)$
   b. $4\,NH_3(g) + 5\,O_2(g) \rightleftharpoons 4\,NO(g) + 6\,H_2O(g)$
   c. $2\,H_2(g) + O_2(g) \rightleftharpoons 2\,H_2O(g)$

12. For each of the following, state whether the equilibrium favors reactants or products.
   a. $N_2(g) + 3\,H_2(g) \rightleftharpoons 2\,NH_3(g)$
      K (at 300 K) $= 6.85 \times 10^5$
   b. $N_2(g) + 3\,H_2(g) \rightleftharpoons 2\,NH_3(g)$
      K (at 720 K) $= 2.5 \times 10^{-5}$
   c. $2\,NO_2(g) \rightleftharpoons N_2O_4(g)$
      K (at 300 K) $= 9.1$

13. In the Haber process, the reaction between N_2 and H_2 to form NH_3 has such a high energy barrier that it must be carried out at 720 K rather than at room temperature (300 K). Refer to the equilibrium constants at these two temperatures in Exercise 12.
   a. Is the reaction endothermic or exothermic?
   b. What specific problem would be created by carrying out the reaction at 720 K?
   c. How could this problem be overcome so as to produce as much NH_3 as possible?

14. Write solubility product expressions for the following.
   a. $PbCrO_4(s) \rightleftharpoons Pb^{2+}(aq) + CrO_4^{2-}(aq)$
   b. $BaSO_4(s) \rightleftharpoons Ba^{2+}(aq) + SO_4^{2-}(aq)$

15. How could the common ion effect be used to remove as much Hg_2^{2+} as possible from polluted water by precipitation of Hg_2Cl_2? The equation is:

$$Hg_2^{2+}(aq) + 2\,Cl^-(aq) \rightleftharpoons Hg_2Cl_2(s)$$

16. Calculate the amount of Ag^+ in a solution containing 1.0 M NaBr and solid AgBr. (The K_{sp} of AgBr is 5.2×10^{-13}.)

17. Solid $PbCrO_4$ is at equilibrium with its solution. What must be the concentration of Pb^{2+} to keep the CrO_4^{2-} concentration down to 1.0×10^{-8} M? (The K_{sp} of $PbCrO_4$ is 2.0×10^{-16}.)

18. For each of the following acids, write the equilibrium constant expressions and arrange the acids in order of increasing acid strength.
   a. $HC_2H_3O_2$: $K_a = 1.8 \times 10^{-5}$
   b. HCO_3^-: $K_a = 4.7 \times 10^{-11}$
   c. H_3PO_4: $K_a = 7.1 \times 10^{-3}$
   d. HSO_4^-: $K_a = 1.0 \times 10^{-2}$

19. The blood buffer system $H_2PO_4^-/HPO_4^{2-}$ has a K_a of 6.3×10^{-8}. The following concentrations are found in a sample of blood: $[HPO_4^{2-}] = 2.6 \times 10^{-4}$ M; $[H_2PO_4^-] = 1.8 \times 10^{-4}$ M. Calculate the buffer ratio and its associated pH.

20. Use the blood sample in Exercise 19.
   a. Calculate the concentrations of $H_2PO_4^-$ and

HPO_4^{2-} that would remain if $[H_3O^+]$ equivalent to 1.0×10^{-5} M were added.

b. Calculate the buffer ratio and its associated pH.

c. What pH change would be caused by this addition?

d. Comparing this pH change with the change for the H_2CO_3/HCO_3^- buffer system on page 372, state which is the more effective buffer.

21. Calculate the pH change that would be produced on the buffer system of Exercise 19 if $[OH^-]$ were added equivalent to 1.0×10^{-5} M.

22. Would you expect the $H_2PO_4^-/HPO_4^{2-}$ buffer in blood to be able to withstand an addition of $[H_3O^+]$ equivalent to 1.0×10^{-4} M? Explain, and prove your answer with appropriate calculations.

23. An industrial fermentation process requires that the pH be maintained at 5.40. Which of the following buffer systems would be the best choice? Explain. (Use Figure 13.3 to convert pH to $[H_3O^+]$.)

a. $HC_2H_3O_2(aq) + H_2O(l) \rightleftharpoons$
$$C_2H_3O_2^-(aq) + H_3O^+(aq)$$
$$K_a = 1.8 \times 10^{-5}$$

b. $H_2PO_4^-(aq) + H_2O(l) \rightleftharpoons$
$$HPO_4^{2-}(aq) + H_3O^+(aq)$$
$$K_a = 6.3 \times 10^{-8}$$

c. $NH_4^+(aq) + H_2O(l) \rightleftharpoons NH_3(aq) + H_3O^+(aq)$
$$K_a = 5.7 \times 10^{-10}$$

16

Nuclear Reactions

When the alchemists tried to change lead into gold, they were really trying to change one element into another. Little did they know that similar reactions were happening all around them. And they are happening all around us, too. In the ground, for instance, uranium is changing into thorium, thorium into protactinium, radium into radon, and radon into polonium. On the sun, hydrogen is changing into helium, releasing the energy that we need to live on earth. These changes are all spontaneous nuclear reactions.

nuclear reaction

Nuclear reactions are different from the chemical reactions we've been studying up to now. In chemical reactions, the elements keep their identities, even though they are bonded in different ways. Only the outer electrons are involved in chemical reactions. In *nuclear reactions,* the nuclei and sometimes the inner electrons are involved, and different elements are formed because the nuclei themselves change.

Humans can cause nuclear reactions to happen, too, and make one element change into another. The change that the alchemists wanted—lead into gold—isn't practical, but many other changes can be made to happen that are just as valuable. Humans can use nuclear reactions to make radioactive isotopes for medicine, industry, and atomic power plants.

The words "radioactivity," "nuclear reactor," "radioisotope," and "atomic power plant" are all part of our modern vocabulary. We'll take a closer look at the nuclear reactions that are behind them.

16.1 RADIOACTIVITY

All the spontaneous nuclear changes mentioned above happen with a release of energy. When something releases energy, sooner or later someone is going to notice it. In 1896, Henri Becquerel (1852 to 1908) noticed that a photographic plate on which he had laid a sample of a uranium salt had been exposed. The plate had been packaged to protect it from light, so he correctly concluded that the film had been exposed by some other kind of rays coming from the uranium. This spontaneous emission of radiation he named *radioactivity. Radiation* is energy traveling in a straight line.

radioactivity

radiation

This discovery opened the door to a whole world of nuclear reactions no one knew existed. Scientists started looking for and finding other radioactive substances. In 1898, Marie and Pierre Curie isolated two previously unknown elements, which they named polonium and radium. These are also radioactive. Since then, many other radioactive substances have been found in nature.

If we had a sample of a radioactive substance, we too would notice the energy it released. Radioactive substances glow in the dark, expose photographic film—and can burn and damage tissue. Placed in a glass of water, a radioactive substance will cause the water to warm up. This energy is released as the nucleus of the substance changes into another nucleus.

THE PRODUCTS OF RADIOACTIVITY.

Scientists soon discovered that radioactive substances give off more than one kind of radiation. Some have more energy than others. Some radiations have mass and charge; some don't. Three kinds of radiation were recognized at first. They were named after the first three letters in the Greek alphabet—alpha, beta, and gamma—because no one knew exactly what they were. Later, when scientists found out what each kind of radiation was, the Greek names stuck. An *alpha particle* (symbolized with the Greek letter α) is a helium nucleus. A *beta particle* (β) is a high-energy electron. And a *gamma ray* (γ) is pure high-energy radiation (without mass or charge). These and other nuclear particles are shown in Table 16.1, where we use this shorthand notation:

alpha particle (α)

beta particle (β)

gamma ray (γ)

$$\text{Mass number} \longrightarrow {}^{4}_{2}\text{He} \longleftarrow \text{Symbol of element or particle}$$
$$\text{Atomic number or charge} \longrightarrow$$

Different radiations have different abilities to penetrate skin and tissue. When it penetrates matter, nuclear radiation knocks electrons off the molecules it contacts, forming ions. These ions, too, have high energy and react with molecules near them. Radiation damage to tissue happens when the structures of important biological molecules are changed as a result of this ionization. Our bodies can repair small amounts of this kind of damage but not large amounts. The early nuclear scientists didn't realize the danger. All of them suffered from radiation burns, and some developed cancer as a result of exposure to radioactivity. Today, scientists protect themselves with lead shields and remote-control devices, but accidents causing exposure can still happen.

WRITING NUCLEAR EQUATIONS.

When a radioactive substance emits any of the particles in Table 16.1, except gamma rays, its nucleus changes. The new nucleus will contain whatever is left afterward. A substance that emits an alpha particle is called an *alpha emitter*, and the process is *alpha emission*.

alpha emitter

alpha emission

EXAMPLE 16.1: Uranium-238 is an alpha emitter. Write the equation for this reaction and identify the new nucleus.

Solution: First, we look on the table of atomic numbers on pages 14–15, where we find that the atomic number of uranium is 92. That lets us write U-238 in shorthand notation. Next, we write the incomplete equation.

$${}^{238}_{92}\text{U} \xrightarrow{\;\;\;} {}^{4}_{2}\text{He} + ?$$

Nuclear equations, like chemical equations, must obey conservation of mass and charge. Mass is conserved, so the same number of atomic mass units must appear on each side. Our new nucleus must therefore have a mass number of 234. Charge is conserved, so the sum of the atomic num-

Table 16.1
Characteristics of some nuclear particles

Name	Symbols	Mass No.	Mass[a] (amu)	Charge	Identity	Comments
Alpha particle	$^4_2$He, α	4	4.00260	2+	Helium nucleus (He^{2+})	Can penetrate tissue only to a depth of 0.01 cm. Can be stopped by a sheet of paper.
Beta particle	$^0_{-1}$e, β	0	0.000549	1−	High-energy electron	Can penetrate tissue to a depth of 1 cm. Goes through a sheet of paper but can be stopped by a 1-cm piece of aluminum.
Gamma ray	γ	0	0	0	High-energy radiation, like X rays	Can penetrate tissue to a depth of 100 cm, or pass completely through the body. Can go through paper and aluminum but can be stopped by a 5-cm sheet of lead.
Neutron	$^1_0$n	1	1.008665	0	Neutron	Can penetrate tissue to a depth of 10 cm.
Positron	$^0_1$e	0	0.000549	1+	Electron with positive charge (positive electron)	Same penetrating power as beta particle.
Proton	$^1_1$H	1	1.007825	1+	Proton	Not usually a product of radioactivity.

[a]In Chapter 2, we used rounded amu values. Now we'll use exact values of amu.

bers on each side must be equal. Our new nucleus must therefore have an atomic number of 90. Next, we look again in the table of atomic numbers to identify the new nucleus. We see that the element having an atomic number of 90 is thorium.

Answer: $^{238}_{92}$U $\longrightarrow$ $^4_2$He + $^{234}_{90}$Th
Alpha emission decreases the mass number by 4 and the atomic number by 2.

beta emitter

beta emission

A substance that emits a beta particle is called a *beta emitter,* and the process is *beta emission.*

Example 16.2: Carbon-14, a naturally occurring radioactive isotope of carbon, is a beta emitter. Write the equation for its beta emission and identify the new nucleus.

Solution: $^{14}_{6}C \not\longrightarrow {}_{-1}^{0}e + ?$
Our new nucleus must have a mass number of 14 and an atomic number of 7. We find that this element is nitrogen.

Answer: $^{14}_{6}C \longrightarrow {}_{-1}^{0}e + {}_{7}^{14}N$
Beta emission doesn't change the mass number, and it increases the atomic number by 1.

A substance that emits a gamma ray is a *gamma emitter,* and the process is *gamma emission.* Usually, gamma emission accompanies other kinds of nuclear reactions. Since a gamma ray has no charge or mass number, it doesn't change the nucleus, and it usually isn't included in the nuclear equation. Just as energy from chemical reactions is usually liberated in the form of heat, energy from nuclear reactions can be released in the form of gamma rays.

From Table 16.1 we can deduce that positron emission will not affect the mass number but will decrease the atomic number by 1. Neutron emission will decrease the mass number by 1 but won't affect the atomic number.

gamma emitter

gamma emission

NUCLEAR STABILIZATION.
All isotopes of all elements having atomic numbers higher than 83 (bismuth) are radioactive. In addition, some isotopes of other elements, such as carbon-14, are also radioactive. Twenty-two elements found in nature contain radioactive nuclei; of these, ten elements have atomic numbers less than 83.

When a nucleus emits radiation and changes to another nucleus, it *decays.* Nuclei decay because they are unstable, or have high potential energy, relative to their decay products. The new nucleus may also be unstable and decay even further. Decay will stop when a stable nucleus is reached. To see what causes certain nuclei to be unstable, we should first look at the stable nuclei.

decay

Figure 16.1 shows a plot of atomic number (number of protons) against the number of neutrons for the stable nuclei. The stable nuclei fall within a narrow band. Nuclei that aren't in this band are unstable. A nucleus is unstable either because it has an atomic number greater than 83, because it has too many neutrons per proton (left of the stable band), or because it has too many protons per neutron (right of the band).

If a nucleus is unstable because it has too high an atomic number, it often emits an alpha particle. By alpha emission, the nucleus can decrease its atomic number by 2. All alpha emitters have an atomic number greater than 83, but not all substances with an atomic number over 83 are alpha emitters.

If a nucleus is unstable because it has too many neutrons per proton, it can emit a neutron (rare) or it can change a neutron to a proton. To understand how this can happen, we can oversimplify a bit and think of a neutron as being made of a proton and an electron. Then, a neutron can change to a proton like this:

$$_{0}^{1}n \longrightarrow {}_{1}^{1}H + {}_{-1}^{0}e$$

**FIGURE 16.1
Neutron-proton
relationship for
stable nuclei**

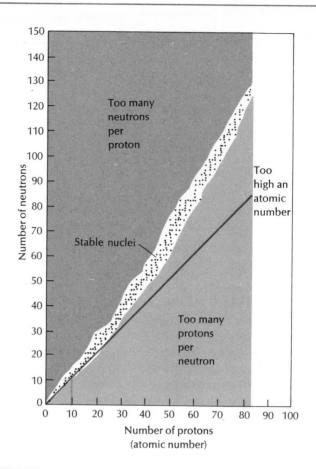

(The masses and charges balance.) The new proton stays behind in the nucleus, and the electron leaves as a beta particle. Nuclei that have too many neutrons per proton to be stable are usually beta emitters. C-14, a beta emitter, falls to the left of the band of stable nuclei.

If a nucleus is unstable because it has too many protons per neutron, it changes a proton to a neutron in one of two ways. In one way, a proton reacts with an electron in the reverse of the above equation. When the electron is one of the atom's own inner electrons, the process is called *electron capture.*

**electron
capture**

EXAMPLE 16.3:   Molybdenum-90 falls to the right of the band of stable nuclei and undergoes electron capture. Write the equation.

Solution: $^{90}_{42}\text{Mo} + {}_{-1}^{0}e \longrightarrow$?

Our new nucleus will have a mass number of 90 and an atomic number of 41: niobium. We write "electron capture" with the arrow to show that the electron came from within the atom itself.

In electron capture, no particles are emitted, but gamma rays are always released.

We can think of a proton as being made of a positron and a neutron. Then, the second way a proton can change to a neutron is by emitting a positron.

$$^{1}_{1}H \longrightarrow ^{1}_{0}n + ^{0}_{1}e$$

Example 16.4: C-11 has too many protons per neutron and is a positron emitter. Write the equation.

Solution: $^{11}_{6}C \nrightarrow ^{0}_{1}e + ?$

Our new nucleus has a mass number of 11 and an atomic number of 5: boron.

Answer: $^{11}_{6}C \longrightarrow ^{0}_{1}e + ^{11}_{5}B$

ARTIFICIAL RADIOACTIVITY AND TRANSMUTATION.

Besides the naturally occurring radioactive isotopes, many more have been made by humans. This is done by shooting a high-energy particle, called a *projectile,* at a target nucleus. The projectiles are given their high energies in instruments such as cyclotrons, linear accelerators, betatrons, and nuclear reactors. The word *transmutation* strictly means one element changing to another, but the current usage is applied mostly to changes caused by human beings. The first human-caused transmutation—but one that didn't result in a radioactive nucleus—was done by Ernest Rutherford in 1919. He bombarded nitrogen with alpha particles.

projectile

transmutation

$$^{14}_{7}N + ^{4}_{2}He \longrightarrow ^{17}_{8}O + ^{1}_{1}H$$

Then, in 1934, Irène Joliot-Curie did the first transmutation to result in a radioactive nucleus.

$$^{27}_{13}Al + ^{4}_{2}He \longrightarrow ^{30}_{15}P + ^{1}_{0}n$$

When aluminum-27 was bombarded with alpha particles, the resulting phosphorus-30 was found to be radioactive. Since a radioactive substance was produced from nonradioactive substances, this was called *artificial radioactivity.* Naturally occurring phosphorus is stable P-31, and so this process had created a new radioactive isotope (*radioisotope*). Today, many other radioisotopes are produced artificially by transmutation.

artificial radioactivity

radioisotope

Uranium has the highest atomic number (92) of any of the naturally occurring elements. The elements with atomic numbers greater than 92— up to 106 at the time of this writing—have been made artificially by similar transmutation reactions. These are called *transuranium elements.* Some reactions used to produce them are shown in Table 16.2. Of course, all these elements are radioactive.

transuranium element

TABLE 16.2
Some transmutation reactions used to produce transuranium elements

Atomic Number	Name and Symbol	Target Nucleus	Projectile		
93	Neptunium, Np	$^{238}_{92}U$	$+$ $^{1}_{0}n$	$\longrightarrow$ $^{239}_{93}Np$	$+$ $^{0}_{-1}e$
94	Plutonium, Pu	$^{238}_{92}U$	$+$ $^{2}_{1}H$	$\longrightarrow$ $^{238}_{94}Pu$	$+$ $2^{1}_{0}n$ $+$ $^{0}_{-1}e$
95	Americium, Am	$^{239}_{94}Pu$	$+$ $^{1}_{0}n$	$\longrightarrow$ $^{240}_{95}Am$	$+$ $^{0}_{-1}e$
96	Curium, Cm	$^{239}_{94}Pu$	$+$ $^{4}_{2}He$	$\longrightarrow$ $^{242}_{96}Cm$	$+$ $^{1}_{0}n$
97	Berkelium, Bk	$^{241}_{95}Am$	$+$ $^{4}_{2}He$	$\longrightarrow$ $^{243}_{97}Bk$	$+$ $2^{1}_{0}n$
98	Californium, Cf	$^{242}_{96}Cm$	$+$ $^{4}_{2}He$	$\longrightarrow$ $^{245}_{98}Cf$	$+$ $^{1}_{0}n$
99	Einsteinium, Es	$^{238}_{92}U$	$+$ $15^{1}_{0}n$	$\longrightarrow$ $^{253}_{99}Es$	$+$ $7^{0}_{-1}e$
100	Fermium, Fm	$^{238}_{92}U$	$+$ $17^{1}_{0}n$	$\longrightarrow$ $^{255}_{100}Fm$	$+$ $8^{0}_{-1}e$
101	Mendelevium, Md	$^{253}_{99}Es$	$+$ $^{4}_{2}He$	$\longrightarrow$ $^{256}_{101}Md$	$+$ $^{1}_{0}n$
102	Nobelium, No	$^{246}_{96}Cm$	$+$ $^{12}_{6}C$	$\longrightarrow$ $^{254}_{102}No$	$+$ $4^{1}_{0}n$
103	Lawrencium, Lr	$^{252}_{98}Cf$	$+$ $^{10}_{5}B$	$\longrightarrow$ $^{257}_{103}Lr$	$+$ $5^{1}_{0}n$
104	Kurchatovium, Ku (tentative)	$^{242}_{94}PU$	$+$ $^{22}_{10}Ne$	$\longrightarrow$ $^{260}_{104}Ku$	$+$ $4^{1}_{0}n$
105	Hahnium, Ha (tentative)	$^{249}_{98}Cf$	$+$ $^{15}_{7}N$	$\longrightarrow$ $^{260}_{105}Ha$	$+$ $4^{1}_{0}n$
106	Unnamed	$^{249}_{98}Cf$	$+$ $^{18}_{8}O$	$\longrightarrow$ $^{263}_{106}?$	$+$ $4^{1}_{0}n$

Radioactive decay reactions are spontaneous and take place with a release of energy. Artificial transmutation reactions are not spontaneous, and great quantities of energy must be supplied to make them happen.

16.2 SOME CONSEQUENCES OF RADIOACTIVE DECAY

Radioisotopes have many uses—and many hazards. They can be used as energy sources, as tracers in medicine, industry or research, and as "clocks" to determine ages or events in natural history. The hazards, of course, have to do with biological damage that can occur from exposure. To use radioisotopes, and to guard against exposure, we need ways of detecting radiation.

Geiger-Müller counter

RADIATION DETECTORS. The best-known radiation detector is the *Geiger-Müller counter*, sometimes called simply a Geiger counter. The part of the counter that receives the radiation is a tube with a window. The tube is filled with a gas and has a wire sticking into its center. A voltage source makes the wire an anode and the jacket of the tube a cathode. The same ionizing effect of radiation on matter that causes biological damage lets the radiation be detected in a Geiger counter. When radiation goes through the window of the tube, it hits the gas molecules inside the tube and knocks electrons off them. The electrons hit the anode and cause a current to flow, which registers as a click or a light flash. Geiger counters work best for beta and gamma emitters rather than for alpha emitters, because alpha particles don't have enough energy to get through the tube's window.

Each time a click or flash is registered, it means that a nucleus has decayed. Most radiation detectors count the number of such nuclear events and collect them on a digital readout. The usual way of measuring radioactivity is in counts per minute. The SI unit of radioactivity is the *becquerel (Bq)*, which is one nuclear event per second (sixty counts per minute). Since an event may result in alpha, beta, or gamma radiation, all of which have different energies and produce different amounts of biological damage, the becquerel isn't an exact measure of how much damaging radiation is present. However, we can say roughly that exposure to between 10^4 and 10^5 becquerels will endanger the life of a human being.

becquerel

More sophisticated counters are used in research and medicine. One is the *scintillation counter.* The substance to be measured is placed in a container holding a solution of a radiation-sensitive dye. When radiation hits the dye, the dye gives a flash of light that is picked up by a light detector and translated into counts per minute.

scintillation counter

Light-sealed photographic film badges are worn by people who work around radiation. These badges are checked frequently to determine how much radiation their wearers have been exposed to. Photographic film is also used in *autoradiography,* in which a radioactive substance contained in a given sample takes its own picture, showing its location in the sample.

auto-radiography

HALF-LIVES OF RADIOACTIVE SUBSTANCES. Each radio-isotope decays at a certain rate. Nothing will stop it from decaying or make it decay faster or slower. The time it takes for half of any specific amount of any radioactive substance to decay is its *half-life*. If an isotope's half-life is twenty-eight years and we start with one gram of it, then after twenty-eight years we'll have half a gram left. After another twenty-eight years, we'll have one-fourth of a gram left, as shown in Figure 16.2. Half-lives range from fractions of a second to billions of years. Some of the heavier artificial elements have very short half-lives (that of element 106 is 0.9 seconds).

half-life

Archaeologists use half-lives to determine how long once-living things have been dead. In a process called *carbon dating,* they measure the amount of radioactive carbon-14 a substance contains. Most naturally occurring carbon is C-12, but small amounts of C-14 are formed in the atmosphere by high-energy neutrons.

carbon dating

$$^{14}_{7}N + ^{1}_{0}n \longrightarrow ^{14}_{6}C + ^{1}_{1}H$$

FIGURE 16.2
Strontium-90
has a half-life
of 28 years

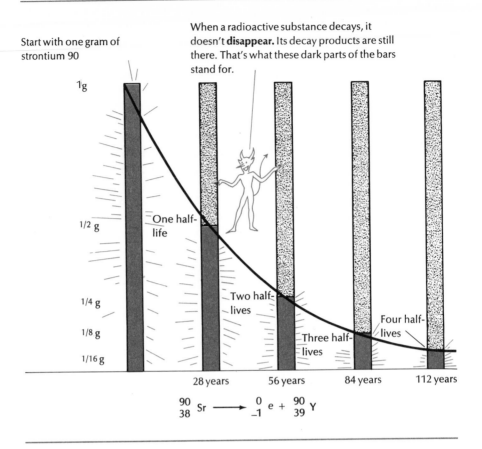

Start with one gram of strontium 90

When a radioactive substance decays, it doesn't **disappear.** Its decay products are still there. That's what these dark parts of the bars stand for.

1g

1/2 g — One half-life

1/4 g — Two half-lives

1/8 g — Three half-lives

Four half-lives

1/16 g

28 years   56 years   84 years   112 years

$$^{90}_{38}\text{Sr} \longrightarrow ^{0}_{-1}e + ^{90}_{39}\text{Y}$$

The formation and decay of C-14 are at equilibrium in the atmosphere, so the ratio of C-12 to C-14 is always constant. Living plants and animals take in C-14, and the amount they contain is also at equilibrium with the amount in the atmosphere. When a plant or animal dies, though, it stops taking in new C-14 while the C-14 it contains still decays.

One gram of carbon from anything alive contains about enough C-14 to release sixteen beta particles per minute. The half-life of C-14 is 5730 years. Thus if a gram of carbon from a dead substance releases only eight beta particles per minute, that means it's been dead for one half-life of C-14, or 5730 years.

EXAMPLE 16.5: A 0.50-gram sample of carbon isolated from a fossilized plant specimen measures two beta emissions per minute. How long has the plant been dead?

Solution: Two beta emissions per minute for 0.50 gram of carbon means four beta particles per minute for one gram of carbon. Since one-fourth of the original activity remains, two half-lives must have elapsed.

Answer: 11,460 years.

The alchemists believed that baser metals like lead "ripened" by changing first to silver and finally gold. Such a series of changes does occur among some metals, but it's nearly the reverse of what the alchemists wanted. One series starts with uranium-238, goes through fourteen changes, and finally ends with lead-206, instead of starting with it. This is called a *radioactive decay series*. The U-238 series is shown in Figure 16.3.

radioactive decay series

FIGURE 16.3
Uranium-238 decay series

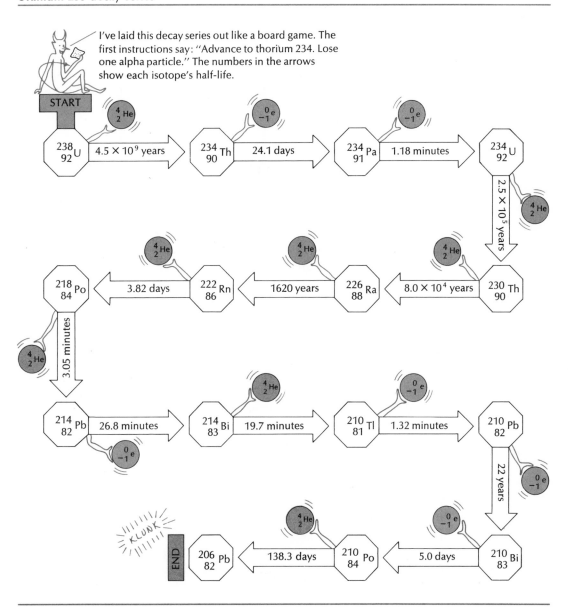

There are three naturally occurring decay series. Besides the U-238 decaying to Pb-206, Th-232 decays to Pb-208, and U-235 decays to Pb-207. For a decay series to exist, the parent isotope (for example, U-238) must have a long half-life, and the daughter (product) isotopes must be relatively short-lived. This explains why some naturally occurring isotopes have relatively short half-lives (for instance, Pa-234, with a half-life of only 1.18 minutes). They are being continuously replaced by their parent isotope. U-238 has a half-life of 4.5 billion years. The earth is believed to be about 4.6 billion years old, so it isn't surprising that there's still plenty of U-238 and its daughter isotopes around.

Lead-206 is not a natural isotope but is formed only through the U-238 decay series. If Pb-206 turns up in a rock, it must have come from the decay of U-238. Because we know U-238's half-life, we can tell how long it took that much uranium to decay to Pb-206. The larger the lead-to-uranium ratio, the older the rock is. Samples of moon rock have been analyzed by **uranium dating** *uranium dating* and found to be about 4.6 billion years old, or about the same age as the earth.

SOME USES OF RADIOISOTOPES.

Table 16.3 shows a few of the many useful radioisotopes. They can sterilize food, because the radiations kill microorganisms that cause spoilage. They can be used to control insect populations by sterilizing male insects. The males are then released to mate with females, whose eggs won't be fertilized. Once a female has mated, she doesn't mate again. Radioisotopes will also destroy cancerous tissue. Radiation from cobalt-60 is aimed at affected areas. Chromium-51 wires are implanted directly into tumors to destroy them. Iodine-131 concentrates in the thyroid gland and can destroy cancerous tissue there.

Radioisotopes are also used as tracers, in the same way that a detective might rig a suspicious vehicle with a radio transmitter so that the vehicle could always be located. Radioisotopes behave chemically in exactly the same way as their stable isotopes, but they send out signals telling where they are. Because of this, they can be substituted for their stable isotopes in compounds, and the compounds can be traced. Such labeled or tagged compounds are used in medicine to diagnose illnesses. For instance, blockages in the circulatory system can be located by injecting radioactive sodium-24 in the form of NaCl. In industry, pipe leaks can be detected by adding a radioisotope and detecting where it appears.

Radioisotopes that are placed into human beings must be carefully chosen. First, no alpha emitters are used. Even though external exposure to alpha radiation isn't serious because of its low penetrating power, alpha emission is the most harmful type of radiation if taken internally. The large massive particles can do a great deal of damage to nearby tissues or organs. Second, substances with relatively short half-lives are used, so that they will disappear from the body as soon as possible after their job is done.

TABLE 16.3
Some useful
radioactive
substances

389

Isotope	Half-Life	Emission	Uses
Cobalt-58	71.3 days	$_1^0e$, γ	Used to determine intake of vitamin B-12, a cobalt-containing vitamin.
Cobalt-60	5.3 years	β, γ	A strong beta and gamma emitter Used in cancer radiation therapy.
Carbon-14	5730 years	β	Used in carbon dating and in chemical and biological research to determine reaction paths. Also used to check wear on tires.
Iodine-131	8 days	β, γ	Iodine concentrates in the thyroid gland. Used to diagnose thyroid malfunction and to treat thyroid cancer, since it concentrates in thyroid gland; its beta and gamma radiations destroy cancerous thyroid tissue without harming other cells.
Iron-59	45.6 days	β, γ	Used to study formation of red blood cells (hemoglobin contains iron).
Phosphorus-32	14.3 days	β	Used in biochemical research and to treat leukemia and skin lesions. Also used in industry to measure tire wear and thickness of films.
Radium-226	1602 years	α, γ	Like cobalt-60, used in cancer radiation therapy.
Sodium-24	15.0 hours	β, γ	Used as NaCl in water solution to check for proper function of circulatory system.
Hydrogen-3	12.3 years	β	Used in chemical and biochemical research in the form of various compounds. As H_2O, used to determine a person's total body water.

16.3 NUCLEAR ENERGY

Stable nuclei have lower energies than unstable ones. Stable nuclei also have lower energies than their separate neutrons and protons. If they didn't, the nuclei would fly apart. Just as energy is released when compounds are formed from atoms, energy is released when nuclei are formed from neutrons and protons.

ENERGY AND THE MASS DEFECT.

If we add up the individual masses of the subatomic particles that make up an atom, we always find that the sum of these masses is greater than the actual mass of the nucleus itself. For instance, we can add up the masses of the ingredients of a helium nucleus.

$$
\begin{array}{rl}
\text{2 protons, each 1.007825 amu} & = 2.015650 \text{ amu} \\
\text{2 neutrons, each 1.008665 amu} & = \underline{2.017330 \text{ amu}} \\
\text{Total} & 4.032980 \text{ amu}
\end{array}
$$

mass defect

However, the actual mass of a helium nucleus is only 4.002600 amu. The difference of 0.03038 amu is called the *mass defect*. Every nucleus has a mass defect, and each value is different. Energy equivalent to the mass defect goes into holding the nucleus together.

E = mc²

Mass-energy equivalence was discovered by Albert Einstein (1879–1955) and stated in his famous equation, $E = mc^2$. E stands for energy, m for mass, and c for the speed of light (3×10^8 meters/second). He said that it should be possible to convert energy to mass and vice versa, because they are both different forms of the same thing. This relationship can be used to calculate exactly how much energy is equivalent to how much mass. The mass defect in one mole of helium is equivalent to about 6×10^8 kcal of energy. We see that a little bit of mass produces a lot of energy, because the speed of light is a very large number.

nuclear binding energy

The energy equivalent to the mass defect is the energy released when the nucleus is formed from the neutrons and protons, or the energy required to take the nucleus apart into its separate particles. This is the *nuclear binding energy*. Figure 16.4 shows a plot of binding energy per neutron or proton against mass number. The binding energy decreases sharply with mass number at first, then levels off and increases slowly toward the elements of very high mass number. Changing from nuclei with larger binding energies to nuclei with smaller binding energies will release energy. We can do this by going downhill on the curve from left to right or from right to left. Iron is the dividing line.

NUCLEAR FUSION.

nuclear fusion

Putting two nuclei together to make a larger nucleus is called *nuclear fusion*. On Figure 16.4, putting hydrogens together to form helium means going downhill from left to right. Quite a lot of energy should be released in this process, and it is. One of the many fusion reactions that takes place on the sun is this one:

$$
{}^{2}_{1}\text{H} + {}^{2}_{1}\text{H} \longrightarrow {}^{4}_{2}\text{He}
$$

Fusion reactions have very high activation energies, because a lot of energy is needed to force the two positive nuclei close enough together to fuse. But much more energy is released once the reaction starts, as in many reactions we saw in Chapter 15. High temperatures like those found on the sun (about 40 million degrees) are needed to overcome the high activation energy. For this reason, using nuclear fusion as a controlled

FIGURE 16.4
Nuclear binding
energies of some
of the elements

391

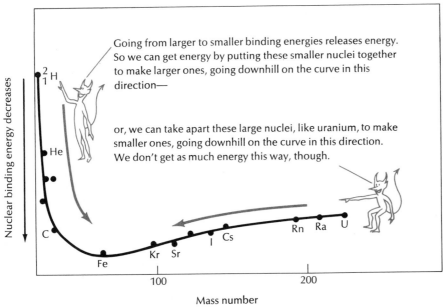

Going from larger to smaller binding energies releases energy.
So we can get energy by putting these smaller nuclei together
to make larger ones, going downhill on the curve in this
direction—

or, we can take apart these large nuclei, like uranium, to make
smaller ones, going downhill on the curve in this direction.
We don't get as much energy this way, though.

energy source is a long way in the future for us. Meanwhile, though, we
do have a fusion reactor: the sun.

The hydrogen bomb is a fusion bomb. It also contains a fission bomb,
which we'll talk about later. The fission bomb is needed to provide the
high temperature for the fusion reaction.

NUCLEAR FISSION.
Nuclear fusion occurs going downhill from
left to right on the binding energy curve, and it releases a lot of energy.
Going downhill from right to left also releases energy, but not as much.
We can see about how much energy we'd get from breaking a uranium
nucleus apart into a strontium nucleus (atomic number 38) and a xenon
nucleus (atomic number 54). Breaking a nucleus apart into pieces of com-
parable size is *nuclear fission*.

nuclear fission

At the time of this writing, only three isotopes—U-235, U-233, and Pu-239
—are known to have *fissionable nuclei* (nuclei capable of fission). Nuclear
fission happens when a slow-moving neutron hits a fissionable nucleus.
The nucleus, already unstable, is distorted by the impact of the neutron
and elongated. This makes it easy for the nucleus to break apart, as shown
in Figure 16.5, releasing energy and neutrons.

**fissionable
nuclei**

Many different products are obtained from nuclear fission, because each
nucleus breaks apart randomly. If we hit a lot of marbles with a hammer,
most of them would break more or less in half, but we'd get a variety of
different-sized pieces. We'd also get some little splinters of glass, just as

FIGURE 16.5
Nuclear fission of U-235

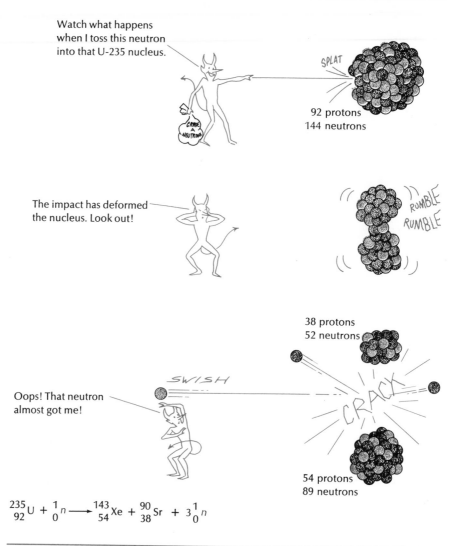

we get a few neutrons along with the big fragments. Some possible fission products of U-235 are these.

$$^{139}_{56}\text{Ba} + ^{95}_{36}\text{Kr} + 2^{1}_{0}n$$

$$^{140}_{57}\text{La} + ^{94}_{35}\text{Br} + 2^{1}_{0}n$$

$$^{135}_{53}\text{I} + ^{97}_{39}\text{Y} + 4^{1}_{0}n$$

$$^{103}_{42}\text{Mo} + ^{131}_{50}\text{Sn} + 2^{1}_{0}n$$

$$^{139}_{54}\text{Xe} + ^{95}_{38}\text{Sr} + 2^{1}_{0}n$$

Of the three fissionable nuclei, only U-235 occurs in nature; the other two are produced artificially by transmutation. U-235 itself is only about 1 percent of the total amount of uranium; the rest is U-238, which isn't fissionable. In naturally occurring uranium, fission of U-235 does happen. Now and then a stray neutron will strike a U-235 nucleus and that nucleus will undergo nuclear fission instead of radioactive decay. The neutrons produced by the fission will simply be lost to the surroundings. We wouldn't notice this isolated event.

However, if we had a great many U-235 nuclei close together, the neutrons (two or more) from the fission of a single nucleus could go out and hit other fissionable nuclei and cause more fission. The snowballing effect of more neutrons causing fission and producing more neutrons to cause still more fission is called a *chain reaction,* shown in Figure 16.6. In a chain reaction more than one neutron per nucleus is released, so that the fission keeps going and releases a lot of energy. For a chain reaction to happen, enough of the fissionable nuclei have to be in the same place, so that few neutrons can escape without hitting other nuclei. The amount of a fissionable material needed for a chain reaction is called the *critical mass.* The critical mass of U-235 is about 10 kilograms; for Pu-239, it's about 3 kilograms.

chain reaction

critical mass

If a chain reaction is allowed to proceed uncontrolled, the result is an atomic explosion. The atomic bombs of World War II were fission bombs, one using U-235 and the other Pu-239. In these bombs, several pieces of the fissionable material, equal to the critical mass when combined, were kept apart. To trigger the explosion, the parts were forced together with ordinary explosives.

In nuclear reactors, chain reactions are controlled. Neutrons from fission have rather high energy. Slow-moving neutrons are needed for fission; fast ones just bounce off. Nuclear reactors usually contain something to slow the neutrons down. The first nuclear reactor, built in 1942 by Enrico Fermi (1901–1954), contained a critical mass of U-235, with graphite blocks and cadmium rods stuck all through it. The graphite served to slow the neutrons down, and the cadmium absorbed neutrons. The rate of energy release could be controlled by pushing the cadmium rods in, to slow down the fission reaction, or by pulling them out, to speed it up.

Although nuclear reactors have become more sophisticated since that of Fermi, the principle is the same: the reaction is kept from getting out of hand by absorbing some of the neutrons when necessary. The first major nuclear power plant for producing electricity began operating in 1957 in Shippingport, Pennsylvania. Since then, over a hundred nuclear power plants have been or are being built in the United States. The method of power generation is the same as for conventional electrical power plants: heat is used to turn water into steam to drive a turbine to make electricity. The difference is that the source of heat is controlled fission and not burning fuel. Of course, the nuclear reactor part of the plant is also much more complex than the fuel-burning part of a conventional power plant.

The energy produced by the fission of 1 kilogram of U-235 is equivalent to that produced by burning about 2800 tons of coal. But there are problems with nuclear reactors. First, U-235 is scarce and hard to separate from U-238. Second, there is danger of releasing radioactive materials to the surroundings during fission. And third, the products of nuclear fission are themselves radioactive. That presents the problem of disposing safely of large amounts of radioactive waste products, some with very long half-lives.

FIGURE 16.6
Chain reaction involving uranium-235

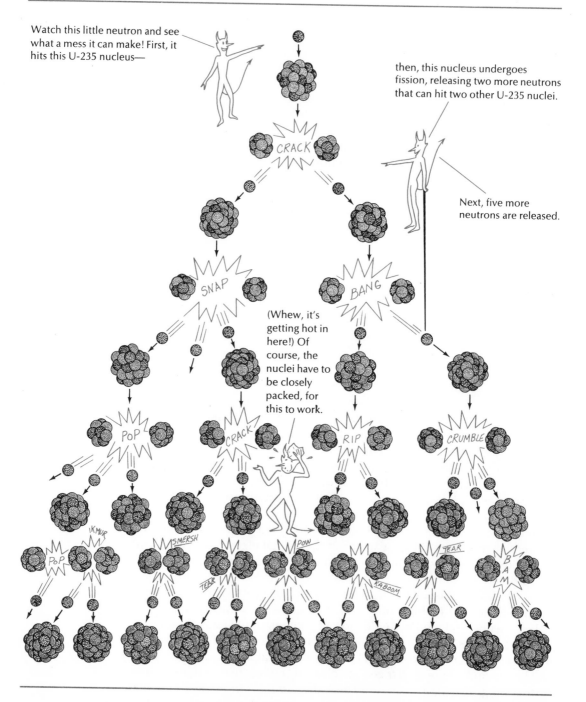

The *breeder reactor* would solve the first of these problems. A breeder reactor makes its own fuel by causing transmutation reactions that produce either U-233 from Th-232 or Pu-239 from U-239, using neutrons from fission.

$$^{232}_{90}\text{Th} + {}^{1}_{0}n \longrightarrow {}^{233}_{92}\text{U} + 2\,{}^{0}_{-1}e$$

$$^{239}_{92}\text{U} + {}^{1}_{0}n \longrightarrow {}^{239}_{94}\text{Pu} + 2\,{}^{0}_{-1}e + {}^{1}_{0}n$$

Several prototype breeder reactors are now functioning in Europe, but as yet none are operating in the United States. A commercial-sized breeder reactor may be operating here by 1980.

While the breeder reactor would partially solve the fuel problem, it wouldn't remove the considerable environmental threat posed by all nuclear reactors. Even during normal operation, nuclear power plants inevitably release radioactive substances to the atmosphere. Many radioactive products, such as xenon and krypton, are gases, and preventing

Isotope	Half-Life	Emission	Comments
Krypton-85	10.8 years	β, γ	These noble gases escape directly from nuclear power plants. In the atmosphere, they expose skin and lungs to radiation.
Xenon-133	5.3 days	β, γ	
Xenon-135	9.14 hours	β, γ	
Strontium-90	27.7 years	β	A member of Group IIA that behaves like calcium, and collects in bones. Can cause bone cancer. Also absorbed by plants.
Radium-226	1,602 years	α, γ	Same as strontium-90.
Iodine-131	8 days	β, γ	A major contaminent from nuclear accidents. Concentrates in thyroid and causes thyroid cancer.
Hydrogen-3 (Tritium)	12.3 years	β	Escapes as H_2 or water vapor from reactors. Can be incorporated into most parts of the body. Not as serious as others because its radiation has relatively low energy.
Cesium-137	30 years	β, γ	A member of Group IA that imitates the behavior of sodium and potassium, finding its way into all animal and plant systems. Exposes the entire body to radiation.
Plutonium-239	24,390 years	α, γ	Also collects in bone. Extremely dangerous to ingest because of alpha emission.
Carbon-14	5,730 years	β	Collects in all parts of plants and animals.

TABLE 16.4
Some dangerous products of nuclear fission

their escape is difficult. In 1967, one power plant alone released about 4×10^{17} becquerels of radioactivity. The contamination would be even more serious if accidents occurred—leaks, ruptures, or runaway reactions that might cause melting and breakage. Some of the radioactive waste products, and their significance and half-lives, are shown in Table 16.4.

A lesser but still serious problem is that of thermal pollution. Nuclear power plants use huge amounts of cooling water, which is then released to natural water systems. We saw some of the consequences of thermal pollution in Chapter 12.

Even with all its problems, nuclear energy holds great promise as an energy source. Someday it may completely replace the fuels—coal, oil, natural gas—that we now use in large quantities.

REVIEW QUESTIONS

1. What are some differences between chemical reactions and nuclear reactions?

Radioactivity

2. What is *radioactivity?* What is *radiation?* How can we tell whether a substance is radioactive?
3. What are *alpha particles, beta particles,* and *gamma rays?* Why were they so named?
4. Write the symbols for six nuclear particles, and give their mass numbers and charges. Which type of external radiation exposure is most dangerous?
5. Give examples of *alpha emission* and *beta emission.* State how each type of emission changes the nucleus of the radioactive substance.
6. How are mass and charge conserved in a nuclear equation? How can the new nucleus be identified?
7. State how the following will affect the mass number and atomic number of a radioactive nucleus: *gamma emission,* positron emission, neutron emission.
8. Give three reasons why a nucleus might be unstable. How might a nucleus stabilize itself in each case?
9. Define and give an example of *electron capture.*
10. How are radioactive isotopes made by humans? What is the current usage of the word *transmutation?*
11. What is meant by *artificial radioactivity?* Give an example.
12. What are *transuranium elements?* Where do they come from? Why are they all radioactive?

Some Consequences of Radioactive Decay

13. Name and describe some radiation detectors. What is the usual way of measuring radioactivity?
14. What is the SI unit of radioactivity? What does it mean?

15. What is meant by *half-life?* Describe what happens to a certain amount of radioactive substance after one, two, and three half-lives.
16. Explain how *carbon dating* works. Why is there always a constant amount of C-14 in the atmosphere?
17. What is a *radioactive decay series?* What element is the end product of the three known radioactive decay series?
18. Protactinium-234 has a half-life of 1.18 minutes. Why is there still any of it around?
19. How can the ages of rocks be estimated by *uranium dating?*
20. Name some uses of radioisotopes.
21. Explain how radioactive tracers work. Give a few examples.

Nuclear Energy

22. How do we know that stable nuclei have lower energy than their separate neutrons and protons do?
23. What is the *mass defect?* How can it be calculated?
24. What is mass-energy equivalence? Why does a little bit of mass produce a lot of energy?
25. What is *nuclear binding energy?* How is it related to the mass defect?
26. What is *nuclear fusion?* Where does it happen naturally? Why does it require very high temperatures?
27. What is *nuclear fission?* How is it different from nuclear fusion?
28. What are the three *fissionable nuclei?* Describe what happens when one of these undergoes fission.
29. Are the same products always obtained from fission? Explain.

30. U-235 occurs in uranium ore. Why doesn't an atomic explosion happen in the ore?
31. What is a *chain reaction?* A *critical mass?*
32. How do nuclear reactors generate power? What are some problems connected with nuclear reactors?
33. What is a *breeder reactor?* Why might it be desirable?
34. Why is it impossible to prevent release of radio-activity from nuclear power plants?
35. Name a few hazardous fission products and say why they are dangerous.

EXERCISES

1. Write nuclear equations for alpha emission of the following nuclei.
    a. U-235
    b. Th-232
    c. Pu-239
    d. Ra-223
2. Write nuclear equations for the following beta emitters.
    a. P-32
    b. I-131
    c. Co-60
    d. Na-24
3. None of the naturally occurring radioactive substances emits positrons. However, the following artificial nuclei do. Write their nuclear equations.
    a. P-30
    b. Na-22
    c. F-18
4. Helium is often found trapped in small holes in rocks. Where did it come from?
5. Nitrogen-14 is a stable nucleus; N-13 and N-16 are unstable. Give probable reasons for their insta-bilities and suggest possible methods of stabiliza-tion. Write nuclear equations for each.
6. Potassium-40 is a naturally occurring radioactive isotope that occurs in about 30 percent of the existing potassium (a large percentage). It is inter-esting because it can undergo either beta emission or electron capture. Write nuclear equations for each reaction.
7. Beryllium-7 undergoes electron capture.
    a. Write the equation.
    b. Explain why this happens with more difficulty when beryllium is in the form of Be^{2+}.
8. Some radioisotopes are made by transmutation. Fill in the missing numbers, symbols, or both for the following transmutation reactions.
    a. $^{59}_{26}Fe + ^{1}_{0}n \longrightarrow ^{60}_{?}Co + ^{?}_{?}?$
    b. $^{35}_{17}Cl + ^{?}_{?}? \longrightarrow ^{35}_{16}? + ^{1}_{1}H$
    c. $^{27}_{?}Al + ^{1}_{0}? \longrightarrow ^{24}_{11}Na + ^{?}_{?}?$
    d. $^{130}_{52}? + ^{?}_{1}? \longrightarrow ^{?}_{53}I$
    e. $^{?}_{?}? + ^{0}_{-1}e \longrightarrow ^{32}_{15}P$
9. Which would be the more dangerous to be exposed to internally?
    a. 1000 becquerels of an alpha emitter, or 1000 becquerels of a gamma emitter
    b. 500 becquerels of a beta emitter, or 1000 bec-querels of a gamma emitter
10. How many counts per minute would be registered by each sample in Exercise 9?
11. Element 106 has a half-life of 0.9 second. If 1,000,000 atoms of it were prepared, how many would remain after 4.5 seconds?
12. How old is a bone sample if 0.152 grams of car-bon from the sample emit 1.2 counts per minute?
13. Explain how carbon-14 might be used to measure wear on tires.
14. Phosphorus-32, in the form of phosphate, can be used to measure the amount of fertilizer plants take up. Explain how this might be done.
15. Small amounts of radioactive substances are added to automobile piston material to test how well lubricating oils are doing their job. If, after equal time of operation, oil sample A measures 42 counts per minute and oil sample B measures 15 counts per minute, which oil causes the least wear?
16. Why do you think cobalt-58, and not cobalt-60, is used to determine intake of vitamin B-12 in human beings? (Refer to Table 16.3.)
17. The mass of a Hg-200 nucleus is 199.9683 amu. Using the values for the masses of the neutron and proton in Table 16.1, calculate the mass defect of Hg-200.
18. Could we get energy from the fusion of krypton with strontium? Explain.
19. Could we get energy by breaking apart a carbon atom into two lithium atoms? Explain.
20. In Figure 16.4, which element has the largest nuclear binding energy? The smallest?
21. One of the reactions that takes place in the hydrogen bomb is this one:

$$^{7}_{3}Li + ^{1}_{1}H \longrightarrow 2 ^{4}_{2}He$$

If a lithium-7 nucleus has a mass of 7.0160 amu calculate the mass difference between the reac-tants and products. Would this reaction release or absorb energy?
22. Zirconium-97, a radioactive fission product that can concentrate in bone tissue, results from fission of U-235. Two neutrons are also released. What is the other product? Write the equation.
23. Could a chain reaction occur from a fission reac-tion that produced only one neutron? Explain.
24. Bromine-90, a fission product, decays to the hazardous strontium-90. Write the equation.
25. Iodine-131 is formed by the loss of three beta particles from another fission product. What is that fission product? Write the equations.

17

Introduction to Organic Chemistry

Photosynthesis began on the earth about three billion years ago. In photo-synthesis, energy from the sun joins together atmospheric carbon dioxide and water molecules to form larger molecules. Energy stored in the bonds of these molecules was used by primitive organisms to carry out bodily functions. In the bodies of plants and animals, carbon atoms were arranged into complex chains and interlocking structures—some stiff enough to make a giant redwood or to help support the weight of a brontosaurus.

The dinosaurs and early plants died, decayed, and became the coal and petroleum deposits that we use today. These deposits are treasure chests of energy and of structure. Energy from the sun that went into making bonds is stored in them. Many molecules that existed in these early life forms still remain as chains or rings of carbon atoms in petroleum and coal. Now we harvest the stored energy as fuel and the molecular structure to make other structures like plastics, rubber, and fabrics.

Photosynthesis is still going on, and all organisms still use carbon to build their bodies. Carbon-based compounds are the foundation of living organisms, and for this reason were dubbed *organic compounds* in the late eighteenth century. *Organic chemistry* is the study of organic compounds. In addition to providing structure and energy, organic compounds provide function. Small organic molecules—vitamins, hormones, drugs, insecticides—perform certain functions because of how they are put together. Many of these are now made synthetically from raw materials found in petroleum and coal. Figure 17.1 shows just a few pathways from petroleum and coal to some of the products we use today. In all, about three million organic compounds are known. This number contrasts sharply with the hundred thousand or so *inorganic compounds,* which are not carbon based.

Up to now, we've studied mostly inorganic compounds. But our bodies, the food we eat, the clothes that cover us, the drugs that keep us well, the fuel that gives us heat—all are organic compounds. We'll take a brief look at the broad spectrum of organic chemistry and, in the next chapter, at some special molecules of the life processes. Here, we'll consider the structure of organic compounds themselves; in the next chapter we'll see how they provide us with energy and function and are used to produce other structures.

**organic
compound**

**organic
chemistry**

**inorganic
compound**

17.1 THE STRUCTURES OF
ORGANIC COMPOUNDS

structure

So far, we've used the word "structure" in a broad sense. But compounds have structure, too, just as a tree or a bridge does. By *structure* of a compound, we mean the arrangement of the elements' atoms in the compound

FIGURE 17.1 Consumer products from petroleum and coal

401

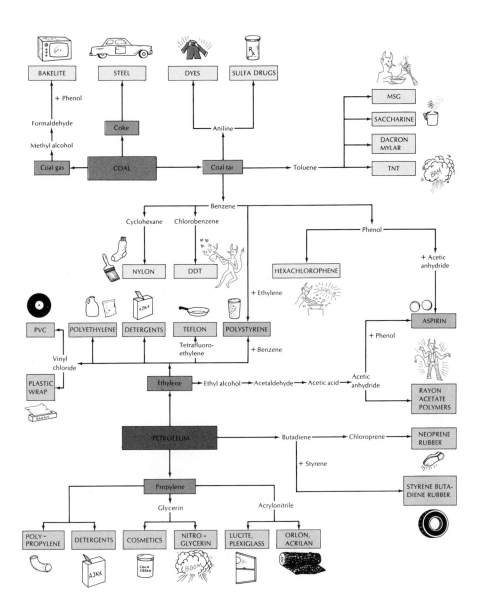

relative to each other, or the way the compound is put together. Structures of organic compounds determine how they behave.

THE CARBON SKELETON.

In the huge continuous structure of a diamond crystal, shown in Chapter 2 (Figure 2.7, p. 26), each single carbon atom is bonded to four others, each at the corner of a tetrahedron. In the graphite structure, also shown in Chapter 2, carbon atoms are joined together in flat connected six-membered rings, with carbon forming only three bonds. Most carbon compounds contain structures that are similar to those between carbon atoms in diamond and graphite, but often other elements are involved in addition to carbon.

carbon skeleton

The *carbon skeleton* of a compound shows only how the carbon atoms themselves are connected to each other. Figure 17.2 shows a few of the limitless possibilities. If we look back at Figure 1.1 in Chapter 1 (p. 3) we recognize these as skeletons of the organic compounds there. Styrofoam and rubber have carbon skeletons that are long and continuous and can provide structural material. Sugar has breaks in its carbon skeleton where there are oxygen atoms. Elements that interrupt the carbon skeleton provide a vulnerable spot where the molecule can be broken, and it's at the oxygen between the two carbon rings that our bodies begin breaking down sugar to obtain its energy.

The remaining bonds on the carbon atoms in each skeleton are connected to other elements. Hydrogen is usually present on most of the bonds. If hydrogen is the only other element in an organic compound, the com-

hydrocarbon

pound is a *hydrocarbon*. The other elements besides carbon and hydrogen that are most often on the bonds are oxygen, nitrogen, a halogen, or sulfur. Some compounds in Figure 17.2—ethyl alcohol, vinegar, and PAN (a component of smog)—have the same carbon skeletons but vastly different properties. In these and most other cases, the elements other than carbon and hydrogen provide the function.

These considerations will be important in all the organic compounds we'll study in this chapter. Now, though, we'll see how to represent the structures of organic compounds in the simplest way possible.

STRUCTURAL FORMULAS.

All the atoms that are connected to the carbon skeleton and all the single, double, and triple bonds are shown in the *structural formulas*. Unlike Lewis structures, structural formulas

structural formula

don't show nonbonding electron pairs. Like Lewis structures, however, structural formulas are drawn on a two-dimensional sheet of paper and don't show the three-dimensional nature of the molecules. We know from Chapter 8 that when carbon or other nonmetallic elements form four single bonds, the geometry is tetrahedral. With three single bonds, the geometry is triangular. And with two single bonds, the geometry is linear.

FIGURE 17.2
Carbon skeletons of some common substances

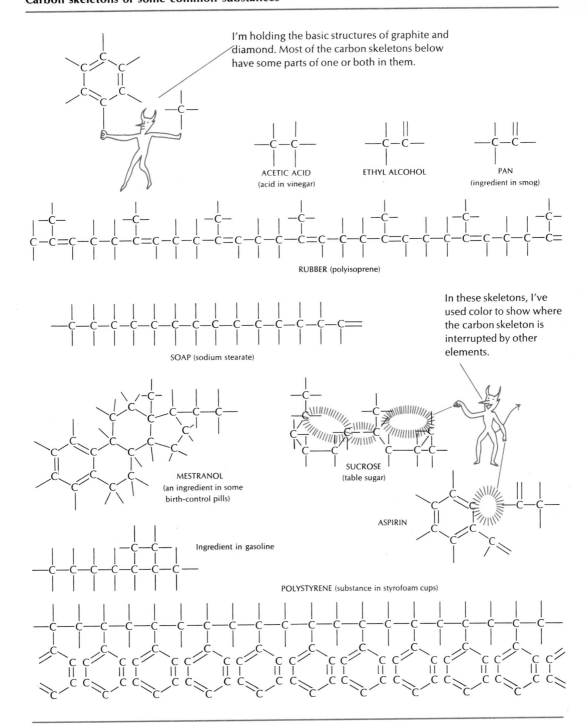

I'm holding the basic structures of graphite and diamond. Most of the carbon skeletons below have some parts of one or both in them.

ACETIC ACID
(acid in vinegar)

ETHYL ALCOHOL

PAN
(ingredient in smog)

RUBBER (polyisoprene)

In these skeletons, I've used color to show where the carbon skeleton is interrupted by other elements.

SOAP (sodium stearate)

MESTRANOL
(an ingredient in some birth-control pills)

SUCROSE
(table sugar)

ASPIRIN

Ingredient in gasoline

POLYSTYRENE (substance in styrofoam cups)

To illustrate structural formulas, let's take two ingredients of gasoline, whose structural formulas are shown below.

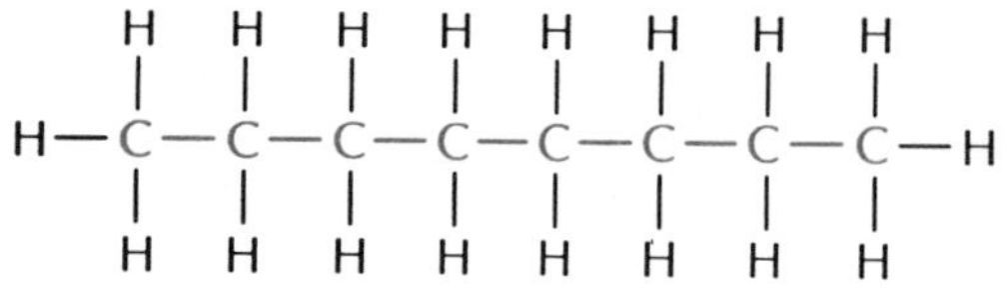

Normal octane

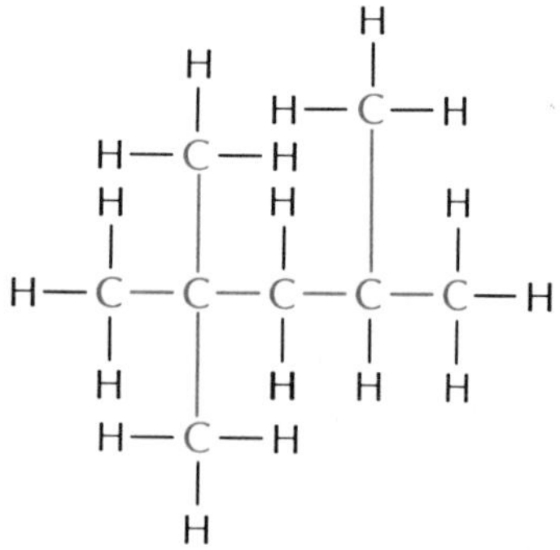

Isooctane

straight chain hydrocarbon

branched chain hydrocarbon

isomer

The two carbon skeletons, marked in color, are different from one another. Normal octane is an example of a *straight chain hydrocarbon*, while isooctane is a *branched chain hydrocarbon*. Even though these two compounds have the same molecular formula, C_8H_{18}, they have different structural formulas. Such compounds are called *isomers*. There are eighteen other isomers of these two compounds. We need the structural formula to know which isomer we're talking about.

Differences in structure cause isomers to behave differently from one another. The two substances above have different melting and boiling points and different densities because of differing attractions between adjacent molecules. Isooctane has an octane rating of 100, meaning that it's a very good antiknock ingredient in gasoline. Normal octane has an octane rating of only −19, meaning that it's a terrible antiknock ingredient. We'll learn more about this later.

Structural formulas have their drawbacks. For large molecules, they're tedious to write and sometimes they tend to be cluttered. Instead, we use *condensed structural formulas,* which let us see the carbon skeleton more clearly. These formulas show each carbon atom and the noncarbon atoms bonded to it all on the same line. Everything that comes between two carbon atoms is bonded to the carbon atom to the left. The formulas of normal octane and isooctane, written as condensed structural formulas, are shown below.

condensed structural formula

$$CH_3-CH_2-CH_2-CH_2-CH_2-CH_2-CH_2-CH_3$$

or

$$CH_3(CH_2)_6CH_3$$

Normal octane

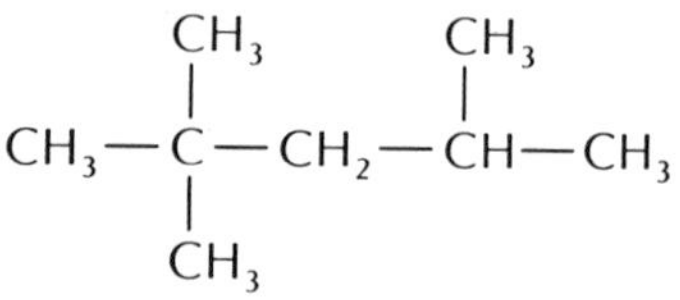

$$CH_3-\overset{\overset{\displaystyle CH_3}{|}}{\underset{\underset{\displaystyle CH_3}{|}}{C}}-CH_2-\overset{\overset{\displaystyle CH_3}{|}}{CH}-CH_3$$

Isooctane

For ring hydrocarbons, we often leave the carbon and hydrogen atoms out altogether and just draw the rings. A carbon atom is understood to be where two straight lines intersect. If double bonds are present, they are shown. Each carbon atom is assumed to have as many bonded hydrogen atoms as it needs to satisfy its four single bonds, or two singles and a double. Table 17.1 illustrates condensed structural formulas involving carbon and hydrogen. We see that compounds with single bonds contain more hydrogen than those with double bonds. Compounds with double or triple bonds between carbons are *unsaturated;* compounds without double or triple bonds are *saturated.*

unsaturated

saturated

WHY CARBON?   Of all the elements, carbon is the only one that bonds to itself and to other elements in such infinite variety. Forming a maximum of four bonds allows more possibilities than forming only three or two. This explains why elements like nitrogen, boron, and oxygen don't provide the backbone for organic compounds, whereas carbon does. But what about the other elements in Group IVA? Silicon, germanium, tin, and lead also have four valence electrons and can form four bonds. Why don't they also form the backbone of organic compounds?

The answer lies in the bond energies. We saw in Chapter 8 that bond energy means the energy needed to break a bond. Thus a higher bond energy means a stronger or more stable bond. Carbon bonds to itself and to other elements with high bond energy. Also, the strengths of the C—C bond and the C—O bond are about the same, giving a C—C bond about the same stability as a C—O bond. Silicon, on the other hand, forms a much weaker bond with itself than it does with oxygen. This means that an Si—Si bond is unstable relative to an Si—O bond, and if there is any oxygen around, an Si—O bond will form instead of an Si—Si bond.

Why should an Si—Si bond be weaker than a C—C bond? From Chapter 8, we know that the longer the bond, the lower the bond energy. Silicon, in the third period, has valence electrons one energy level further from the nucleus than carbon. When silicon bonds to itself, its atoms have to be further away from each other than carbon atoms are in a C—C bond. An Si—Si bond is longer and therefore weaker than a C—C bond. This trend continues with Ge—Ge, Sn—Sn, and Pb—Pb bonds becoming weaker and weaker. Carbon is thus the only element that forms strong bonds with itself and with other elements at the same time.

17.2 ENERGY FROM
CARBON COMPOUNDS

Some fuels obtained from petroleum and coal are shown in Figure 17.3. All of these are hydrocarbons. When we burn these fuels, we're releasing

TABLE 17.1
Condensed structural formulas of hydrocarbons

Condensed Structural Formula	Meaning	Example	Name
$-CH_3$ or CH_3-	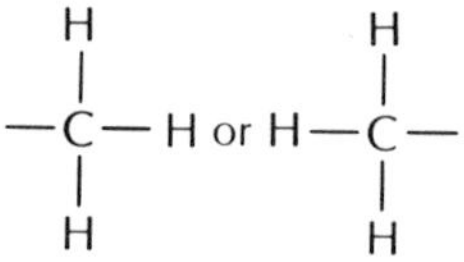 $-\overset{\displaystyle H}{\underset{\displaystyle H}{C}}-H$ or $H-\overset{\displaystyle H}{\underset{\displaystyle H}{C}}-$	CH_3-CH_2-OH	Ethyl alcohol
$-CH_2-$	 $-\overset{\displaystyle H}{\underset{\displaystyle H}{C}}-$	$CH_3-CH_2-CH_3$	Propane
$-CH-$	$-\overset{\displaystyle \vert}{\underset{\displaystyle H}{C}}-$	$CH_3-\overset{\displaystyle OH}{CH}-CH_3$	Isopropyl alcohol (rubbing alcohol)
$CH_2=$	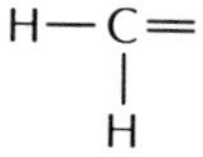 $H-\overset{\displaystyle}{\underset{\displaystyle H}{C}}=$	$CH_2=CH_2$	Ethylene
$-CH=$	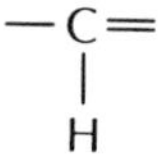 $-\overset{\displaystyle}{\underset{\displaystyle H}{C}}=$	$CH_3-CH=CH_2$	Propylene
$-\overset{\vert}{C}=$	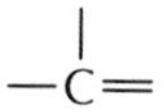 $-\overset{\vert}{C}=$	$CH_3-\overset{\displaystyle CH_3}{C}=CH_2$	Isobutylene (used to make synthetic rubber)
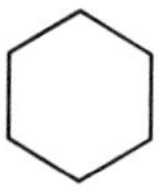 (cyclohexane ring)	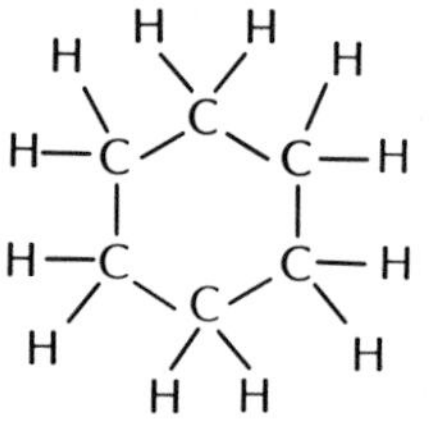 (cyclohexane structure)	 (cyclohexane ring)	Cyclohexane (used to make nylon)
 (benzene ring) or  (benzene ring)	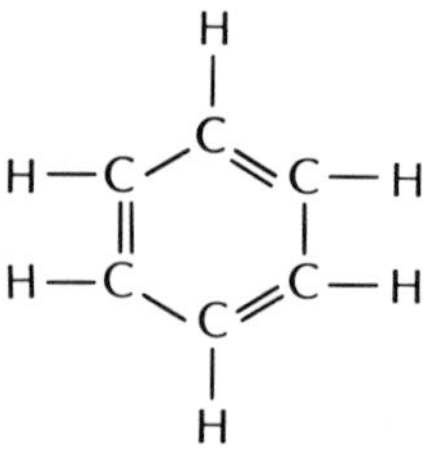 (benzene ring structure) Benzene ring	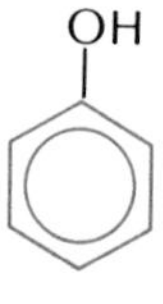 (phenol structure with OH)	Phenol (used to make aspirin)

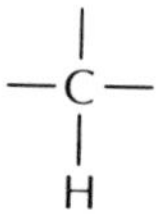

FIGURE 17.3
Fuel products of petroleum and coal

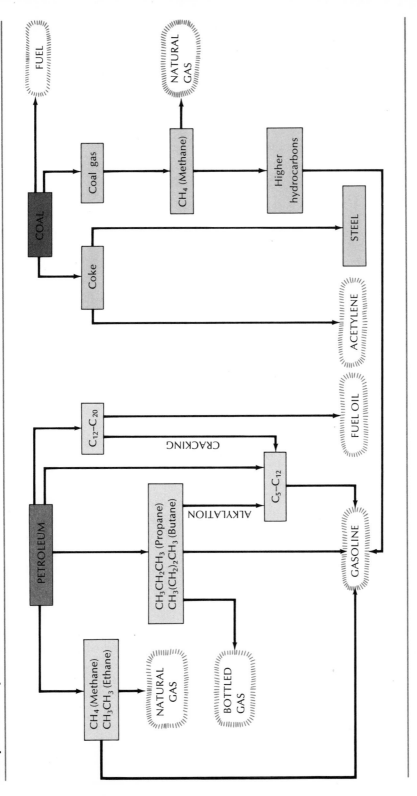

the sun's energy stored in the bonds of their hydrocarbons. We'll be able to talk about hydrocarbons more easily once they are classified.

**aromatic
hydrocarbon**

THE CLASSIFICATION OF HYDROCARBONS. An *aromatic hydrocarbon* is any hydrocarbon that contains a benzene ring or has a benzene-like structure.

 or

Benzene   Naphthalene (moth balls)

(A circle inside the ring instead of the three alternating double bonds is a shorthand way of showing that the sequence of bonds is continuous.) The alternating double and single bonds around a ring are the characteristic feature of an aromatic hydrocarbon. Thus, neither of the two hydrocarbons below is aromatic even though they might look nearly the same as benzene. They lack the sequence of alternating single and double bonds.

Cyclohexane   Cyclohexene

Aromatic hydrocarbons come mostly from coal. They got their name because some early compounds isolated from coal and shown to contain benzene rings had characteristic aromas.

**aliphatic
hydrocarbon**

An *aliphatic hydrocarbon* is any hydrocarbon that does not contain a benzene ring or benzenelike structure. In Table 17.1, all the examples except phenol are aliphatic. Aliphatic hydrocarbons come mostly from petroleum. They got their name from a Greek word meaning "oil." Even though coal contains mostly aromatic compounds and petroleum contains mostly aliphatic compounds, modern technology can synthesize (make) aromatic compounds from petroleum products and aliphatic compounds from coal products.

The classification of hydrocarbons appears in Figure 17.4. We learned in Chapter 4 that inorganic chemicals have common and systematic names. This is true of organic chemicals, too. So that chemists could discuss organic compounds, a system of naming was developed by the International Union of Pure and Applied Chemistry (IUPAC). In this system, the names of all alkanes end in -*ane*, alkenes in -*ene*, and alkynes in -*yne*. We won't go into this system here, although we should know that it exists. Usually we'll use the common name of a substance, sometimes indicating its IUPAC name in parentheses. If the common name is nonexistent—or unfamiliar—we'll use only the IUPAC name. The common names "ethylene," "propylene," and "acetylene" are so much more widely used than their IUPAC names "ethene," "propene," and "ethyne" that we'll use only the common names of these.

If a hydrogen atom is removed from an alkane, leaving a bonding position that can hold another atom or group, the rest of the alkane is an *alkyl group*. A particular alkyl group is named by dropping the *-ane* and adding *-yl,* as in the examples at the top of the next page.

alkyl group

FIGURE 17.4
The classification of hydrocarbons

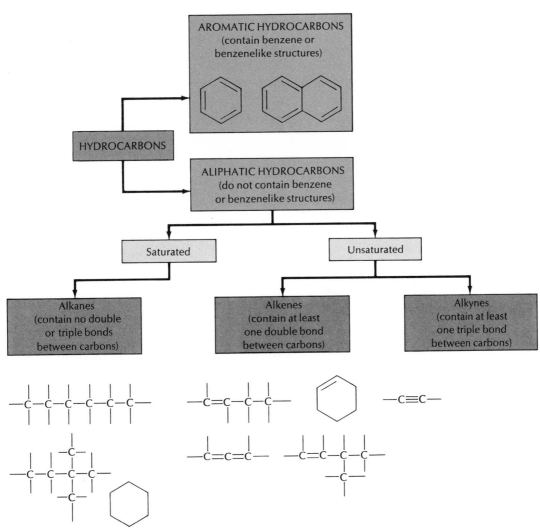

All categories may contain branched chain, straight chain, or cyclic hydrocarbons.

$$CH_4 \qquad CH_3- \qquad CH_3-OH$$

Methane   Methyl   Methyl
          group   alcohol

$$CH_3CH_3 \qquad CH_3CH_2- \qquad CH_3CH_2-OH$$

Ethane   Ethyl   Ethyl
         group   alcohol

COAL AS AN ENERGY SOURCE. Coal is mostly carbon with the graphite structure. Some other atoms—sulfur, nitrogen, and oxygen—are bonded chemically to carbon in coal's organic structure. When coal is burned, oxides of nitrogen and sulfur are products as well as carbon dioxide. This is why coal has been labeled a "dirty" fuel.

In Chapter 11, we discussed the possibilities of removing sulfur from coal before it's burned, or removing SO_2 from the smokestack afterward. The sulfur dioxide from burning coal comes from two places: the sulfur that's bound chemically in the coal, and the sulfur from the pyrite (FeS_2) that's mixed in with the coal. The pyrite can be removed, with difficulty, by grinding up the coal and separating the coal particles from the pyrite particles using gravity. But the chemically bound sulfur stays behind; no good way has yet been found to remove it.

About 70 percent of the coal that is mined is burned to give heat, and the energy yield is about 7.8 kilocalories per gram of coal. The other 30 percent is used to make coke (charcoal) for the steel industry. In the coking process, coal is heated to about 1000°C without any air, as shown by this unbalanced equation:

$$Coal(C, H, O, N, S) \not\longrightarrow Coke(C) + Coal\ tar + CH_4 + H_2S + HCN$$
$$+ NH_3 + CO + H_2 + H_2C{=}CH_2 + CH_3{-}CH{=}CH_2$$

coal gas   The mixture of gases produced as a by-product of the coking industry is called *coal gas*. This gas is usually passed through a water scrubber that removes the obnoxious gases—H_2S, HCN, and NH_3—leaving mostly CO and H_2, with some ethylene and propylene. This relatively clean gas can itself be burned as a fuel, or it can be made into other gases by using a nickel catalyst.

$$CO(g) + 3\,H_2(g) \xrightarrow{\text{nickel}} CH_4(g) + H_2O(g)$$

Higher hydrocarbons (those having more carbon atoms) can be obtained by using an iron catalyst. These higher hydrocarbons can be made into gasoline.

PETROLEUM AS AN ENERGY SOURCE. Petroleum is a mixture of hydrocarbons having from one to about thirty carbon atoms. Most are straight chain saturated hydrocarbons, but some are branched chain and some are cyclic. To get some idea of the relative energies of

Energy from
Carbon
Compounds

411

heat of
combustion

these hydrocarbons, we can compare their heats of combustion. For example, in the burning of methane:

$$CH_4(g) + 2\,O_2(g) \longrightarrow CO_2(g) + 2\,H_2O(g) + 211 \text{ kcal}$$

The *heat of combustion*, 211 kcal/mole in this case, is the energy released when a mole of any substance burns completely. Energy is released because the energy required to break the reactants' bonds is more than paid for by the energy released when the products' bonds are formed.

Heats of combustion of some hydrocarbons are shown in Table 17.2. Of course, the total energy in kilocalories/mole increases with the number of carbon and hydrogen atoms, but it's more useful to compare energy released per gram. The heat of combustion in kilocalories/gram is greatest for methane, less for ethane, and levels off for the rest of that series. The amount of energy released compares roughly with the number of C—H bonds per carbon atom. This is because a C—H bond changing into an O—H bond releases more energy than does a C—C bond changing into a C=O bond. Unsaturated hydrocarbons have fewer C—H bonds and therefore lower heats of combustion than saturated hydrocarbons. All the heats of combustion are greater than that of coal (7.8 kcal/g), indicating that coal has even fewer C—H bonds per carbon atom than benzene. In fact, as we mentioned previously, coal resembles graphite in its structure, with many unsaturated rings fused together.

Heat of combustion is an important consideration when heat is the desired product of a fuel. As we saw in Chapter 6, though, we don't want

Name	Condensed Structural Formula	Heat of Combustion (kcal/mole)	(kcal/g)	Number of C—H Bonds Per Carbon Atom
Methane	CH_4	211	13	4
Ethane	$CH_3—CH_3$	368	12	3
Propane	$CH_3—CH_2—CH_3$	526	11.9	2.7
Butane	$CH_3—(CH_2)_2—CH_3$	684	11.8	2.5
Pentane	$CH_3—(CH_2)_3—CH_3$	838	11.5	2.4
Hexane	$CH_3—(CH_2)_4—CH_3$	990	11.5	2.3
Heptane	$CH_3—(CH_2)_5—CH_3$	1150	11.5	2.3
Octane	$CH_3—(CH_2)_6—CH_3$	1303	11.5	2.3
Ethylene (ethene)	$CH_2=CH_2$	337	10.5	2
Acetylene (ethyne)	$HC{\equiv}CH$	302	10.1	1
Benzene		781	10	1

**TABLE 17.2
Heats of combustion of some hydrocarbons**

all of gasoline's heat of combustion in a car engine. Instead, we want the fuel to burn evenly and produce gases that expand and push the pistons out when ignited with a spark. If the gasoline explodes when it's compressed, before the spark ignites it, the result is engine knock or preignition. Engine knock causes poor engine performance and low gasoline mileage. The octane rating of a gasoline tells how much engine knock it causes. The higher the octane rating, the less the engine knock. *Octane ratings* are based on a score of 100 for isooctane, and the others measured relative to that. Much of gasoline technology is aimed at improving the octane ratings of gasolines.

**octane
rating**

We already saw the difference in octane rating between normal octane and isooctane. Straight chain hydrocarbons cause much more engine knock than branched chain or cyclic ones. Among the straight chain hydrocarbons, longer chains cause more engine knock than shorter chains. Compact molecules seem to burn more evenly and cause less engine knock than long, stringy molecules.

PETROLEUM REFINING.

Crude petroleum is a thick black sludge. Distillation is used to separate it into natural gas, kerosene, gasoline, and so forth. The only attractive force between the nonpolar hydrocarbon molecules is van der Waals attraction, so the boiling points are roughly proportional to molecular weight and therefore to the number of carbon atoms. When petroleum is heated and changed into a mixture of gases, the gases condense in different temperature ranges as the mixture cools. A mixture of substances that condenses within a given range is called a *fraction*. Because the number of carbon atoms in hydrocarbons is related to their molecular weights, each fraction will contain hydrocarbons having a certain range of numbers of carbon atoms. The lightest molecules—those having from one to four carbon atoms (C_1 to C_4)—do not condense at all and make up the lowest-boiling fraction, below 20°C. The next fraction, with a boiling range of 20°C to 60°C, includes hydrocarbons in the C_5 to C_6 range. And so forth. Figure 17.5 shows a diagram of an industrial distillation tower with its petroleum fractions.

fraction

The gasoline fraction presents two basic problems. First, there isn't enough of it. Petroleum is only about 30 percent to 40 percent gasoline, but the demand is for over 50 percent. Two things can be done to make more gasoline:

alkylation

1. Combine smaller molecules in the C_1 to C_5 range to make molecules in the C_6 to C_{12} range. This is called *alkylation*.

cracking

2. Break apart larger molecules in the fuel oil range (C_{15} to C_{20}) to make molecules in the C_6 to C_{12} range. This is called *cracking*.

Another problem with the gasoline fraction is that it's not good enough for modern high-compression car engines that need an octane rating of about 90. Various substances have to be added to gasoline to raise its octane rating. Tetraethyl lead [$Pb(C_2H_5)_4$] was once added, but the resulting leaded gasoline can't be used with catalytic converters, as we saw in Chapter 13. Also, leaded gasoline releases harmful lead compounds to the air. To produce unleaded gasoline with an increased octane rating, straight chain hydrocarbons have to be changed into more compact cyclic or branched chain hydrocarbons. This process is called *reforming*. Some un-

reforming

FIGURE 17.5
A petroleum distillation tower separates light molecules from heavy molecules

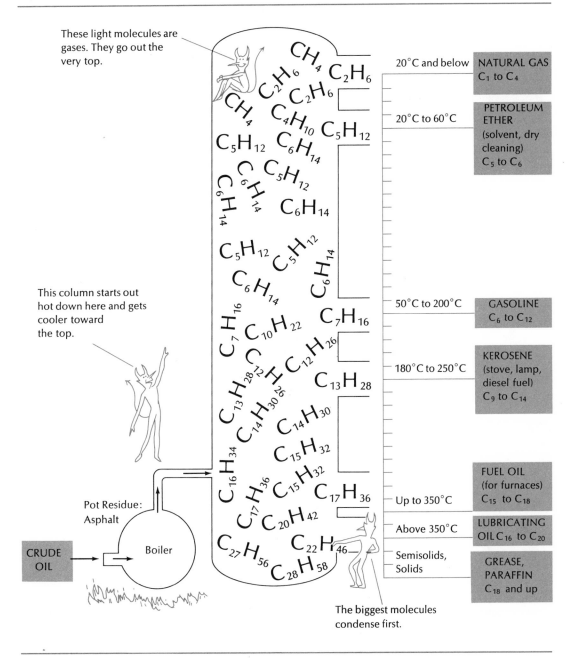

These light molecules are gases. They go out the very top.

This column starts out hot down here and gets cooler toward the top.

Pot Residue: Asphalt

Boiler

CRUDE OIL

The biggest molecules condense first.

20°C and below	NATURAL GAS C_1 to C_4
20°C to 60°C	PETROLEUM ETHER (solvent, dry cleaning) C_5 to C_6
50°C to 200°C	GASOLINE C_6 to C_{12}
180°C to 250°C	KEROSENE (stove, lamp, diesel fuel) C_9 to C_{14}
Up to 350°C	FUEL OIL (for furnaces) C_{15} to C_{18}
Above 350°C	LUBRICATING OIL C_{16} to C_{20}
Semisolids, Solids	GREASE, PARAFFIN C_{18} and up

leaded gasolines have a characteristic smell because they contain benzene, a good antiknock agent. Unleaded gasolines are more expensive than leaded, because reforming is an expensive process.

17.3 FUNCTION FROM CARBON COMPOUNDS

functional group

We said earlier that elements other than carbon and hydrogen often determine function. Atoms or combinations of atoms that cause an organic compound to react in a certain way are called *functional groups*. We've already had a little experience with organic functional groups. In Chapter 13, we learned that the —COOH group causes an organic compound to behave like an acid. We've also seen the —OH, or alcohol, group in ethyl alcohol.

Some important functional groups, and a typical compound containing each one, are shown in Table 17.3 Textbooks of organic chemistry contain a discussion of each functional group, how it's made, how it reacts, and varying examples of compounds. In this brief introduction to organic chemistry, we can't cover every aspect of functional groups, any more than we could see all of Europe on a five-day whirlwind tour. Instead, we're going to focus on a few important compounds and some industrial reactions or reaction types that convert raw materials from petroleum or coal to products that we use.

ORGANIC COMPOUNDS DERIVED FROM WATER AND FROM AMMONIA.

alcohol

The substance that we usually think of as alcohol is ethyl alcohol. But any organic compound that contains the —OH functional group is an *alcohol*, and there are many of them. Here are the formulas of ethyl alcohol and water side by side:

$$CH_3-CH_2-O-H \qquad H-O-H$$

We see that ethyl alcohol is derived from water by substituting an ethyl group for one of water's hydrogen atoms. In the same way, we could substitute methyl, propyl, butyl, and so forth, and obtain a series of simple alcohols derived from alkanes. Besides these simple alcohols, more complex ones exist that contain more than one —OH group or are derived from aromatic or cyclic hydrocarbons. Table 17.4 shows a few common examples.

Simple alcohols are part water and part alkane, with properties somewhere in between. The —OH functional group can hydrogen-bond to itself and to water. Alcohols having one, two, and three carbon atoms (methyl, ethyl, and propyl) are miscible with water in all proportions.

But as the alkyl group gets larger (four carbon atoms and higher), the alcohol becomes more like the alkane, less like water, and therefore less water soluble.

Some reactions of alcohols are like those of water. For instance, alcohols react with the Group IA metals to liberate hydrogen.

TABLE 17.3
Structural formulas of some functional groups

Name of Functional Group	Condensed Structural Formula	Meaning	Example	
Chloro, Fluoro, Bromo, Iodo	$-Cl$ $-F$ $-Br$ $-I$	Same	CCl_2F_2	Freon
				DDT (dichlorodi-phenyltrichloro-ethane)
Alcohol	$-OH$	$-O-H$	CH_3-OH	Wood alcohol (methyl alcohol)
Ether	$-O-$	$-O-$	$CH_3CH_2-O-CH_2CH_3$	Ether (diethyl-ether)
Amino	$-NH_2$		$NH_2-(CH_2)_5-NH_2$	Cadaverine (odor of rotting flesh)
Nitro	$-NO_2$			TNT (trinitro-toluene)
Aldehyde	$-CHO$		$H-CHO$	Formaldehyde
Ketone	$-CO-$		$CH_3-CO-CH_3$	Acetone
Carboxylic acid	$-COOH$		CH_3-COOH	Acetic acid
Ester	$-COO-$			Aspirin (acetylsalicylic acid)
Amide	$-CONH_2$		NH_2-CONH_2	Urea (animal waste product)

$$2\,CH_3CH_2OH(l) + 2\,Na(s) \longrightarrow H_2(g) + 2\,CH_3CH_2ONa(solution)$$
$$\text{Sodium ethoxide}$$

We obtain a solution of sodium ethoxide in ethyl alcohol in much the same way that we obtain a solution of sodium hydroxide in water when sodium reacts with water.

Other reactions involve both the alkyl group and the —OH group. If an alcohol is treated with sulfuric acid (which acts as a catalyst) at a fairly high temperature (180°C), the alcohol loses a water molecule to form an alkene.

$$CH_3CH_2OH(g) \xrightarrow[180°C]{H_2SO_4} CH_2{=}CH_2(g) + H_2O(g)$$

dehydration

A reaction like this, where a single molecule loses the elements of water to form a more simple molecule, is called *dehydration*.

If, however, an alcohol is treated with sulfuric acid at a lower temperature, an ether is formed.

$$CH_3CH_2OH(l) + CH_3CH_2OH(l) \xrightarrow[\text{low temp.}]{H_2SO_4} CH_3CH_2OCH_2CH_3(l) + H_2O(l)$$
$$\text{Diethyl ether}$$

TABLE 17.4
Some common alcohols

Formula	Name	Source	Comments
$CH_3{-}OH$	Methyl alcohol (wood alcohol)	Older source: distillation of wood chips. Modern source: from coal gas: $CO(g) + 2\,H_2(g) \xrightarrow{Cat.} CH_3{-}OH$	Very poisonous; can cause blindness and death. Used to "denature" ethyl alcohol or make it unfit for drinking.
$CH_3{-}CH_2{-}OH$	Ethyl alcohol (grain alcohol)	For beverages: fermentation of sugar. Industrial source: from ethylene: $CH_2{=}CH_2(g) + H_2O(g) \xrightarrow{H_2SO_4} CH_3{-}CH_2{-}OH(l)$	The active ingredient in alcoholic drinks.
$CH_3{-}\underset{\underset{OH}{\|}}{CH}{-}CH_3$	Isopropyl alcohol	From propylene: $CH_3{-}CH{=}CH_2(g) + H_2O(g) \longrightarrow CH_3{-}\underset{\underset{OH}{\|}}{CH}{-}CH_3(l)$	Best known as "rubbing alcohol," but also important industrially.
$\underset{\underset{CH_2}{\|}}{\overset{\overset{OH}{\|}}{}}{-}\underset{\underset{CH_2}{\|}}{\overset{\overset{OH}{\|}}{}}$	Ethylene glycol	Derived from ethylene.	Used as antifreeze. Two —OH groups on one molecule make it very water soluble.
$\underset{\underset{CH_2}{\|}}{\overset{\overset{OH}{\|}}{}}{-}\underset{\underset{CH}{\|}}{\overset{\overset{OH}{\|}}{}}{-}\underset{\underset{CH_2}{\|}}{\overset{\overset{OH}{\|}}{}}$	Glycerin (glycerol)	By-product of soap manufacture. Occurs naturally in animal fats. Also made from propylene.	Very water soluble. Used to make cosmetics and nitroglycerin.

Here, the elements of water are taken from two molecules instead of one. A reaction where two or more molecules form a more complex molecule with the loss of water is called *condensation*. This meaning is somewhat different from the one we saw in Chapter 10, where condensation meant going from a less dense phase (such as a gas) to a more dense phase (such as a liquid). However, in the broad sense—going from something less dense to something more dense—the meaning of the word "condensation" still applies. We'll be seeing many more examples of condensation reactions throughout this and the next chapter.

condensation

Now let's look at the formulas of diethyl ether and of water side by side.

$$CH_3CH_2-O-CH_2CH_3 \qquad H-O-H$$
Diethyl ether $\qquad\qquad$ Water

We see that diethyl ether is derived from water by substituting an ethyl group for each of water's hydrogen atoms. As with alcohols, we can substitute different alkyl groups to form different *ethers*. On a given ether molecule, the alkyl groups can be the same or they can be different.

ether

Ethers are much less like water than alcohols are. With two alkyl groups, only the oxygen of water is left, there is no hydrogen to hydrogen-bond with, and the ether behaves much more like an alkane than like water. Ethers are mostly low boiling and water insoluble. Because they lack a hydrogen bonded to oxygen, ethers don't participate in reactions similar to the ones we've mentioned for alcohols. (Ethers do burn and participate in some reactions, but we won't discuss them here.)

Amines are organic compounds derived from ammonia in the same way that alcohols and ethers are derived from water.

amine

$$\begin{array}{cccc} -N-H & CH_3-N-H & CH_3-N-H & CH_3-N-CH_3 \\ | & | & | & | \\ H & H & CH_3 & CH_3 \end{array}$$

Ammonia $\qquad$ Methylamine $\qquad$ Dimethylamine $\qquad$ Trimethylamine

We see that there are three possibilities, since ammonia has three hydrogen atoms. All three types of compounds are amines: *primary* (one alkyl group), *secondary* (two alkyl groups), and *tertiary* (three alkyl groups). These compounds have some of the properties of alkanes and some of ammonia. The more alkyl groups that are substituted, the fewer hydrogens that are left to hydrogen-bond, and the less water soluble and lower boiling the compounds become. As with alcohols, increasing the number of carbon atoms also decreases the water solubility. Most amines are foul smelling. The characteristic smell of putrid meat or rotten fish is caused by the amines they contain.

primary amine

secondary amine

tertiary amine

Some reactions of amines are like those of ammonia. For instance, amines can act as weak bases.

$$CH_3NH_2(aq) + HCl(aq) \longrightarrow CH_3NH_3^+(aq) + Cl^-(aq)$$
Methylammonium ion

$$(CH_3)_3N(aq) + HCl(aq) \longrightarrow (CH_3)_3NH^+(aq) + Cl^-(aq)$$
Trimethylammonium ion

Since it is the nonbonding electron pair on nitrogen that makes ammonia a base, the primary, secondary, and tertiary amines alike can also be bases.

Primary and secondary, but not tertiary, amines can undergo condensation reactions as alcohols can. We'll see some important condensation reactions later.

REACTIONS OF HYDROCARBONS.

In Chapter 10, we talked about the use of Freons—carbon compounds containing fluorine and chlorine—as refrigerants. These are made from the raw materials methane and ethane in petroleum. Saturated hydrocarbons don't have any functional groups, so their reactions are limited. We've already seen that they can burn and can be broken into smaller hydrocarbons (cracked). About the only reaction left is to trade one or more hydrogen atoms for one or more atoms of a different kind. This is called *substitution*.

substitution

chlorination

The first step in making one kind of Freon from methane is the substitution of a chlorine atom for one of methane's hydrogen atoms. The process is called *chlorination*.

$$CH_4(g) + Cl_2(g) \longrightarrow CH_3Cl(g) + HCl(g)$$
Methyl chloride

When this process is carried out three more times, the product is carbon tetrachloride (CCl_4), with four molecules of HCl as a by-product. Chlorination of hydrocarbons is an important commercial source of HCl. To make Freon 11 (trichlorofluoromethane), carbon tetrachloride is treated with HF, and one fluorine is substituted for one chlorine.

$$CCl_4(g) + HF(g) \longrightarrow CCl_3F(g) + HCl$$
Freon-11

Other Freons are these:

CCl_2F_2	$CClF_3$	CCl_2FCClF_2	$CClF_2CF_3$
Freon-12	Freon-13	Freon-113	Freon-115

Most organic compounds can be chlorinated. Bacteria and viruses will stop multiplying when their biological molecules are chlorinated, which is why chlorine is a good disinfectant. However, a side effect is that organic matter dissolved in water is also being chlorinated, putting chlorinated hydrocarbons into some public water supplies. Chlorinated hydrocarbons have been associated with various liver ailments, including cancer.

We see from Figure 17.1 that ethylene and propylene are very important raw materials from petroleum. They don't occur naturally in petroleum but are produced during the cracking process. These unsaturated hydrocarbons have a functional group: a double bond. Double bonds can serve as "handles" to get other functional groups onto hydrocarbons. The first step usually involves addition to the double bond. In *addition*, a two-part reactant such as Cl_2 (Cl—Cl) causes the double bond to open up and form two single-bonding positions, one for each part of the reactant. The

addition

resulting compound is saturated. Addition is different from substitution because atoms are added to the compound while none are taken away.

Addition is best illustrated by example. Looking at Figure 17.1, we see that the path from ethylene to PVC includes a compound called vinyl chloride. The first step in making PVC, then, is to change ethylene to vinyl chloride. This is done by addition of chlorine to ethylene.

$$CH_2{=}CH_2 \ + \ Cl_2 \ \xrightarrow{\text{low temp.}} \ \underset{\displaystyle \substack{| \quad | \\ Cl \quad Cl}}{CH_2{-}CH_2} \ \xrightarrow{500°C} \ CH_2{=}CH{-}Cl \ + \ HCl$$

1,2-Dichloroethane   Vinyl chloride

The 1,2-dichloroethane decomposes at high temperature to vinyl chloride. We'll see how to get from vinyl chloride to PVC in Section 17.4.

In the pathway from ethylene to aspirin, the first step is changing ethylene to ethyl alcohol. As we saw in Table 17.4, this is done industrially by adding water, which we can think of as a two-part reactant H—OH.

$$CH_2{=}CH_2 \ + \ H_2O \ \xrightarrow{H_2SO_4} \ \underset{\displaystyle \substack{| \quad | \\ H \quad OH}}{CH_2{-}CH_2} \quad \text{(written } CH_3CH_2OH)$$

Another reaction involving addition to a double bond is *hydrogenation*, where the two-part reactant is H_2 (H—H). Polyunsaturated fats and oils have several double bonds and are liquids. To make solid shortening, polyunsaturated fats can be hydrogenated like this:

hydrogenation

$$CH_3(CH_2)_4CH{=}CHCH_2CH{=}CH(CH_2)_7COOH + 2\,H_2(g) \xrightarrow{\text{cat.}} CH_3(CH_2)_{16}COOH$$

Linoleic acid   Stearic acid

(found in cottonseed oil)   (found in beef tallow)

Saturated fats have recently been linked to heart disease, such as hardening of the arteries. Emulsifying agents are now being used to turn unsaturated fats into solids while they still keep their double bonds.

Figure 17.6 illustrates addition to a double bond.

CHANGING CARBON'S OXIDATION NUMBER.

If we look again at the pathway from ethylene to aspirin in Figure 17.1, we find the sequence ethyl alcohol to acetaldehyde to acetic acid. Here are the formulas for these, plus the oxidation number of the carbon atom that contains or is part of the functional group:

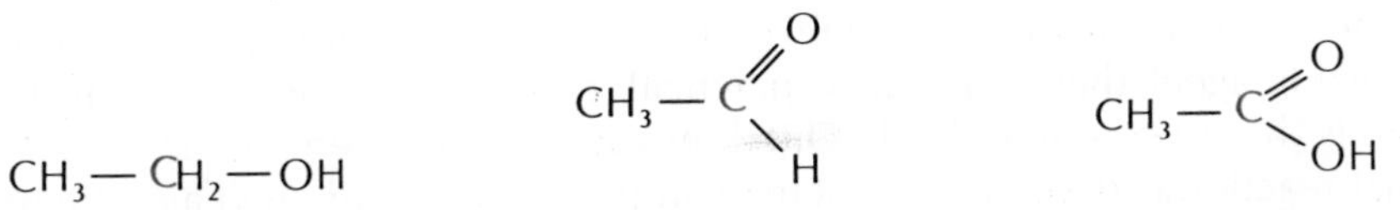

$$CH_3{-}CH_2{-}OH \qquad CH_3{-}C\underset{\textstyle H}{\overset{\textstyle O}{\diagup\!\!\!\diagdown}} \qquad CH_3{-}C\underset{\textstyle OH}{\overset{\textstyle O}{\diagup\!\!\!\diagdown}}$$

Ethyl alcohol   Acetaldehyde   Acetic acid

oxidation number: 1−   oxidation number: 1+   oxidation number: 3+

**FIGURE 17.6
Addition to a
double bond
involves a
two-part
reactant**

I'm going to make this two-part chlorine
molecule add to the double bond.

First, I'll open up this double bond. Then
each carbon atom can form one more
single bond.

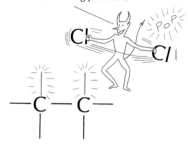

Now, I'll take apart this chlorine molecule.
Then I'll have one chlorine ready to go on
each of those new bonding positions—

and here's the end
of the reaction.
The product is
saturated.

aldehyde

We know about ethyl alcohol and acetic acid, but acetaldehyde and the
aldehyde functional group.

are unfamiliar. The carbon atom in the aldehyde group has an oxidation
number in between that of ethyl alcohol's —CH$_2$OH group and acetic
acid's —COOH group. (In organic chemistry, "oxidation" usually means
loss of hydrogen or gain of oxygen. Thus the —CH$_2$OH group loses two
hydrogens to become the —CHO group, which gains one oxygen to become the —COOH group.) Acetaldehyde is an important industrial
chemical. The largest part of it is used to make acetic acid.

The sequence alcohol to aldehyde to acid is important in industry. The
oxidizing agent that is the most practical, economical, and readily available is the oxygen in air itself. Different catalysts are used, depending on
what reaction is desired. For instance, in the sequence of ethyl alcohol to
acetic acid, these reactions are used:

$$CH_3CH_2OH + \tfrac{1}{2}O_2 \xrightarrow[450°C]{Ag} CH_3-C{\overset{\displaystyle O}{\underset{H}{\big<}}} + H_2O$$

Ethyl alcohol   Acetaldehyde

$$CH_3-C{\overset{\displaystyle O}{\underset{H}{\big<}}} + \tfrac{1}{2}O_2 \xrightarrow{Mn(C_2H_3O_2)_2} CH_3-C{\overset{\displaystyle O}{\underset{OH}{\big<}}}$$

Acetaldehyde   Acetic acid

In Figure 17.1, the sequence of coal gas to methyl alcohol to formaldehyde leads to the formation of Bakelite resin. Again we use oxidation, but this time we stop at the aldehyde stage. We saw in Table 17.4 that methyl alcohol is made from coal gas. The methyl alcohol is then oxidized.

$$CH_3OH + \tfrac{1}{2}O_2 \xrightarrow[600°C]{Cu} HC{\overset{\displaystyle O}{\underset{H}{\big<}}} + H_2O$$

Methyl alcohol   Formaldehyde

About half the methyl alcohol produced is used to make formaldehyde, and, in turn, most of the formaldehyde is used to make the hard plastic Bakelite. Formaldehyde is a gas, so it's used mostly as a water solution called *formalin*. A minor use of formalin is to preserve biological specimens.

formalin

The carbon atom in the ketone functional group has the same oxidation number as that in the aldehyde group. The difference between an aldehyde and a ketone can be seen by comparing the structures of acetaldehyde and acetone.

$$CH_3-C{\overset{\displaystyle O}{\underset{H}{\big<}}} \qquad CH_3-C{\overset{\displaystyle O}{\underset{CH_3}{\big<}}}$$

Acetaldehyde   Acetone
(an aldehyde)   (a ketone)

We see that an alkyl group appears in a *ketone* where a hydrogen does in an aldehyde. Ketones can be obtained by oxidizing alcohols where the —OH group appears somewhere in the middle of the carbon chain rather than at the end. For instance, acetone is made commercially by oxidizing isopropyl alcohol.

ketone

$$CH_3-\overset{\displaystyle OH}{\underset{\displaystyle |}{C}}H-CH_3(g) \xrightarrow{cat.} CH_3-\overset{\displaystyle O}{\overset{\displaystyle \|}{C}}-CH_3(g) + H_2(g)$$

If formaldehyde were oxidized still further, the product would be formic acid, HCOOH. Formic acid occurs naturally in the sting of ants and other insects. Although formic acid has some industrial uses, the demand for formaldehyde is far greater. Enough formic acid is obtained from other sources without oxidizing formaldehyde.

CONDENSATION REACTIONS AND THEIR PRODUCTS.

We've seen one example of a condensation reaction. The formations of detergents, aspirin, and many synthetic plastics and fibers also depend on condensation reactions.

In making synthetic detergents, alcohols with six or more carbon atoms are allowed to react with sulfuric acid. For example:

$$CH_3(CH_2)_{10}CH_2OH \;+\; HO{-}\overset{\displaystyle O}{\underset{\displaystyle O}{\overset{|}{\underset{|}{S}}}}{-}OH \;\longrightarrow\; CH_3(CH_2)_{10}CH_2O{-}\overset{\displaystyle O}{\underset{\displaystyle O}{\overset{|}{\underset{|}{S}}}}{-}OH \;+\; H_2O$$

Lauryl alcohol   Sulfuric acid   Lauryl hydrogen sulfate

ester

The product of condensation between an alcohol and an acid is an *ester.* In this case, the product is a sulfate ester. Since sulfuric acid had two protons to begin with and one still remains, it could react with one more alcohol molecule in the same way, just as H_2SO_4 can react with one or two moles of NaOH. However, lauryl hydrogen sulfate is much more useful the way it is. To make a detergent, the remaining proton is neutralized with NaOH.

$$CH_3(CH_2)_{10}CH_2O{-}\overset{\displaystyle O}{\underset{\displaystyle O}{\overset{|}{\underset{|}{S}}}}{-}OH \;+\; NaOH \;\longrightarrow\; CH_3(CH_2)_{10}CH_2O{-}\overset{\displaystyle O}{\underset{\displaystyle O}{\overset{|}{\underset{|}{S}}}}{-}O^-Na^+ \;+\; H_2O$$

Sodium lauryl sulfate

Sodium lauryl sulfate is one of a class of alkyl sulfate detergents. These all have the long hydrophobic ends and the ionic hydrophilic ends that are necessary for detergent action, as we saw in Chapter 12. Sodium lauryl sulfate, one of the first synthetic detergents, is now commonly used as a detergent in toothpaste.

Lauryl alcohol is obtained from natural products, but many alcohols for making synthetic detergents are made from ethylene or propylene by complex processes. Another class of synthetic detergents is the benzene-sulfonates.

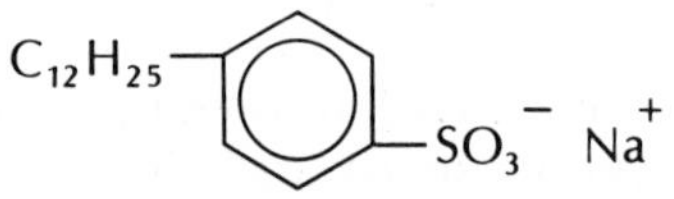

$$C_{12}H_{25}{-}\!\!\bigcirc\!\!{-}SO_3^-\;Na^+$$

Earlier detergents of this type had highly branched alkyl groups attached to the benzene ring. This made the detergent incapable of being broken down by microorganisms (nonbiodegradable), so that natural waters became full of soap suds. Now, processes have been developed for attaching straight chain instead of branched chain alkyl groups, and these detergents are biodegradable.

Like sulfuric acid and alcohols, carboxylic acids and alcohols form condensation products that are also esters. Aspirin (acetylsalicylic acid) is an ester of salicylic acid and acetic acid.

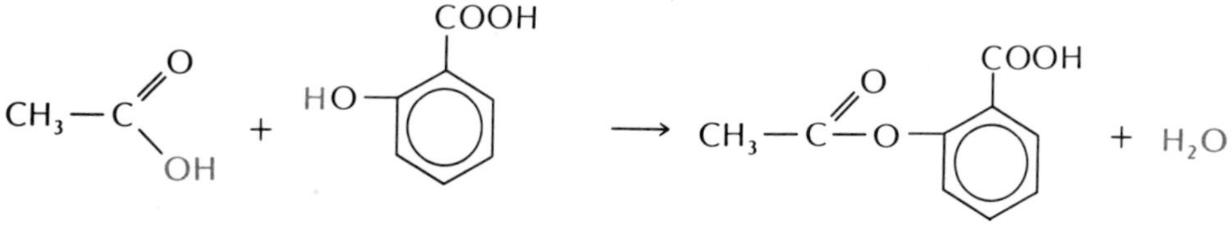

Acetic acid   Salicylic acid   Aspirin

Salicylic acid has both a carboxylic acid and an alcohol functional group. Only the alcohol group reacts with acetic acid to form an ester group.

We find it convenient to show where an ester came from by condensing a water molecule from an acid and an alcohol, but esters usually aren't made this way. This is because the reaction is reversible, and for most esters the position of equilibrium lies far to the side of the acid and the alcohol. This principle is illustrated by the way aspirin works in the system. The real pain reliever is salicylic acid. When the aspirin passes through our intestines and blood stream, bases catalyze this reaction:

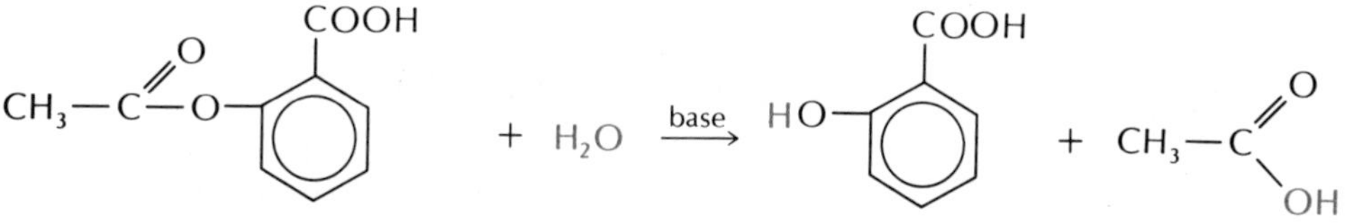

Aspirin   Salicylic acid   Acetic acid

This kind of reaction is called *hydrolysis* (*hydro* means "water"; *lysis* means "breaking apart"). Here we have a good example of something we said earlier: interruptions in the carbon skeleton provide vulnerable spots where an organic molecule may be broken apart. The carbon skeleton of an ester is interrupted by oxygen. As a result, most esters can be hydrolyzed easily in the presence of water and an acid or a base. Figure 17.7 illustrates the formation and hydrolysis of esters.

hydrolysis

If we can't make an ester from an acid and an alcohol, then how *do* we make one? Figure 17.1 shows a substance called acetic anhydride coming between acetic acid and aspirin in the chain of production. An *anhydride* is a condensation product of two carboxylic acid molecules. We arrive at the structure of acetic anhydride this way:

anhydride

Introduction to
Organic
Chemistry

$$CH_3-C\overset{O}{\underset{OH}{}} \quad + \quad CH_3-C\overset{OH}{\underset{O}{}} \quad \longrightarrow \quad CH_3-C\overset{O}{\underset{O}{}} \quad CH_3-C\overset{O}{\underset{O}{}} \quad + \quad H_2O$$

Anhydrides are very high-energy compounds that react with alcohols much more readily than their parent acids do. For this reason, anhydrides are often used to make esters. In the final step of making aspirin, acetic anhydride made from petroleum products is allowed to react with salicylic acid made from coal products.

FIGURE 17.7
Formation and
Hydrolysis
of Esters

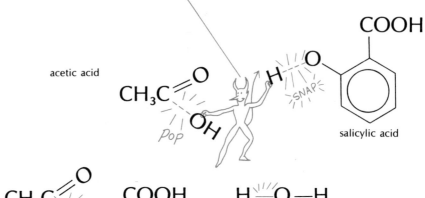

I'm going to make an ester out of acetic acid and salicylic acid. First, I take off an H and an OH to make water.

acetic acid

salicylic acid

Then I put the broken pieces together like this, which makes an ester and a water molecule.

Hydrolysis is just the opposite. That colored bond can be attacked by a water molecule if there's acid or base around. Then the bond just breaks and the water adds in two parts, as I've shown here. We get back our original acid and alcohol.

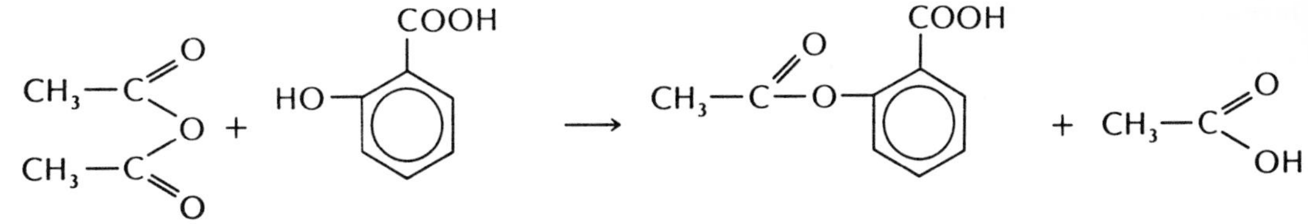

The structural diagram shows:

Acetic anhydride + Salicylic acid → Aspirin + Acetic acid

Acetic anhydride   Salicylic acid   Aspirin   Acetic acid

The acetic acid produced as a by-product is recycled and used over again.

17.4 POLYMERS: STRUCTURE FROM CARBON ATOMS

Polymers are huge molecules that contain many repeating parts (*poly* means "many"; *mer* means "part"). Wool, hair, and rubber are natural polymers. Humans have imitated these natural polymers in synthetic polymers that have many different uses.

polymer

ADDITION POLYMERS.

Painting a table with linseed oil or oil-based paint will eventually cause a hard surface to form on the table. These oils contain double bonds and form natural addition polymers when exposed to air. Synthetic addition polymers imitate them.

We've seen that substances can add to an alkene's double bond. Two or more alkenes can also add to one another's double bonds and form a polymer. The simplest synthetic addition polymer, polyethylene, comes from the reaction of many ethylene molecules with one another.

$$CH_2{=}CH_2 + CH_2{=}CH_2 + CH_2{=}CH_2 + \cdots \xrightarrow{\text{cat.}} \cdots CH_2CH_2CH_2CH_2CH_2CH_2 \cdots$$

Formation of polymers is called *polymerization*. The small molecules that react to produce the polymer are called *monomers*. Usually we find it convenient to write the polyethylene polymer like this: $-(CH_2CH_2)-_n$. The *n* stands for a large number (at least 1000) whose value isn't known exactly.

polymerization

monomer

If other groups are substituted for one or more of the hydrogen atoms on the ethylene monomer, different polymers result. All these—including polyethylene—are called *vinyl polymers*. Table 17.5 shows some common vinyl polymers. Polyethylene itself is the most important plastic made in the United States. Natural rubber and one of its synthetic relatives, neoprene rubber, can stretch because their long chains of molecules form coils. The coils straighten out when they're pulled and spring back when they're released. Notice in the table that some polymers, such as plastic wrap, are made from more than one monomer. These are called *copolymers*.

vinyl polymer

copolymer

TABLE 17.5
Some vinyl polymers

Monomer	Polymer	Name, Use
Ethelene, $CH_2=CH_2$	$-(CH_2-CH_2)_n-$	Polyethlene. Used for squeeze bottles, toys, packaging.
Propylene, $CH_2=CH$ $\mid$ CH_3	$-(CH_2-CH)_n-$ $\mid$ CH_3	Polypropylene. Used in bottles, pipes, valves, carpets.
Vinyl chloride, $CH_2=CH$ $\mid$ Cl	$-(CH_2-CH)_n-$ $\mid$ Cl	Polyvinyl chloride, PVC. Used in vinyl tile, pipes, phonograph records.
Tetrafluoroethylene, $CF_2=CF_2$	$-(CF_2-CF_2)_n-$	Teflon. Used in cooking utensils, bearings, valves.
Acrylonitrile, $CH_2=CH_2$ $\mid$ CN	$-(CH_2-CH)_n-$ $\mid$ CN	Polyacrylonitrile. Used to make Orlon and Acrilan textile fibers.
Styrene, $CH_2=CH$	$-(CH_2-CH)_n-$	Polystyrene. Used for Styrofoam, toys, knobs.
Methyl methacrylate, $CH_2=CCH_3$ $\mid$ $COOCH_3$	CH_3 $\mid$ $-(CH_2-C)_n-$ $\mid$ $COOCH_3$	Polymethylmethacrylate. Lucite, Plexiglas. Used in transparent surfaces, furniture, jewelry.
Chloroprene, $CH_2=C-CH=CH_2$ $\mid$ Cl	$-(CH_2-C=CH-CH_2)_n-$ $\mid$ Cl	Neoprene rubber.
Isoprene, $CH_2=C-CH=CH_2$ $\mid$ CH_3	$-(CH_2-C=CH-CH_2)_n-$ $\mid$ CH_3	Natural rubber.
Vinyl chloride + vinylidene chloride, $CH_2=CCl_2$	Cl $\mid$ $-(CH_2-C-CH_2-CH)_n-$ $\mid$ $\quad\quad$ Cl $\quad$ Cl	Plastic wrap (a copolymer).
Styrene + butadiene, $CH_2=CH-CH=CH_2$	$-(CH_2CHCH_2CH=CHCH_2)_n-$	Styrene-butadiene rubber. Used in automobile tires.

POLYESTERS.

We've already seen that an ester is a condensation product. A *polyester* is a condensation polymer. If we have a monomer that has an alcohol group on each end, and another monomer that has a carboxylic acid group on each end, then we can link them together in a continuous chain. The synthetic fiber Dacron is such a polymer.

HOOC—⬡—COOH + HOCH$_2$CH$_2$OH +

      Terephthalic acid   Ethylene glycol

+ HOOC—⬡—COOH + HOCH$_2$CH$_2$OH + ··· ⟶

      Terephthalic acid   Ethylene glycol

··· OOC—⬡—COOCH$_2$CH$_2$OOC—⬡—CO   CH$_2$OOC—⬡—COOCH$_2$CH$_2$ ···

                 Dacron

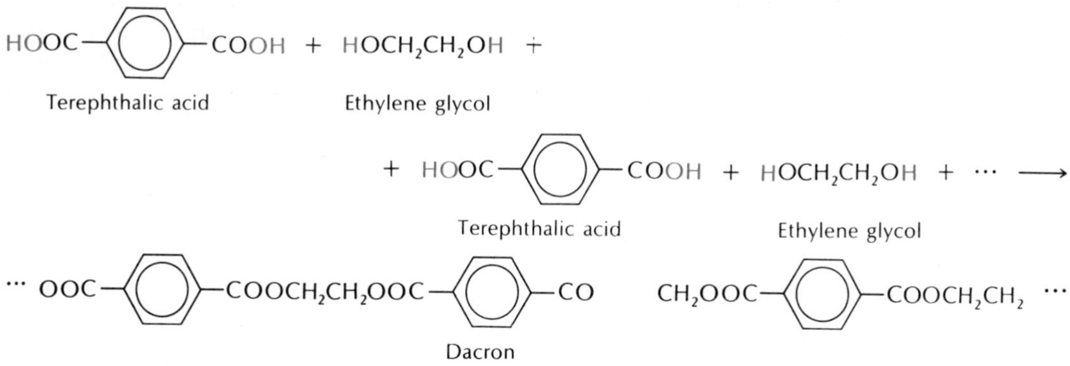

To make a fiber, the polymer is extruded, or pushed through many small holes. The polymer can also be formed into sheets; then it's Mylar.

The ethylene glycol monomer is made from ethylene. The terephthalic acid monomer is made by oxidizing paraxylene.

CH$_3$—⬡—CH$_3$

Paraxylene is found in small amounts in coal tar, but it is in such great demand for making Dacron that ways have been found to produce it from petroleum.

NYLON.

There are many kinds of nylons, but they're all condensation polymers. Nylon 66 (so named because both monomers have six carbon atoms) is made by this reaction:

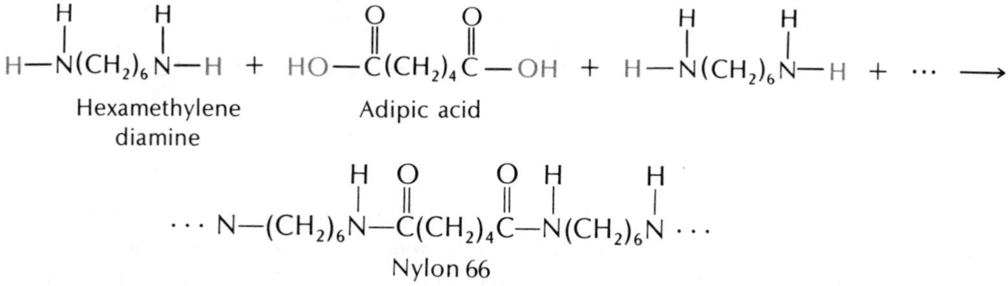

H—N(CH$_2$)$_6$N—H + HO—C(CH$_2$)$_4$C—OH + H—N(CH$_2$)$_6$N—H + ··· ⟶

    Hexamethylene   Adipic acid
     diamine

··· N—(CH$_2$)$_6$N—C(CH$_2$)$_4$C—N(CH$_2$)$_6$N ···

               Nylon 66

Hexamethylene diamine is an example of an amine that has two amino groups, as shown in Table 17.3. The condensation product between an amine and a carboxylic acid is called an *amide*. Nylons are all *polyamides*. As we'll see in the next chapter, proteins are polyamides, too. By using the amide linkage, nylon imitates the protein polymers wool and silk.

amide

polyamide

Both of Nylon 66's monomers are made from cyclohexane, which in turn is made by hydrogenating benzene from coal tar. Thus nylon is a product of coal.

BAKELITE. Bakelite is a condensation polymer between formaldehyde and phenol. We've already seen how formaldehyde is made from coal gas. Since phenol is made from benzene, both are products of coal. In Bakelite, formaldehyde condenses with the hydrogen atoms that are on the benzene ring of phenol.

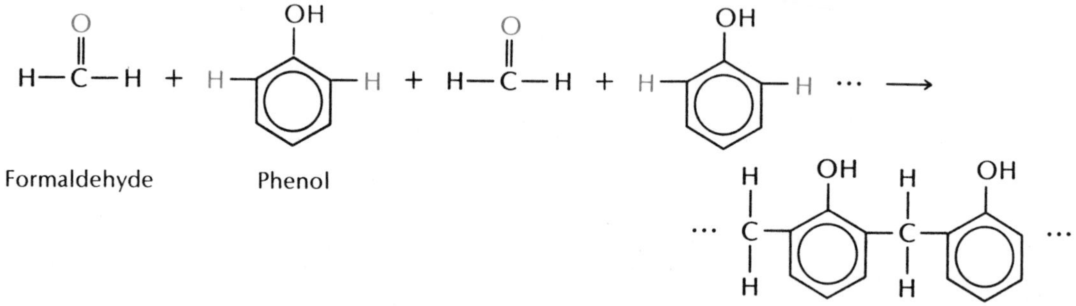

Formaldehyde   Phenol

cross-link

Condensation can also occur with hydrogen atoms that are across the ring from the OH group, as well as with those that are next to it. This lets the chains join, or *cross-link*. Bakelite is a very hard resin because it's highly cross-linked. A portion of its structure looks like this:

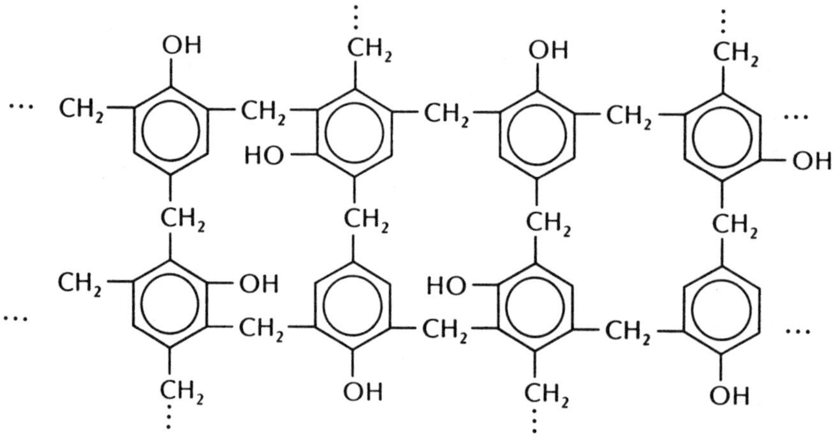

Bakelite is used for electrical insulation, knobs, switches, and plugs. Formica and Melmac are related polymers that are condensation products of formaldehyde with other substances. Cross-linking makes them hard and tough, too—suitable for kitchen counters and unbreakable dishes.

We've touched on the major types of polymers, but there are many others that are variations of the ones we've seen. The properties of polymers can be changed in a number of ways, including regulating the amount of cross-linking, the length of the carbon chain of monomers, and the nature of the groups attached to them.

REVIEW QUESTIONS

1. What are *organic compounds?* What are the two major sources of organic compounds, and where did they come from?

The Structures of Organic Compounds

2. What do we mean by the *structure* of a compound?
3. What is an organic compound's *carbon skeleton?* Give an example. What can happen where a substance's carbon skeleton is interrupted by another element?
4. What is the name for compounds that contain only carbon and hydrogen? What other elements are often present in organic compounds?
5. What is a *structural formula?* How is it like a Lewis structure, and how is it different? Give an example.
6. What is the difference between a *straight chain* and a *branched chain* hydrocarbon? Give examples of each.
7. What are *isomers?* Do isomers all have the same properties?
8. How do we write *condensed structural formulas?* Write one for any compound and tell how it is different from the structural formula.
9. Write condensed structural formulas for two ring compounds.
10. What do we mean by *saturated* and *unsaturated* compounds?
11. Why does carbon and no other element form the backbone of organic compounds?

Energy from Carbon Compounds

12. What is the difference between an *aromatic* and an *aliphatic* hydrocarbon? What is the main feature of an aromatic hydrocarbon?
13. What are *alkanes, alkenes,* and *alkynes?* How are they alike? How are they different?
14. What is an *alkyl group?* Give some examples.
15. What are the compounds in *coal gas?* Where does coal gas come from? Name one of its uses.
16. What is a substance's *heat of combustion?* How does structure affect a hydrocarbon's heat of combustion?
17. What is the purpose of petroleum distillation?
18. What are *reforming* and *cracking?* What are their purposes?

Function from Carbon Compounds

19. What are *functional groups?* Write condensed structural formulas for five, and give their names.
20. How are alcohols related to water? Give examples of some waterlike chemical and physical properties of alcohols.
21. What are *dehydration* and *condensation?* In equation form, give an example of each involving an alcohol.
22. How are ethers related to water? Why are they less like water than alcohols are?
23. Write formulas for a primary, a secondary, and a tertiary amine, and explain how they are related to ammonia.
24. What reactions of amines are like those of ammonia? Write an equation.
25. What is *substitution?* Show how substitution reactions are used to make one kind of Freon.
26. How are the raw materials ethylene and propylene obtained from petroleum? Why are ethane and propane not as useful as starting materials?
27. How is *addition* different from substitution? Explain how a reactant can add to a double bond, and give an example.
28. What is *hydrogenation?* How is it used? Give an example.
29. Arrange aldehyde, acid, and alcohol in order of increasing oxidation number of the functional group carbon atom, and write condensed structural formulas for their functional groups. Write the equations for an industrial process that takes advantage of this sequence.
30. What is the difference between an aldehyde and a ketone? What type of compound must be oxidized to obtain a ketone?
31. What is the product of condensation between an acid and an alcohol? Write the formula of one. What is it used for?
32. What is *hydrolysis?* Write an equation for a hydrolytic reaction.
33. Write the structure of an *anhydride.* How are anhydrides useful?
34. Write the equation for the preparation of aspirin.

Polymers: Structure from Carbon Atoms

35. What are *polymers?* What are some natural polymers?
36. Give an example of an *addition polymer.* What is the *monomer?*
37. Name some *vinyl polymers* and their monomers.
38. What is a *copolymer?* Give an example.
39. What kind of a polymer is Dacron? Draw part of its structure.
40. Write part of the structure for Nylon 66 and identify the *amide* linkages.
41. What is a *cross-linked* polymer? Show part of the structure of one.

EXERCISES

1. Make hydrocarbons out of the following carbon skeletons by putting hydrogen atoms wherever they are needed.

   a. $C-C-C-C-C$ c. $C=C-C-C$

   b. 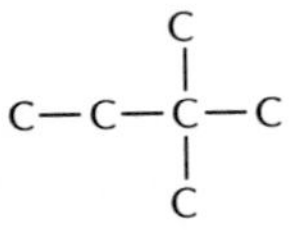
   $$C-C-\overset{\displaystyle C}{\underset{\displaystyle C}{C}}-C$$

   d. 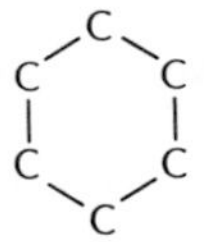 (hexagonal carbon ring skeleton)

2. Write condensed structural formulas for the following.

   a. 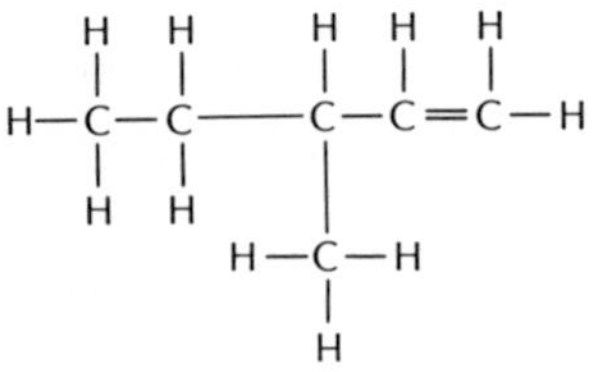 (full structural formula)

   b. 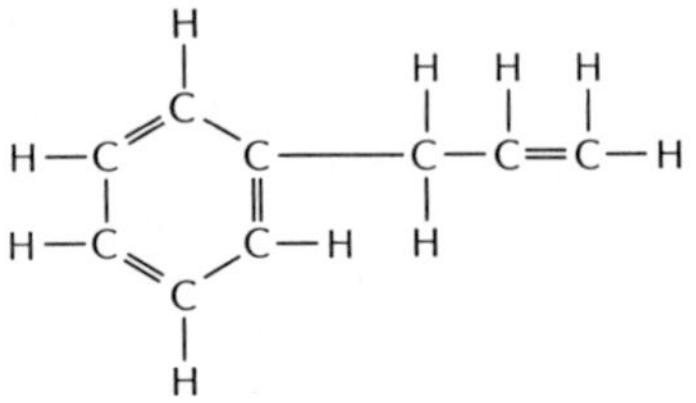 (full structural formula with benzene ring)

   c. 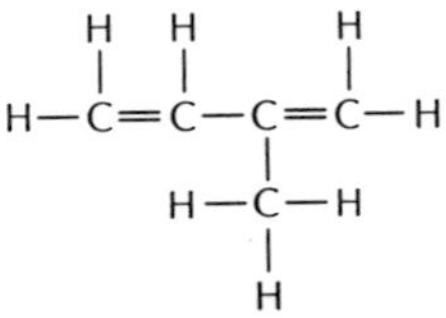 (full structural formula)

3. Write full structural formulas for the following condensed structural formulas.

   a. 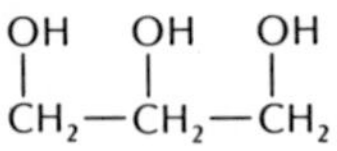
   $$\overset{OH}{\underset{}{CH_2}}-\overset{OH}{\underset{}{CH_2}}-\overset{OH}{\underset{}{CH_2}}$$

   Glycerin

   b. 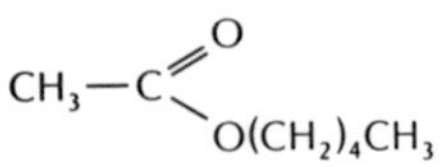 $CH_3-C\overset{\displaystyle O}{\underset{\displaystyle O(CH_2)_4CH_3}{}}$

   Pentyl acetate (banana flavoring)

   c. 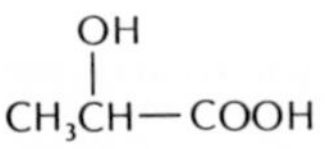 $CH_3\overset{OH}{\underset{}{CH}}-COOH$

   Lactic acid (acid in sour milk)

   d. 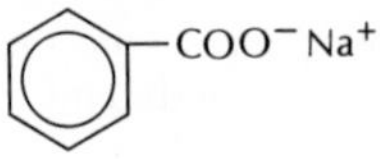 $\bigcirc -COO^-\ Na^+$

   Benzoate of soda (preservative)

   e. 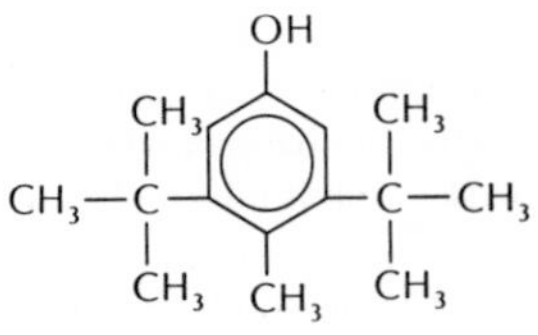
   $$CH_3-\overset{CH_3}{\underset{CH_3}{C}}\bigcirc\overset{OH}{}\overset{CH_3}{\underset{CH_3}{C}}-CH_3$$

   BHT (preservative)

4. Identify the functional groups in each compound in Exercise 3.

5. Which of the following are isomers?

   a. $CH_3-CH_2-CH_2-CH_2-CH_3$

   b. 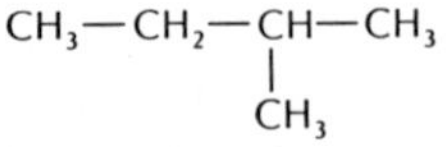 $CH_3-CH_2-\overset{}{\underset{CH_3}{CH}}-CH_3$

   c. 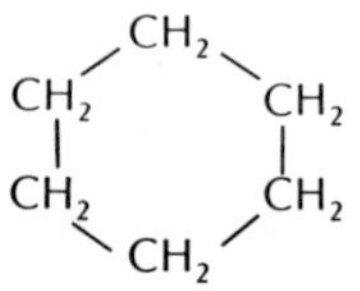 (cyclohexane ring of CH_2 groups)

   d. 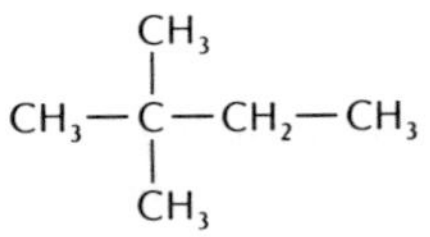 $CH_3-\overset{CH_3}{\underset{CH_3}{C}}-CH_2-CH_3$

   e. $CH_2=CH-CH_2-CH_2-CH_2-CH_3$

   f. 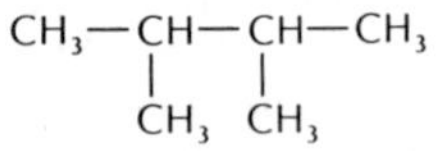 $CH_3-\overset{}{\underset{CH_3}{CH}}-\overset{}{\underset{CH_3}{CH}}-CH_3$

6. Classify each of the following as an alkane, alkene, or alkyne.

   a. $CH_2=CH-CH=CH_2$

   Butadiene

   b. 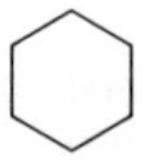 (cyclohexane ring)

   Cyclohexane

c. $HC\equiv CH$

Acetylene

d. $CH_3=CH-CH_3$
$\qquad\quad |$
$\qquad\quad CH_3$

Isobutene

e.

Cyclohexene

7. Which compound in each of the following pairs would have the higher heat of combustion (kilocalories/gram)?

a. $HC\equiv CCH_3$ or $CH_3-CH_2-CH_3$

b. CH_3CH_3 or ⬡

c. $CH_2=C=CH_2$ or $CH_2=CH-CH_3$

d. $CH_2=CH-CH=CH_2$ or ⬡

e. (CH₃-phenyl) CH_3 or CH_4

8. Which compound in each of the following pairs would have the higher octane rating?

a. $CH_3CH_2CH_2CH_2CH_3$ or ⬡

b. $CH_3CHCH_2CH_3$ or CH_3CCH_3
$\qquad\quad |$ $\qquad\qquad\quad |$
$\qquad\quad CH_3$ $\qquad\qquad\quad CH_3$
(with CH₃ on top of second structure)

c. CH_4 or $CH_3CH_2CH_2CH_3$

9. Which of the following would be expected to be more water soluble?
a. CH_3OH or $CH_3(CH_2)_4OH$
b. CH_3OH or CH_3OCH_3
c. $CH_3CH_2CH_2OH$ or CH_3OCH_3

10. State which compounds in the previous exercise would be expected to have the higher boiling point, and explain.

11. Write complete, balanced equations showing the following.
a. methyl alcohol reacting with potassium metal
b. propyl alcohol undergoing dehydration
c. methyl alcohol undergoing condensation
d. methyl and ethyl alcohols undergoing condensation with one another

12. Write formulas for ethylamine, diethylamine, and triethylamine, and write an equation showing one of them acting as a base.

13. Why can't tertiary amines undergo condensation reactions?

14. The first step in the manufacture of Freon 115, $CClF_2CF_3$, is the chlorination of ethane. Write the equation.

15. The plastic Teflon is made of tetrafluoroethylene, $CF_2=CF_2$, which is manufactured by this reaction:

$$2\ CHClF_2 \xrightarrow{\Delta} CH_2=CF_2 + 2\ HCl$$

Chloro-
difluoromethane

Suggest a sequence of reactions that might be used to make chlorodifluoromethane from methane.

16. Substitute the correct compound for each question mark.

a. $? + H_2O \not\rightarrow CH_3-\overset{\overset{\displaystyle OH}{|}}{CH}-CH_3$

Isopropyl alcohol
(rubbing alcohol)

b. $CH_2=CH_2-CH_3 + Cl_2 \not\rightarrow ?$

Propylene

c. ⬡ $+ ? \not\rightarrow$ ⬡

d. $CH_3-CH_2-\overset{\overset{\displaystyle OH}{|}}{CH}-CH_3 + \tfrac{1}{2}O_2 \not\rightarrow$

e. $CH_3-CH_2-CH_2-OH + \tfrac{1}{2}O_2 \not\rightarrow ?$

f. $? + \tfrac{1}{2}O_2 \not\rightarrow H-C\overset{\displaystyle O}{\underset{\displaystyle OH}{}}$

g. ⬡$-CHO + \tfrac{1}{2}O_2 \not\rightarrow ?$

17. Fill in the blanks in the following table of related alcohols, aldehydes or ketones, and acids.

Alcohol	Aldehyde or Ketone	Acid
CH$_3$—OH	H—CHO	H—COOH
CH$_3$(CH$_2$)$_2$—OH	_____	_____
_____	CH$_3$(CH$_2$)$_2$C$\overset{\displaystyle O}{\underset{\displaystyle CH_3}{<}}$	None
_____	_____	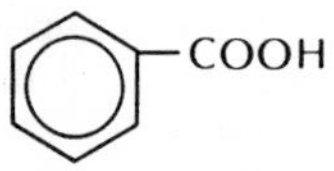 ⬡—COOH

18. Write condensation products for the following pairs.

a. CH$_3$—CH$_2$—C$\overset{\displaystyle O}{\underset{\displaystyle OH}{<}}$

and CH$_3$—CH$_2$—OH

b. CH$_3$—OH

and H—C$\overset{\displaystyle O}{\underset{\displaystyle OH}{<}}$

c. H$_2$SO$_4$

and CH$_3$—(CH$_2$)$_8$—CH$_2$—OH

19. Write formulas for the alcohol and the carboxylic acid that are parents of these esters.

a. CH$_3$—(CH$_2$)$_{14}$—C$\overset{\displaystyle O}{\underset{\displaystyle O(CH_2)_9CH_3}{<}}$

Myricyl palmitate (beeswax)

b. CH$_3$—C$\overset{\displaystyle O}{\underset{\displaystyle O—CH_2—CH_3}{<}}$

Ethyl acetate (nail polish remover)

c. CH$_3$—CH$_2$—C$\overset{\displaystyle O}{\underset{\displaystyle OCH_2—CH—CH_3}{<}}$
$\qquad\qquad\qquad\qquad\quad$|
$\qquad\qquad\qquad\qquad\quad$CH$_3$

Isobutyl propionate (rum flavor)

20. Write equations for the hydrolysis of the esters in Exercise 19.

21. Oxalic acid, HOOC—COOH, is the simplest acid that has two carboxylic acid groups. Write an equation and show the structure of a polyester that might be made from oxalic acid and ethylene glycol.

22. A natural material used to make nylon is sebacic acid, HOOC(CH$_2$)$_8$COOH, found in castor oil. Sebacic acid and hexamethylenediamine, NH$_2$(CH$_2$)$_6$NH$_2$, make nylon 610. Write an equation showing condensation and the product's partial structure.

23. Melmac, a polymer similar to Bakelite, is made with formaldehyde and melamine. Melamine has this structure:

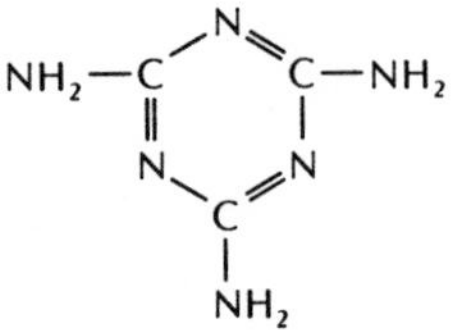

The —NH$_2$ groups each use one of their hydrogen atoms to condense with the oxygen of the formaldehyde. Write a partial structure of this polymer, showing cross-linking.

18

Introduction to Biochemistry

A baby is born. Suddenly there is a human being where once there was not. And yet, as amazing as birth is, the events leading up to it are even more amazing. At the moment of conception, cells from each parent fuse to form a single fertile egg cell, destined to become a human being. From that single cell come arms, legs, eyes, nose, ears. From that single cell comes the ability to walk, talk, see, hear, think.

A tiny seed sprouts in the ground. Nourishing itself on simple inorganic materials in the soil and air and on the sun's energy, the seedling builds complex structures. After a time, there is a huge tree where once there was not. From a single cell contained in the seed come trunk, roots, stems, leaves, flowers. From a single cell comes the ability to produce, or synthesize, large organic molecules from inorganic compounds.

A tree and a human being are very different, but they and all other living organisms share the same ingredients. From a single cell of each comes the ability to grow, reproduce, and repair. Molecules within the single cell in a fertile egg or a seed determine that a tree will be a tree and a person a person. As the organisms grow, more molecules are formed. As more molecules are formed, the organisms grow. Life from molecules, and molecules from life—that's what *biochemistry* is about.

biochemistry

18.1 NUCLEIC ACIDS

Figure 18.1 shows a diagram of a typical cell. The outside is a semipermeable membrane, which lets certain molecules pass into and out of the cell. Most of the inside is water, with many small molecules dissolved in it. Various solid bodies, called *organelles,* are dotted all around the cell like islands. Each organelle has a function.

organelle

**FIGURE 18.1
A generalized
animal cell**

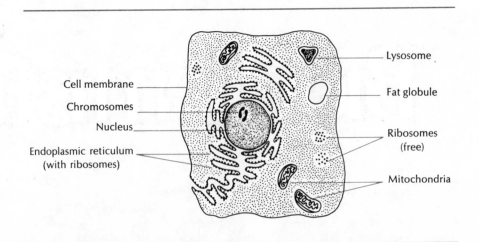

Lysosome

Cell membrane

Chromosomes

Nucleus

Endoplasmic reticulum
(with ribosomes)

Fat globule

Ribosomes
(free)

Mitochondria

A newly formed cell comes with packages of information, called *chromosomes*. The information tells the cell how to make others just like it and also how to make cells with different functions—eye cells, for instance, or liver or leaf cells. The cell makes other cells by first making proteins. Some of the proteins will form the structural parts of the new cells, whereas others will control or regulate the production of other kinds of molecules that provide structure or function. Within the chromosomes are *genes*—directions for making individual protein molecules. A human being has forty-six chromosomes, which contain over a hundred thousand genes.

The chromosomes are located in the *nucleus,* the organelle that contains the cell's "brains." The molecules in the chromosomes that contain information, plus others found in the nucleus, are called *nucleic acids.*

gene

nucleus

nucleic acid

deoxyribonucleic acid (DNA)

This is a double helix.

DNA STRUCTURE AND REPLICATION.

As soon as the cell is formed, long slender threads unravel from each chromosome. These threads are the nucleic acid *deoxyribonucleic acid* (DNA). The DNA in human chromosomes, originally contained in a nucleus only 8×10^{-4} centimeters in diameter, has a combined length of over 2 meters when it's all unraveled.

DNA has two functions. The first, which it performs when the cell isn't dividing, is to direct the synthesis of proteins. Some of these proteins are catalysts called *enzymes.* Every reaction in a cell needs a special enzyme to make it go, and thus enzymes are second in command to DNA when it comes to getting things done in the cell.

DNA's second function is *replication,* or copying itself. It stops directing protein synthesis and starts replicating as soon as the cell is ready to begin dividing. When the DNA has completely replicated itself, the two sets that result pack themselves back up into separate chromosomes and the cell divides. Each of the two new cells will have a copy of the directions.

A closer look at a strand of DNA reveals that it's actually two strands twisted together in a double helix (or spiral). This structure of DNA was discovered in 1953 by James Watson and Francis Crick. DNA is a polymer whose monomers are *deoxyribonucleotides.* There are four kinds of these monomers, and we'll look at their structures a little later. Right now we'll abbreviate them as dA, dT, dC, and dG. The two strands in a DNA double helix are held together by hydrogen bonding between dA and dT and between dC and dG. Each DNA strand is said to be complementary to the other.

The order in which these four monomers appear in the DNA molecule is the code that will later tell the cells how to make proteins. When DNA is replicated, this order must be copied exactly so that the right information gets into the new cells. To do this, the DNA double helix untwists and the two strands separate from each other, a little at a time. Each untwisted single DNA strand is used as a model for making a new strand, which will be complementary to its model. To make the strand, single monomers that are dissolved in the cell's water come up to the DNA strand. Each mono-

enzyme

replication

deoxyribo-nucleotide

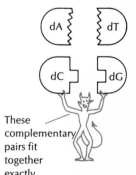

These complementary pairs fit together exactly.

mer hydrogen-bonds to its complement on the model strand. When two new monomers are hydrogen-bonded next to each other on the model, then an enzyme comes along and fastens the monomers to each other, forming the new strand. Figure 18.2 illustrates DNA replication.

ribonucleic acid (RNA)

RNA STRUCTURE AND TRANSCRIPTION. *Ribonucleic acid (RNA)* is the middleman between DNA and protein. It reads the orders on DNA and helps them to be carried out. Unlike DNA, which is carried along from one cell to another, RNA is made as it's needed. The process of making RNA is called *transcription,* because the directions on the DNA are being transcribed into a form that's used directly to make proteins.

transcription

**FIGURE 18.2
DNA replication**

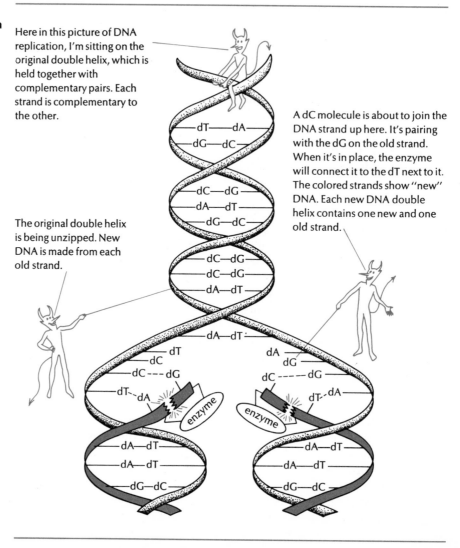

Here in this picture of DNA replication, I'm sitting on the original double helix, which is held together with complementary pairs. Each strand is complementary to the other.

A dC molecule is about to join the DNA strand up here. It's pairing with the dG on the old strand. When it's in place, the enzyme will connect it to the dT next to it. The colored strands show "new" DNA. Each new DNA double helix contains one new and one old strand.

The original double helix is being unzipped. New DNA is made from each old strand.

RNA is a polymer made of monomers called *ribonucleotides*. There is only one kind of DNA, but there are three kinds of RNA.

ribonucleotide 437

1. Ribosomal RNA (rRNA) goes into making ribosomes, one kind of organelle in Figure 18.1 *Ribosomes* are where protein synthesis occurs.
2. Messenger RNA (mRNA) carries the code for making a specific protein.
3. Transfer RNA (tRNA) fetches a protein monomer unit from somewhere in the cell and takes it to the ribosome, where the protein is being put together.

ribosome

As with DNA, there are four RNA monomers, which we'll abbreviate A, U, C, and G, with a different letter prefix for each kind of RNA. There are sets of complementary pairs between the monomer units of DNA and of RNA. These are:

DNA	rRNA	mRNA	tRNA
dA	rU	mU	tU
dT	rA	mA	tA
dC	rG	mG	tG
dG	rC	mC	tC

All RNA is single-stranded. It's made from DNA by pairing. The DNA double helix unzips and RNA monomers bind to their mates on one of the DNA strands. Then an enzyme bonds the RNA monomers together. The process of transcription is illustrated in Figure 18.3.

Figure 18.4 summarizes the relationships among DNA, RNA, and protein.

NUCLEOTIDE STRUCTURE.

Both deoxyribonucleotides and ribonucleotides are included in the general term *nucleotide*. Figure 18.5 shows the chemical structure of part of a double-stranded DNA molecule, with the nucleotide monomers shown. Both DNA and RNA can be hydrolyzed to their individual nucleotides. The nucleotides themselves can be hydrolyzed to three parts: a phosphate ion, a sugar molecule, and a base molecule.

nucleotide

The sugar is ribose in RNA and deoxyribose in DNA. Here are their structures:

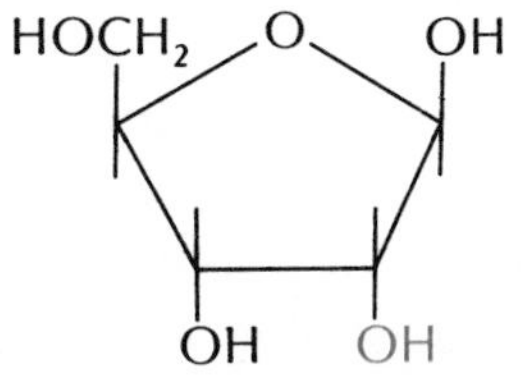

Ribose 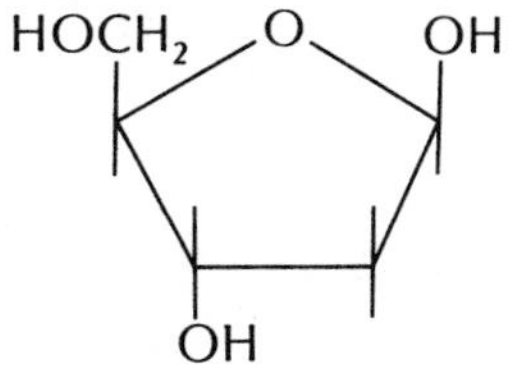   Deoxyribose

FIGURE 18.3
RNA transcription

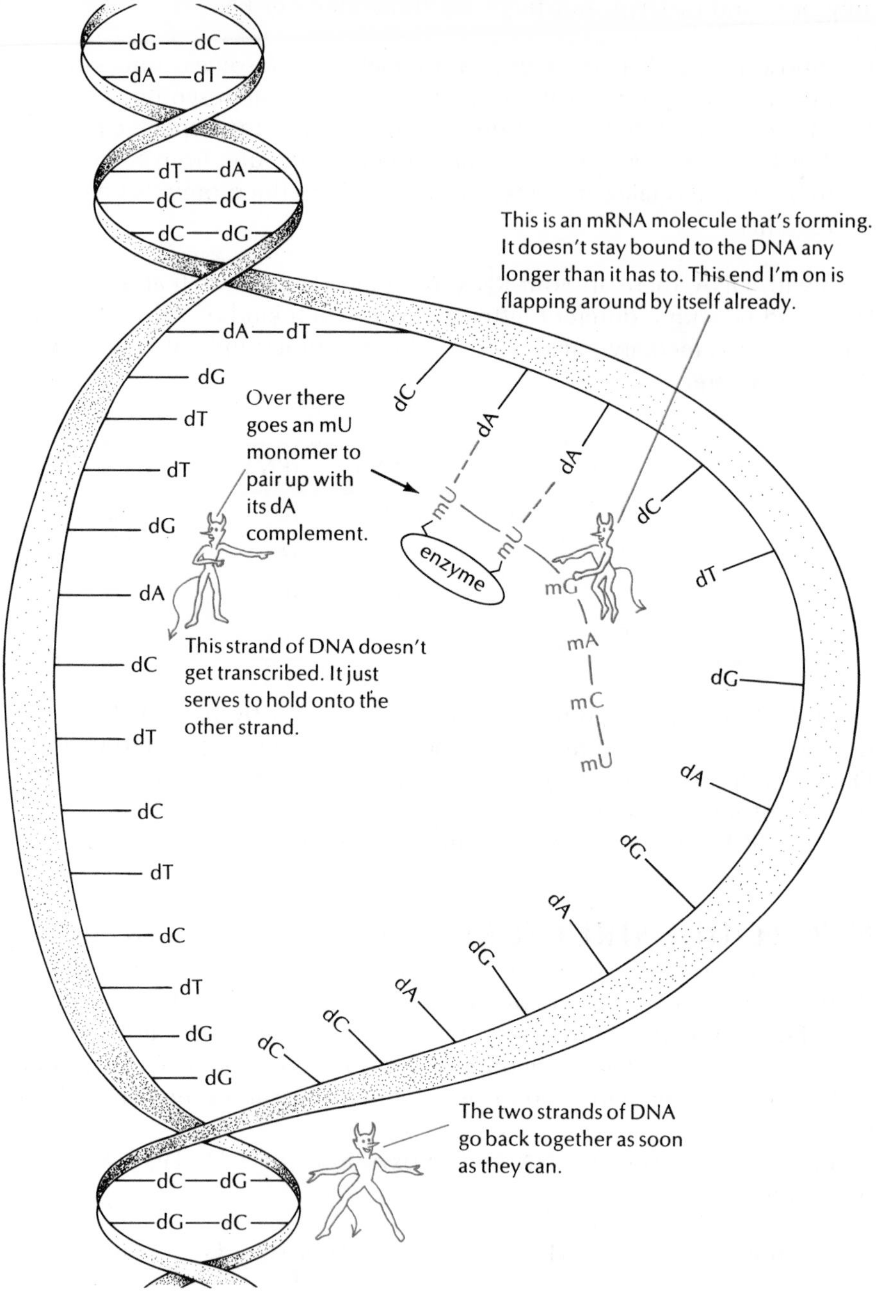

—dG—dC—
—dA—dT—

—dT—dA—
—dC—dG—
—dC—dG—

This is an mRNA molecule that's forming. It doesn't stay bound to the DNA any longer than it has to. This end I'm on is flapping around by itself already.

—dA—dT—

— dG

Over there goes an mU monomer to pair up with its dA complement.

— dT

— dT

— dG

— dA

This strand of DNA doesn't get transcribed. It just serves to hold onto the other strand.

— dC

— dT

— dC

— dT

— dC

— dT

— dG

— dG

dC

dA

dG

dA

dG

dA

dG

dC

dT

dG

dA

dC

dA

mU

mU

mG

mA

mC

mU

enzyme

The two strands of DNA go back together as soon as they can.

—dC—dG—
—dG—dC—

This shorthand notation is slightly different from that used in other ring compounds. If we imagine that we're looking at the ring sideways, then the groups at the ends of the straight lines can be seen as sticking up and

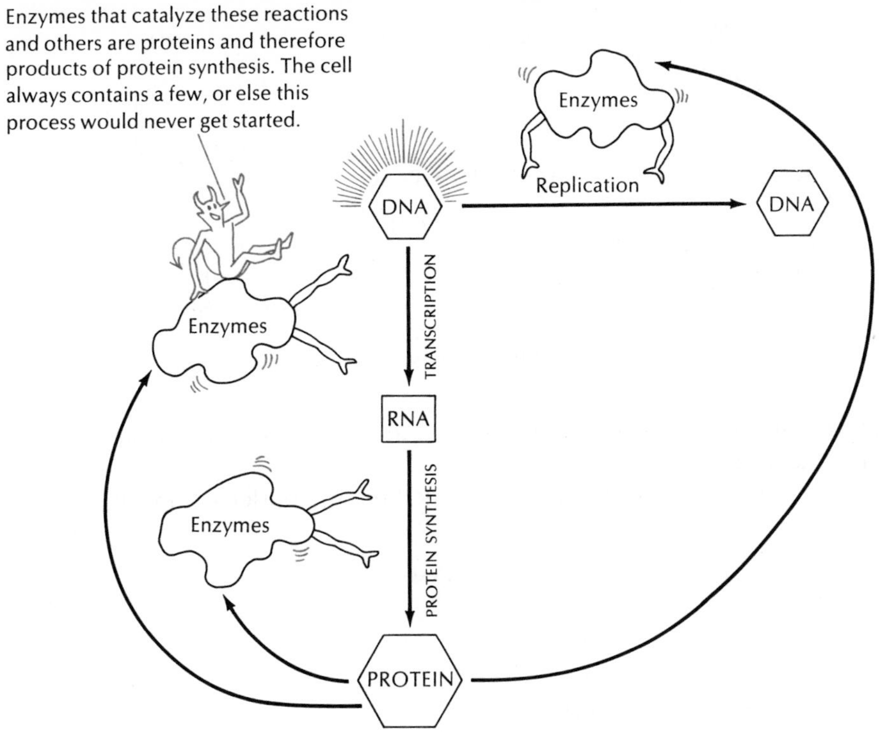
Enzymes that catalyze these reactions and others are proteins and therefore products of protein synthesis. The cell always contains a few, or else this process would never get started.
Enzymes
Replication
DNA
DNA
TRANSCRIPTION
Enzymes
RNA
PROTEIN SYNTHESIS
Enzymes
PROTEIN

FIGURE 18.4 The Relationships Among DNA, RNA, and Protein

down from the ring. If there is no group shown, we assume it's a hydrogen. This type of ring structure is characteristic of sugars. They contain an oxygen as part of the ring and usually an —OH group on nearly every carbon. The difference between ribose and deoxyribose is the presence or absence of the OH shown in color.

The bases are ring compounds containing nitrogen. These are the five in both DNA and RNA.

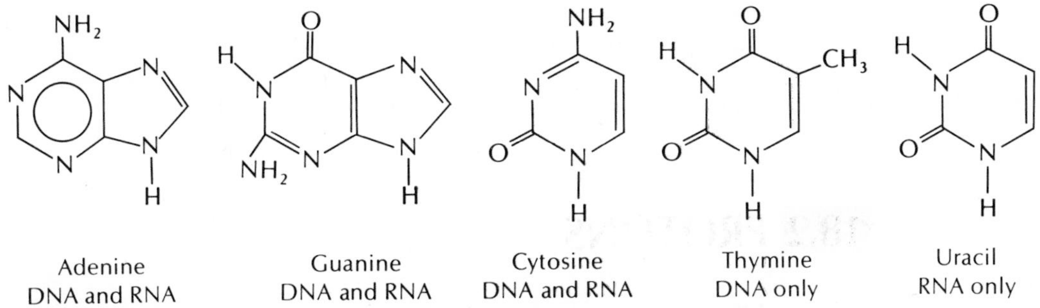
Adenine
DNA and RNA
Guanine
DNA and RNA
Cytosine
DNA and RNA
Thymine
DNA only
Uracil
RNA only

We can think of nucleotides as being formed from their parts by condensation. One example is:

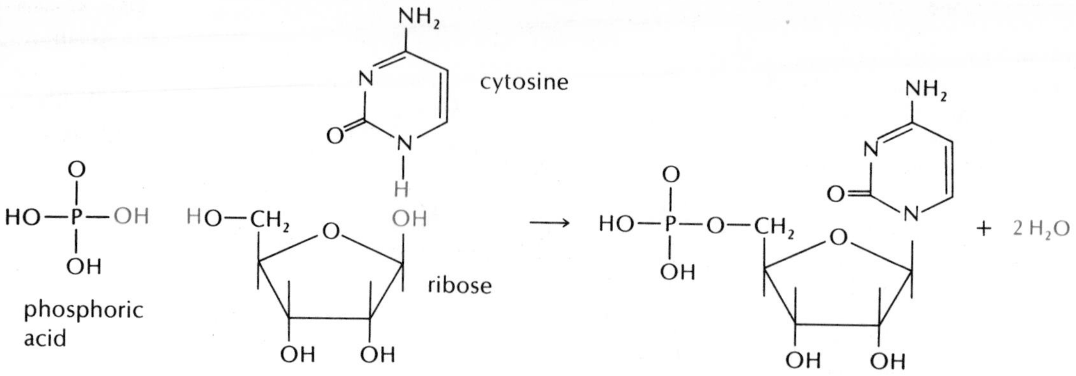

Cytosine monophosphate (CMP)

The correct names for all the nucleotides, and what they contain, are shown in Table 18.1.

The individual nucleotides join together by condensation like this:

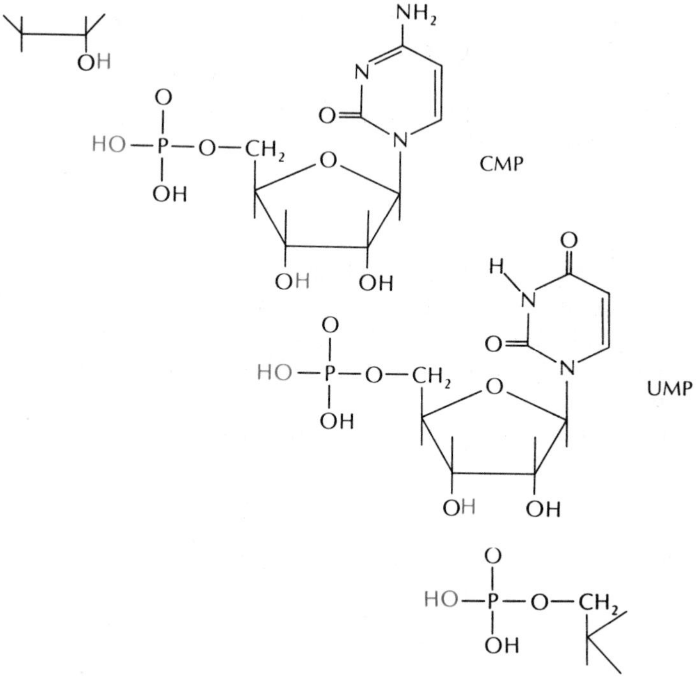

18.2 PROTEINS

protein

The word "protein" comes from the Greek word "proteios" meaning "of first importance." *Proteins* are high-molecular-weight (from about six thousand to forty million atomic mass units) polymers whose monomers are connected by amide linkages. The same type of compounds having lower molecular weight are called *polypeptides*. About 50 percent of the dry weight of most organisms is protein.

FIGURE 18.5
The Chemical Structure of DNA

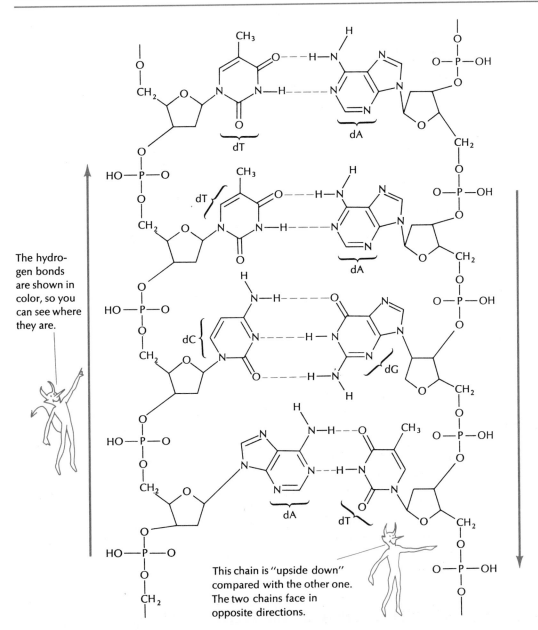

The hydrogen bonds are shown in color, so you can see where they are.

This chain is "upside down" compared with the other one. The two chains face in opposite directions.

TABLE 18.1
The composition of nucleotides

Name and Abbreviation[a]	Where Found	Sugar	Base
Adenosine monophosphate (AMP)	RNA	Ribose	Adenine
Cytidine monophosphate (CMP)	RNA	Ribose	Cytosine
Guanosine monophosphate (GMP)	RNA	Ribose	Guanine
Uridine monophosphate (UMP)	RNA	Ribose	Uracil
Deoxyadenosine monophosphate (dAMP)	DNA	Deoxyribose	Adenine
Deoxycytidine monophosphate (dCMP)	DNA	Deoxyribose	Cytosine
Deoxyguanosine monophosphate (dGMP)	DNA	Deoxyribose	Guanine
Thymidine monophosphate (TMP)	DNA	Deoxyribose	Thymine

[a]These abbreviations replace the A,C,G,U, and T, etc., used earlier in the chapter.

We've already been introduced to one important class of proteins: the enzymes. But proteins perform other functions besides catalyzing reactions. **antibody** Proteins in the blood, called *antibodies,* protect us from disease by combining with foreign substances. Other proteins are organic buffers in the blood, supplementing the inorganic buffers we learned about in Chapter 15. The hemoglobin that carries our life-giving oxygen is mostly protein.

Besides function, proteins provide structure to the greater part of animal cells. All the organelles shown in Figure 18.1 contain varying amounts of protein. The outer packaging of the chromosomes is protein. Ribosomes contain protein as well as RNA. On a larger scale, skin, hair, and muscle tissue are mostly protein. Bone is a protein network filled in with calcium phosphate.

AMINO ACIDS AND PROTEIN SYNTHESIS. In Chapter 17,
we saw that nylon is a polymer containing amide linkages. In fact, nylon is an imitation of wool, a protein fiber. Unlike nylon, which is made of just

one or two monomers, proteins can be made from any of twenty-six monomers. The monomers in proteins are *amino acids* and have this general structure:

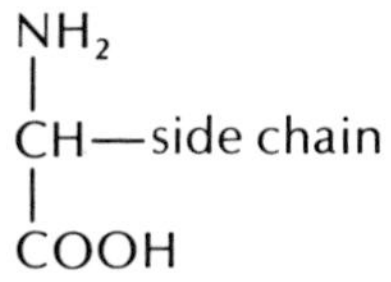

$$
\begin{array}{c}
NH_2 \\
| \\
CH\text{—side chain} \\
| \\
COOH
\end{array}
$$

The amide linkages in proteins are formed by condensation between amino acid molecules, like this:

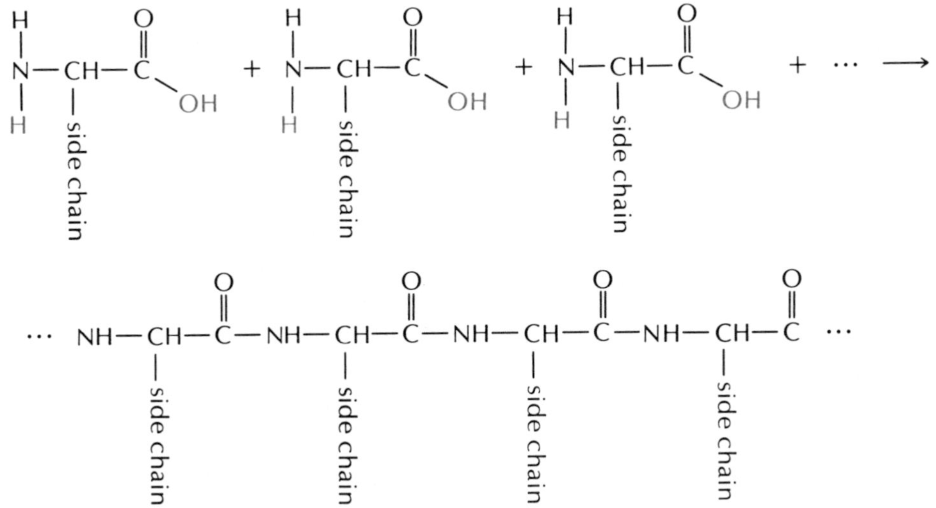

As with any condensation product, the new linkages provide points where the substance can be hydrolyzed.

Each of the twenty-six amino acids has a different side chain: these can contain nonpolar (hydrocarbon) groups, polar groups, or ionic groups. The names and side chains of some amino acids are shown in Table 18.2. Side chains that have acidic (—COOH) or basic (—NH_2) groups react with each other or with water to form their ionic conjugate bases (—COO^-) or conjugate acids (—NH_3^+). In this way, side chains with ionic groups are formed.

From these twenty-one monomer units, protein synthesis takes place in this sequence. (1) The messenger RNA (mRNA), freshly transcribed from DNA, fastens itself to a ribosome. (2) Elsewhere in the cell, each transfer RNA (tRNA) molecule binds an amino acid and carries it to the mRNA on the ribosome. (3) The tRNA molecules fasten themselves to the mRNA. (4) An enzyme forms the amide linkage between adjacent amino acids. (5) The mRNA moves along the ribosome. (6) After its amino acid is joined to the protein chain, each tRNA is released and goes to find an identical amino acid. (7) The process goes on until the whole protein chain is formed.

There are at least twenty-six different tRNA molecules, each having a shape that lets it bind to one and only one kind of amino acid. The mRNA tells the tRNA where to put its amino acid by means of the *genetic* **genetic code**

TABLE 18.2
Amino acid side chains

Nonpolar				Polar (Uncharged)		
Name	Abbr.	Side Chain		Name	Abbr.	Side Chain
Glycine	Gly	$-H$		Serine	Ser	$-CH_2-OH$
Alanine	Ala	$-CH_3$		Threonine	Thr	$-CH-OH$
Valine	Val	$-CH-(CH_3)_2$				$\quad\ \ CH_3$
Leucine	Leu	$-CH_2-CH-(CH_3)_2$				
Isoleucine	Ileu	$-CH-CH_2-CH_3$		Cysteine	Cys	$-CH_2-SH$
		$\quad CH_3$				
				Tyrosine	Tyr	$-CH_2-\bigcirc-OH$
Proline[a]	Pro	(ring structure with $-COOH$ and $N-H$)				
				Asparagine	AspN	$-CH_2-C{\overset{O}{\underset{NH_2}{}}}$
Phenylalanine	Phe	$-CH_2-\bigcirc$				
Methionine	Met	$-CH_2CH_2SCH_3$		Glutamine	GluN	$-CH_2-CH_2-C{\overset{O}{\underset{NH_2}{}}}$

Ionic (Conjugate Acids Are +)				Ionic (Conjugate Bases are −)		
Name	Abbr.	Side Chain		Name	Abbr.	Side Chain
Lysine	Lys	$-CH_2-CH_2-CH_2-CH_2-NH_2$		Aspartic acid	Asp	$-CH_2-COOH$
				Glutamic acid	Glu	$-CH_2-CH_2-COOH$
Arginine	Arg	$-CH_2-CH_2-CH_2-NH-C{\overset{NH}{\underset{NH_2}{}}}$				
Histidine	His	$-CH_2-$ (imidazole ring)				

[a]Proline does not have the normal $-NH_2$ group, so its whole structure is shown.

codon

anticodon

code. In the genetic code, a sequence of three nucleotides on mRNA— called a *codon*—codes for a single amino acid. In addition to having a binding position for an amino acid, each tRNA molecule has a place where it binds to the mRNA. This binding position contains a sequence of three nucleotides—called an *anticodon*—that is complementary to the codon of that tRNA. In this way, each amino acid is added to the protein chain in its proper place. Figure 18.6 shows the process of protein synthesis.

fibrous protein

PROTEIN STRUCTURE.
Proteins in muscle and cartilage are examples of *fibrous proteins*. An overcooked pot roast shows just how fibrous muscle protein is. Fibrous proteins have straight chains and are water insoluble because they contain large numbers of nonpolar hydrophobic side chains. Single fibrous protein molecules twist themselves into a helix

because of the hydrogen bonding between the —C=O and the —N—H groups in the chain. Several of these helixes twist together to form thicker strands, which in turn twist to form tough ropelike muscle fibers. The protein in hair, which is also fibrous, contains *disulfide bridges* between adjacent protein chains.

disulfide bridge

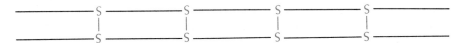

These disulfide bridges are created by the presence of cysteine, which has

FIGURE 18.6
Protein Synthesis

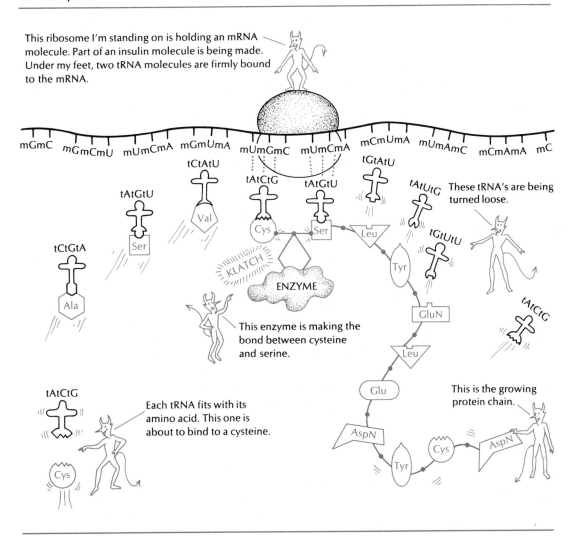

mercapto an —SH (*mercapto*) group. A very mild oxidizing agent can cause two adjacent —SH groups to form a disulfide bridge.

$$\text{—SH} + \text{SH—} \longrightarrow \text{—S—S—} + 2(\text{H})$$

Disulfide bridges can be broken easily by reduction. Permanent waving reduces the disulfide bridges, then re-forms them again while the hair is molded into the desired shape.

globular protein Enzymes, hemoglobin, and antibodies are examples of *globular proteins*. These are roundish (like globes) and water soluble because of the large numbers of polar and ionic side chains they contain. Attractions among the polar and ionic side chains, plus disulfide bridges, give each globular protein the shape it needs to do its particular job. Figure 18.7 illustrates the difference between a fibrous and a globular protein.

denatured Anything that destroys the shape of a globular protein also destroys its function. When this happens, the protein has been *denatured*. Table 18.3 shows some ways of denaturing proteins.

Just as the meaning of a sentence depends on the words and their order, so the identity and function of a protein depends on the amino acids it contains and on their order. If a mistake is made, either in the kinds of amino acids or in their order, it may change the protein's shape or charge, or both. The disease sickle-cell anemia is caused by a mistake of one out of the three hundred amino acids contained in hemoglobin. An amino acid with a nonpolar side chain is wrongly substituted for an amino acid with an ionic one, changing the hemoglobin's charge and making it less soluble. The hemoglobin precipitates, and the red blood cells that contain it become lopsided. The cells clump together and block blood vessels, or sometimes break. These cells don't carry oxygen well, and the person becomes weak **genetic defect** and less resistant to infections. This is an example of a *genetic defect*—a mistake in the cell's DNA, which is passed on by heredity and causes an incorrect protein structure.

ENZYMES.

The many biochemical reactions that happen in organisms have to take place fast. If we tried to carry them out in a test tube, they'd either go very slowly or not at all. Enzymes, like all catalysts, speed up the rates of reactions by lowering their activation energies.

Consider a factory with assembly lines. There are a lot of processes going on that involve just one thing, like putting on a nut, tightening a bolt, or taking out a screw. Usually these jobs are done by specialists. One kind of worker only puts on a certain nut. That worker has a special tool and a supply of nuts. The kind of worker who takes out a screw needs a special tool and a place to put the screws. The worker who tightens a bolt needs a special tool, but he or she doesn't need a supply or a place to put anything.

substrate Enzymes are like the workers. The molecule that an enzyme is working on, which is like the piece of work on the assembly line, is called the *substrate*. The shape and charge of an enzyme cause it to hold onto its particular substrate like a vise. Somewhere near is the enzyme's "tool," called its *active site*. The active site is a functional group or groups on certain of the enzyme's amino acid side chains.

Each reaction that happens in an organism needs at least one enzyme. Some enzymes can work on one reaction; others can work on several similar reactions involving different substrates. The most common reactions involve either hydrolysis or condensation—the addition or removal of water molecules. Since cells are mostly water, there is always plenty of it around when and where an enzyme needs it.

FIGURE 18.7
Shapes of Fibrous and Globular Proteins

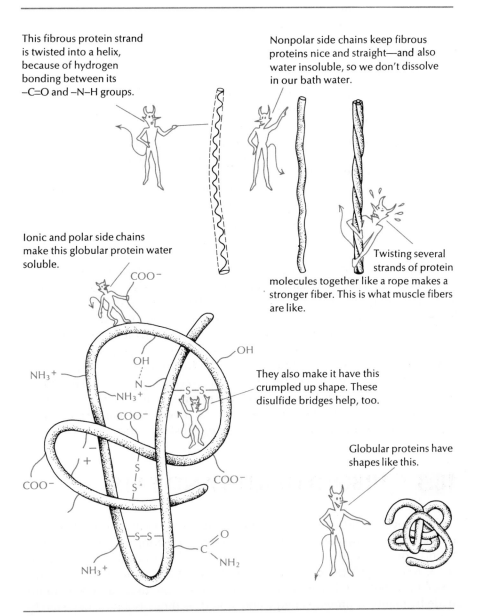

This fibrous protein strand is twisted into a helix, because of hydrogen bonding between its –C=O and –N–H groups.

Nonpolar side chains keep fibrous proteins nice and straight—and also water insoluble, so we don't dissolve in our bath water.

Twisting several strands of protein molecules together like a rope makes a stronger fiber. This is what muscle fibers are like.

Ionic and polar side chains make this globular protein water soluble.

They also make it have this crumpled up shape. These disulfide bridges help, too.

Globular proteins have shapes like this.

TABLE 18.3
Ways to denature proteins

Method	Effect	Comments
Add acid or base	Breaks up ionic attractions by destroying acidic or basic groups.	Milk curdles when lemon juice or vinegar is added. The casein (milk protein) is denatured.
Add concentrated salt or urea (NH_2CONH_2)	These interact with the protein's polar or ionic groups and prevent them from interacting with each other.	This kind of denaturing can sometimes be reversed just by washing the protein free of the salt or urea.
Heat	Breaks up most interactions.	Frying an egg denatures the albumin (egg protein).
Add alcohol	This disrupts the ionic and polar interactions through hydrogen bonding.	Alcohol is a good disinfectant because it denatures the proteins of bacteria and viruses.
Add heavy metal ions (Hg^{2+}, Pb^{2+})	React with the disulfide linkages and usually precipitate the protein.	Mercury and lead denature important enzymes and other proteins so that they no longer function. *Mercury* is named after the Roman god Mercury, because it flows so rapidly.

coenzyme

However, many other reactions involve putting on or taking off hydrogen, electrons, methyl groups, sulfate, and amino or acetate groups. Since these aren't so readily available, the enzyme must have either a supply or a place to put them. This service is provided by compounds called *coenzymes*, which are small soluble nonprotein molecules that hold pieces of molecules for enzymes. Each coenzyme can hold only one of a certain kind of part or piece. However, a coenzyme can give its part to or take it from any enzyme that needs to use it or to get rid of it. If an enzyme's job is to take a piece off its substrate, it gives the piece to a coenzyme. That coenzyme can give the part to another enzyme in the cell that needs the part. Figure 18.8 illustrates the relationship among enzyme, substrate, and coenzyme.

18.3 CARBOHYDRATES AND FATS

carbohydrate

Besides nucleic acids and proteins, living organisms contain carbohydrates and fats. A *carbohydrate,* meaning "hydrate of carbon," is usually a compound containing a carbon, hydrogen, and oxygen in the proportion of one C to one H_2O. (Since H_2O as such does not appear in these, the term "hydrate" is not strictly correct.) The simple sugar glucose is a carbohydrate made by plants to provide energy and stored by them as a polymer, starch.

Another polymer of glucose is cellulose, used by plants as structural material. Many cell membranes and walls contain carbohydrates.

Fats are made from carbohydrates in the bodies of both plants and animals. One type of fat is used for energy storage. Other types make up the large part of brain and nerve tissue in animals. Still other types make up parts of cell membranes and walls.

MONOSACCHARIDES. Starch can be hydrolyzed to glucose, but glucose can't be hydrolyzed to any simpler carbohydrate. *Monosaccharides,* **monosaccharide** or simple sugars, are carbohydrates that can't be hydrolyzed any further. We've already seen two monosaccharides: ribose and deoxyribose. These have five carbon atoms. Glucose has six carbon atoms and exists in both these ring structures:

α-Glucose β-Glucose

The difference between these two kinds of glucose lies in the position of the —OH group printed in color. All other —OH groups in glucose keep their positions—up or down—on the ring. Changing one or more of these will change the identity of the sugar.

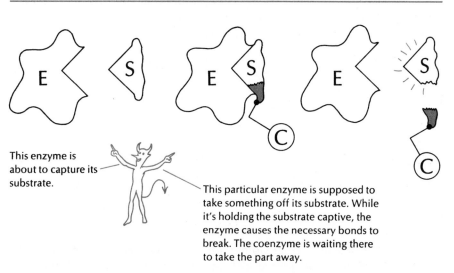

FIGURE 18.8
The
Relationship
Among Enzyme,
Substrate,
and Coenzyme

This enzyme is about to capture its substrate.

This particular enzyme is supposed to take something off its substrate. While it's holding the substrate captive, the enzyme causes the necessary bonds to break. The coenzyme is waiting there to take the part away.

Glucose is also called "dextrose," or "corn sugar." Its commercial use is almost exclusively in candy and sweeteners.

Two other important monosaccharides are galactose, found in milk sugar, and fructose, found in honey and fruits.

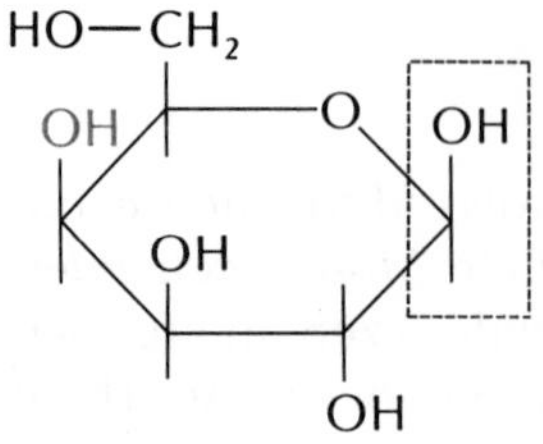

Galactose

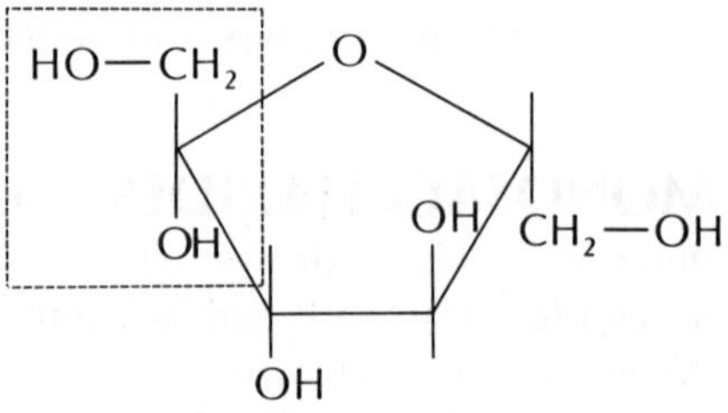

Fructose

These also exist in α and β forms by reversing the position of the groups in the boxes. Galactose differs from glucose in the position of the —OH group printed in color.

It is often convenient to abbreviate these ring structures by leaving out some or all of the —OH groups. When this is done, the sugar must be clearly specified.

DI- AND POLYSACCHARIDES.

Plants make glucose and use it for energy. But they also store it for their own future needs—at night, when the sun's energy isn't available, or literally for a rainy day, when some of the sun's energy is blocked by clouds. Plants also store glucose in seeds and tubers so that their offspring will have energy to live on until they have leaves and can make their own glucose. We can store a lot of small, regularly shaped objects more efficiently by stacking them neatly than by throwing them in a heap. In the same way, monosaccharides can be stored more efficiently by condensing them, like this:

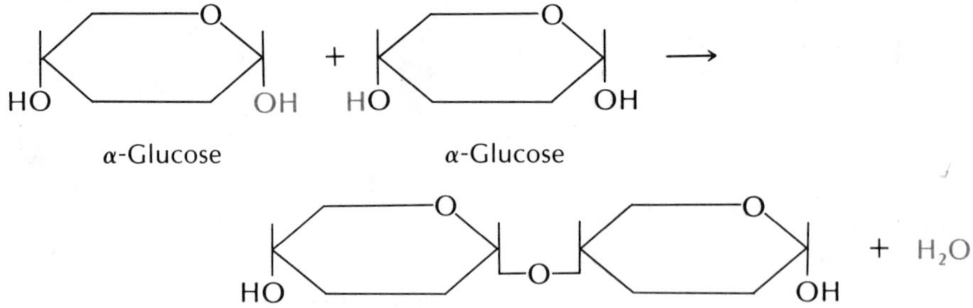

α-Glucose α-Glucose

Maltose
(malt sugar)

disaccharide   Two monosaccharides that are joined form a *disaccharide*. The point where the monosaccharides are joined is also where they can be hydrolyzed. Two other important disaccharides have these structures:

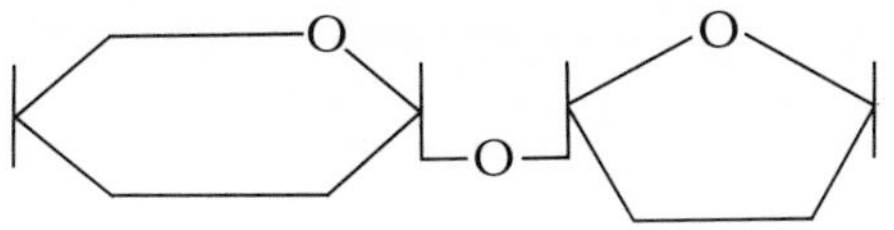

(glucose) (fructose)

Sucrose
(table sugar, beet sugar,
cane sugar)

(galactose) (glucose)

Lactose
(milk sugar)

Polysaccharides are composed of many monosaccharides and are an even more condensed way to store them. Plants store glucose in their seeds and tubers as starch, a polysaccharide made of α-glucose. Animals get glucose from plants and store it in their livers as glycogen, or animal starch. Plant starch and glycogen have very similar structures and are easily hydrolyzed by enzymes when the organism needs glucose. **polysaccharide**

Another way that plants put glucose together is in the polysaccharide cellulose, made of β-glucose. Unlike starch, cellulose is a building material and not an energy storehouse. Cellulose is the most abundant organic material of the plant world; it is to plants what fibrous proteins are to animals. Woody stems and tree trunks are mostly cellulose. The roughage we eat in celery, carrots, and leafy vegetables is cellulose. We use cellulose mostly in paper, made from wood, and in cotton, a natural fiber.

Cellulose is useful as a structural material because it isn't easily hydrolyzed, and most organisms don't have enzymes that will hydrolyze it at all. However, it can be hydrolyzed by heating with a strong acid, such as HCl. Depending on the cost of other sugar sources, this method is sometimes used as a commercial source of glucose.

Figure 18.9 shows the structures of starch and of cellulose.

LIPIDS. Biological substances that are soluble in ether—that is, fats and oils—are *lipids*. Like carbohydrates, they are both energy sources and building materials. Some of them also provide function. Some simple lipids are glyceryl esters, esters of glycerol with fatty acids (long straight chain organic acids). Glycerol has three —OH groups, so it can form esters with three fatty acids. The acids can be the same or different, but they're usually different. A typical glyceryl ester might have this structure: **lipid**

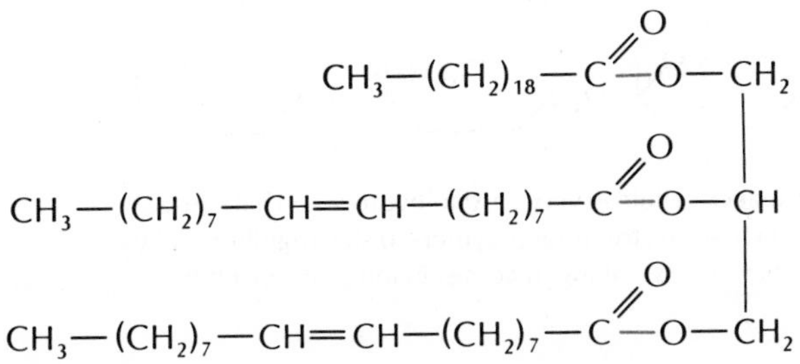

FIGURE 18.9
Starch and Cellulose Structures

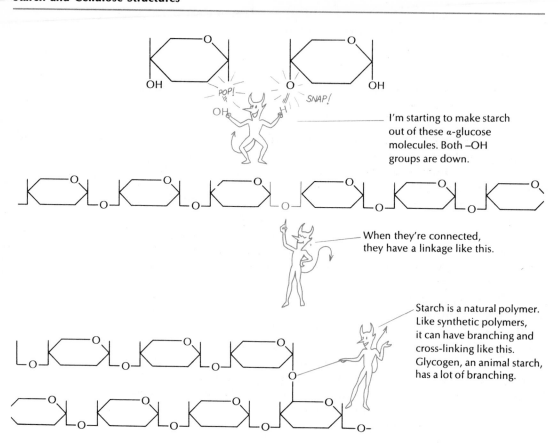

I'm starting to make starch out of these α-glucose molecules. Both –OH groups are down.

When they're connected, they have a linkage like this.

Starch is a natural polymer. Like synthetic polymers, it can have branching and cross-linking like this. Glycogen, an animal starch, has a lot of branching.

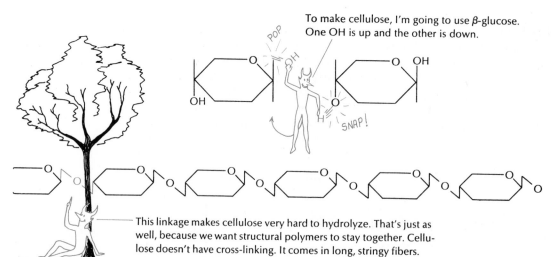

To make cellulose, I'm going to use β-glucose. One OH is up and the other is down.

This linkage makes cellulose very hard to hydrolyze. That's just as well, because we want structural polymers to stay together. Cellulose doesn't have cross-linking. It comes in long, stringy fibers.

The ester linkages, indicated in color, provide points where the fat can be hydrolyzed. Such a lipid is a *triglyceride*, because each of the three —OH groups on glycerol is now part of an ester group. Most animal triglycerides contain saturated fatty acids and are fats (solids). Most plant triglycerides contain unsaturated fatty acids and are oils (liquids). Fats and oils are used as energy sources directly, or are stored in the form of fat globules.

triglyceride 453

Other, more complex lipids may contain phosphate, monosaccharide, or other molecules. These are found in nerve and brain tissue and in cell membranes. One such lipid is the following, called a *lecithin* and found in nerve tissue:

lecithin

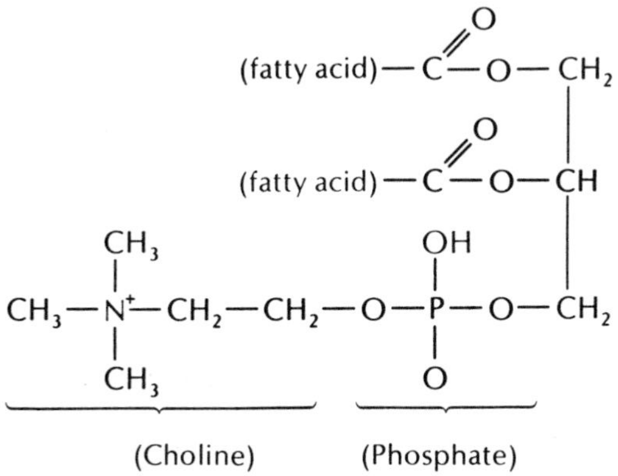

(Choline)   (Phosphate)

The structure of a lecithin is similar to that of a triglyceride, but in place of one of the fatty acid groups there is a phosphate and a choline group. It is because these lipids are soluble in ether that ether is such an effective anesthetic. When we breathe ether, it dissolves in nerve cell lipids, changing them temporarily.

Another class of lipids includes the *steroids*, which have this basic structure:

steroid

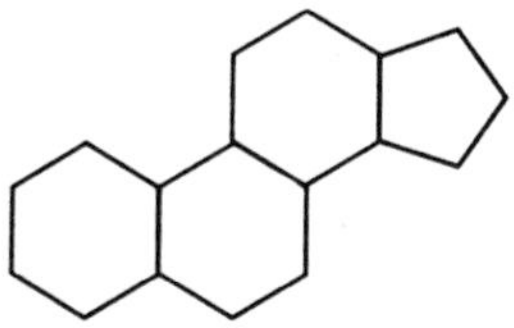

Table 18.4 shows the complete structures for some important steroids. One of them is cholesterol. The others are all *hormones*, relatively small molecules that are produced in one part of an organism and sent to another part. Their function is to trigger a reaction or reactions in the part of the organism to which they are sent.

hormone

18.4 SOME BIOCHEMICAL PROCESSES

Only a certain number of each element's atoms exist on earth. For plants and animals to reproduce and grow, atoms must be recycled and used over and over again. The atoms that make up our bodies now are only tempo-

TABLE 18.4
The structures of some steroids

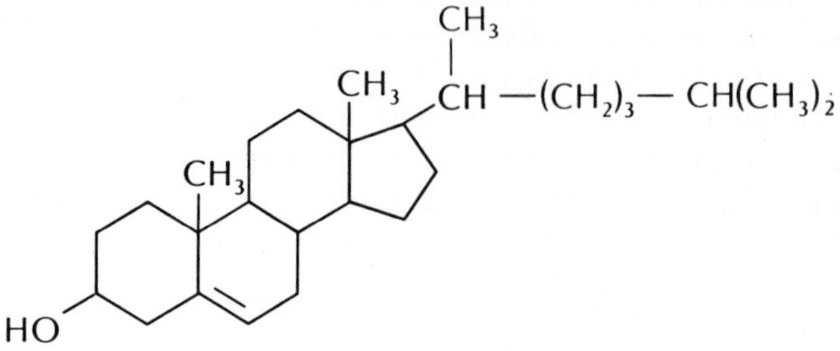

Cholesterol

A steroid alcohol, or sterol. Found in nearly all vertebrates, mostly in the brain and spinal cord, and in gallstones. Has been associated with hardening of the arteries. Function is probably to be made into steroid hormones and bile acids.

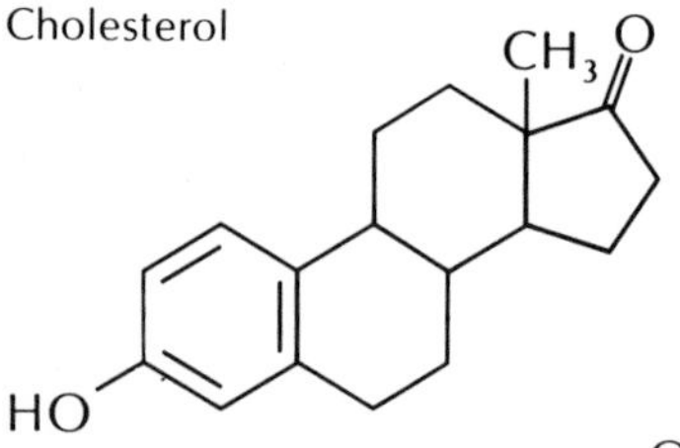

Estrone

A female sex hormone. Prevents release of eggs. Secreted in greater amounts during pregnancy.

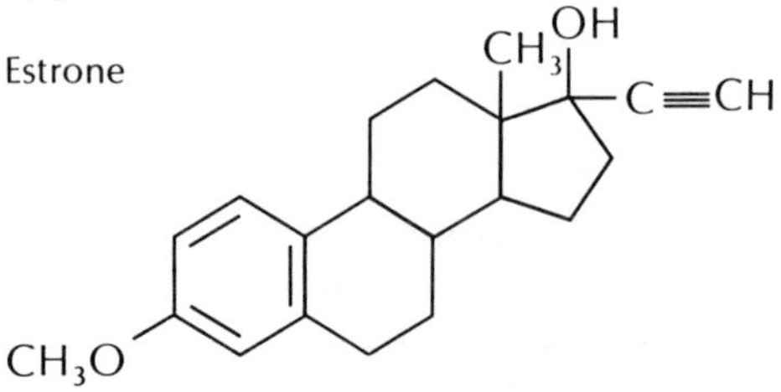

Mestranol

A synthetic hormonelike compound, used in birth-control pills. Imitates estrone and others by simulating pregnancy and preventing release of egg.

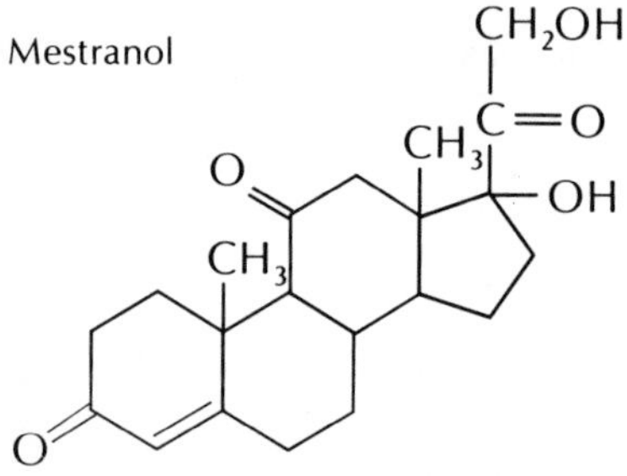

Cortisone

A hormone that regulates the use of carbohydrates. Also effective in relieving inflammation, such as that from arthritis.

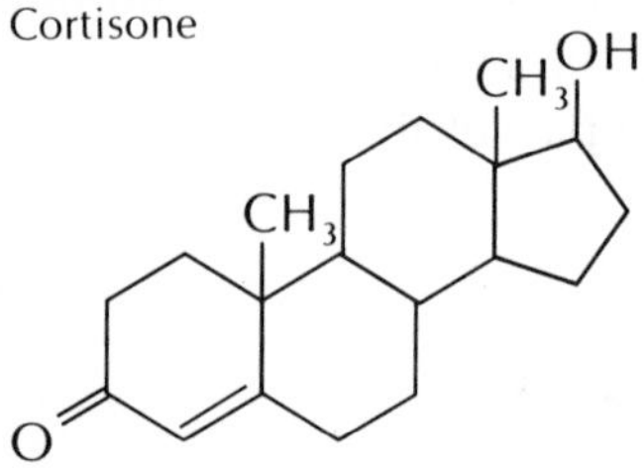

Testosterone

A male sex hormone. Regulates the development of reproductive organs.

rarily ours. These atoms probably belonged at one time to prehistoric plants and animals, and they will belong to other organisms in the future. Figure 18.10 shows roughly how carbon and nitrogen are recycled in nature.

Plants make glucose by photosynthesis, and they use the energy from it to make amino acids out of inorganic nitrogen—ammonia and nitrates—in the soil. Then the plants make proteins for their own use. Herbivorous (plant-eating) animals eat the plants, taking amino acids from the plants' proteins and re-forming them into their own protein structures. Carnivorous (meat-eating) animals eat the herbivorous animals to obtain protein for their own structure and to store fat for their energy. All animals and plants die, and microorganisms in the soil turn their complex organic structures back into simple inorganic compounds that can be used again by plants.

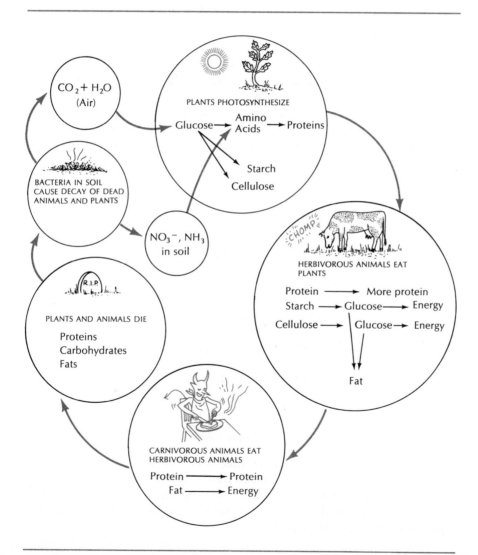

**FIGURE 18.10
The Biological
Cycle of
Elements**

Animals can't make amino acids, so they depend on plants for them. Plants can't use organic compounds, so they depend on the bacteria in the soil to break them down. If decay didn't occur, the elements would reach a literal dead end as organic compounds, and the cycle would be incomplete. Our production of certain plastics and other substances that do not decay is beginning to interrupt this cycle.

Although the biological cycle of elements depends on each segment, it is logical to start at photosynthesis, the process that directly and indirectly furnishes all organisms with energy from the sun.

PHOTOSYNTHESIS. This equation for photosynthesis sums up a very complex series of biochemical reactions that happen in a green plant.

$$6\,CO_2(g) + 6\,H_2O(l) \longrightarrow C_6H_{12}O_6(aq) + 6\,O_2(g)$$

The important end result is that the product, glucose, contains seven C—H bonds, while the CO_2 from which it is made contains none. We saw in Chapter 17 that C—H bonds are the main energy source when organic compounds are burned, and it's the same with biochemical compounds. The energy that went into making glucose is stored mostly in its C—H bonds. Hydrogen to make these bonds is stripped off the water molecules, leaving their oxygen to be released to the atmosphere as the free element.

Only green plants can carry out photosynthesis, because the first step depends on absorbing the sun's energy by means of the green pigment chlorophyll.

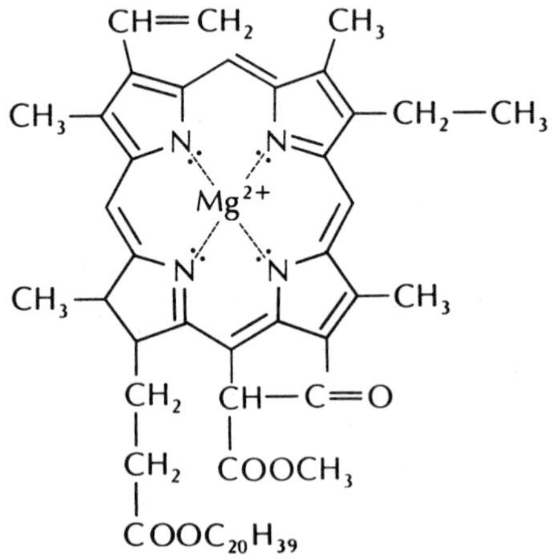

Chlorophyll a

This is one of several chlorophylls that have similar structure. In these compounds, Mg^{2+} acts as a Lewis acid—that is, as an electron-pair acceptor. The available electron pair on each nitrogen belonging to the ring system is donated to four coordinate covalent bonds. As we'll see a bit later, hemoglobin contains a similar system.

Scientists still don't understand all the processes that occur during photosynthesis. However, the initial reaction is the absorption of energy by chlorophyll.

$$\text{chlorophyll} + \text{energy} \longrightarrow \text{chlorophyll (higher energy)}$$

Then, the chlorophyll provides energy for removing hydrogen from water and giving it to a hydrogen-accepting coenzyme.

$$\text{chlorophyll} + H_2O + \text{coenzyme} \xrightarrow{\text{enzymes}}$$
$$\text{chlorophyll} + O_2 + H_2 \text{coenzyme}$$

After that, the hydrogen is passed around through many other coenzymes until it ends up bonded to carbon in glucose.

All of the other reactions we'll look at are involved in *metabolism*—an organism's use of raw materials from its environment to provide its energy and structural materials.

metabolism

RESPIRATION. The controlled burning of fuel by cells to obtain energy is called *respiration,* and it is carried out by both plants and animals. Most respiration reactions occur in the *mitochondrion,* one of the cell's organelles shown in Figure 18.1. When the fuel is glucose, the result is almost the opposite of the photosynthesis reaction.

respiration

mitochondrion

$$C_6H_{12}O_6(aq) + 6\,O_2(g) \longrightarrow 6\,CO_2(g) + 6\,H_2O(g) + 277 \text{ kcal}$$

Hydrogen is stripped from the C—H bonds and made into water molecules, with a release of energy. Every day, the average adult generates about 2500 kilocalories from food, needs about 500 liters of oxygen, and generates about 400 liters of carbon dioxide. The heat of combustion of glucose is 690 kilocalories per mole. Since the respiration of glucose yields only 277 kilocalories, the human body manages to use about 40 percent of glucose's energy.

How do cells harvest this energy? Obviously not all as heat (though some is needed to maintain body temperature) or the organism would burn up. Most of the energy is captured in other chemical bonds. The main chemical substance that performs this function in all organisms is adenosine triphosphate (ATP), which has this structure:

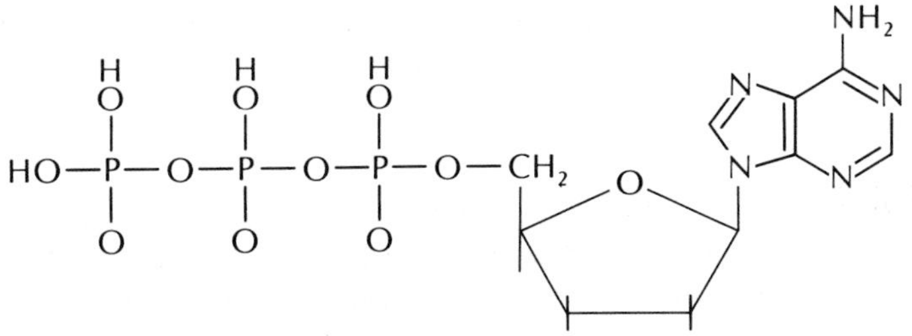

ATP is a coenzyme that stores and transfers energy and a phosphate group according to this reversible reaction:

$$ATP \rightleftharpoons ADP + PO_4^{3-} + 7.3 \text{ kcal}$$

Here, ADP (adenosine diphosphate) is simply ATP without one of its phosphate groups. Both ATP and ADP are abundant in cells. If a process releases energy (as respiration does), the energy is invested by driving the above reaction from right to left and forming ATP. We thus have an energy conversion factor: 7.3 kilocalories per mole of ATP. Expressing the energy from respiration in moles of ATP instead of kilocalories, we then write:

$$C_6H_{12}O_6(aq) + 6\,O_2(g) + 38\,ADP + 38\,PO_4^{3-}(aq) \longrightarrow$$
$$6\,CO_2(g) + 6\,H_2O(g) + 38\,ATP$$

Or, the respiration of 1 mole of glucose yields 38 moles of ATP.

Any kind of food that contains C—H bonds and can be broken down by an organism's enzymes can be used as an energy source in respiration, provided that it's soluble and can be carried to the cells by blood or plant sap. Glucose, amino acids, and fatty acids are such substances. A 6-carbon-atom fatty acid yields 42 moles of ATP, so it's a slightly more efficient energy source than glucose. If animals take in more fuel than they need immediately for energy, they store the excess as fat. About 30 percent of the carbohydrates eaten by humans go to make stored fat.

We can think of respiration as happening from two extreme points: the C—H bonds in the food, and the O_2 we breathe. Getting these two together to form H_2O and release energy involves a long chain of reactions in which coenzymes pass hydrogen and electrons around. The reactions begin on one end with the binding of oxygen by hemoglobin. We've said that hemoglobin contains a protein (called globin) and a nonprotein (called heme). The heme part binds the oxygen to Fe^{2+} in the center of a ring system similar to that of chlorophyll. Fe^{2+} has six binding positions. Four are used by the nitrogens in the ring; one is used to bind the heme to the globin; and the remaining one is for binding oxygen. Hemoglobin's structure and a simplified version of the respiratory chain are shown in Figure 18.11.

Coenzymes are clearly very important in respiration. Many of the vitamins we need are used to make parts of these coenzymes. The word "vitamin" comes from "vital amine," because it was once thought that all vitamins were amines. Now *vitamin* means any substance that an organism needs but can't make itself and therefore must have in its diet. Table 18.5 shows a few important coenzymes and the vitamins that we need to make them. In addition to these, there are many other vitamins that aren't converted to coenzymes, and some whose exact functions aren't well known.

vitamin

DIGESTION.

digestion

We saw that cell respiration requires soluble food. The process of converting food from an insoluble form (such as starch or protein) to a soluble form (such as glucose or amino acids) is called *digestion*. All the digestive reactions involve hydrolysis and are catalyzed by hydrolytic enzymes.

Digestion begins in the mouth, where the enzyme amylase in saliva begins breaking starch molecules into smaller polysaccharides. In the

stomach, the enzyme pepsin, along with the stomach's HCl, begins breaking protein chains down into smaller units. In the intestines, other enzymes
complete the breakdown to glucose and amino acids, which pass through
the walls of the intestines and into the blood. Bile salts from the liver act
as emulsifying agents for fats and let them mix with fluid so that they, too,

FIGURE 18.11
Hemoglobin's Structure and the Respiratory Chain

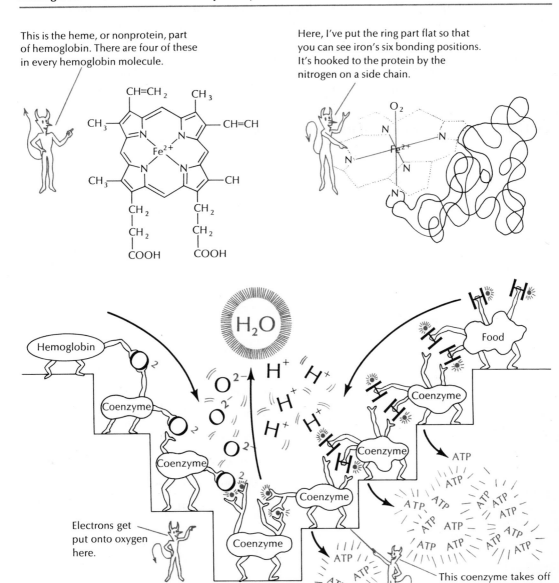

This is the heme, or nonprotein, part
of hemoglobin. There are four of these
in every hemoglobin molecule.

Here, I've put the ring part flat so that
you can see iron's six bonding positions.
It's hooked to the protein by the
nitrogen on a side chain.

Electrons get
put onto oxygen
here.

This coenzyme takes off
hydrogen's electron.

can be attacked by enzymes. Fatty acids and glycerol then also pass into the blood. Bacteria that are normal residents of the intestinal tract aid in the final digestion. Feces contain large quantities of dead bacteria, as well as indigestible substances such as cellulose.

The intestines of ruminating animals like cattle contain bacteria that can digest cellulose and make its glucose available to the animal. These bacteria, and others in the soil, are among the few organisms that have the enzyme **cellulase** *cellulase*, which catalyzes the hydrolysis of cellulose. Microorganisms in the digestive systems of some wood-eating insects, such as termites and carpenter ants, also have this enzyme.

Besides digesting food they eat, organisms also digest food that's stored in their own bodies. Enzymes in a sprouting seed begin to digest its starch so the seedling can have glucose for its growth. Beer brewing takes advantage of this enzymatic process. To make malt, barley is moistened and

TABLE 18.5 Some important coenzymes and their vitamins

Vitamin	Coenzyme and Function
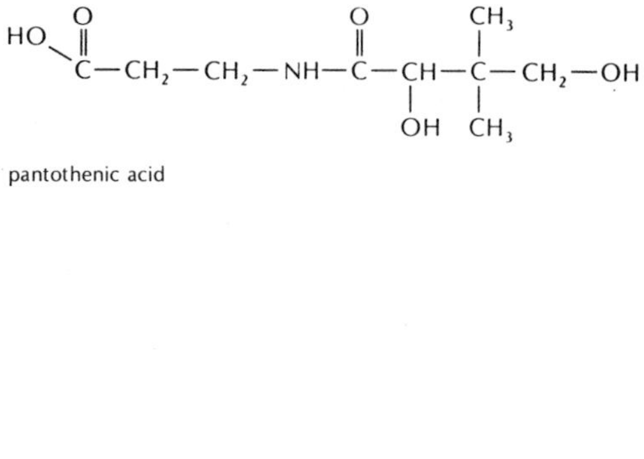 pantothenic acid	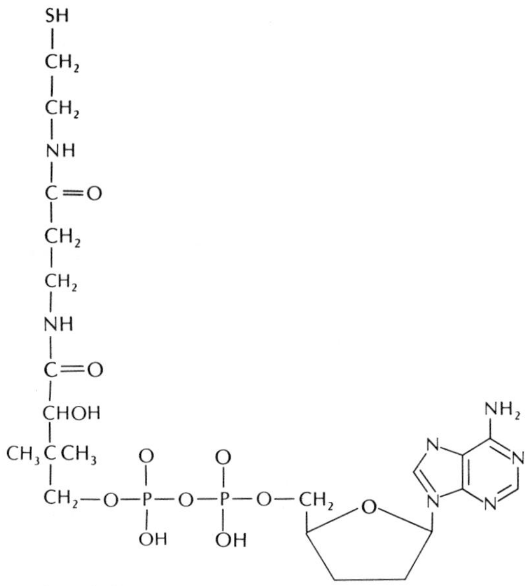 coenzyme A (CoA) Transfers acetyl group important in the metabolic processes.
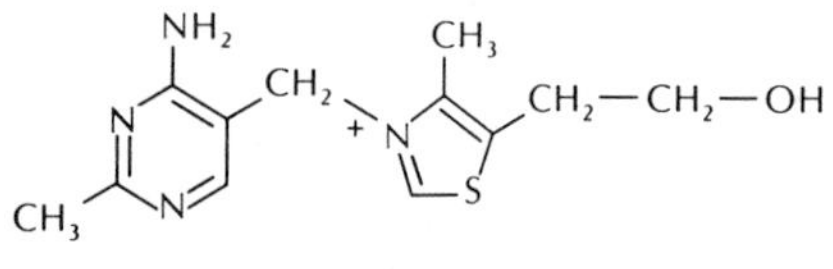 thiamine (vitamine B₁)	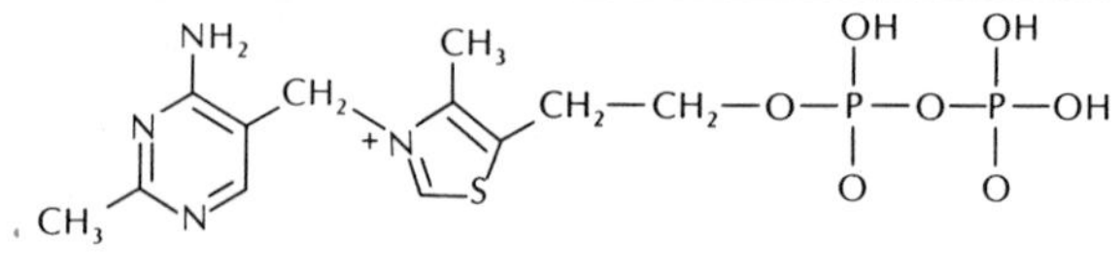 thiamine pytrophosphate (TPP) Also transfers acetyl group

allowed to sprout, then cooked and mashed. The enzymes have converted starch, an unacceptable food for yeast, into maltose, which yeast can convert into alcohol. Brewer's yeast is then added to the malt, along with other things. The resulting fermentation produces beer.

When our diets aren't supplying enough energy, our bodies call on their energy reserves by digesting their glycogen or stored fat. Fat is the most deeply stored of all the reserves, sort of like money tied up in stocks and bonds. Glycogen is a bit more available, like money in a savings account. Blood sugar (glucose) is still more available, like money in a checking account. And ATP is like having cash on hand. The amount of sugar in blood will last only a few minutes. The sugar from glycogen in the liver will last several hours. After that, if we're not taking in any food, we start tapping our reserve of stored fat. An average adult (not overweight) has enough reserve fat to last 30 to 40 days.

Vitamin	Coenzyme and Function

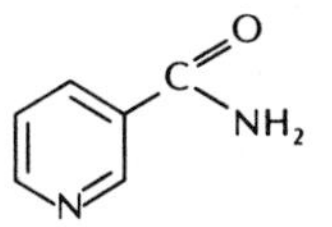

niacin
(nicotinamide)

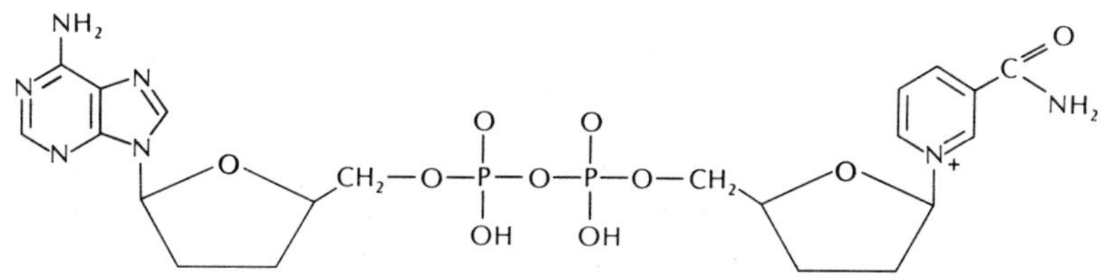

nicotinamide adenine dinucleotide (NAD)

A hydrogen-accepting coenzyme, important in the respiratory chain.

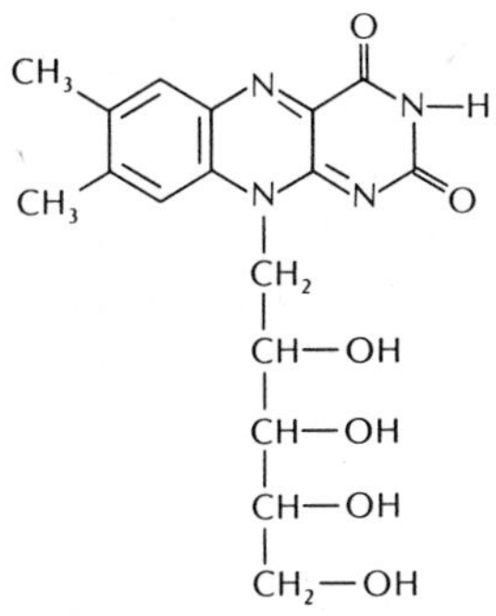

riboflavin

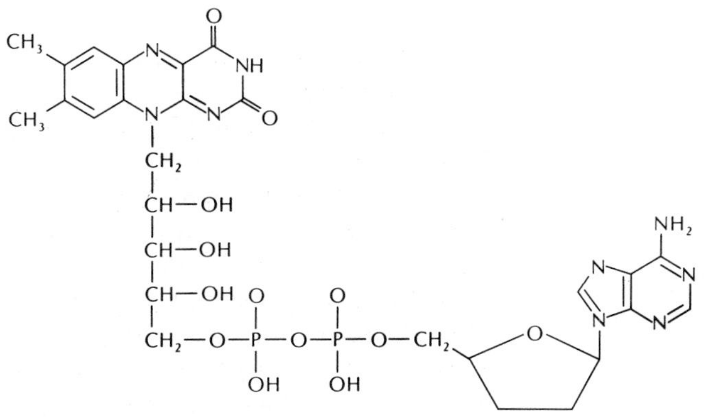

flavin adenine dinucleotide (FAD)

Like NAD, an important hydrogen-accepting coenzyme in the respiratory chain.

The enzymes that break down liver glycogen are controlled by the hormone *adrenalin*, which has this structure:

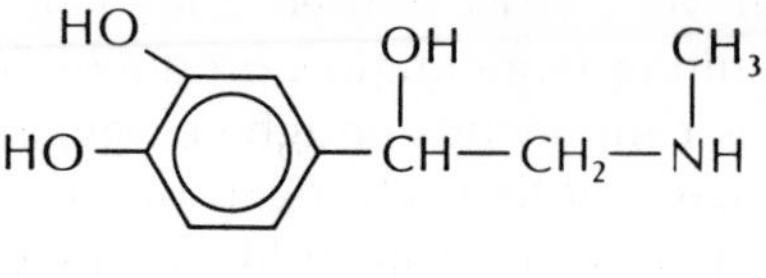

$$HO-\underset{HO}{\bigcirc}-\underset{\overset{|}{OH}}{CH}-CH_2-\underset{\overset{|}{CH_3}}{NH}$$

Adrenalin

In stressful situations, adrenalin is secreted and triggers the conversion of glycogen to glucose, probably by somehow activating a key enzyme. One molecule of adrenaline causes the release of about thirty thousand molecules of glucose. This gives the brain and muscles a lot of extra energy that might be needed in an emergency.

EXCRETION.

A lot of the amino acids in cells are used to make new proteins, but the surplus is used for energy. The first step in converting an amino acid to energy is removal of the amino group by enzymes.

$$H_2 \text{ coenzyme} + \underset{\underset{\text{side chain}}{|}}{NH_2-CH-COOH} \xrightarrow{\text{enzymes}} \underset{\underset{\text{side chain}}{|}}{CH_2-COOH} + NH_3 + \text{coenzyme}$$

Now the amino acid has become a fatty acid and is available for respiration. (If enough fuel is already available, this fatty acid is combined with glycerol and stored as fat. Thus proteins, as well as fats and carbohydrates, can end up as fat if more is eaten than the body needs to use.)

The ammonia that results from the above reaction is toxic to cells and is immediately converted to urea.

$$2\,NH_3(aq) + CO_2(aq) \longrightarrow NH_2-\overset{\overset{O}{\|}}{C}-NH_2(aq) + H_2O(l)$$

urea

The urea is returned to the blood. Urea isn't as toxic as ammonia, but it must still be removed or it will cause uremic poisoning. The process of removing the waste products of metabolism is called *excretion,* and in human beings is done by the kidneys and urine. Blood constantly filters through the kidneys, like water through a filter pump in an aquarium. The kidneys remove excess water and salt along with urea and various small ions. Over a 24-hour period, the same average adult we've been talking about will produce about 30 grams of urea, 15 grams of sodium chloride, and 15 grams of miscellaneous substances, contained in about 1.5 liters of urine. People on high-protein diets will produce more urea and should drink plenty of water so that the urea can be excreted frequently.

Besides urea, salt and other ions are removed to maintain a constant osmotic pressure of blood. In Chapter 12, we saw that larger amounts of dissolved solutes increase the osmotic pressure of a solution. The osmotic

excretion

pressure of blood is maintained by a hormone called *vasopressin,* which consists of nine amino acids joined together.

$$
\begin{array}{c}
\text{Phe—GluN} \\
\diagup \qquad \diagdown \\
\text{Tyr} \qquad\qquad \text{AspN} \\
\diagdown \qquad\qquad \diagup \\
\text{Cys—S—S—Cys—Pro—Arg—Gly}
\end{array}
$$

Vasopressin

When we eat salted popcorn or peanuts, we get thirsty because of the action of vasopressin. When a lot of salt is consumed, it goes into the blood, raising blood's osmotic pressure and triggering the secretion of vasopressin. Vasopressin represses the production of urine and puts the water back into the blood, lowering its osmotic pressure by diluting the salt. This is only a temporary method, though, and so the thirst response is also turned on. With a fresh supply of water to further dilute the blood, the secretion of vasopressin is turned off and urine is produced normally.

Diuretics are substances that increase urine production. Frequent production of urine removes more solute from the blood and lowers its osmotic pressure. For this reason, diuretics are sometimes given to people with high blood pressure.

diuretic

REVIEW QUESTIONS

Nucleic Acids

1. What are *nucleic acids?* In what part of the cell are they found?
2. What are *chromosomes?* What happens to the chromosomes after a cell divides?
3. What information is contained in DNA? What is a *gene?*
4. What is *replication?* Why must replication occur before a cell divides?
5. How do complementary pairs of monomers hold the two DNA strands together?
6. Describe, with the aid of a sketch, the process of DNA replication.
7. What is RNA? What are its monomers called?
8. Describe and sketch the process of *transcription.*
9. List the three types of RNA and describe the function of each.
10. Explain the relationship among DNA, RNA, and protein.
11. What are *nucleotides?* What are their three parts?
12. What are the differences between the nucleotides found in DNA and those found in RNA?

Proteins

13. What are *proteins?* What are some of their functions in organisms?

14. Give the general structure of an *amino acid.* Show how amino acids are linked in proteins.
15. What is meant by the *genetic code? Codon? Anticodon?*
16. Sketch and describe the process of protein synthesis.
17. Describe the structure of a *fibrous protein.*
18. What amino acid must be present to make a *disulfide bridge?*
19. What are *globular proteins?* What gives them their shape and solubility? Why must they be water soluble?
20. What does it mean to *denature* a protein? What are some ways of denaturing proteins?
21. Why are enzymes needed in biological systems? What is an enzyme's *substrate?* Its *active site?*
22. What are *coenzymes?* Are they always needed? Explain.
23. Explain the relationship among enzyme, substrate, and coenzyme.

Carbohydrates and Fats

24. What is a *carbohydrate?* Name some carbohydrates.
25. What are *monosaccharides?* Give examples.

26. Name three *polysaccharides,* and describe each. Which is used for energy, and which for structure?
27. What are *lipids?* What kind of lipids are found in nerve tissue?
28. What are *steroids? Hormones?* Give some examples of steroid hormones.

Some Biochemical Processes

29. Sketch the biological cycle of elements. What is the key energy source for both plants and animals?
30. What is the first step in photosynthesis? Describe the role of chlorophyll and of coenzymes in photosynthesis.
31. What is meant by *metabolism?*
32. How do cells receive energy from *respiration?* How do they store and use energy?
33. What is the conversion factor between kilocalories and moles of ATP?

34. Do we get more energy from glucose or from fat? What happens to excess glucose or fat that isn't needed for energy?
35. Describe the two parts of hemoglobin. Show where the oxygen is bound.
36. Sketch and describe the respiratory chain.
37. What are *vitamins?* Show how some vitamins are related to coenzymes.
38. What is *digestion?* Why do some substances need to be digested?
39. Describe the digestive process in human beings. Why are bile salts needed?
40. Compare the energy availabilities of starch, glycogen, glucose, and ATP.
41. What happens to amino acids after they reach the cells?
42. What is *excretion?* Why do organisms need to excrete?
43. How does the hormone vasopressin maintain the blood's osmotic pressure?

EXERCISES

1. Suppose one strand of a small segment of DNA has this sequence:

    dA—dA—dT—dC—dT—dC—dG—dT—
    dA—dT—dC—dC—dA—dC—dG—dT—dC

    a. Write the sequence for the complementary strand.
    b. Use diagrams to show how this piece of DNA would be replicated.
2. Assume that the DNA segment in Exercise 1 is the strand that is transcribed into RNA. Write the sequence of the RNA that would be transcribed from it.
3. For this piece of mRNA:

    mU—mU—mG—mG—mG—mC—mA—mU—
    mA—mC—mG—mA—mU—mU

    write the sequence for the DNA strand that would code for its transcription.
4. Arsenic and phosphorus are both in Group V of the periodic table. How might this fact account for arsenic's poisonous nature?
5. Consider these two protein fragments:

    Gly—Ala—Pro—Gly—Gly—Lys—Pro
    Asp—Glu—Lys—Val—His—Ser—Gly

    a. Which would most likely be part of a fibrous protein? A globular protein? Explain.
    b. Which would be the most water soluble, and why?
6. Show what would happen if this polypeptide were mildly oxidized:

    Gly—Cys—Ser—Glu—Gly—Ala—Cys—Met

7. Show where hydrogen bonds might form between amino acid side chains in this polypeptide:

    Ser—Gly—GluN—Gly—Met—Ala—Tyr—Thr
8. Using amino acids that can form disulfide bridges, ionic attractions, and hydrogen bonding, design polypeptide molecules that could have the following shapes.

    a. S-shaped   c. 8-shaped
    b. H-shaped   d. T-shaped
    Use ten or fewer amino acids, and indicate what interactions are causing the structures.
9. The antidote for immediate poisoning with a heavy metal like lead or mercury is to take egg white and then induce vomiting. Why would this work?
10. Write the products of the hydrolysis of the glyceryl ester shown on page 451.
11. House plants placed in dark corners tend to grow greener leaves than those placed in direct sunlight. Suggest a reason for this.
12. Why is magnesium an important plant nutrient?
13. One of the processes by which nucleotides are synthesized in cells requires 9 moles of ATP. How many kilocalories is this?
14. How many moles of oxygen would have to be breathed to produce the equivalent of 100 kilocalories of energy via the respiratory chain?
15. Muscle contains about 5×10^{-6} moles of ATP per gram. Assuming no other source of energy, calculate the amount of energy (kilocalories) available in a 500-gram muscle.

16. Calculate the number of kilocalories of energy that can be obtained from one gram of glucose.

17. Structures of four vitamins are given below.

Vitamin A

Vitamin D

Vitamin B$_6$

Vitamin C

Vitamins A and D tend to collect in fatty tissues, while vitamins B$_6$ and C tend to be excreted in urine. Suggest structural features of these vitamins that would explain this behavior.

18. The earth's atmosphere contains about 2×10^{12} metric tons of CO_2. If this were all converted to glucose via photosynthesis, calculate the following.
   a. the metric tons of glucose that could be produced
   b. the moles of ATP this could yield in metabolism
   c. the energy equivalent in kilocalories

19. Trace the path of the following through the digestive process.

   a. the triglyceride

   b. table sugar (sucrose)
   c. muscle protein (meat)
   d. cellulose

20. Insulin, a protein hormone used for the treatment of diabetes, must be administered by injection. Explain why it is not effective if taken orally.

21. Calculate the effect of 0.001 moles of adrenalin on a blood-sugar level that starts at 60 mg/ml. Assume a total blood volume of 5 liters.

22. How much energy, in kilocalories, would be produced in Exercise 21?

23. Papain, an enzyme that hydrolyzes protein, is the active ingredient in meat tenderizer. Explain its function.

24. "Enyzme detergents" contained enzymes that hydrolyze proteins and thus destroy protein stains. However, these detergents had to be removed from the market because many people suffered respiratory irritation from breathing the dust. Suggest a reason for this undesirable side effect.

25. How much urea would be produced by removing the amino acid group from 1 gram of glycine?

26. Alcohol represses the secretion of vasopressin. With this in mind, explain why people urinate frequently while drinking liquor and then wake up thirsty the "morning after."

27. Vasopressin is sometimes used to prevent low blood pressure caused by shock following surgery. Explain how this might work.

28. Since fatty acids are slightly better energy sources than carbohydrates, why do we depend on carbohydrates and not on fats for energy? Explain what would happen to the biological cycle if suddenly no carbohydrates were available to animals.

APPENDIX A
WORKING WITH NUMBERS

A.1 ROUNDING OFF

Suppose you're buying a new electronic calculator to help you in this chemistry course. The price is $14.95. The local sales tax is 3.5%. Just for fun, you try out your new calculator to figure out how much the tax will be. When you push 14.95 × .035 =, the calculator gives an answer of 0.52325. What's this? The clerk looks at the tax table and says, "That's $14.95, plus 52 cents tax." Of course. Obviously you can't pay fractions of a cent, because cents are the smallest unit of money we have. So, the answer on the tax table has been rounded off to the nearest cent.

Many times in chemistry we'll need to round off numbers. *Rounding off* means eliminating all digits to the right of a specified place and then adjusting the numbers in the places to the left to reflect this change. Rules for rounding off, with examples, are shown in Table A.1.

rounding off

A.2 SIGNIFICANT FIGURES

WHAT THEY ARE. For any object that's being measured, the accuracy of the measurement is limited by the measuring device. You might get on the bathroom scale and say, "I weigh 125 pounds," but not, "I weigh 125.456 pounds." The lines on most bathroom scales only occur at every pound, and we can only guess at the nearest pound. The last figure—the nearest pound—is uncertain.

The last figure in any measurement is always uncertain. For instance, an automobile odometer usually gives mileage to the nearest tenth of a mile.

	Example	*Round to*	*Answer*
Rule 1. If the number to be eliminated is 5 or greater, add 1 to the number in front of it.	$3.489	Nearest cent	$3.49
	$3503.75	Nearest dollar	$3504
	93.99	One decimal place	94.0
	11595	Three digits	11600
Rule 2. If the number to be eliminated is less than five, drop it.	$4.5219	Nearest cent	$4.52
	$97.34	Nearest dollar	$97
	5.54	One decimal place	5.5
	0.05453	Three digits	0.0545

TABLE A.1
Rules for rounding off, with examples

If we want to know the mileage at any given time, we might look at the odometer and see something like this:

| 1 | 1 | 4 | 5 | 0 | 3/4 |

The last number is between 3 and 4. We can only guess at whether it's closer to the 3 or to the 4, and certainly we wouldn't know whether it's 11450.32 or 11450.36. The best we can do is guess at the first decimal place, but we do know that it's either a 3 or a 4. This figure is uncertain.

significant figure

Significant figures are the figures in any measurement that we know accurately, plus one figure that is uncertain. If we decide that the last digit above is a 4, then 11450.4 is our number. This number contains six significant figures: the first five are known accurately and the last, 4, is uncertain but significant. This case is easy to understand, but some won't be. We need a set of rules for deciding how many significant figures a number has. Table A.2 lists and illustrates significant figure rules.

MULTIPLYING AND DIVIDING WITH SIGNIFICANT FIGURES.

Suppose that, in the course of trying out your new calculator, you do this operation: 7 divided by 3 times 3. Your calculator gives you the answer 6.9999999. This is puzzling, because you know that if you set it up as a fraction, the threes would cancel, like this:

$$\frac{7 \times \cancel{3}}{\cancel{3}} = 7$$

Clearly, the answer should be 7, but you got a six and all those nines instead. We can see why this happened if we take the operation in steps. Dividing 7 by 3 gives us 2.3333333 (the calculator cut it off at eight significant figures). If we then multiply 2.3333333 by 3, we of course get 6.9999999. The calculator didn't know that we were going to give it another 3 to cancel with the previous 3. We know, though, that we should round off this number to 7 and not keep it at 6.9999999.

The point is that when we're working with an electronic calculator, many times it'll give us an answer with far more places than we're justified in keeping. But how do we always know how many places we *are* justified in keeping? The example above is simple and obvious, but most are not. The rule for multiplying and dividing with significant figures is that the answer can't have more significant figures than the input number that has the fewest significant figures. When the calculator gives us more figures than this, we round off the calculator answer to the correct number of significant figures. Table A.3 illustrates how to use this rule.

ADDING AND SUBTRACTING WITH SIGNIFICANT FIGURES.

When the president talks about the projected budget for the coming year, numbers like 52 billion dollars get thrown around right and left. These numbers are rounded numbers, because they're only an estimate.

Table A.2
Significant figure rules, with examples

Rule	Example	Number of Significant Figure	Reason
1. Always begin counting significant figures with the first nonzero integer.	0.0000345	Three: 3, 4, and 5.	3 is the first nonzero integer.
2. All nonzero integers are significant.	1543	Four: 1, 5, 4, and 3.	All are integers.
3. **Zeros.**			
a. A zero is significant if it is not needed to fix the decimal point.	24.00	Four: 2, 4, 0, and 0.	Both zeros are significant. Writing 24 without them still places the decimal in the same spot.
	27,000	Two: 2 and 7.	These zeros are not significant because we do need them to fix the decimal point.
	0.004500	Four: 4, 5, 0, and 0.	The end zeros are significant. Writing 0.0045 without them still places the decimal in the same spot.
b. A decimal point placed after the end zeros in a number greater than one makes those zeros significant.	500.	Three: 5, 0, and 0.	Zeros before the point are significant. Without the point, they wouldn't be.
c. A zero between two significant figures is significant.	1.0087	Five: 1, 0, 0, 8, and 7.	The two zeros are between the 1 and the 8, both of which are significant.

Suppose we then ask, "How will an additional expenditure of $3.47 for coffee cups affect the projected budget?" We might add it like this:

$$\begin{array}{r} 52{,}000{,}000{,}000 \\ 3.47 \\ \hline 52{,}000{,}000{,}003.47 \end{array}$$

Is this reasonable? No: 52 billion has only two significant figures, and we're trying to add 3.47 out there in the noise. 52,000,000,000 plus 3.47 is still 52,000,000,000.

TABLE A.3 Examples of multiplying and dividing with significant figures

Example	Calculator Answer	Limiting Input Number	No. Significant Figures	Corrected Answer
Rule: In multiplication or division, the answer may not have more significant figures than the input number that has the fewest significant figures.				
$2.36 \times 3.4 = ?$	8.024	3.4	2	8.0
$2.00 \times 0.003345 = ?$	0.00669	2.00	3	0.00669
$5.040 \times 3000 = ?$	15120	3000	1	20000
$6251 \times 93.0 = ?$	581343	93.0	3	581000
$\dfrac{11.95}{3.00} = ?$	3.9833333	3.00	3	3.98
$\dfrac{0.555}{9.070} = ?$	0.0611907	0.555	3	0.0612
$\dfrac{45.9}{15{,}000} = ?$	0.00306	15,000	2	0.0031
$\dfrac{5}{3.0} = ?$	1.6666666	5	1	2
$\dfrac{2100.0}{7.0000} = ?$	300	Either	5	300.00[a]

[a]Electronic calculators often do not give final zeroes that are significant. These must be added if they are needed, as they are in this case.

In adding and subtracting, we round off the answer to the first column that contains an uncertain digit. In the operation above, we see that the second column (2) is the first one that has an uncertain digit, so our answer can't have any significant figures after that. Table A.4 illustrates this rule.

PURE NUMBERS.

pure number

We've seen how to handle numbers used with measurements. Some things, though, can be counted exactly. These are *pure numbers.* If we counted four apples, the number would be exactly four, no more and no less. We can write the number as simply 4, or as 4.00, or with as many zeros after the decimal as we want or need in calculations. Numbers that are defined exactly are also pure numbers. An example is the atomic weight of carbon-12, which is defined as 12, or 12.00000. . . . We'll see later that some conversion factors are known as pure numbers because they're defined.

When we work with these pure numbers in problems, we may find that we want to alter the number of significant figures they seem to contain. This will be so when we're multiplying a pure number by a measured number that has limited significant figures. A pure number never limits the number of significant figures an answer can have.

A.3 NEGATIVE NUMBERS

One of the added bonuses of your new calculator is that you can use it to compute your checking account balance. Your computation might look something like this:

		Running Balance
Starting balance	134.56	
Electronic calculator	−15.47	119.09
Chemistry book	−13.95	105.14
Aspirin, No-Doz	−5.43	99.71
Room and board	−125.00	−25.29
New balance	−25.29	

TABLE A.4 Examples of adding and subtracting with significant figures

Example	Column with Uncertain Digit		Answer
Rule: In addition and subtraction, the answer must be rounded off to the first column that contains an uncertain digit.			
6.54 + 1.2766 = ?	6.54 1.2766 7.8166	Third column	7.82
9.5433 − 0.002 = ?	9.5433 − 0.002 9.5413	Fourth column	9.541
5400 + 0.122 = ?	5400 0.122 5400.122	Second column	5400[a]
155 + 100 + 206 = ?	155 100 206 461	First column	500
47,000 − 368 = ?	47000 − 368 46632	Second column	47,000
500. + 12 = ?	500. 12 512	Third column	512

[a]Note that the small addition is insignificant.

Your calculator gives you an answer with a negative sign. What does that mean? It means that you're overdrawn. You'll have to go and quickly deposit at least 25.29 to cover yourself.

algebraic addition   A calculator adds numbers algebraically. To *add algebraically* means to combine two or more numbers according to their signs (+ or −). If we're adding a positive number and a negative number, the result will be the dif-

TABLE A.5
Examples of algebraic addition and subtraction

Operation	Calculator Setup	Manual Setup	Explanation
Add 3.4 to 4.3.	$3.4 + 4.3 = 7.7$ or $4.3 + 3.4 = 7.7$	3.4 + 4.3 ——— 7.7	Signs of both numbers are (+).
Subtract 3.4 from 4.3.	$4.3 - 3.4 = 0.9$ or $-3.4 + 4.3 = 0.9$	4.3 − 3.4 ——— 0.9	"Subtract 3.4" means that 3.4 becomes −3.4. Numbers may be given to calculator in any order.
Subtract 4.3 from 3.4.	$3.4 - 4.3 = -0.9$ or $-4.3 + 3.4 = -0.9$	−4.3 3.4 ——— −0.9	Since the negative number is larger than the positive number, the answer is negative.
Add (−3.4) to 4.3.	$-3.4 + 4.3 = 0.9$ or $4.3 - 3.4 = 0.9$	4.3 −3.4 ——— 0.9	Numbers are combined according to their signs.
Subtract (−3.4) from 4.3.	$4.3 + 3.4 = 7.7$ or $3.4 + 4.3 = 7.7$	4.3 − (−3.4) ——— 7.7	"Subtract (−3.4)" means that − (−3.4) becomes (+3.4). We change the sign and add.
Subtract (−3.4) from (−4.3).	$-4.3 + 3.4 = -0.9$ or $3.4 - 4.3 = -0.9$	−4.3 − (−3.4) ——— −0.9	Again, a − (−3.4) becomes +3.4.
Add (−3.4) to (−4.3).	$-3.4 - 4.3 = -7.7$ or $-4.3 - 3.4 = -7.7$	−3.4 −4.3 ——— −7.7	Both numbers are negative. Their sum is negative.
Add 3.4 to −4.3.	$3.4 - 4.3 = -0.9$ or $-4.3 + 3.4 = -0.9$	−4.3 + 3.4 ——— −0.9	Again, answer is negative because negative number is larger than positive number.

ference between the two numbers. The sign of the answer depends on whether the positive number or the negative number is larger.

To illustrate this, imagine two towns: Town A, at elevation 2000 feet, and Town B, at 8000 feet. If we ask the question, "How much higher is Town B than Town A?" the answer is "6000 feet." But if we ask, "How much higher is Town A than Town B?" the answer is "−6000 feet." Our answer has a negative sign because Town A is *lower* than Town B. Positive and negative signs are an indication of direction. The difference in elevation between the two towns is always 6000 feet, but its sign can be + or − depending on which direction we take.

To *subtract* means to change the sign and add algebraically. Table A.5 illustrates various possibilities of addition and subtraction.

subtraction

A.4 EXPONENTIAL NOTATION

WRITING NUMBERS AS EXPONENTIALS.

Try multiplying Avogadro's number, 602,000,000,000,000,000,000,000, by anything. We can't even get that huge number onto a calculator. A calculator doesn't have enough windows. And why should it? We only need calculator windows for significant figures, and few measurement numbers even approach eight significant figures. All of those zeros are just excess baggage—important, of course, but something we can just count and set aside. We count them and keep track of them by writing them in *exponential notation*. We can write that huge number above as 6.02×10^{23}. The "10^{23}" is read, "ten to the twenty-third." The "23" is an *exponent* or *power* of ten. It tells us the number of times ten has to be multiplied by itself. To get the exponent, we count the number of places to the left that the decimal point must be moved (in this case, 23) in order to put it after the first significant figure (in this case, 6).

Exponential notation can be used for very small numbers, too: for example, 0.00000000000000000000000167. In exponential notation, this is 1.67×10^{-24}. The "10^{-24}" is read, "ten to the minus twenty-fourth." To get this exponent, we count the number of places to the right that the decimal point must be moved (in this case, 24) in order to put it after the first significant figure (in this case, 1).

We see that here, too, positive and negative signs indicate direction. A negative exponent always means a number less than 1—that is, the original decimal point lies to the left of the first significant figure. A positive exponent always means a number greater than 1—that is, the original decimal point lies to the right of the first significant figure.

Numbers between 1 and 10 are usually written without exponents, but they could also be written as multiples of 10^0 ($10^0 = 1$). Whether the number is less than or greater than 1, we always put the decimal point after the

exponential notation

exponent (power)

first significant figures in the number. Thus we write "6.02 × 10²³" instead of "60.2 × 10²²" or "0.602 × 10²⁴," although they all mean the same thing.

SIGNIFICANT FIGURES AND EXPONENTIAL NOTATION.

coefficient

exponential

exponent

All digits in the coefficient of an exponential number are significant. The coefficient and other parts of an exponential number are shown below.

$$\text{coefficient} \longrightarrow 6.02 \times 10^{23} \longleftarrow \text{exponent}$$
$$\underbrace{\qquad\qquad}_{\text{exponential}}$$

Now we can show significant figures easily, by writing numbers in exponential notation. We also see that we can now specify significant figures for some numbers that we couldn't do any other way—for instance, expressing a number like 7,000 to two significant figures. We write this as 7.0×10^3, and there is no doubt as to how many significant figures this number has. We can't do it in its nonexponential form. Table A.6 shows some cases.

JUSTIFICATION OF EXPONENTIAL NUMBERS.

justification

An exponential number is *justified* when the decimal point of the coefficient appears directly after the first significant figure. 6.02×10^{23} is justified; 60.2×10^{22} is not. When we write numbers directly from the nonexponential form, they'll be justified. But often the answer that we get by adding, subtracting, multiplying, or dividing two or more exponential numbers will not be justified. The last step, therefore, is justifying the answer.

To justify a number, first write the coefficient itself as an exponential. Then multiply the two exponentials together. Multiplying exponentials is easy: we just add the exponents. For example, to justify 669×10^{-2}, we write:

TABLE A.6 Exponential numbers, their nonexponential forms, and significant figures

Exponential Number	Nonexponential Form	Number of Significant Figures
3.47×10^3	3470	Three: 3, 4, and 7.
1.2×10^{-2}	0.012	Two: 1 and 2.
9.000×10^3	9000.	Four: 9, 0, 0, and 0.
6.720×10^5	67200	Four: 6, 7, 2, and 0. Note that this number cannot specify its significant figures in the nonexponential form.
8.14×10^{-4}	0.000814	Three: 8, 1, and 4.
1×10^2	100	One: 1.
1.000×10^2	100.0	Four: 1, 0, 0, and 0.

$$(6.69 \times 10^2)(10^{-2}) = 6.69 \times 10^0 = 6.69$$

We added the exponents like this: $2 - 2 = 0$. We'll talk about multiplication and division of exponentials in the next section.

MULTIPLYING AND DIVIDING WITH EXPONENTIAL NUMBERS.
To multiply exponential numbers, we multiply the coefficients and add the exponents algebraically. To divide exponential numbers, we divide the coefficient in the numerator by the coefficient in the denominator. We subtract the exponent in the denominator from the exponent in the numerator. Table A.7 shows multiplication and division of exponential numbers, with justification of answers.

Some calculators are equipped to handle exponentials. Instructions vary from one calculator to the other, so it's best to consult the instruction manual.

ADDING AND SUBTRACTING WITH EXPONENTIAL NUMBERS.
To add and subtract exponential numbers, the exponents have to be the same. If they aren't, then we have to change one of the exponents so that it is the same as the other exponent. Then we add and sub-

Table A.7
Multiplication and division of exponential numbers, with justified answers

| Example | Coefficient Answer | | Exponent Answer | Full Answer |
	Calculator	Corrected		
$3.55 \times 10^4 \times 2.05 \times 10^3 = ?$	7.2775	7.28	$10^{(4+3)} = 10^7$	7.28×10^7
$4.32 \times 10^{-1} \times 1.19 \times 10^{-7} = ?$	5.1408	5.14	$10^{(-1-7)} = 10^{-8}$	5.14×10^{-8}
$6.4 \times 10^{-2} \times 9.88 \times 10^8 = ?$	63.232	63	$10^{(-2+8)} = 10^6$	63×10^6 $(6.3 \times 10^1)(10^6) =$ 6.3×10^7
$\dfrac{10.1 \times 10^7}{5.22 \times 10^2} = ?$	1.9348659	1.93	$10^{(7-2)} = 10^5$	1.93×10^5
$\dfrac{4.21 \times 10^{-4}}{8.22 \times 10^{-2}} = ?$	0.5121654	0.512	$10^{(-4-(-2))} = 10^{-2}$	0.512×10^{-2} $(5.12 \times 10^{-1})(10^6) =$ 5.12×10^{-3}
$\dfrac{8.2 \times 10^3}{2.6 \times 10^5} = ?$	3.1538461	3.2	$10^{(3-5)} = 10^{-2}$	3.15×10^{-2}
$\dfrac{1.02 \times 10^{-2}}{9.75 \times 10^{-8}} = ?$	0.1046153	0.105	$10^{(-2-(-8))} = 10^6$	$0.105 \times 10^6 =$ $(1.05 \times 10^{-1})(10^6) =$ 1.05×10^5

tract the coefficients, but we *don't* add and subtract the exponents. One rule of thumb for deciding which exponent to change is to change the exponent of the smaller number. This usually eliminates the need to justify the answer.

Changing an exponent is simply *un*justifying the number. We reverse the steps that we took to justify numbers. For instance, if we want to write 6.02×10^{23} as some number times 10^{20}, we do it this way:

$$6.02 \times 10^{23} = (6.02)(10^3)(10^{20}) = 6020 \times 10^{20}$$

Table A.8 shows problems in adding and subtracting, with and without changing exponents.

We notice that when exponents are very far apart relative to the numbers of significant figures in the coefficients, the smaller number becomes insignificant. What if you tried to do this: you get on the bathroom scale and weigh yourself. Then you get on the same scale with a letter, and you try to see how much more the letter weighs to know the postage. Ridiculous. The accuracy of a bathroom scale doesn't even come close to the weight of the letter, so you'd notice no difference. We don't usually add or subtract very large numbers with very small numbers, because the effect of the small number is lost.

A.5 APPROXIMATE ANSWERS

Another use you've discovered for your new electronic calculator is in the grocery store. You can add up the contents of your shopping cart as you go

Table A.8
Addition and subtraction of exponential numbers

Example	Change	To	Method	Solution	Correct, Justified Answer
4.35×10^3 $+9.22 \times 10^3$?	No change. Both exponents are the same.			4.35×10^3 $+9.22 \times 10^3$ 13.57×10^3	1.357×10^4
2.79×10^3 -1.62×10^2 ?	1.62×10^2	? $\times 10^3$	$(1.62)(10^{-1})(10^3)$ $= 0.162 \times 10^3$	2.79×10^3 -0.162×10^3 2.628×10^3	2.63×10^3
6.44×10^{-4} -2.33×10^{-5} ?	2.33×10^{-5}	? $\times 10^{-4}$	$(2.33)(10^{-1})(10^{-4})$ $= 0.233 \times 10^{-4}$	6.44×10^{-4} -0.233×10^{-4} 6.207×10^{-4}	6.21×10^{-4}
8.65×10^5 $+2.28 \times 10^2$?	2.28×10^2	? $\times 10^5$	$(2.28)(10^{-3})(10^5)$ $= 0.00228 \times 10^5$	8.65×10^5 $+0.00228 \times 10^5$ 8.65228×10^5	8.65×10^5 [a]

[a]Note that 2.28×10^2 is insignificant compared with 8.65×10^5.

along, so that you don't spend too much money. But, unfortunately, today you accidentally left it at home. You only have $5 to spend and you want to make sure you don't go over that amount. You estimate the cost of your groceries like this: One dozen eggs at 59¢—that's about 60¢; a head of lettuce, 29¢ (about 30¢)—90¢ so far. A box of crackers is 83¢ (about 80¢)—$1.70 so far. One T-bone steak is $2.46 (about $2.50)—that's $4.20 so far. Probably can get a pound of potatoes for 35¢ (about 40¢). That comes to approximately $4.60. When you check out, the register slip says $4.52, plus 16¢ tax: $4.68. Whew, just made it.

In chemistry, we need to be able to do approximate calculations like that. It's handy if we don't happen to have a calculator, and it's useful even if we do. In doing a calculation that involves a long string of numbers, it's easy to push the wrong button in one or more of the operations, and get the wrong answer. We'd never know whether or not this happened unless we had some feeling for what sort of answer we were expecting. For instance, in the example above, you were expecting an answer of about $4.60,

TABLE A.9
Approximate answers

Example	Approximate Answer	Calculator Answer	Conclusion
$454 \times 22.4 = ?$	$5 \times 10^2 \times 2 \times 10^1 =$ $10 \times 10^3 = 1 \times 10^4$	$10169.6 =$ 1.02×10^4	OK
$\dfrac{1.986}{760} = ?$	$\dfrac{1}{\dfrac{\cancel{2}}{\cancel{8} \times 10^2}} = 0.25 \times 10^{-2} = 3 \times 10^{-3}$	$0.0026131 =$ 2.6×10^{-3}	OK
$22.4 \times \dfrac{749}{760} = ?$	$2 \times 10^1 \times \dfrac{\cancel{7} \times \cancel{10^2}}{\cancel{7} \times \cancel{10^2}} = 2 \times 10^1$	$22.075789 =$ 2.21×10^1	OK
$\dfrac{18.9}{111 \times 100.} = ?$	$\dfrac{2 \times 10^1}{1 \times 10^2 \times 1 \times 10^2} = 2 \times 10^{-3}$	$0.0017027 =$ 1.70×10^{-3}	OK
$\dfrac{1.45 \times 62.4 \times 298}{1.00 \times 756} = ?$	$\dfrac{3}{\dfrac{1 \times \cancel{6} \times 10^1 \times 3 \times 10^2}{1 \times \cancel{8} \times 10^2}} = \dfrac{9}{4} \times 10^1 =$ 2×10^1	$20384058 =$ 2.04×10^7	Something is wrong. Answers differ too much. Do calculator answer again.
		$35.665396 =$ 3.57×10^1	OK now.
$\dfrac{0.0821 \times 11.2 \times 40.0}{273 \times 2.98 \times 0.760} = ?$	$\dfrac{\cancel{8} \times 10^{-2} \times 1 \times 10^1 \times 4 \times 10^1}{3 \times 10^2 \times 3 \times \cancel{8} \times 10^{-4}} =$ $\dfrac{4}{9} \times 10^{-1} = 5 \times 10^{-2}$	$0.0594879 =$ 5.95×10^{-2}	OK

more or less. If the clerk had said, "$46.80, please," you'd have known that something was wrong with the cash register, the clerk, or your approximate answer.

To do approximate calculations, first simultaneously round off each number to one significant figure and express it as an exponential. Then compute the answer in your head, rounding off any intermediate steps to the nearest single significant figure. Cancel numbers or exponents above and below the fraction line wherever possible. If the calculator answer is way out of line with the approximate answer, you should check both the calculator answer and the approximate answer. Table A.9 shows how to calculate approximate answers and relate them to calculator answers.

EXERCISES

Note: The answers and numerical solutions for the first half of the questions in each multi-part question are provided on p. 508.

1. Round off the following numbers as indicated.
   a. 3.489 to two decimal places
   b. 45.219 to one decimal place
   c. 67,432 to the nearest thousand
   d. $3.42 to the nearest dollar
   e. 0.122 to two decimal places

2. State the number of significant figures in each of the following.
   a. 0.00123   e. 8.040
   b. 6789   f. 98600
   c. 0.0070   g. 200.
   d. 9.87   h. 101.0

3. Perform these operations, and correct the significant figures.
   a. $3.0 \times 4.00 =$ e. $12.00/2.0 =$
   b. $6.00 \times 10.0 =$ f. $8.0/2.00 =$
   c. $2.000 \times 0.0017 =$ g. $9.54/2000 =$
   d. $400 \times 1.98 =$

4. Perform these operations, and correct the significant figures.

   a. $\begin{array}{r} 3.980 \\ +0.001 \\ \hline \end{array}$ d. $\begin{array}{r} 777.12 \\ -98.1 \\ \hline \end{array}$

   b. $\begin{array}{r} 54.09 \\ +0.230 \\ \hline \end{array}$ e. $\begin{array}{r} 9.12 \\ +11.9760 \\ \hline \end{array}$

   c. $\begin{array}{r} 143.9 \\ -40. \\ \hline \end{array}$ f. $\begin{array}{r} 12.0 \\ -9.4711 \\ \hline \end{array}$

5. In arithmetic, we learned that $4 \times 4 = 16$. Is this always true when we're talking about scientific measurements? What circumstances would cause this equality to not be true?

6. Add algebraically.
   a. $8.2 - 4.3 =$ e. $-4.6 + 9.0 =$
   b. $9.7 + 2.2 =$ f. $-6.6 - 4.7 =$
   c. $6.2 - 10.2 =$ g. $4.4 - (-1.9) =$
   d. $-3.3 + 2.1 =$ h. $-(-3.2) - 2.2 =$

7. Subtract.
   a. 3.3 from 7.9   e. -3 from 6
   b. 7.9 from 3.3   f. 2.7 from (-1.3)
   c. 0.2 from (-7.7) g. (-9.8) from 3.3
   d. -2 from -4 h. (-3) from (-5)

8. Write these numbers in exponential notation with the correct number of significant figures.
   a. 52800   d. 0.0000000650
   b. 0.00000897   e. 980
   c. 21000   f. 6

9. State the number of significant figures in each of the following, and justify.
   a. 39.8×10^7 d. 101.0×10^{-3}
   b. 4.30×10^4 e. 454×10^2
   c. 0.198×10^{-3} f. 233×10^{-9}

10. Perform the following multiplications, and justify the answers (use the correct number of significant figures).
    a. $(1.03 \times 10^{-5}) \times (7.22 \times 10^2) =$
    b. $(4.87 \times 10^9) \times (9.22 \times 10^{10}) =$
    c. $(6.34 \times 10^{-2}) \times (2.37 \times 10^{-3}) =$
    d. $(5.61 \times 10^{22}) \times (6.02 \times 10^{23}) =$

11. Perform the following divisions, and justify the answers (use the correct number of significant figures).

    a. $\dfrac{4.18 \times 10^8}{2.63 \times 10^2} =$ c. $\dfrac{7.23 \times 10^{-4}}{3.49 \times 10^2} =$

    b. $\dfrac{5.99 \times 10^2}{9.81 \times 10^6} =$ d. $\dfrac{3.75 \times 10^8}{4.99 \times 10^{-2}} =$

12. Perform the following additions or subtractions, and justify the answers (use the correct number of significant figures).

a. $\begin{aligned} & 1.22 \times 10^{-5} \\ & -3.45 \times 10^{-5} \end{aligned}$

d. $\begin{aligned} & 5.72 \times 10^{-9} \\ & +4.61 \times 10^{-10} \end{aligned}$

b. $\begin{aligned} & 4.68 \times 10^{4} \\ & +3.99 \times 10^{3} \end{aligned}$

e. $\begin{aligned} & 8.53 \times 10^{-2} \\ & -6.47 \times 10^{-3} \end{aligned}$

c. $\begin{aligned} & 2.97 \times 10^{-4} \\ & -3.42 \times 10^{-3} \end{aligned}$

f. $\begin{aligned} & 1.46 \times 10^{5} \\ & +7.21 \times 10^{6} \end{aligned}$

13. Compute approximate answers.

a. $0.0234 \times 34.6 =$

d. $\dfrac{2.58 \times 88.7}{0.333} =$

b. $\dfrac{5670}{19.8} =$

e. $\dfrac{5.95}{3.4 \times 75.2} =$

c. $22.4 \times 760 \times 273 =$

f. $\dfrac{4.42 \times 189}{0.0012 \times 450} =$

g. $\dfrac{79.8 \times 0.221 \times 899}{3.34 \times 454 \times 1.986} =$

14. By computing approximate answers, state which of the following calculator answers are incorrect.

a. $98.6 \times 2.54 \times 454 = 113701.57$

b. $\dfrac{22.4 \times 32 \times 23.0}{760 \times 2.2 \times 0.0821} = 69370302$

c. $\dfrac{44.0 \times 0.621 \times 8700}{77.2 \times 3 \times 88.0} = 11.663859$

d. $\dfrac{33.8 \times 0.11}{6.02 \times 10^{23}} = 0.6176079 \times 10^{-23}$

e. $\dfrac{1752 \times 1.67 \times 10^{-24} \times 888}{5.75 \times 98.0 \times 3.4 \times 10^{10}} = 15676.478 \times 10^{-34}$

15. For the correct answers in Exercise 14, express the calculator answer in justified exponential form with corrected significant figures.

APPENDIX B
WORKING WITH UNITS

In scientific calculations, each number usually has a label, which we call a unit. In mathematics, people work just with numbers, such as $2 \times 3 = 6$, but in science we usually want to know, "2 what? 3 what? 6 what?" The unit is the "what." A *unit* is a word or words that describe what is being measured or counted. It can be anything at all: 2 dollars, 2 atoms, 2 kilometers.

In Appendix A, working with numbers alone is discussed. In this appendix, we'll work with units that usually come with numbers. All the rules for working with numbers will be followed here. Appropriate sections of Appendix A should be consulted, if necessary, to find out about numbers.

B.1 METRIC UNITS

metric system

Scientists (including American and British scientists) use the metric system of units. The *metric system* is a decimal system of weights and measures based on the kilogram and on the meter. For us Americans, the metric system may at first seem more difficult than the English system, which we're used to. At the time of this writing, steps are being taken to convert the United States to the metric system, which really is much simpler and more convenient.

Our money system is a decimal system: 100 cents to the dollar. To change from one of these money units to the other, all we have to do is move a decimal point two places. Moving a decimal point two places to the right is the same as multiplying by 10^2, and moving a decimal point two places to the left is the same as multiplying by 10^{-2}. (For a review of exponential numbers, see Appendix A.4, p. 472.) The metric system is about as easy, once we've studied it awhile. Like our money system, we move a decimal point to change from one unit to another.

METRIC PREFIXES. In the metric system, there are prefixes that tell us what to multiply a given unit by to get another unit, just as we know to multiply dollars by 10^2 to get cents and cents by 10^{-2} to get dollars. Table B.1 shows the metric prefixes expressed as exponentials as well as rational (fractional) numbers. For instance, the prefix *centi-* tells us to multiply by 10^{-2} (or to divide by 100). That's where the word "cent" comes from. The prefix *kilo-* means to multiply by 10^3, or 1000. The prefix *milli-* means to multiply by 10^{-3} (or to divide by 1000).

TABLE B.1
Metric prefixes and their origins

Prefix	Symbol	Means Multiply by Exponential	Means Multiply by Rational	Origin	Original Meaning
exa-	E	10^{18}	1,000,000,000,000,000,000	Greek "hexa"	Six groups of three zeros
peta-	P	10^{15}	1,000,000,000,000,000	Greek "penta"	Five groups of three zeros
tera-	T	10^{12}	1,000,000,000,000	Greek	Monstrous
giga-	G	10^{9}	1,000,000,000	Greek	Gigantic
mega-	M	10^{6}	1,000,000	Greek	Great
kilo-	k	10^{3}	1,000	Greek	Thousand
hecto-	h	10^{2}	100	Greek	Hundred
deca-	da	10^{1}	10	Greek	Ten
deci-	d	10^{-1}	1/10	Latin	Tenth
centi-	c	10^{-2}	1/100	Latin	Hundredth
milli-	m	10^{-3}	1/1000	Latin	Thousandth
micro-	μ	10^{-6}	1/1,000,000	Greek	Small
nano-	n	10^{-9}	1/1,000,000,000	Greek	Very small
pico-	p	10^{-12}	1/1,000,000,000,000	Spanish	Extremely small
femto-	f	10^{-15}	1/1,000,000,000,000,000	Scandinavian	Fifteen
atto-	a	10^{-18}	1/1,000,000,000,000,000,000	Scandinavian	Eighteen

SI UNITS.

The International Bureau of Weights and Measures in 1960 established a system of units to simplify communication among all scientists throughout the world. This is called the *International System of Units* (abbreviated SI, for the French Système International). It's constructed from seven basic units, given in Table B.2. The SI system recognizes other units derived from these, shown in Table B.3. Larger or smaller units from the basic or derived units should preferably be in multiples of three powers of ten. Thus the metric prefixes *deca-, deci-,* and *centi-* aren't technically approved SI prefixes. However, they were introduced before the SI system

TABLE B.2
Basic SI units

Unit	Symbol	Physical Quantity
Meter	m	Length
Kilogram	kg	Mass
Second	s (sec)	Time
Ampere[a]	A (amp)	Electric current
Kelvin	K	Temperature
Candela[a]	cd	Light intensity
Mole	mol	Amount of substance

[a]These units are not used in this book.

**TABLE B.3
Units derived
from
basic SI units**

Unit	Symbol	Physical Quantity	Definition
Newton[a]	N	Force	$(kg \times m)/s^2$
Pascal[a]	Pa	Pressure	N/m^2
Joule[a]	J	Energy	$(kg \times m^2)/s^2$
Coulomb[a]	C	Electric charge	$A \times s$
Cubic meter[a]	m^3	Volume	m^3

[a]These units are not used in this book.

was established, and they are sometimes tolerated. Other units that were introduced before the SI system are still used by scientists, but some are recommended to be phased out. At the time of this writing, though, many of these units are still in use by chemists because of their greater convenience. Table B.4 shows commonly used units, both SI and non-SI. Values in terms of SI units are given, as well as useful conversion factors.

**conversion
factor**

A *conversion factor* is a factor that tells how many of a given unit is contained in exactly one of another unit. If we say that there are 1000 grams in a kilogram, the conversion factor is 1000 grams per kilogram, written 1000 g/kg, or 10^3 g/kg. To find a conversion factor in kilograms per gram (kg/g), we just invert the previous conversion factor, like this:

$$\frac{10^3 \text{ g}}{\text{kg}} \text{ inverted is } \frac{1 \text{ kg}}{10^3 \text{ g}} = \frac{10^{-3} \text{ kg}}{\text{g}}$$

We see that inverting a metric conversion factor changes the sign of the power of ten (Appendix A.4, p. 475). Conversion factors in both directions are given in Table B.4.

SIGNIFICANT FIGURES IN THE METRIC SYSTEM.

Conversion factors within a system of measurement are defined numbers. One kilogram contains *exactly* 1×10^3 (or 1000) grams, because a gram is defined that way. These conversion factors are pure numbers. (See Appendix A.2, p. 470). Thus we can write 10^3 g/kg as 1.00×10^3 g/1.00 kg, or with as many zeros after the decimal as we want or need in calculations. Defined conversion factors never limit the number of significant figures that an answer may have.

B.2 NONMETRIC UNITS

Since we live in the United States, which uses nonmetric units, and we're studying chemistry, which uses metric units, we need to be able to convert between the two systems. In addition, there are many other conversions that we'll need to be able to do in chemistry.

Table B.5 shows some useful metric-nonmetric conversion factors. These have all been exactly defined in terms of SI units. For convenience, we list these to only three significant figures. For example, the conversion factor between pounds and kilograms is exactly 0.45359237 kg/lb. We round this off to 0.454 kg/lb to make it more manageable. (For a discussion of rounding off, see Appendix A.1, p. 467). Thus these metric-nonmetric conversion factors aren't pure numbers, as the metric-metric conversion factors are. We can't write 0.4540 kg/lb just because we need four significant figures. If more significant figures are needed, another table can be consulted. (We *can*, however, assume that the bottom unit has as many significant figures as the top one. Thus 0.454 kg/lb is the same as 0.454 kg/1.00 lb.) The conversion factors that are expressed in the table to three significant figures can limit the number of significant figures an answer may have.

Table B.4
Some commonly used metric units and their conversion factors

Basic SI Unit	Conversion Factors		SI Conversion Factor
Length: meter (m)			
1 kilometer (km) = 10^3 meters (m)	10^3 m/km	10^{-3} km/m	10^{-3} km/m
1 centimeter (cm)[a] = 10^{-2} meters (m)	10^2 cm/m	10^{-2} m/cm	10^2 cm/m
1 millimeter (mm) = 10^{-3} meters (m)	10^3 mm/m	10^{-3} m/mm	10^3 mm/m
1 micron (μ) = 10^{-6} meters (m)	10^6 μ/m	10^{-6} m/μ	10^6 μ/m
1 Angstrom (Å)[b] = 10^{-8} centimeters (cm)	10^8 Å/cm	10^{-8} cm/Å	10^{10} Å/m
1 nanometer (nm) = 10^{-7} centimeters (cm)	10^7 nm/cm	10^{-7} cm/nm	10^9 nm/m
Volume: cubic meter (m^3)			
1 liter (l) = 10^{-3} cubic meters (m^3)	10^3 l/m^3	10^{-3} m^3/l	10^3 l/m^3
1 milliliter (ml) = 10^{-3} liters (l)	10^3 ml/l	10^{-3} l/ml	10^6 ml/m^3
1 cubic centimeter (cm^3) = 1 milliliter	1 cm^3/ml	1 ml/cm^3	10^6 cm^3/m^3
Mass: kilogram (kg)			
1 metric ton (t) = 10^3 kilograms (kg)	10^3 kg/t	10^{-3} t/kg	10^{-3} t/kg
1 gram (g) = 10^{-3} kilograms (kg)	10^3 g/kg	10^{-3} kg/g	10^3 g/kg
1 milligram (mg) = 10^{-3} grams (g)	10^3 mg/g	10^{-3} g/mg	10^6 mg/kg
Energy:			
1 kilocalorie (kcal)[c] = 10^3 calories (cal)	10^3 cal/kcal	10^{-3} kcal/cal	0.239 cal/J

[a]The centimeter is not an approved SI unit, but it is used in chemistry for convenience.
[b]The Angstrom is not an approved SI unit, and it is being replaced by the nanometer, which is ten times larger.
[c]The kilocalorie is not an approved SI unit, but it is still used by chemists.

B.3 USING CONVERSION FACTORS.

We've listed a lot of conversion factors, and now we'll see how to use them to solve conversion problems. First we need to look at some properties of conversion factors.

PROPERTIES OF CONVERSION FACTORS. There are three properties that we will consider here.

Table B.5
Metric-nonmetric conversion factors

Metric Unit	Nonmetric Unit	Conversion Factors
Length		
centimeter (cm)	inch (in)	2.54 cm/in 0.394 in/cm
meter (m)	inch (in)	0.0254 m/in 39.4 in/m
meter (m)	foot (ft)	0.305 m/ft 3.28 ft/m
kilometer (km)	mile (mi)	1.61 km/mi 0.621 mi/km
Volume		
liter (l)	pint (pt)	0.473 l/pt 2.11 pt/l
liter (l)	quart (qt)	0.946 l/qt 1.06 qt/l
liter (l)	gallon (gal)	3.78 l/gal 0.264 gal/l
Mass		
gram (g)	pound (lb)	454 g/lb 2.20×10^{-3} lb/g
gram (g)	ounce (oz)	28.4 g/oz 3.52×10^{-2} oz/g
kilogram (kg)	pound (lb)	0.454 kg/lb 2.20 lb/kg
Pressure		
pascal (Pa)	atmosphere (atm)	1.01×10^5 Pa/atm 9.90×10^{-6} atm/Pa
pascal (Pa)	torr (torr)[a]	1.33×10^2 Pa/torr 7.52×10^{-3} torr/Pa
pascal (Pa)	millimeter of mercury (mm Hg)[a]	1.33×10^2 Pa/mm Hg 7.52×10^{-3} mm Hg/Pa
Energy		
joule (J)	calorie (cal)	4.18 J/cal 0.239 cal/J

[a]Torr and millimeter of mercury are equivalent.
Conversion factors useful to learn are printed in color.

1. The *reciprocal* of a conversion factor means one over the conversion factor. A reciprocal can be calculated simply by inverting the conversion factor and dividing the numerator by the denominator. For instance, 2.54 cm/in inverted is 1.00 in/2.54 cm = 0.394 in/cm. The two columns of conversion factors in Table B.5 are reciprocals of each other.
2. Conversion factors can be used right side up or upside down. Thus 0.454 kg/lb is the same as 1.00 lb/0.454 kg = 2.20 lb/kg.
3. Units in conversion factors must be multiplied, divided, and canceled just like numbers. Thus:

$$\frac{cm}{in} \times cm = \frac{cm^2}{in}$$

$$\frac{qt}{l} \times \frac{pt}{qt} = \frac{pt}{l}$$

WORKING PROBLEMS. Conversion factors are used to convert one unit to another. To solve a problem in conversion, first we decide what units are to be converted to what other units. Next, we choose appropriate conversion factors to accomplish the conversion. The rest is arithmetic.

Let's see how this works by following an example. In Europe, gasoline is sold by the liter. A typical tankful of gas might be 54.4 liters. We want to know how many gallons this is.

Step 1: Decide what units are to be converted to what other units. Write the starting units on the left and the desired new units on the right.
We want to convert 54.4 liters to gallons.

$$54.4 \ l = \underline{\hspace{2cm}} gal$$

Step 2: Choose appropriate conversion factors.
We need a conversion factor that contains liters and gallons. Since we want to get rid of liters and substitute gallons, our conversion factor should contain liters on the bottom and gallons on the top. The liters will cancel and we'll be left with gallons. From Table B.5, we see that 0.264 gal/l is what we want.

Step 3: Set up the problem with the conversion factors, check units, and solve the problem.

$$54.4 \ l \times \frac{0.264 \ gal}{l} = 14.4 \ gal$$

The unit check in Step 3 is a good way to check the correctness of your answer. (Another way is by approximate answers; see Appendix A.5, p. 476.) If the units aren't right, chances are the problem is set up wrong. For instance, suppose we chose the conversion factor 3.78 l/gal and set it up like this:

$$54.4 \ l \times \frac{3.78 \ l}{gal} = \underline{\hspace{2cm}} \frac{l^2}{gal}$$

Without doing the arithmetic, we know this is wrong because we wanted gallons, and instead we got l²/gal, which doesn't have any meaning in this problem, or anywhere else, for that matter.

However, we can use this conversion factor if we invert it, like this:

$$54.4 \text{ l} \times \frac{1.00 \text{ gal}}{3.78 \text{ l}} = 14.4 \text{ gal}$$

We get the same answer, with the units canceling as they should.

In the examples above and in the ones that follow, calculator answers are rounded off to the proper number of significant figures. Where convenient, exponential notation is used as well. (For a complete discussion of these topics, see Appendix A, pp. 467–470 and 472–476.)

EXAMPLE B.1: In Germany, there is no speed limit on the superhighway called the "autobahn." Speeds there often reach as high as 195 km/hr (and higher). How many miles per hour is this?

Solution:

Step 1: We want to convert 195 km/hr to miles per hour (mi/hr):

$$195 \frac{\text{km}}{\text{hr}} = \underline{\hspace{1cm}} \frac{\text{mi}}{\text{hr}}$$

Step 2: Only the kilometer part needs to change, so we can use the conversion factor 0.621 mi/km from Table B.5.

Step 3:

$$195 \frac{\cancel{\text{km}}}{\text{hr}} \times 0.621 \frac{\text{mi}}{\cancel{\text{km}}} = \underline{\hspace{1cm}} \frac{\text{mi}}{\text{hr}}$$

The units are correct.

Answer: 121 mi/hr (frightening!).

EXAMPLE B.2: Convert 121 mi/hr in Example B.1 to centimeters per second (cm/sec).

Solution:

Step 1: We want to convert 121 mi/hr to centimeters per second (cm/sec).

$$121 \frac{\text{mi}}{\text{hr}} = \underline{\hspace{1cm}} \frac{\text{cm}}{\text{sec}}$$

Step 2: Here, both miles and hours change, so we need more than one conversion factor. We need to go from miles to kilometers to meters to centimeters, and from hours to minutes to seconds. To get rid of miles first, we choose the conversion factor 1.61 km/mi.

$$121 \frac{\cancel{\text{mi}}}{\text{hr}} \times 1.61 \frac{\text{km}}{\cancel{\text{mi}}}$$

This leaves us with kilometers, which we can change to meters and then to centimeters by using conversion factors from Table B.4: 10^3 m/km and 10^2 cm/m.

$$121 \frac{\cancel{\text{mi}}}{\text{hr}} \times 1.61 \frac{\cancel{\text{km}}}{\cancel{\text{mi}}} \times 10^3 \frac{\cancel{\text{m}}}{\cancel{\text{km}}} \times 10^2 \frac{\text{cm}}{\cancel{\text{m}}}$$

Now we've taken care of changing miles to centimeters. We still have to change hours to seconds. We use 1.00 hr/60.0 min and 1.00 min/60.0 sec.

$$121 \frac{\text{mi}}{\text{hr}} \times 1.61 \frac{\text{km}}{\text{mi}} \times 10^3 \frac{\text{m}}{\text{km}} \times 10^2 \frac{\text{cm}}{\text{m}} \times \frac{1.00 \text{ hr}}{60.0 \text{ min}} \times \frac{1.00 \text{ min}}{60.0 \text{ sec}} = \underline{\quad} \frac{\text{cm}}{\text{sec}}$$

The units are correct, so we do the arithmetic and get the answer.

Answer: 5.41×10^3 cm/sec.

Most of the conversions we'll run into in this book won't need so many conversion factors.

Notice that we really need only one conversion factor for each type of physical quantity. Three convenient ones are shaded in Table B.5. These can be memorized, so that conversions can always be made even if a table isn't available. From them, we can even make conversion factors that we don't have.

EXAMPLE B.3: Calculate a conversion factor for converting feet to kilo-meters (ft/km).

Solution:

Step 1: We need to select our starting unit. Looking at Table B.5, we see a conversion between feet and meters, so that'll be what we'll use to convert to feet per kilometer.

$$3.28 \frac{\text{ft}}{\text{m}} = \underline{\quad} \frac{\text{ft}}{\text{km}}$$

Step 2: We need a conversion factor to convert meters to kilometers. This is 10^3 m/km.

Step 3:

$$3.28 \frac{\text{ft}}{\text{m}} \times 10^3 \frac{\text{m}}{\text{km}} = \underline{\quad} \frac{\text{ft}}{\text{km}}$$

The units are correct.

Answer: 3.28×10^3 ft/km.

Notice that no arithmetic was involved in this calculation. That was because we were converting one metric unit to another, and this kind of conversion involves only powers of ten. With a little practice and experience, we can do calculations like that in our heads. We can say, "Well, it takes a thousand meters to make a kilometer, so I multiply feet/meter by a thousand to get feet/kilometer." At first, though, it's best to write the problem out so we don't multiply where we should be dividing, or vice versa. We'll know whether it is set up right if the units cancel properly.

B.4 TEMPERATURE SCALES

Temperature conversions are a little different from the unit conversions of the last section. We've seen how one unit can be converted to another unit by multiplying by a conversion factor. In temperature conversions, addition and subtraction are involved as well.

THE KELVIN SCALE.

The basic SI temperature scale is the *Kelvin scale,* and its units are called Kelvins (K). The zero point on the Kelvin scale (0 K) is the point at which everything is frozen and all motion stops. On this scale, water freezes at 273.16 K and boils at 373.16 K. Room temperature is about 295 K. When we're working with gases, we use this temperature scale.

THE CELSIUS (CENTIGRADE) SCALE.

Celsius scale

The one that we often find more convenient to use for ordinary laboratory measurements is the *Celsius scale.* Its units are called degrees Celsius (°C). The zero point on the Celsius scale (0°C) is the freezing point of water, and 100°C is the boiling point of water. That's how the scale was defined. The difference between the freezing and boiling points of water was divided into one hundred equal parts, which are the degrees. That's why it's sometimes called the centigrade scale (*centi-* means "one hundredth").

The size of a Celsius degree is the same as the size of a Kelvin. The distinction between the two scales is the difference in their zero points. 0°C is the same as 273.16 K and 0 K is the same as −273.16°C.

THE FAHRENHEIT SCALE.

Fahrenheit scale

The scale we use in the United States to measure temperature, but isn't used in science at all, is the *Fahrenheit scale.* Its units are called degrees Fahrenheit (°F). On the Fahrenheit scale, water freezes at 32.0°F and boils at 212°F. The 0°F and 100°F points don't have any special significance to us. The size of a Fahrenheit degree isn't the same as the size of a Kelvin or a Celsius degree. A Fahrenheit degree is smaller than the other two.

Figure B.1 shows the three temperature scales side by side.

KELVIN-CELSIUS TEMPERATURE CONVERSIONS.

We've said that the size of a Celsius degree is the same as the size of a Kelvin. Because their zero points are different, we convert between these two scales by adding and subtracting. To change from Kelvin to Celsius, we subtract 273.16 (the difference in zero points on these scales) from the Kelvin temperature. In the opposite direction, to convert from Celsius to Kelvin, we add 273.16 to the Celsius temperature. Strictly speaking, though, if we add or subtract two numbers, their units have to be the same. We can take care of this easily with the conversion factor 1°C/K, and formalize the conversions with these equations:

$$°C = K \times \frac{1°C}{K} - 273.16°C$$

$$K = °C \times \frac{1K}{°C} + 273.16 \ K$$

In practice, we'd obviously just subtract or add the number. These are easy formulas to use, because they involve only addition or subtraction.

EXAMPLE B.4: Express the temperature 18.0°C in Kelvins.

Solution:

$$K = 18.0°\cancel{C} \times 1\frac{K}{°\cancel{C}} + 273.16\ K$$

Answer: 291.2 K.

FIGURE B.1
Comparison of temperature scales

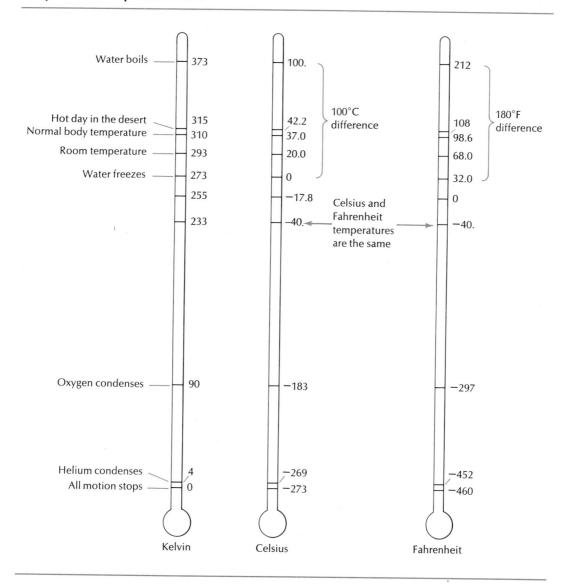

	Kelvin	Celsius	Fahrenheit
Water boils	373	100.	212
Hot day in the desert	315	42.2	108
Normal body temperature	310	37.0	98.6
Room temperature	293	20.0	68.0
Water freezes	273	0	32.0
	255	−17.8	0
	233	−40.	−40.
Oxygen condenses	90	−183	−297
Helium condenses	4	−269	−452
All motion stops	0	−273	−460

100°C difference

180°F difference

Celsius and Fahrenheit temperatures are the same

EXAMPLE B.5: Express the temperature 18.0 K in °C.

Solution:

$$°C = 18.0 \, \cancel{K} \times 1\frac{°C}{\cancel{K}} - 273.16°C$$

Answer: $-255.2°C$.

CELSIUS-FAHRENHEIT TEMPERATURE
CONVERSIONS.
Looking at the Celsius and Fahrenheit temperature scales side by side (as in Figure B.1), we see that we need 180°F and only 100°C to measure the same difference between the boiling and freezing points of water. This distance is the same, no matter which scale we use to measure it. Using the distance as a standard of reference, we can get a conversion factor between Celsius and Fahrenheit degrees. There are 180 Fahrenheit degrees for every 100 Celsius degrees, or:

$$\frac{180°F}{100°C} = \frac{9°F}{5°C}$$

FIGURE B.2
Derivation of conversion factor between Fahrenheit and Celsius degrees

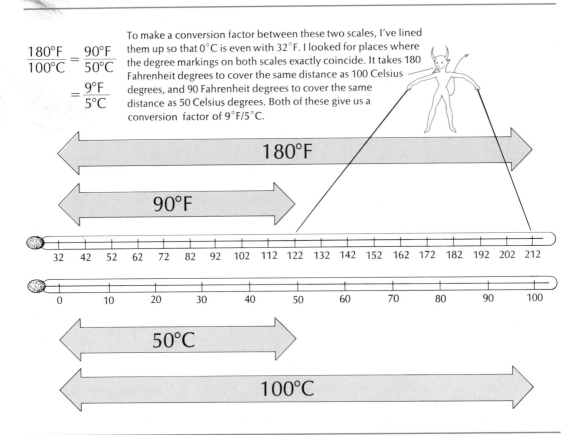

$$\frac{180°F}{100°C} = \frac{90°F}{50°C}$$

$$= \frac{9°F}{5°C}$$

To make a conversion factor between these two scales, I've lined them up so that 0°C is even with 32°F. I looked for places where the degree markings on both scales exactly coincide. It takes 180 Fahrenheit degrees to cover the same distance as 100 Celsius degrees, and 90 Fahrenheit degrees to cover the same distance as 50 Celsius degrees. Both of these give us a conversion factor of 9°F/5°C.

180°F

90°F

32 42 52 62 72 82 92 102 112 122 132 142 152 162 172 182 192 202 212

0   10   20   30   40   50   60   70   80   90   100

50°C

100°C

FIGURE B.3
Add 40 degrees
as the first
step in
Fahrenheit-
Celsius
conversion

491

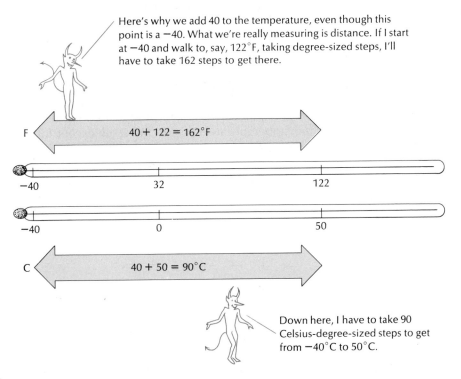

Here's why we add 40 to the temperature, even though this point is a −40. What we're really measuring is distance. If I start at −40 and walk to, say, 122°F, taking degree-sized steps, I'll have to take 162 steps to get there.

F   40 + 122 = 162°F

−40   32   122

−40   0   50

C   40 + 50 = 90°C

Down here, I have to take 90 Celsius-degree-sized steps to get from −40°C to 50°C.

So, our conversion factor is 9°F/5°C, or 5°C/9°F (this conversion factor is a pure number). If we remember that Fahrenheit degrees are smaller, and that therefore it takes more of them to cover the same distance, we'll always get the conversion factor right. (See Figure B.2.)

But that's not all. We've accounted for the different degree sizes, but we also have to account for the difference in zero points. We see that 0°C is 32°F, and that 0°F is −17.8°C. Another thing to notice is that both scales have the same value at −40°. If we start at this common "zero" point, which is really a "−40" point, then we see that we have to add 40° to a temperature reading on either scale to measure the distance from −40 to any temperature. (See Figure B.3.) Then, these relationships are true.

$$°F + 40°F = \frac{9°F}{5°C}(°C + 40°C)$$

$$°C + 40°C = \frac{5°C}{9°F}(°F + 40°F)$$

Now, to get temperatures in °F and °C, we subtract 40° from both sides of each equation.

$$°F = \frac{9°F}{5°C}(°C + 40°C) - 40°F$$

$$°C = \frac{5°C}{9°F}(°F + 40°F) - 40°C$$

(Note: Both the 40° and the 5/9 are pure numbers, and may have as many significant figures as needed in a given instance.) This gives us these two working formulas for converting between Celsius and Fahrenheit temperatures. They're easy to remember, because they're the same except for the inversion of the conversion factor.

EXAMPLE B.6: Express the temperature 37.0°C in °F.

Solution: We want to convert °C to °F, so we use the first equation above.

$$°F = \frac{9°F}{5°C}(37.0°C + 40.0°C) - 40.0°F$$

$$= \frac{9°F}{5°C}(77.0°C) - 40.0°F$$

$$= 138.6°F - 40.0°F$$

Answer: 98.6°F (normal body temperature).

EXAMPLE B.7: Express the temperature 68°F in °C.

Solution: We want to convert degrees Fahrenheit to Celsius, so we use the second formula.

$$°C = \frac{5°C}{9°F}(68°F + 40°F) - 40°C$$

$$= \frac{5°C}{9°F}(108°F) - 40°C$$

$$= 60°C - 40°C$$

Answer: 20°C (room temperature).

The above formulas are easier to remember than the ones that are often given, which are:

$$°F = \frac{9°F}{5°C}(°C) + 32°F$$

$$°C = \frac{5°C}{9°F}(°F - 32°F)$$

We could rework Examples B.6 and B.7 with these formulas, and we'd get the same answers. The first pair of formulas show where the two temperature scales are equal. The second pair show that there is a difference of 32 Fahrenheit degrees between their zero points. Both show the 9°F/5°C conversion factor. Which pair we use is merely a matter of which we remember more easily.

EXERCISES

1. Metric prefixes have permeated the financial world. Financiers use words like "kilobucks" and "megabucks." What do these units mean in terms of dollars?

2. Fill in the blanks.

   a. 1 deciliter (dl) = _____ liters (l)

   b. 1 kilogram (kg) = _____ micrograms (μg)

   c. 5 cubic centimeters = _____ milliliters (ml)

   d. 500. kilograms (kg) = _____ metric tons

   e. _____ centimeters (cm) = 0.75 meters

   f. _____ liters (l) = 500. cubic centimeters (cm³)

   g. _____ grams (g) = 200. milligrams (mg)

   h. _____ meters (m) = 0.400 kilometers (km)

   i. 800. calories (cal) = _____ kilocalories (kcal)

3. Which of the following conversion factors may be treated as pure numbers?
   a. 1000 mg/g
   b. 0.621 mi/km
   c. 1 cm³/ml
   d. 1.06 qt/l
   e. 2.20×10^{-3} lb/g
   f. 60 sec/min

4. Write reciprocals of the conversion factors in Exercise 3.

5. Some of the following conversions are set up incorrectly. Select the incorrect ones and explain why they are incorrect.

   a. $15.7 \text{ cm} \times \dfrac{1.00 \text{ in}}{2.54 \text{ cm}} = 6.18 \text{ in}$

   b. $2.25 \text{ l} \times 0.946 \dfrac{l}{qt} = 2.13 \text{ qt}$

   c. $121 \text{ lb} \times 0.454 \dfrac{kg}{lb} = 54.9 \text{ kg}$

   d. $547 \text{ cm}^3 \times 10^3 \dfrac{cm^3}{l} \times 2.11 \dfrac{pt}{l} = 1.15 \times 10^6 \text{ pt}$

   e. $1.50 \text{ atm} \times 760 \dfrac{torr}{atm} = 1.14 \times 10^3 \text{ torr}$

   f. $495 \text{ oz} \times 28.4 \dfrac{g}{oz} \times \dfrac{1.00 \text{ g}}{10^{-3} \text{ kg}} = 14.1 \text{ kg}$

   g. $1.55 \text{ ft} \times 0.305 \dfrac{m}{ft} \times 10^3 \dfrac{mm}{m} = 4.27 \times 10^2 \text{ mm}$

6. You are having a physical examination in Europe, and the doctor asks you for your height in centimeters and your weight in kilograms. Perform the conversion.

7. You are driving through Europe, and Paris, your destination, is 115 kilometers away. How many miles do you have to go?

8. You put 40.0 liters of gas in the car you're driving. How many gallons is that?

9. The 40.0 liters of gas cost 45.0 francs. How many cents per gallon is that, if the exchange rate is 4.00 francs to the dollar?

10. Your car weighs 2.51 tons. How many kilograms is that?

11. The distance between the earth and the sun is 9.3×10^7 miles. How many kilometers is that?

12. A polio virus particle is about 34.5 nanometers in diameter. How many inches is that?

13. The speed of light is 3.0×10^{10} cm/sec. Convert this to miles/hour.

14. A whimsical unit among some scientists is "furlongs per fortnight." Convert this to miles per hour. (A furlong is 220 yards, and a fortnight is 14 days.)

15. Calculate a conversion factor that tells how many milliliters are in a cup (ml/c). (1 pt = 2 cups.)

16. Calculate a conversion factor for converting ounces to kilograms (kg/oz).

17. Calculate a conversion factor for converting centimeters to yards (yd/cm).

18. A good temperature for baking bread is 375°F. Express this temperature in Kelvins and in degrees Celsius.

19. Make the following temperature conversions.
    a. 34.0°C to Kelvins
    b. 89.6°C to °F
    c. 125 K to °C
    d. 66°F to °C
    e. −90.0°C to Kelvins
    f. −21.0°F to °C
    g. 22.0 K to °F
    h. 250 K to °C

20. A certain antifreeze claims to protect water from freezing down to −40°. Whether this is degrees Celsius or Fahrenheit is not specified. Which do you think it is? Explain.

ANSWERS TO ODD-NUMBERED EXERCISES WITH NUMERICAL SOLUTIONS

Chapter 2

1. Yes. When added together, the masses and charges of the proton and electron give the mass (1) and charge (0) of the neutron.
3. a. 13 protons, 13 electrons, 14 neutrons; b. 18 protons, 18 electrons, 22 neutrons; c. 29 protons, 29 electrons, 35 neutrons; d. 79 protons, 79 electrons, 118 neutrons; e. 28 protons, 28 electrons, 31 neutrons; f. 27 protons, 27 electrons, 33 neutrons
5. a is an isotope of hydrogen ($Z = 1$); b, e, and g are isotopes of lithium ($Z = 3$); c, f, and h are isotopes of beryllium ($Z = 4$); and d is an isotope of helium ($Z = 2$).
7. Barium, zirconium, and aluminum are metals; oxygen and sulfur are nonmetals; arsenic, astatine, and antimony are metalloids.
9. a. Na reacts violently with water, Mg does not; b. H is a gas, Li is a metal; c. Hg is shiny and metallic and Br is reddish-brown; d. Ca reacts violently with water; Mg does not; e. Si shatters when pounded with a hammer, Al is a malleable metal; f. Br is a reddish-brown liquid, Cl is a yellowish-green gas; g. N is a gas, P is a solid; h. S is a solid, Ar is a gas; i. H burns when ignited, O does not; j. Cu is a reddish-brown shiny metal, I is a brownish nonmetal; k. Br is a liquid, I is a solid; l. Ca reacts with water; Pb does not; m. Au is a solid, Hg is a liquid; n. Mg burns brightly when lit with a match, Fe does not.
11. Fe. The nonmetal Se does not conduct electricity; Ca is a metal but too reactive.
13. a. Na; b. Mn; c. Hg; d. lithium; e. potassium; f. phosphorus; g. tin; h. copper; i. silver; j. Pb; k. Fe; l. bromine.

Chapter 3

1. $1\ \text{doz doughnuts} \times \dfrac{12\ \text{doughnuts}}{\text{doz doughnuts}} \times \dfrac{225\ \text{g}}{\text{doughnut}}$
$$= 2700\ \text{g}$$

3. $2.50\ \text{moles H atoms} \times \dfrac{1.01\ \text{g}}{\text{mole H atoms}} = 2.53\ \text{g}$

5. $1\ \text{mole } H_2 \text{ molecules} \times \dfrac{2\ \text{moles H atoms}}{\text{mole } H_2 \text{ molecules}}$
$$\times \dfrac{1.01\ \text{g}}{\text{mole H atoms}} = 2.02\ \text{g}$$

7. $8 \times 10^4\ \text{kg water} \times (25 - 10)°C = 1 \times 10^6\ \text{kcal}$
9. Tungsten has the highest melting and boiling points.
11. Group IA metals tend to have lower melting points than Group IIA metals.
13. Highest melting point: carbon as graphite (3550 °C). Lowest melting point: helium (-272 °C).

15. Copper: $\dfrac{500\ \text{cal}}{0.092\ \text{cal}/(\text{g} \times °C) \times 10\ \text{g}} = 500\ °C$

Aluminum: $\dfrac{500\ \text{cal}}{0.215\ \text{cal}/(\text{g} \times °C) \times 10\ \text{g}} = 200\ °C$

Aluminum, with a smaller temperature change, would be better able to maintain a constant temperature.

17. $155\ \text{g Zn} \times 0.0928\ \dfrac{\text{cal}}{\text{g Zn} \times °C} \times (58.4 - 35.2)\ °C$
$$= 334\ \text{cal}$$

19. $10.5\ \text{cm}^3 Br_2 \times 3.12\ \dfrac{\text{g}}{\text{cm}^3 Br_2} = 32.8\ \text{g}$

21. $95.2\ \text{g Os} \times \dfrac{1.00\ \text{cm}}{22.6\ \text{g Os}} = 4.21\ \text{cm}^3$

23. Magnesium (density 1.74 g/cm³)
25. H, He
27. Oil has lower density and floats on water.
29. Sink. CO_2 is more dense than air.
31. One liter of butter weighs 0.86 kg; of water, 1 kg; of salt, 2.16 kg; of sugar, 1.59 kg. Grandma's saying works well only for water.

Chapter 4

1. a. covalent; b. ionic; c. ionic; d. covalent; e. covalent; f. ionic
3. a. oxygen difluoride; b. chlorine iodide; c. dinitrogen tetrahydride; d. sulfur hexafluoride
5. a. H_2S; b. HBr; c. HF; d. H_2Se
7. a. O^{2-}; b. Ag^+; c. N^{3-}; d. K^+; e. Br^-; f. Sr^{2+}
9. a. lithium hydride; b. beryllium oxide; c. iron(II) sulfide; d. nickel(II) chloride; e. potassium nitride; f. mercury(II) bromide
11. a. sulfate ion; b. nitrite ion; c. perchlorate ion;

d. permanganate ion
13. a. H_2SO_4; b. HNO_2; c. HIO_3; d. H_3PO_3
15. a. potassium perchlorate; b. iron(II) sulfate; c. ammonium dichromate; d. silver acetate; e. sodium phosphate; f. copper(II) carbonate.
17. a. covalent, HNO_3; b. ionic, lithium sulfiite; c. ionic, $Cr(OH)_3$; d. covalent, sulfuric acid; e. ionic, ammonium phosphate; f. covalent, chloric acid; g. covalent, H_2SO_4; h. ionic, $PbCO_3$; i. covalent, hypoiodous acid; j. ionic, $KMnO_4$

19.

	OH^-	CN^-	SO_4^{2-}	PO_4^{3-}	HCO_3^-	NO_3^-	ClO_2^-	O_2^{2-}
NH_4^+	NH_4OH^a	NH_4CN	$(NH_4)_2SO_4$	$(NH_4)_3PO_4$	NH_4HCO_3	NH_4NO_3	NH_4ClO_2	$(NH_4)_2O_2{}^a$
Co^{2+}	$Co(OH)_2$	$Co(CN)_2$	$CoSO_4$	$Co_3(PO_4)_2$	$Co(HCO_3)_2$	$Co(NO_3)_2$	$Co(ClO_2)_2$	CoO_2
K^+	KOH	KCN	K_2SO_4	K_3PO_4	$KHCO_3$	KNO_3	$KClO_2$	$K_2O_2{}^b$
Hg_2^{2+}	$Hg_2(OH)_2{}^{a,b}$	$Hg_2(CN)_2{}^b$	Hg_2SO_4	$(Hg_2)_3(PO_4)_2$	$Hg_2(HCO_3)_2{}^b$	$Hg_2(NO_3)_2{}^b$	$Hg_2(ClO_2)_2{}^b$	$Hg_2O_2{}^{a,b}$
Mn^{2+}	$Mn(OH)_2$	$Mn(CN)_2$	$MnSO_4$	$Mn_3(PO_4)_2$	$Mn(HCO_3)_2$	$Mn(NO_3)_2$	$Mn(ClO_2)_2$	$MnO_2{}^c$
Pb^{4+}	$Pb(OH)_4$	$Pb(CN)_4$	$Pb(SO_4)_2$	$Pb_3(PO_4)_4$	$Pb(HCO_3)_4$	$Pb(NO_3)_4$	$Pb(ClO_2)_4$	$Pb(O_2)_2$
Sn^{2+}	$Sn(OH)_2$	$Sn(CN)_2$	$SnSO_4$	$Sn_3(PO_4)_2$	$Sn(HCO_3)_2$	$Sn(NO_3)_2$	$Sn(ClO_2)_2$	$SnO_2{}^c$
Ca^{2+}	$Ca(OH)_2$	$Ca(CN)_2$	$CaSO_4$	$Ca_3(PO_4)_2$	$Ca(HCO_3)_2$	$Ca(NO_3)_2$	$Ca(ClO_2)_2$	CaO_2
Li^+	$LiOH$	$LiCN$	Li_2SO_4	Li_3PO_4	$LiHCO_3$	$LiNO_3$	$LiClO_2$	Li_2O_2

[a]These compounds do not exist, but we may still write their formulas.
[b]Note that these formulas may not be simplified without destroying a polyatomic ion.
[c]These formulas are the same as for manganese(IV) oxide and tin(IV) oxide.

21. NaH_2PO_4; b. NH_4HSO_4; c. $NaKSO_3$; d. $Al(HCO_3)_3$
23. a. Hydrate, chromium(II) sulfate tetrahydrate (or 4-hydrate)
    b. Ternary covalent (oxyacid), perchloric acid (or hydrogen perchlorate)
    c. Mixed ionic, sodium potassium sulfite

    d. Binary covalent, phosphorus pentachloride
    e. Binary covalent, silicon dioxide
    f. Ionic, ammonium cyanide
    g. Ternary ionic, barium chromate
    h. Binary covalent, sulfur trioxide

Chapter 5

1. a. correct; b. incorrect ($NaBr_2$ should be NaBr); c. incorrect (S should be Si); d. incorrect (O should be O_2); e. correct
3. a. balanced; b. unbalanced; c. balanced, d. unbalanced; e. unbalanced
5. The "balanced" equations given will be unbalanced when their formulas are corrected.
   a. H should be H_2, O should be O_2; b. FeBr should be $FeBr_2$, HS should be H_2S; c. H_2F_2 should be HF; d. Na_2Cl_2 should be NaCl; e. Cl_3 should be Cl_2; f. $Li_2(OH)_2$ should be LiOH; g. $AlCl_2$ should be $AlCl_3$; h. $PbNO_3$ should be $Pb(NO_3)_2$, PbCl should be $PbCl_2$; i. O_4 should be O_2
7. a. $2\,P + 3\,Cl_2 \longrightarrow 2\,PCl_3$
   b. $Mg_3N_2 + 6\,H_2O \longrightarrow 3\,Mg(OH)_2 + 2\,NH_3$
   c. $4\,Fe + 3O_2 \longrightarrow 2\,Fe_2O_3$
   d. $Ni(OH)_2 + H_2SO_4 \longrightarrow NiSO_4 + 2\,H_2O$
   e. $Fe + 2\,AgNO_3 \longrightarrow Fe(NO_3)_2 + 2\,Ag$
   f. $BaCl_2 + (NH_4)_2CO_3 \longrightarrow BaCO_3 + 2\,NH_4Cl$
   g. $2\,NaNO_2 + H_2SO_4 \longrightarrow 2\,HNO_2 + Na_2SO_4$
   h. $2\,NaOH + CO_2 \longrightarrow Na_2CO_3 + H_2O$

   i. $2\,B + 3\,F_2 \longrightarrow 2\,BF_3$
   j. $2\,HNO_2 \longrightarrow N_2O_3 + H_2O$

9. a. "Solid calcium (or calcium metal) reacts with hydrobromic acid to yield aqueous calcium bromide and hydrogen gas (or gaseous hydrogen)."
   b. "Hydrogen iodide gas decomposes to form hydrogen gas and solid iodine."
   c. "Solid beryllium reacts with oxygen gas to form solid beryllium oxide."
   d. "Aqueous manganese(II) nitrate reacts with aqueous sodium sulfide to yield a precipitate of manganese(II) sulfide and aqueous sodium nitrate."
   e. "Liquid dichlorine heptoxide reacts with liquid water to form aqueous perchloric acid."

11. a. combination; b. double replacement; c. single replacement; d. decomposition; e. single replacement; f. combination; g. double replacement; h. double replacement; i. decomposition; j. combination

13. a. $2 \text{Li}(s) + \text{Cl}_2(g) \longrightarrow \text{LiCl}(s)$ (Rule 1)
 b. $2 \text{Cr}(s) + \text{O}_2(g) \longrightarrow 2 \text{CrO}(s)$ (Rule 1)
 c. $2 \text{NO}(g) + \text{O}_2(g) \longrightarrow 2 \text{NO}_2(g)$ (Rule 2)
 d. $\text{CO}_2(g) + \text{H}_2\text{O}(l) \longrightarrow \text{H}_2\text{CO}_3(aq)$ (Rule 3)
 e. $\text{K}_2\text{O}(s) + \text{H}_2\text{O}(l) \longrightarrow 2 \text{KOH}(aq)$ (Rule 4)
 f. $\text{BeO}(s) + \text{CO}_2(g) \longrightarrow \text{BeCO}_3(s)$ (Rule 5)
 g. $\text{ZnO}(s) + \text{SO}_2(g) \longrightarrow \text{ZnSO}_3(s)$ (Rule 5)
 h. $\text{Rb}_2\text{O}(s) + \text{SO}_3(g) \longrightarrow \text{Rb}_2\text{SO}_4(s)$ (Rule 5)

15. a. $\text{Ca}(s) + 2 \text{H}_2\text{O}(l) \longrightarrow \text{Ca(OH)}_2(aq) + \text{H}_2(g)$
 (Rule 10)
 b. $2 \text{Rb}(s) + 2 \text{H}_2\text{O}(l) \longrightarrow 2 \text{RbOH}(aq) + \text{H}_2(g)$
 (Rule 10)
 c. $\text{Cr}(s) + 2 \text{HCl}(aq) \longrightarrow \text{CrCl}_2(aq) + \text{H}_2(g)$
 (Rule 11)
 d. $3 \text{Cd}(s) + 2 \text{H}_3\text{PO}_4(aq) \longrightarrow$
 $\text{Cd}_3(\text{PO}_4)_2(aq) + 3 \text{H}_2(g)$ (Rule 11)
 e. $\text{Ni}(s) + \text{Hg(NO}_3)_2(aq) \longrightarrow$
 $\text{Ni(NO}_3)_2(aq) + \text{Hg}(l)$ (Rule 12)
 f. $\text{Zn}(s) + \text{CuCl}_2(aq) \longrightarrow \text{ZnCl}_2(aq) + \text{Cu}(s)$
 (Rule 12)
 g. $2 \text{KBr}(aq) + \text{F}_2(aq) \longrightarrow 2 \text{KF}(aq) + \text{Br}_2(aq)$
 (Rule 13)

h. $\text{BaI}_2(aq) + \text{Br}_2(aq) \longrightarrow \text{BaBr}_2(aq) + \text{I}_2(s)$
 (Rule 13)
 i. $\text{K}_2\text{S}(aq) + \text{I}_2(s) \longrightarrow \text{S}(s) + 2 \text{KI}(aq)$ (Rule 13)
17. a. no rule, insufficient information; b. Rule 1; c. Rule 18; d. Rule 11; e. Rule 20; f. Rule 9A; g. Rule 15; h. no rule, insufficient information; i. no rule, insufficient information; j. no rule, insufficient information
19. $2 \text{ZnS}(s) + 3 \text{O}_2(g) \longrightarrow 2 \text{ZnO}(s) + 2 \text{SO}_2(g)$
 $\text{HgS}(s) + \text{O}_2(g) \longrightarrow \text{Hg}(l) + \text{SO}_2(g)$
 The first reaction involves burning a binary compound to yield oxides of both elements (Rule 19). The second is single replacement.
21. a. $\text{N}_2(g) + \text{O}_2(g) \longrightarrow 2 \text{NO}(g)$ (combination)
 b. $2 \text{NO}(g) + \text{O}_2(g) \longrightarrow 2 \text{NO}_2(g)$ (combination)
 c. $\text{H}_2\text{O}(g) + 3 \text{NO}_2(g) \longrightarrow 2 \text{HNO}_3(aq) + \text{NO}(g)$
 (unclassified)
23. $2 \text{Al}(s) + 3 \text{Ag}_2\text{S}(s) \longrightarrow \text{Al}_2\text{S}_3 + 6 \text{Ag}(s)$ (Rule 12)
 (solubility unknown)
25. $\text{Ca(OH)}_2(aq) + \text{Na}_2\text{CO}_3(aq) \longrightarrow 2 \text{NaOH} + \text{CaCO}_3$
 (solubilities unknown)

Chapter 6

1. a. $1/3 \text{ mole He} \times \dfrac{6.02 \times 10^{23} \text{ He atoms}}{\text{mole He}}$
 $= 2 \times 10^{23}$ He atoms

 b. $3.21 \text{ g S} \times \dfrac{1.00 \text{ moles S}}{32.1 \text{ g S}} \times \dfrac{6.02 \times 10^{23} \text{ S atoms}}{\text{mole S}}$
 $= 6.02 \times 10^{22}$ S atoms

 c. $6 \text{ moles Ar} \times \dfrac{6.02 \times 10^{23} \text{ Ar atoms}}{\text{mole Ar}}$
 $= 4 \times 10^{24}$ Ar atoms

 d. $20.0 \text{ g Ar} \times \dfrac{1.00 \text{ mole Ar}}{39.9 \text{ g Ar}} \times \dfrac{6.02 \times 10^{23} \text{ Ar atoms}}{\text{mole Ar}}$
 $= 3.02 \times 10^{23}$ Ar atoms

 e. $2 \text{ moles O}_2 \times \dfrac{6.02 \times 10^{23} \text{ O}_2 \text{ molecules}}{\text{mole O}_2}$
 $\times \dfrac{2 \text{ O atoms}}{\text{O}_2 \text{ molecule}} = 2 \times 10^{24}$ O atoms

 f. $0.100 \text{ moles Na} \times \dfrac{6.02 \times 10^{23} \text{ Na atoms}}{\text{mole Na}}$
 $= 6.02 \times 10^{22}$ Na atoms

3. There are no N atoms in b, c, e, and f.

 a. $3.01 \times 10^{23} \times \text{NO molecules} \times \dfrac{1 \text{ N atom}}{\text{NO molecule}}$
 $= 3.01 \times 10^{23}$ N atoms

 d. $6.02 \times 10^{23} \text{ N}_2\text{O}_5 \text{ molecules} \times \dfrac{2 \text{ N atoms}}{\text{N}_2\text{O}_5 \text{ molecule}}$
 $= 1.20 \times 10^{24}$ N atoms

5. a. 2 N atoms, each 14.0 g/mole $= 28.0$ g/mole

 b. 1 H atom, each 1.01 g/mole $= 1.01$ g/mole
 1 N atom, each 14.0 g/mole $= 14.0$ g/mole
 3 O atoms, each 16.0 g/mole $= \underline{48.0}$ g/mole
 63.0 g/mole

 c. 2 Na atoms, each 23.0 g/mole $= 46.0$ g/mole
 1 S atom, each 32.1 g/mole $= 32.1$ g/mole
 4 O atoms, each 16.0 g/mole $= \underline{64.0}$ g/mole
 142.1 g/mole

 d. 6 C atoms, each 12.0 g/mole $= 72.0$ g/mole
 12 H atoms, each 1.01 g/mole $= 12.1$ g/mole
 6 O atoms, each 16.0 g/mole $= \underline{96.0}$ g/mole
 180.1 g/mole

 e. 1 Ca atom, each 40.1 g/mole $= 40.1$ g/mole
 1 S atom, each 32.1 g/mole $= 32.1$ g/mole
 6 O atoms, each 16.0 g/mole $= 96.0$ g/mole
 4 H atoms, each 1.01 g/mole $= \underline{4.04}$ g/mole
 172.2 g/mole

 f. 3 N atoms, each 14.0 g/mole $= 42.0$ g/mole
 12 H atoms, each 1.01 g/mole $= 12.1$ g/mole
 1 P atom, each 31.0 g/mole $= 31.0$ g/mole
 4 O atoms, each 16.0 g/mole $= \underline{64.0}$ g/mole
 149.1 g/mole

7. a. I_2: 253.8 g/mole

 $2.00 \text{ moles I}_2 \times \dfrac{253.8 \text{ g I}_2}{\text{mole I}_2} = 508 \text{ g I}_2$

 b. H: 1.01 g/mole
 Cl: 35.5 g/mole
 O_3: $\underline{48.0}$ g/mole
 HClO_3: 84.5 g/mole

$$1.57 \text{ moles } HClO_3 \times \frac{84.5 \text{ g } HClO_3}{\text{mole } HClO_3} = 133 \text{ g } HClO_3$$

c. $0.122 \text{ mole Fe} \times \dfrac{55.8 \text{ g Fe}}{\text{mole Fe}} = 6.81 \text{ g Fe}$

d. N: 14.0 g/mole
O$_2$: 32.0 g/mole
NO$_2$: 46.0 g/mole

$$10.0 \text{ moles } NO_2 \times \frac{46.0 \text{ g } NO_2}{\text{mole } NO_2} = 460 \text{ g } NO_2$$

e. Cr$_2$: 104. g/mole
O$_3$: 48.0 g/mole
Cr$_2$O$_3$: 152 g/mole

$$5.93 \text{ moles } Cr_2O_3 \times \frac{152 \text{ g } Cr_2O_3}{\text{mole } Cr_2O_3} = 901 \text{ g } Cr_2O_3$$

f. C$_3$: 36.0 g/mole
H$_8$: 8.08 g/mole
C$_3$H$_8$: 44.1 g/mole

$$0.500 \text{ moles } C_3H_8 \times \frac{44.1 \text{ g } C_3H_8}{\text{mole } C_3H_8} = 22.1 \text{ g } C_3H_8$$

9. a.

$$\frac{2 \text{ moles } C_2H_2}{5 \text{ moles } O_2} \qquad \frac{1 \text{ mole } C_2H_2}{2 \text{ moles } CO_2}$$

$$\frac{1 \text{ mole } C_2H_5}{\text{mole } H_2O} \qquad \frac{5 \text{ moles } O_2}{4 \text{ moles } CO_2}$$

$$\frac{5 \text{ moles } O_2}{2 \text{ moles } H_2O} \qquad \frac{2 \text{ moles } CO_2}{\text{mole } H_2O}$$

b.

$$\frac{1 \text{ mole } Fe_2O_3}{3 \text{ moles } CO} \qquad \frac{1 \text{ mole } Fe_2O_3}{2 \text{ moles } Fe}$$

$$\frac{1 \text{ mole } Fe_2O_3}{3 \text{ moles } CO_2} \qquad \frac{3 \text{ moles } CO}{2 \text{ moles } Fe}$$

$$\frac{1 \text{ mole } CO}{\text{mole } CO_2} \qquad \frac{2 \text{ moles } Fe}{3 \text{ moles } CO_2}$$

c.

$$\frac{3 \text{ moles } Cl_2}{\text{mole } CH_4} \qquad \frac{3 \text{ moles } Cl_2}{\text{mole } CHCl_3}$$

$$\frac{1 \text{ mole } Cl_2}{\text{mole } HCl} \qquad \frac{1 \text{ mole } CH_4}{\text{mole } CHCl_3}$$

$$\frac{1 \text{ mole } CH_4}{3 \text{ moles } HCl} \qquad \frac{1 \text{ mole } CHCl_3}{3 \text{ moles } HCl}$$

11. a. $1.18 \times 10^{13} \text{ g } NH_3 \times \dfrac{1.00 \text{ mole } NH_3}{17.0 \text{ g } NH_3}$

$$= 6.94 \times 10^{11} \text{ moles } NH_3$$

b. $6.94 \times 10^{11} \text{ moles } NH_3 \times \dfrac{1 \text{ mole } N_2}{2 \text{ moles } NH_3}$

$$= 3.47 \times 10^{11} \text{ moles } N_2$$

$$6.94 \times 10^{11} \text{ moles } NH_3 \times \frac{3 \text{ moles } H_2}{2 \text{ moles } NH_3}$$

$$= 1.04 \times 10^{12} \text{ moles } H_2$$

13. $2 C_4H_{10} + 13 O_2 \longrightarrow 8 CO_2 + 10 H_2O$

$$1050 \text{ g } C_4H_{10} \times \frac{1 \text{ mole } C_4H_{10}}{58.1 \text{ g } C_4H_{10}} \times \frac{13 \text{ moles } O_2}{2 \text{ moles } C_4H_{10}}$$

$$= 118 \text{ moles } O_2$$

15. $50.0 \text{ g } Cr_2O_3 \times \dfrac{1 \text{ mole } Cr_2O_3}{152 \text{ g } Cr_2O_3}$

$$\times \frac{1 \text{ mole } (NH_4)_2Cr_2O_7}{\text{mole } Cr_2O_3} \times \frac{252 \text{ g } (NH_4)_2Cr_2O_7}{\text{mole } (NH_4)_2Cr_2O_7}$$

$$= 82.9 \text{ g } (NH_4)_2Cr_2O_7$$

17. $5.00 \times 10^3 \text{ g } C_6H_{12}O_6 \times \dfrac{1 \text{ mole } C_6H_{12}O_6}{180.1 \text{ g } C_6H_{12}O_6}$

$$= 27.8 \text{ moles } C_6H_{12}O_6$$

$$27.8 \text{ moles } C_6H_{12}O_6 \times \frac{2 \text{ moles } CO_2}{\text{mole } C_6H_{12}O_6} \times \frac{44.0 \text{ g } CO_2}{\text{mole } CO_2}$$

$$= 2.45 \times 10^3 \text{ g } CO_2$$

$$27.8 \text{ moles } C_6H_{12}O_6 \times \frac{2 \text{ moles } C_2H_5OH}{\text{mole } C_6H_{12}O_6}$$

$$\times \frac{46.1 \text{ g } C_2H_5OH}{\text{mole } C_2H_5OH} = 2.56 \times 10^3 \text{ g } C_2H_5OH$$

19. a. $5.00 \text{ t } H_2SO_4 \times \dfrac{1 \text{ t-mole } H_2SO_4}{98.1 \text{ t } H_2SO_4} \times \dfrac{1 \text{ t-mole } H_2S}{\text{t-mole } H_2SO_4}$

$$\times \frac{34.1 \text{ t } H_2S}{\text{t-mole } H_2S} = 1.74 \text{ t } H_2S$$

b. $1.73 \text{ t } H_2S \times \dfrac{1 \text{ t-mole } H_2S}{34.1 \text{ t } H_2S} \times \dfrac{1 \text{ t-mole } H_2O_2}{\text{t-mole } H_2S}$

$$\times \frac{34.0 \text{ t } H_2O_2}{\text{t-mole } H_2O_2} = 1.72 \text{ t } H_2O_2$$

We get nearly the same answer in a and b because H_2S and H_2O_2 have very nearly the same molecular weights.

21. a. $855 \text{ kcal} \times \dfrac{2 \text{ moles } KCl}{21.4 \text{ kcal}} \times \dfrac{74.6 \text{ g } KCl}{\text{mole } KCl}$

$$= 5960 \text{ g } KCl$$

b. $855 \text{ kcal} \times \dfrac{1 \text{ mole } CaO}{42 \text{ kcal}} \times \dfrac{56.1 \text{ g } CaO}{\text{mole } CaO}$

$$= 1100 \text{ g } CaO$$

23. Hg: 200.59 $\quad Hg = \dfrac{200.59}{454.39} \times 10^2 = 44.14\%$

$$
\begin{array}{lll}
2 \text{ I:} & 253.80 & I = \dfrac{253.80}{454.39} \times 10^2 = \dfrac{55.86\%}{} \\
HgI_2: & 454.39 & \phantom{I = \dfrac{253.80}{454.39} \times 10^2 = } 100.00\%
\end{array}
$$

$$
\begin{array}{lll}
\text{N:} & 14.01 & N = \dfrac{14.01}{30.01} \times 10^2 = 46.68\%
\end{array}
$$

$$
\begin{array}{lll}
\text{O:} & 16.00 & O = \dfrac{16.00}{30.00} \times 10^2 = \dfrac{53.32\%}{} \\
\text{NO:} & 30.00 & \phantom{O = \dfrac{16.00}{30.00} \times 10^2 = } 100.00\%
\end{array}
$$

$$
\begin{array}{lll}
\text{Ca:} & 120.3 & Ca = \dfrac{120.3}{310.2} \times 10^2 = 38.78\%
\end{array}
$$

$$
\begin{array}{lll}
\text{P:} & 61.94 & P = \dfrac{61.94}{310.2} \times 10^2 = 19.97\%
\end{array}
$$

$$
\begin{array}{lll}
\text{O:} & 128.0 & O = \dfrac{128.0}{310.2} \times 10^2 = \dfrac{41.26\%}{} \\
Ca_3(PO_4)_2: & 310.2 & \phantom{O = \dfrac{128.0}{310.2} \times 10^2 = } 100.01\%
\end{array}
$$

25. N: 28.02 $\quad \dfrac{28.02}{80.06} \times 10^2 = 35.00\%$ N

    H: 4.04

    O: 48.00

    NH_4NO_3: 80.06

    N: 14.01 $\quad \dfrac{14.01}{17.04} \times 10^2 = 82.22\%$ N

    H: 3.03

    NH_3: 17.04

    NH_3 would be a better buy.

27. C: $\dfrac{85.59\ g}{12.01\ g/mole} = \dfrac{7.13\ \text{moles C}}{7.13\ \text{moles C}} = \dfrac{1\ \text{mole C}}{\text{mole C}}$

    H: $\dfrac{14.41\ g}{1.01\ g/mole} = \dfrac{14.3\ \text{mole H}}{7.13\ \text{moles C}} = \dfrac{2\ \text{moles H}}{\text{mole C}}$

    Empirical formula, $CH_2 = 14.03$ g/mole

$\dfrac{56.08\ g/mole\ \text{(molecular weight)}}{14.03\ g/mole\ \text{(wt. of empirical formula)}} = 3.997$

The molecular formula is 4 times the empirical formula: C_4H_8

29. 255 kg Fe $\times \dfrac{120.\ \text{kg FeS}_2}{55.8\ \text{kg Fe}} \times \dfrac{1.00\ \text{kg ore}}{0.328\ \text{kg FeS}_2}$

    $= 1670$ kg ore

31. 1.00 kg SO$_3$ $\times \dfrac{1\ \text{kg-mole SO}_3}{80.1\ \text{kg SO}_3} \times \dfrac{1\ \text{kg-mo H}_2\text{SO}_4}{\text{kg-mole SO}_3}$

    $\times \dfrac{1\ \text{kg-mole CaCO}_3}{\text{kg-mole H}_2\text{SO}_4} \times \dfrac{100.1\ \text{kg CaCO}_3}{\text{kg-mole CaCO}_3}$

    $= 1.25$ kg $CaCO_3$ dissolved by the SO_3

    $\dfrac{1.25\ \text{kg CaCO}_3}{545\ \text{kg CaCO}_3} \times 10^2$

    $= 0.229\%$ of the statue dissolved

Chapter 7

1. a. The bowling ball on the eighth floor; b. a bullet that hasn't been fired; c. separate samples of sodium and chlorine; d. a sample of hydrogen; e. separate Na^+ and Cl^- ions.

3. $2(Na[s]) + 26.0\ \text{kcal} \longrightarrow Na[g]$

   $\tfrac{1}{2}\,O_2(g) + 118.9\ \text{kcal} \longrightarrow O(g)$

   $2(Na[g]) + 118.5\ \text{kcal} \longrightarrow Na^+[g] + e^-[g]$

   $O(g) + 2e^-(g) \longrightarrow O^{2-}(g) - 177\ \text{kcal}$

   $\underline{2\ Na^+(g) + O^{2-}(g) \longrightarrow Na_2O(s) + 602\ \text{kcal}}$

   $2\ Na(s) + \tfrac{1}{2}O_2(g) \longrightarrow Na_2O(s) + 17.1\ \text{kcal}$

   Heat of formation: 17.1 kcal/mole.

5. $S(g) + e^-(g) \longrightarrow S^-(g) + 46\ \text{kcal}$

   $\underline{S^-(g) + e^-(g) \longrightarrow S^{2-}(g) - 118\ \text{kcal}}$

   $S(g) + 2e^-(g) \longrightarrow S^{2-}(g) - 72\ \text{kcal}$

   Total electron affinity: -72 kcal/mole.

7. a. BeO. Small ions with higher charge have higher lattice energy.

   b. CsF. F^- is smaller than I^-.

c. AlN. The ions in AlN have higher charge.

d. LiI. Li^+ is smaller than Cs^+.

e. BeO. Be^{2+} is smaller than Ba^{2+}.

f. $CaCO_3$. The ions in $CaCO_3$ have higher charge.

9. a. Li; b. Ca; c. Tl; d. Bi; e. Sn; f. Sn

11. a. Na; b. Ar; c. He; d. Ca; e. N; f. Br; g. B; h. O; i. Cl

13. a. Li; b. S^{2-}; c. N^{3-}; d. Kr; e. H^-; f. I^-; g. Ba^{2+}; h. Br^-; i. Mg^{2+}; i. S^{2-}; k. O^{2-}

15.

IA	IIA	IIIA	IVA	VA	VIA	VIIA	VIIIA
E·	Ė·	·Ė·	·Ė·	:Ė·	:Ė:	:Ė:	:Ė:

17. Groups IIIA, IVA, and VA

19. Ionization energy and electron affinity decrease going down Group IVA. Carbon is the first element in the group. Its high ionization energy prevents it from losing 4 electrons, and its high electron affinity allows it to gain 4 electrons. Lead has too low an electron affinity to gain electrons, and its lower ionization energy allows it to lose electrons.

Chapter 8

1. :C̈l:C̈l: :B̈r:B̈r: :Ï:Ï:

3. :S̈::S̈:

5. a. :F̈:Ö:F̈:   c. :C̈l:B:C̈l:
                         :C̈l:

   b. :B̈r:P̈:B̈r: d. :S̈::C::S̈:
         :B̈r:

7. $\left[\begin{array}{c} :\ddot{F}: \\ :\ddot{F}:B:\ddot{F}: \\ :\ddot{F}: \end{array}\right]^-$

9. 280. kcal/mole (3 times the bond energy)

11. Longer, because At is further down Group VIIA than I, so its atoms will be larger.

13. a. H—Ō—C̄l—Ō|
              |
              |Ō|

    b. |Ō—S̄=Ō|
              |
              |Ō|

    c. $\left[\begin{array}{c} |\bar{O}—N=\bar{O}| \\ | \\ |\bar{O}| \end{array}\right]^-$

    d. H—Ō—C—Ō—H
                ‖
                Ō|

    e. |Ō|
       |
       H—Ō—S̄—Ō—H
              |
              |Ō|

    f. $\left[\,|\bar{O}—N=\bar{O}|\,\right]^-$

15. H_2SO_4: $H-O-\overset{\displaystyle O}{\underset{\displaystyle O}{S}}-O-H$ (6 pairs)

S:	6 valence electrons
O_4:	24 valence electrons
H_2:	2 valence electrons
H_2SO_4:	32 electrons, 16 pairs

$H-\overline{O}-\overset{\displaystyle |\overline{O}|}{\underset{\displaystyle |\underline{O}|}{S}}-\overline{O}-H$ (16 pairs)

HSO_4^- (H_2SO_4 minus 1 H): $\left[H-\overline{O}-\overset{\displaystyle |\overline{O}|}{\underset{\displaystyle |\underline{O}|}{S}}-\overline{O}| \right]^-$

SO_4^{2-} (HSO_4^- minus 1 H): $\left[|\overline{O}-\overset{\displaystyle |\overline{O}|}{\underset{\displaystyle |\underline{O}|}{S}}-\overline{O}| \right]^{2-}$

All have the same number of electron pairs.

17. NO_3^-: $O-\overset{\displaystyle}{\underset{\displaystyle O}{N}}-O$ (3 pairs)

N:	5 valence electrons
O_3:	18 valence electrons
1−:	1 electron
NO_3^-:	24 electrons, 12 pairs

$\left[|\overline{O}-\overset{\displaystyle}{\underset{\displaystyle |\underline{O}|}{N}}=\overline{O}| \right]^-$ (12 pairs)

(Note: A double bond is necessary to use 12 pairs and still allow N to obey the octet rule.)

CO_3^{2-}: $O-\overset{\displaystyle}{\underset{\displaystyle O}{C}}-O$ (3 pairs)

C:	4 valence electrons
O_3:	18 valence electrons
2−:	2 electrons
CO_3^{2-}:	24 electrons, 12 pairs

$\left[|\overline{O}-\overset{\displaystyle}{\underset{\displaystyle |\underline{O}|}{C}}=\overline{O}| \right]^{2-}$ (12 pairs)

SO_3: $O-\overset{\displaystyle}{\underset{\displaystyle O}{S}}-O$ (3 pairs)

S:	6 valence electrons
O_3:	18 valence electrons
SO_3:	24 electrons, 12 pairs

$|\overline{O}-\overset{\displaystyle}{\underset{\displaystyle |\underline{O}|}{S}}=\overline{O}|$ (12 pairs)

All contain 12 electron pairs, 3 atoms attached to a central atom, and 1 double bond.

19. $H-\overset{\displaystyle}{\underset{\displaystyle H}{N}}-\overset{\displaystyle}{\underset{\displaystyle H}{N}}-H$ (5 pairs)

N_2:	10 valence electrons
H_4:	4 valence electrons
N_2H_4:	14 electrons, 7 pairs

$H-\overset{\displaystyle}{\underset{\displaystyle H}{\overline{N}}}-\overset{\displaystyle}{\underset{\displaystyle H}{\overline{N}}}-H$ (7 pairs)

21. a. $H-\overset{\displaystyle O}{\underset{\displaystyle}{C}}-H$ (3 pairs)

C:	4 valence electrons
O:	6 valence electrons
H_2:	2 valence electrons
CH_2O:	12 electrons, 6 pairs

$H-\overset{\displaystyle \overline{O}|}{\underset{\displaystyle}{C}}-H$ (6 pairs)

b. $H-\overset{\displaystyle H}{\underset{\displaystyle H}{C}}-\overset{\displaystyle H}{\underset{\displaystyle H}{C}}-H$ (7 pairs)

C_2:	8 valence electrons
H_6:	6 valence electrons
C_2H_6:	14 electrons, 7 pairs

c. $H-\overset{\displaystyle}{\underset{\displaystyle H}{C}}-\overset{\displaystyle}{\underset{\displaystyle Cl}{C}}-H$ (5 pairs)

C_2:	8 valence electrons
H_3:	3 valence electrons
Cl:	7 valence electrons
C_2H_3Cl:	18 electrons, 9 pairs

$H-\overset{\displaystyle}{\underset{\displaystyle H}{C}}=\overset{\displaystyle}{\underset{\displaystyle |\underline{Cl}|}{C}}-H$ (9 pairs)

23. a. Se, S, Cl, F; b. Rb, Sr, I, F; c. Li, B, N, F
25. b. Ba ⟷ Br; d. Be ⟷ Se; e. C ⟷ O; f. H ⟷ O;
    h. Pb ⟷ S
27. a. Nonpolar (C—H bonds are not polar).
    b. Nonpolar (C—Cl and C—H bonds are not polar).
    c. Polar (C=O bonds are polar, and the molecule lacks symmetry).
    d. Nonpolar (B—Cl bonds are polar, but the molecule is triangular and has symmetry).
    e. Polar (C=O bond is polar, and the molecule lacks symmetry).
    f. Nonpolar (H—S bonds are not polar).
    g. Polar (H—Cl bonds are polar, and the molecule lacks symmetry).

29.

Formula	Electronic Geometry	Molecular Shape
$HClO_3$	Tetrahedral	Pyramidal
SO_3	Triangular	Triangular
NO_3^-	Triangular	Triangular
H_2CO_3	Triangular	Triangular
H_2SO_4	Tetrahedral	Tetrahedral
NO_2^-	Triangular	Bent
H_3BO_3	Triangular	Triangular
HSO_4^-	Tetrahedral	Tetrahedral
SO_4^{2-}	Tetrahedral	Tetrahedral
PO_4^{3-}	Tetrahedral	Tetrahedral
ClO_4^-	Tetrahedral	Tetrahedral
CCl_4	Tetrahedral	Tetrahedral
CO_3^{2-}	Triangular	Triangular
ClO_2^-	Tetrahedral	Bent

Chapter 9

1. a. An electron in the first energy level; b. an electron in the s sublevel; c. an electron that occupies an orbital alone.
3. a. 3rd energy level, d sublevel, 3 electrons in d sublevel; b. 2nd energy level, s sublevel, 2 electrons in s sublevel; c. 5th energy level, p sublevel, 4 electrons in p sublevel; d. 6th energy level, f sublevel, 10 electrons in f sublevel.
5. a. $1s^2 2s^2 2p^2$; b. (Ne-10) $3s^2 3p^6$;
   c. (Kr-36) $5s^2 4d^{10}$ d. (Ar-18) $4s^1$
7. a. Wrong. The p sublevel can contain only 6 electrons.
   b. Correct.
   c. Wrong. There is no p sublevel in the first energy level.
   d. Wrong. The single orbital in the s sublevel can contain only 2 electrons.
   e. Wrong. After Ne-10, the third energy level, not the second, begins to fill.
   f. Correct.
   g. Wrong. The 3d sublevel is filled *after* the 4s sublevel.
   h. Correct.
   i. Wrong. The second energy must be filled before beginning to fill the third energy level.
   j. Wrong. There is no d sublevel in the second energy level.
9. a. N, P, As, Sb, Bi; b. Eu, Am; c. Sc, Y, La, Ac; d. Cu, Ag, Au; e. Kr, Xe, Rn; f. H, Li, Na, K, Rb, Cs, Fr
11. a. H, He; b. B, C, N, O, F, Ne; c. Na, Mg; d. F; e. V; f. Ag
13. Outer configuration s^1, 6th energy level: $6s^1$.
15. Atomic number 14
17. $s^2 p^2$, Group IVA

19. a. (Kr-36) $5s^2$

    (Kr-36) ⬆⬇
           5s

    b. (Xe-54) $6s^1$

    (Xe-54) 6s

    c. (Kr-36) $5s^2 4d^2$

    (Kr-36) ⬆⬇ ⬆ ⬆ ☐ ☐ ☐
            5s   4d

    d. (Ar-18) $4s^2 3d^{10} 4p^4$

    (Ar-18) ⬆⬇ ⬆⬇⬆⬇⬆⬇⬆⬇⬆⬇ ⬆⬇⬆⬆
            4s   3d   4p

    e. (Ar-18) $4s^2 3d^{10} 4p^1$

    (Ar-18) ⬆⬇ ⬆⬇⬆⬇⬆⬇⬆⬇⬆⬇ ⬆☐☐
            4s   3d   4p

    f. (Kr-36) $5s^2 4d^{10} 5p^5$

    (Kr-36) ⬆⬇ ⬆⬇⬆⬇⬆⬇⬆⬇ ⬆⬇⬆⬇⬆
            5s   4d   5p

    g. (Kr-36) $5s^2 4d^5$

    (Kr-36) ⬆⬇ ⬆⬆⬆⬆⬆
            5s   4d

    h. (Ar-18) $4s^2 3d^6$

    (Ar-18) ⬆⬇ ⬆⬇⬆⬆⬆⬆
            4s   3d

21. a. $3d^3$; b. $3d^5$; c. $3d^{10}$; d. $3d^7$; e. $4d^{10}$; f. (Kr-36); g. $3d^3$; h. (Ar-18)

Chapter 10

1. $1 \text{ kg} \times 0.5 \dfrac{\text{kcal}}{\text{kg} \times K} \times (273 - 233)K = 20 \quad \text{kcal}$

   $1 \text{ kg} \times 79.9 \dfrac{\text{kcal}}{\text{kg}} \qquad\qquad = 79.9 \text{ kcal}$

   $1 \text{ kg} \times 1 \dfrac{\text{kcal}}{\text{kg} \times K} \times (373 - 273)K = 100 \text{ kcal}$

   $1 \text{ kg} \times 540 \dfrac{\text{kcal}}{\text{kg}} \qquad\qquad = \underline{540 \quad \text{kcal}}$

   740 kcal

3. $1 \text{ kg NH}_3 \times \dfrac{327 \text{ kcal}}{\text{kg NH}_3} = 327 \text{ kcal}$

5. a. A gas; b. the first flat part on the left is the heat of fusion, the next is the heat of vaporization; c. solid; d. weaker (melting and boiling points lower than water's).

7. b. Because lowering the temperature decreases water's vapor pressure; d. to prevent the escape of water vapor from the room; e. to help saturate the air with water vapor; g. to prevent the escape of water vapor from the plants.

9. Yes, by decreasing the pressure.

11. The ice would melt.

13. a. Br_2 has only van der Waals attraction, NaCl has ionic bonding; b. they have only van der Waals attraction; c. tungsten has d electrons to contribute to its metallic bonds; d. Br_2 has a higher molecular weight than Cl_2; e. H_2O can form twice as many hydrogen bonds as HF; f. SiO_2 has covalent bonding, which is stronger than NaCl's ionic bonding.

15. a. NH_3; b. NH_3 has H-bonding; the others have only dipole-dipole or van der Waals attraction.

Chapter 11

1. $100 \text{ miles} \times \dfrac{5 \text{ g NO}}{\text{mile}} \times \dfrac{1 \text{ mole NO}}{30 \text{ g NO}} \times \dfrac{22.4 \text{ l NO}}{\text{mole NO}}$
$$= 400 \text{ l NO}$$

3. $2 \times 10^{10} \text{ l NH}_3 \times \dfrac{1 \text{ mole NH}_3}{22.4 \text{ l NH}_3} \times \dfrac{17 \text{ g NH}_3}{\text{mole NH}_3}$
$$\times \dfrac{1 \text{ t NH}_3}{10^6 \text{ g NH}_3} = 2 \times 10^4 \text{ t NH}_3$$

5. $1.35 \dfrac{\text{g}}{\text{l}} \times \dfrac{22.4 \text{ l}}{\text{mole}} = 30.2 \dfrac{\text{g}}{\text{mole}}$

The pollutant is probably NO (molecular weight 30.0 g/mole).

7. $500 \text{ l N}_2 \times \dfrac{1 \text{ mole N}_2}{22.4 \text{ l N}_2} \times \dfrac{2 \text{ moles NO}}{\text{mole N}_2}$
$$= 40 \text{ moles NO}$$

9. $2 \times 10^5 \text{ l NO} \times \dfrac{1 \text{ l CH}_4}{4 \text{ l NO}} = 5 \times 10^4 \text{ l CH}_4$

11. $250 \text{ l H}_2 S \times \dfrac{1 \text{ mole H}_2 S}{22.4 \text{ l H}_2 S} \times \dfrac{1 \text{ mole S}}{\text{mole H}_2 S} \times \dfrac{32.1 \text{ g S}}{\text{mole S}}$
$$= 360 \text{ g S}$$

13. $1.00 \times 10^3 \text{ g NaHCO}_3 \times \dfrac{1 \text{ mole NaHCO}_3}{84.0 \text{ g NaHCO}_3}$
$$\times \dfrac{1 \text{ mole NH}_3}{\text{mole NaHCO}_3} \times \dfrac{22.4 \text{ l NH}_3}{\text{mole NH}_3} = 267 \text{ l NH}_3$$

CO_2 has the same mole-ratio as NH_3, so its volume is also the same (267 l).

15. $V_2 = 525 \text{ l} \dfrac{40 \text{ atm}}{1 \text{ atm}} = 2 \times 10^4 \text{ l}$

17. $V_2 = 1 \text{ l} \times \dfrac{273 \text{ K}}{923 \text{ K}} = 0.3 \text{ l}$

19. Needles: $1.00 \text{ l} \times \dfrac{316 \text{ K}}{273 \text{ K}} = 1.16 \text{ l}$; density $= \dfrac{1.29 \text{ g}}{1.16 \text{ l}}$
$$= 1.11 \text{ g/l}$$

Bozeman: $1.00 \text{ l} \times \dfrac{244 \text{ K}}{273 \text{ K}} = 0.894 \text{ l}$; density
$$= \dfrac{1.29 \text{ g}}{0.894 \text{ l}} = 1.44 \text{ g/l}$$

Density of air in Needles is roughly 3/4 the density of air in Bozeman.

21. $P_2 = 2.5 \text{ atm} \times \dfrac{339 \text{ K}}{296 \text{ K}} = 2.9 \text{ atm}$

23. $V_2 = 89.2 \text{ cm}^3 \times \dfrac{273 \text{ K}}{295 \text{ K}} \times \dfrac{0.978 \text{ atm}}{1.00 \text{ atm}} = 80.7 \text{ cm}^3$

25. $0.234 \text{ atm} + 0.438 \text{ atm} + 0.199 \text{ atm} = 0.871 \text{ atm}$

27. $P_2 = 0.954 \text{ atm} - 0.0261 = 0.928 \text{ atm}$

$V_2 = 97.2 \text{ cm}^3 \times \dfrac{295 \text{ K}}{273 \text{ K}} \times \dfrac{1.00 \text{ atm}}{0.928 \text{ atm}} = 113 \text{ cm}^3$

29. a. $5.5 \times 10^5 \text{ g CaC}_2 \times \dfrac{1 \text{ mole CaC}_2}{64.1 \text{ g CaC}_2} \times \dfrac{1 \text{ mole C}_2 H_2}{\text{mole CaC}_2}$
$$\times \dfrac{22.4 \text{ l C}_2 H_2}{\text{mole C}_2 H_2} = 1.9 \times 10^5 \text{ l C}_2 H_2$$

b. $V_2 = 1.9 \times 10^5 \text{ liters} \times \dfrac{573 \text{ K}}{273 \text{ K}} \times \dfrac{1.00 \text{ atm}}{2.00 \text{ atm}}$
$$= 2.0 \times 10^5 \text{ liters}$$

31. Ideal Gas Equation, $V = \dfrac{nRT}{P}$

Note that moles HgO = moles O_3, from equation.

$$V = \dfrac{(0.012 \text{ moles } O_3)(0.0821 \frac{(l)(atm)}{(mole)(K)})(297 \text{ K})}{0.989 \text{ atm}}$$
$$= 0.30 \text{ l } O_3$$

Alternative method: $0.012 \text{ moles HgO} \times \dfrac{1 \text{ mole } O_3}{\text{mole HgO}}$
$$\times \dfrac{22.4 \text{ l } O_3}{\text{mole } O_3} = 0.269 \text{ l } O_3$$

$0.269 \text{ l } O_3 \times \dfrac{297 \text{ K}}{273 \text{ K}} \times \dfrac{1.00 \text{ atm}}{0.989 \text{ atm}} = 0.30 \text{ l } O_3$

33. a. 2×10^4 moles $H_2 SO_4$ (moles S = moles SO_2
$$= \text{moles } H_2 SO_4)$$

b. $2 \times 10^4 \text{ moles H}_2 SO_4 \times \dfrac{98.1 \text{ g } H_2 SO_4}{\text{mole } H_2 SO_4}$
$$= 2 \times 10^6 \text{ g } H_2 SO_4 \ (2 \times 10^3 \text{ kg})$$

Chapter 12

1. $\dfrac{0.352 \text{ g}}{0.0500 \text{ l}} = 7.04 \dfrac{\text{g}}{\text{l}}$ Answer: 7.04 g/l

3. $1 \text{ g gold} \times \dfrac{1 \text{ l seawater}}{4 \times 10^{-9} \text{ g gold}} = 3 \times 10^8 \text{ l seawater}$

This doesn't seem to be a practical source of gold.

5. Add water to the mixture and stir. NaCl is soluble and will dissolve, leaving the insoluble AgCl behind.

7. Mayonnaise is an emulsion, and the excess ions in the air during an electrical storm could destroy the emulsion.

9. Gases are less soluble at lower pressure.

11. N_2, Ar, O_2 (in increasing order of boiling points).

13. $\dfrac{27.0 \text{ g methyl alcohol}}{0.0730 \text{ kg } H_2O} \times \dfrac{1 \text{ mole methyl alcohol}}{32.0 \text{ g methyl alcohol}}$

$= 11.6 \dfrac{\text{moles methyl alcohol}}{\text{kg } H_2O} = 11.6 \text{ m}$

$T_f = 0.00 \,°C - \left(1.84 \dfrac{°C}{m}\right)(11.6 \text{ m}) = -21.3 \,°C$

15. Yes; any soluble solute will lower the freezing point of the solution. However, care should be taken not to contaminate the ice cream with ethylene glycol.

17. a. The water inside the fruit cells passes through cell membranes, trying to dilute the sugar on the outside; b. water passes through the muscle cells to the outside, trying to dilute the salt; c. water passes into the cells, which are more concentrated in solutes, and is drawn up the tree by osmosis; d. water leaves the snail's cells to dilute the salt, and the snail becomes dehydrated and dies; e. water passes from cells, trying to dilute the salt water.

19. $2 \text{ Al}^{3+}(aq) + 3 \text{ SO}_4^{2-}(aq) + 2 \text{ PO}_4^{3-}(aq) \longrightarrow$
$ 2 \text{ AlPO}_4(s) + 3 \text{ SO}_4^{2-}(aq)$
Net ionic: $\text{Al}^{3+}(aq) + \text{PO}_4^{3-}(aq) \longrightarrow \text{AlPO}_4(s)$
$2 \text{ Fe}^{3+}(aq) + 3 \text{ SO}_4^{2-}(aq) + 2 \text{ PO}_4^{3-}(aq) \longrightarrow$
$ 2 \text{ FePO}_4(s) + 3 \text{ SO}_4^{2-}(aq)$
Net ionic: $\text{Fe}^{3+}(aq) + \text{PO}_4^{3-}(aq) \longrightarrow \text{FePO}_4(s)$

21. a. $MgCO_3$:
$2 \text{ K}^+ + \text{CO}_3^{2-} + \text{Mg}^{2+} + 2 \text{ Cl}^- \longrightarrow$
$ 2 \text{ K}^+ + \text{MgCO}_3(s) + 2 \text{ Cl}^-$
Net ionic: $\text{CO}_3^{2-} + \text{Mg}^{2+} \longrightarrow \text{MgCO}_3(s)$

b. PbI_2:
$\text{Pb}^{2+} + 2 \text{ NO}_3^- + \text{Sr}^{2+} + 2 \text{ I}^- \longrightarrow$
$ \text{PbI}_2(s) + 2 \text{ NO}_3^- + \text{Sr}^{2+}$
Net ionic: $\text{Pb}^{2+} + 2 \text{ I}^- \longrightarrow \text{PbI}_2(s)$

c. No precipitate; all possible compounds are soluble.

d. $Co(OH)_2$ and CaF_2:
$\text{Co}^{2+} + 2 \text{ F}^- + \text{Ca}^{2+} + 2 \text{ OH}^- \longrightarrow$
$ \text{CaF}_2(s) + \text{Co(OH)}_2(s)$
Net ionic equation is the same.

e. No precipitate; all possible compounds are soluble.

f. HgS:
$\text{Hg}^{2+} + 2 \text{ Cl}^- + 2 \text{ NH}_4^+ + \text{S}^{2-} \longrightarrow$
$ \text{HgS}(s) + 2 \text{ Cl}^- + 2 \text{ NH}_4^+$
Net ionic: $\text{Hg}^{2+} + \text{S}^{2-} \longrightarrow \text{HgS}(s)$

23. $500 \text{ cm}^3 \text{ solution} \times \dfrac{2 \times 10^{-17} \text{ moles Ag}_2S}{1.00 \times 10^3 \text{ cm}^3 \text{ solution}}$

$\times \dfrac{247.9 \text{ g Ag}_2S}{\text{mole Ag}_2S} = 2 \times 10^{-15} \text{ g Ag}_2S$

25. $\text{Ag}^+ + \text{Cl}^- \longrightarrow \text{AgCl}(s)$

$2500 \text{ l Ag}^+ \times \dfrac{0.0023 \text{ moles Ag}^+}{\text{l Ag}^+} \times \dfrac{1 \text{ mole KCl}}{\text{mole Ag}^+}$

$\times \dfrac{74.6 \text{ g KCl}}{\text{mole KCl}} = 430 \text{ g KCl, or } 0.43 \text{ kg KCl}$

27. $\text{Mg}^{2+} + 2 \text{ OH}^- \longrightarrow \text{Mg(OH)}_2(s)$

$1500 \text{ l seawater} \times \dfrac{5 \times 10^{-2} \text{ moles Mg}^{2+}}{\text{l seawater}}$

$\times \dfrac{1 \text{ mole Ca(OH)}_2}{\text{mole Mg}^{2+}} \times \dfrac{74.1 \text{ g Ca(OH)}_2}{\text{mole Ca(OH)}_2}$

$= 6 \times 10^3 \text{ g Ca(OH)}_2 \text{, or } 6 \text{ kg Ca(OH)}_2$

Chapter 13

1. a. $\underset{\substack{\text{strong} \\ \text{acid}}}{\text{ClO}_4^-} + \underset{\substack{\text{strong} \\ \text{base}}}{\text{H}_3\text{O}^+ + \text{K}^+ + \text{OH}^-} \longrightarrow$
$ 2 \text{ H}_2\text{O} + \text{K}^+ + \text{HSO}_4^-$
Net: $\text{H}_3\text{O}^+ + \text{OH}^- \longrightarrow 2 \text{ H}_2\text{O}$

b. $2 \underset{\text{weak acid}}{\text{HC}_2\text{H}_3\text{O}_2} + \text{Ca}^{2+} + 2 \underset{\substack{\text{strong} \\ \text{base}}}{\text{OH}^-} \longrightarrow$
$ 2 \text{ C}_2\text{H}_3\text{O}_2^- + \text{Ca}^{2+} + 2 \text{ H}_2\text{O}$
Net: $2\text{HC}_2\text{H}_3\text{O}_2 + 2 \text{ OH}^- \longrightarrow$
$ 2 \text{ C}_2\text{H}_3\text{O}_2^- + 2 \text{ H}_2\text{O}$

c. $\underset{\substack{\text{weak} \\ \text{base}}}{\text{NH}_3} + \underset{\substack{\text{weak} \\ \text{acid}}}{\text{HC}_2\text{H}_3\text{O}_2} \longrightarrow \text{NH}_4^+ + \text{C}_2\text{H}_3\text{O}_2^-$
Net: Same as above

d. $\underset{\text{strong acid}}{\text{Cl}^- + \text{H}_3\text{O}^+} + 3 \underset{\text{weak base}}{\text{Na}^+ + \text{PO}_4^{3-}} \longrightarrow$
$ \text{Cl}^- + \text{H}_2\text{O} + 3 \text{ Na}^+ + \text{HPO}_4^{2-}$
Net: $\text{H}_3\text{O}^+ + \text{PO}_4^{3-} \longrightarrow \text{H}_2\text{O} + \text{HPO}_4^{2-}$

e. $2 \underset{\text{strong acid}}{\text{H}_3\text{O}^+ + 2 \text{ NO}_3^-} + \underset{\text{strong base}}{\text{Sr}^{2+} + 2 \text{ OH}^-} \longrightarrow$
$ 4 \text{ H}_2\text{O} + 2 \text{ NO}_3^- + \text{Sr}^{2+}$
Net: $2 \text{ H}_3\text{O}^+ + 2 \text{ OH}^- \longrightarrow 4 \text{ H}_2\text{O}$

f. $Na^+ + HCO_3^- + HF \longrightarrow$

　　weak base　　　weak
　　　　　　　　　　acid

$$Na^+ + F^- + H_2CO_3(CO_2 + H_2O)$$

Net: $HCO_3^- + HF \longrightarrow$

$$F^- + H_2CO_3(CO_2 + H_2O)$$

3. $H_3O^+ + HSO_4^- + Na^+ + HCO_3^- \longrightarrow$

　　strong acid　　　　　　weak base

$$H_2O + HSO_4^- + Na^+ + H_2CO_3(H_2O + CO_2)$$

Net: $H_3O^+ + HCO_3^- \longrightarrow$

$$H_2O + H_2CO_3(H_2O + CO_2)$$

5. a. $[H_3O^+] = 10^0 = 1$; b. $[H_3O^+] = 10^{-3}$;
c. $[H_3O^+] = 10^{-5}$; d. $[H_3O^+] = 10^{-7}$;
e. $[H_3O^+] = 10^{-8}$; f. $[H_3O^+] = 10^{-12}$

7. a. $[H_3O^+] = 3.6 \times 10^{-2}$, pH $= 1.45$, acid;
b. $[OH^-] = 1.5 \times 10^{-1}$, pH $= 13.18$, base;
c. pH $= 4.13$, acid; d. pH $= 6.63$, acid; e. pH $= 8.06$, base; f. pH $= 13.30$, base

9. Proton donor: $H_2O + CO_3^{2-} \longrightarrow OH^- + HCO_3^-$
Proton acceptor: $H_2O + NH_4^+ \longrightarrow H_3O^+ + NH_3$

11. a. $F^- + H_3O^+ \longrightarrow HF + H_2O$
b. No reaction. HSO_3^- as a base is above $HC_2H_3O_2$ in Table 13.6.
c. $H_3PO_4 + S^{2-} \longrightarrow H_2PO_4^- + HS^-$
d. $NH_4^+ + PO_4^{3-} \longrightarrow NH_3 + HPO_4^{2-}$
e. $HSO_4^- + NH_3 \longrightarrow SO_4^{2-} + NH_4^+$
f. No reaction. Both are acids only.
g. No reaction. Both are bases only.
h. $HCO_3^- + H_3O^+ \longrightarrow$
$$H_2CO_3 + H_2O(CO_2 + H_2O)$$

13. $C_2^{2-} + 2 H_2O \longrightarrow C_2H_2 + 2 OH^-$
　　base　　　acid

15. $HBr(g) + 86.5 \text{ kcal} \longrightarrow H(g) + Br(g)$
$H(g) + 312.0 \text{ kcal} \longrightarrow H^+(g) + e^-(g)$
$Br(g) + e^-(g) \longrightarrow Br^-(g) + 79.5 \text{ kcal}$
$H^+(g) + H_2O(l) \longrightarrow H_3O^+(aq) + 264.0 \text{ kcal}$
$Br^-(g) \longrightarrow Br^-(aq) + 76.4 \text{ kcal}$

$HBr(g) + H_2O(l) \longrightarrow$
$$H_3O^+(aq) + Br^-(aq) + 21.4 \text{ kcal}$$

17. $Ca_3(PO_4)_2(s) + 2 H_3O^+ + 2 HSO_4^- \longrightarrow$
$$3 Ca^{2+} + 2 H_2PO_4^- + 2 H_2O + 2 SO_4^{2-}$$
The insoluble substance contains a negative ion that's a base (PO_4^{3-}).

19. a. $ZnS(s) + 2 H_3O^+ \longrightarrow Zn^{2+} + H_2S + 2 H_2O$
b. Acid won't help, because the negative ion (NO_3^-) is not a base.
c. $CaCO_3(s) + 2 H_3O^+ \longrightarrow$
$$Ca^{2+} + H_2CO_3 + 2 H_2O$$
d. Acid won't help, because Cl^- is not a base.
e. $CaO(s) + 2 H_3O^+ \longrightarrow Ca^{2+} + 3 H_2O$
f. $Al(OH)_3(s) + 3 H_3O^+ \longrightarrow Al^{3+} + 6 H_2O$

21. $V_c = \dfrac{0.016 \text{ M}}{12 \text{ M}}(1.00 \text{ l}) = 0.0013 \text{ l, or 1.3 ml}$

23. $HCl + NH_3 \longrightarrow NH_4Cl$

$0.0241 \text{ l HCl} \times \dfrac{0.0500 \text{ moles HCl}}{\text{l HCl}} \times \dfrac{1 \text{ mole NH}_3}{\text{mole HCl}}$
$$= 1.21 \times 10^{-3} \text{ moles NH}_3$$

$\dfrac{1.21 \times 10^{-3} \text{ moles NH}_3}{0.0100 \text{ l NH}_3} = 0.121 \text{ M NH}_3$

25. $50.0 \text{ g palmitic acid} \times \dfrac{1 \text{ mole palmitic acid}}{256 \text{ g palmitic acid}}$

$\times \dfrac{1 \text{ mole NaOH}}{\text{mole palmitic acid}} \times \dfrac{1.00 \text{ l NaOH}}{1.00 \text{ moles NaOH}}$
$$= 0.195 \text{ l NaOH, or 195 ml}$$

27. $H_2SO_3 + 2 NaOH \longrightarrow Na_2SO_3 + 2 H_2O$

$0.0224 \text{ l NaOH} \times \dfrac{0.0122 \text{ moles NaOH}}{\text{l NaOH}}$

$\times \dfrac{1 \text{ mole H}_2SO_3}{2 \text{ moles NaOH}} = 1.37 \times 10^{-4} \text{ moles H}_2SO_3$

$\dfrac{1.37 \times 10^{-4} \text{ moles H}_2SO_3}{0.100 \text{ l rainwater}} = 1.37 \times 10^{-3} \text{ M H}_2SO_3$

Chapter 14

1.

	Ox. Agent	Red. Agent	Ox. Substance	Red. Substance
a.	S	Cu	Cu	S
b.	O_2	N_2	N_2	O_2
c.	H_3O^+	Fe	Fe	H_3O^+
d.	F_2	Cl^-	Cl^-	F_2
e.	OH^-	Zn	Zn	OH^-
f.	$AgNO_3$	Mg	Mg	$AgNO_3$

3. a. Oxidation happens at the anode, so Al is the anode. Reduction happens at the cathode, so Pb is the cathode.

b.

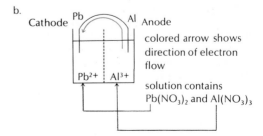

Cathode Pb　　　Al Anode

colored arrow shows direction of electron flow

Pb^{2+}　Al^{3+}

solution contains $Pb(NO_3)_2$ and $Al(NO_3)_3$

5. a.
$$4[Al^{3+}(l) + 3e^- \longrightarrow Al(l)]$$
$$3[2O^{2-}(l) \longrightarrow O_2(g) + 4e^-]$$
$$\overline{4\,Al^{3+}(l) + 6\,O^-(l) \longrightarrow 4\,Al(l) + 3\,O_2(g)}$$

b.

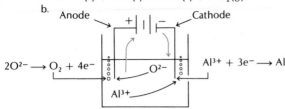

$$2O^{2-} \longrightarrow O_2 + 4e^- \qquad Al^{3+} + 3e^- \longrightarrow Al$$

c. Oxygen gas bubbles off at anode. Aluminum metal plates out onto cathode.

7. a. No reaction

b.
$$2[MnO_4^-(aq) + 8\,H_3O^+(aq) + 5e^- \longrightarrow$$
$$Mn^{2+}(aq) + 12\,H_2O(l)]$$
$$5[2\,I^-(aq) \longrightarrow$$
$$I_2(aq) + 2e^-]$$
$$\overline{2\,MnO_4^-(aq) + 16\,H_3O^+(aq) + 10\,I^-(aq) \longrightarrow}$$
$$2\,Mn^{2+}(aq) + 24\,H_2O + 5\,I_2(aq)$$

c. No reaction

d.
$$3[Ag(s) \longrightarrow$$
$$Ag^+(aq) + e^-]$$
$$NO_3^-(aq) + 4\,H_3O^+(aq) + 3e^- \longrightarrow$$
$$NO(g) + 6H_2O(l)$$
$$\overline{3\,Ag(s) + NO_3^-(aq) + 4\,H_3O^+(aq) \longrightarrow}$$
$$3\,Ag^+(aq) + NO(g) + 6\,H_2O(l)$$

e.
$$MnO_2(s) + 4\,H_3O^+(aq) + 2e^- \longrightarrow$$
$$Mn^{2+}(aq) + 6\,H_2O(l)$$
$$2[Fe^{2+}(aq) \longrightarrow$$
$$Fe^{3+}(aq) + e^-]$$
$$\overline{MnO_2(s) + 4\,H_3O^+(aq) + 2\,Fe^{2+}(aq) \longrightarrow}$$
$$Mn^{2+}(aq) + 6\,H_2O(l) + 2\,Fe^{3+}(aq)$$

f. No reaction

g.
$$Cr_2O_7^{2-}(aq) + 14\,H_3O^+(aq) + 6e^- \longrightarrow$$
$$2\,Cr^{3+}(aq) + 21\,H_2O(l)$$
$$3[H_2O_2(aq) + 2\,H_2O(l) \longrightarrow$$
$$O_2(g) + 2\,H_3O^+(aq) + 2e^-$$
$$\overline{Cr_2O_7^{2-}(aq) + 8\,H_3O^+(aq) + 3\,H_2O_2(aq) \longrightarrow}$$
$$2\,Cr^{3+}(aq) + 3\,O_2(g) + 15\,H_2O(l)$$

h.
$$PbO_2(s) + SO_4^{2-}(aq) + 4\,H_3O^+(aq) + 2e^- \longrightarrow$$
$$PbSO_4(s) + 6\,H_2O(l)$$
$$2\,Br^-(aq) \longrightarrow$$
$$Br_2(aq) + 2e^-$$
$$\overline{PbO_2(s) + SO_4^{2-}(aq) + 4\,H_3O^+(aq) + 2\,Br^-(aq) \longrightarrow}$$
$$PbSO_4(s) + 6\,H_2O(l) + Br_2(aq)$$

9. H_3O^+ will oxidize Al. HCl could be used to remove the oxide coating, but carefuly and quickly to prevent the HCl from dissolving the aluminum, too.

11. Yes. H_3O^+ is below Au.

13.
$$NiO_2(s) + 2\,H_2O(l) + 2e^- \longrightarrow$$
$$Ni(OH)_2(s) + 2\,OH^-(aq)$$
$$+0.49\ V$$
$$Cd(s) + 2\,OH^-(aq) \longrightarrow Cd(OH)_2(s) + 2e^-$$
$$+0.81\ V$$
$$\overline{NiO_2(s) + 2\,H_2O(l) + Cd(s) \longrightarrow}$$
$$Ni(OH)_2(s) + Cd(OH)_2(s)$$
$$+1.30\ V$$

15. $Na^+(l) + e^- \longrightarrow Na(l)$ $-2.71\ V$
$Li^+(l) + e^- \longrightarrow Li(l)$ $-3.01\ V$
Na would be obtained at the cathode, because its negative potential is lower.
$2\,Cl^-(l) \longrightarrow Cl_2(g)$ $-1.36\ V$
$2\,Br^-(l) \longrightarrow Br_2(l)$ $-1.06\ V$
Br_2 would be obtained at the anode, because its negative potential is lower.

17. a. $3\,Fe^{2+}(aq) + 2\,Al(s) \longrightarrow 3\,Fe(s) + Al^{3+}(aq)$
$3\,Pb^{2+}(aq) + 2\,Al(s) \longrightarrow 3\,Pb(s) + 2\,Al^{3+}(aq)$

b. The second reaction would take place, because its positive potential $(-0.13 + 1.66 = +1.53\ V)$ is greater than that of the first reaction $(-0.44 + 1.66 = +1.22\ V)$.

19. Fe^{3+} would oxidize I^-.

21. From Table 14.5, energy for NaCl is -188 kcal/2 moles e^-, and for $MgCl_2$, -172 kcal/2 moles e^-.
$$\frac{-188\ kcal}{2\ moles\ e^-} \times \frac{1\ mole\ e^-}{mole\ Na} = -94\ \frac{kcal}{mole\ Na}$$
$$\frac{-172\ kcal}{2\ moles\ e^-} \times \frac{2\ moles\ e^-}{mole\ Mg} = -172\ \frac{kcal}{mole\ Mg}$$
It takes more energy to produce a mole of Mg than a mole of Na.

23. $454\ g\ NaCl \times \dfrac{1\ mole\ NaCl}{58.5\ g\ NaCl} \times \dfrac{-94\ kcal}{mole\ NaCl}$
$$= -730\ kcal$$
730 kcal required

25. a. H, 1+; O, 1−. b. K, 1+; Cr, 6+; O, 2−. c. Na, 1+; Cl, 5+; O, 2−. d. Hg, 1+; Cl, 1−. e. S, 4+; O, 2−. f. Mn, 2+; S, 4+; O, 2−. g. Ni, 4+; O, 2−

27. a.
$$MnO_2 + 4\,H_3O^+ + 2e^- \longrightarrow Mn^{2+} + 6\,H_2O$$
$$2\,Cl^- \longrightarrow Cl_2 + 2e^-$$
$$\overline{MnO_2 + 4\,H_3O^+ + 2\,Cl^- \longrightarrow}$$
$$Mn^{2+} + Cl_2 + 6\,H_2O$$

b.
$$5[Cl_2 + 2e^- \longrightarrow 2\,Cl^-]$$
$$I_2 + 16\,H_2O \longrightarrow$$
$$2\,HIO_3 + 10\,H_3O^+ + 10e^-$$
$$\overline{I_2 + 16\,H_2O + 5\,Cl_2 \longrightarrow}$$
$$2\,HIO_3 + 10\,H_3O^+ + 10\,Cl^-$$

c.
$$4\,H_3O^+ + O_2^{2-} + 2e^- \longrightarrow 6\,H_2O$$
$$2\,Cl^- \longrightarrow Cl_2 + 2e^-$$
$$\overline{4\,H_3O^+ + O_2^{2-} + 2\,Cl^- \longrightarrow Cl_2 + 6\,H_2O}$$

Chapter 15

1. a. 1; b. 2; c. 1
3. a. left; b. right; c. middle; d. right
5. a. shift to the left; b. shift to the right; c. shift to the right; d. shift to the left; e. shift to the right; f. no effect
7. a. Supply heat, reduce pressure, remove CO_2 as it forms; b. remove heat, reduce pressure, remove CO as it forms; c. supply heat, reduce pressure, remove C_2H_2 as it forms; d. increase pressure, remove heat as reaction proceeds; e. increase pressure, remove product as it forms.

9. a.　　　　　　b.　　　　　c.

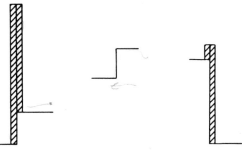

Equilibrium lies to left　　Equilibrium lies to left　　Equilibrium lies to right

11. a. $\dfrac{[NO_2][NO_2]}{[NO][NO][O_2]}$

b. $\dfrac{[NO][NO][NO][NO][H_2O][H_2O][H_2O][H_2O][H_2O][H_2O]}{[NH_3][NH_3][NH_3][NH_3][O_2][O_2][O_2][O_2][O_2]}$

c. $\dfrac{[H_2O][H_2O]}{[H_2][H_2][O_2]}$

13. a. exothermic; b. too little product would be obtained; c. begin the reaction at a high temperature, then remove heat as the reaction proceeds
15. A large excess of Cl^- (in a soluble chloride such as NaCl) will drive the equilibrium in the direction of Hg_2Cl_2.
17. $[Pb^{2+}[= \dfrac{2.0 \times 10^{-16}}{1.0 \times 10^{-8}} = 2.0 \times 10^{-8}\ M\ Pb^{2+}$
19. Buffer ratio $= \dfrac{[H_2PO_4^-]}{[HPO_4^{2-}]} = \dfrac{1.8 \times 10^{-4}}{2.6 \times 10^{-4}} = 6.9 \times 10^{-1}$

$[H_3O^+] = (6.3 \times 10^{-8})(6.9 \times 10^{-1}) = 4.3 \times 10^{-8}$
pH $= 7.36$ (from Figure 13.3)
21. If OH^- added, then $H_2PO_4^- + OH^- \longrightarrow$
$$HPO_4^{2-} + H_2O$$
$[H_2PO_4^{2-}] = 1.8 \times 10^{-4} - 0.1 \times 10^{-4}$
$$= 1.7 \times 10^{-4}\ M$$
$[HPO_4^{2-}] = 2.6 \times 10^{-4} + 0.1 \times 10^{-4}$
$$= 2.7 \times 10^{-4}\ M$$

Buffer ratio $= \dfrac{1.7 \times 10^{-4}}{2.7 \times 10^{-4}} = 6.3 \times 10^{-1}$

$[H_3O^+] = (6.3 \times 10^{-8})(6.3 \times 10^{-1}) = 4.0 \times 10^{-8}$
pH $= 7.40$; pH change $= 7.40 - 7.36 = 0.04$
23. A pH of 5.40 means $[H_3O^+]$ or 4.0×10^{-6}. Acetic acid (a) would be the best choice, since its K_a is closest to the value of the desired $[H_3O^+]$.

Chapter 16

1. a. $^{235}_{92}U \longrightarrow {}^{4}_{2}He + {}^{231}_{90}Th$
   b. $^{232}_{90}Th \longrightarrow {}^{4}_{2}He + {}^{228}_{88}Ra$
   c. $^{239}_{94}Pu \longrightarrow {}^{4}_{2}He + {}^{235}_{92}U$
   d. $^{223}_{88}Ra \longrightarrow {}^{4}_{2}He + {}^{219}_{86}Rn$
3. a. $^{30}_{15}P \longrightarrow {}^{0}_{1}e + {}^{30}_{14}Si$
   b. $^{22}_{11}Na \longrightarrow {}^{0}_{1}e + {}^{22}_{10}Ne$
   c. $^{18}_{9}F \longrightarrow {}^{0}_{1}e + {}^{18}_{8}O$
5. N-13 probably has too few neutrons per proton, and could undergo either electron capture or positron emission:

Electron capture: $^{13}_{7}N + {}^{0}_{-1}e \longrightarrow {}^{13}_{6}C$

Positron emission: $^{13}_{7}N \longrightarrow {}^{0}_{1}e + {}^{13}_{6}C$

N-15 probably has too many neutrons per proton, and could undergo beta-emission:

$^{15}_{7}N \longrightarrow {}^{0}_{-1}e + {}^{15}_{8}O$

7. a. $^{7}_{4}Be + {}^{0}_{-1}e \xrightarrow[\text{capture}]{\text{electron}} {}^{7}_{3}Li$

b. Be^{2+} would not relinquish an additional electron easily.
9. a. 1000 becquerels of an alpha emitter; b. 1000 becquerels of a gamma emitter
11. $\dfrac{4.5\ \text{sec}}{0.9\ \text{sec/half-life}}$

　　　$= 5$ half-lives, leaving $1/32 \times (10^6$ atoms$)$

$\dfrac{10^6\ \text{atoms}}{32} = 3 \times 10^4$ atoms

13. C-14 could be incorporated into the tires, and a test strip of road could be measured for radioactivity.
15. Sample B
17. 80 protons, each 1.007825 amu　$=$　80.626000 amu
　　120 neutrons, each 1.008665 amu $=$ 121.039800 amu

　　　　　　　　　　　　　　　total　　201.665800 amu
　　201.665800 amu$-$199.9683 amu $=$　1.6975 amu

19. No. This would mean going uphill on the curve of Figure 16.4 and expending energy instead of releasing it.

21. Reactants: Li-7 $= 7.0160$ amu
proton $= 1.007825$ amu
8.0238 amu

Products: 2 He, each 4.002600 amu $= 8.0052$ amu
Mass difference $= 8.0238$ amu $- 8.0052$ amu $= 0.0186$ amu. The reaction releases energy.

23. No, because a single neutron could only strike one other nucleus.

25. $^{131}_{50}Sn \longrightarrow ^{131}_{53}I + 3\,^{0}_{-1}e$

Chapter 17

1. a.
$$H-\overset{\overset{\displaystyle H}{|}}{\underset{\underset{\displaystyle H}{|}}{C}}-\overset{\overset{\displaystyle H}{|}}{\underset{\underset{\displaystyle H}{|}}{C}}-\overset{\overset{\displaystyle H}{|}}{\underset{\underset{\displaystyle H}{|}}{C}}-\overset{\overset{\displaystyle H}{|}}{\underset{\underset{\displaystyle H}{|}}{C}}-\overset{\overset{\displaystyle H}{|}}{\underset{\underset{\displaystyle H}{|}}{C}}-H$$

b. [structural formula]

c. [structural formula]

d. [cyclohexane ring structural formula]

e. [structural formula with OH-substituted ring]

3. a. [structural formula with O–H groups]

b. [ester structural formula]

c. [structural formula]

d. [benzoate sodium salt structural formula with O⁻ Na⁺]

5. a, b, and d; c and e

7. a. $CH_3-CH_2-CH_3$ b. CH_3CH_3 c. $CH_2=CH-CH_3$
d. $CH_2=CH-CH=CH_2$ e. CH_4

9. a. CH_3OH b. CH_3OH c. $CH_3CH_2CH_2OH$

11. a. $2\,CH_3OH + 2\,K \longrightarrow 2\,CH_3OK + H_2$

b. $CH_3CH_2OH \xrightarrow[180\,°C]{H_2SO_4} CH_2=CH_2 + H_2O$

c. $2\,CH_3OH \xrightarrow[\text{low temp.}]{H_2SO_4} CH_3OCH_3 + H_2O$

d. $CH_3OH + CH_3CH_2OH \xrightarrow[\text{low temp.}]{H_2SO_4}$
$CH_3OCH_2CH_3 + H_2O$

13. Because they don't have a hydrogen bonded to nitrogen.

15. $CH_4 + Cl_2 \longrightarrow CH_3Cl + HCl$
$CH_3Cl + Cl_2 \longrightarrow CH_2Cl_2 + HCl$
$CH_2Cl_2 + Cl_2 \longrightarrow CHCl_3 + HCl$
$CHCl_3 + HF \longrightarrow CHCl_2F + HCl$
$CHCl_2F + HF \longrightarrow CHClF_2 + CHl$

17. Blank spaces, left to right and top to bottom:
$CH_3-(CH_2)_2-CHO$; $CH_3-(CH_2)_2-COOH$;
$CH_3-(CH_2)_2-\overset{\overset{\displaystyle OH}{|}}{CH}-CH_3$;

[benzene ring]—CH_2OH; [benzene ring]—CHO

19. a. $CH_3-(CH_2)_{14}-COOH$, $CH_3-(CH_2)_9-OH$
b. CH_3-COOH, CH_3-CH_2-OH
c. CH_3-CH_2-COOH, CH_3CH-CH_2OH
$\qquad\qquad\qquad\qquad\qquad\quad |$
$\qquad\qquad\qquad\qquad\qquad CH_3$

21. $HO-CH_2CH_2-OH + HOOC-COOH$
$+ HO-CH_2CH_2-OH + HOOC-COOH + \ldots \longrightarrow$
$\ldots O-CH_2CH_2-OOC-COO-CH_2CH_2-OOC-COO \ldots$

23. —CH₂—NH—C...C—NH—CH₂—NH—C...C—NH—CH₂—

(structure diagram)

Chapter 18

1. a. dT—dT—dA—dG—dA—dG—dC—dA—dT—dA—dG—dG—dT—dG—dC—dA—dG

b. dA—dA—dT—dC—dT—dC—dG—dT—dA — dT—dC—dC—dA—dG—dT—dC
dC—dG—dT—dC—dA—dG

dT—dT—dA—dG—dA—dG—dC—dA—dT—dA—dG—dC—dA—dG—dT—dG—dT—dG—dC—dA—dG
dC—dG—dT—dC—dA—dG—dT—dC—dA—dG

new strands formed

strand unzips

3. dA—dA—dC—dC—dC—dG—dT—dA—dT—dG—
dC—dT—dA—dA

5. a. The first, with nonpolar sidechains, would more likely be a fibrous protein. The second, with polar side chains, would more likely be a globular protein. b. The second would be more water-soluble, for the same reason.

7. Amino acids having polar sidechains are Ser, GluN, Tyr, and Thr. One possible system of hydrogen-bonding:

Gly —— Met
GluN—C=O---H—O Ala
Gly N—H Tyr
H
Ser ~~~ O---H—O ~~~ Thr
H

9. The protein in the egg white would react with the heavy metal ions and precipitate them, preventing them from getting into the bloodstream. Vomiting would then remove them from the stomach.

11. Green plants not receiving much light need to manufacture more green chlorophyll to get as much light energy as possible.

13. $9 \text{ moles ATP} \times \dfrac{7.3 \text{ kcal}}{\text{mole ATP}} = 65.7 \text{ kcal}$

15. $500 \text{ g muscle} \times \dfrac{5 \times 10^{-6} \text{ moles ATP}}{\text{g muscle}} \times \dfrac{7.3 \text{ kcal}}{\text{mole ATP}}$
$= 2 \times 10^{-2} \text{ kcal}$

17. Vitamins A and D have very few or no polar groups and would be fat-soluble rather than water-soluble. Vitamins B_6 and C have many polar groups and would be water-soluble rather than fat-soluble.

19. In the mouth, these things are physically chewed but none are attacked by the enzyme amylase in saliva. In the stomach, the meat protein is partially broken down by HCl and the enzyme pepsin into polypeptides. In the intestines, table sugar is broken into glucose and fructose, polypeptides are broken into amino acids, and the triglyceride is broken into glycerol and fatty acids—all of which can enter the blood. Cellulose is not attacked at all and passes through unchanged.

21. $0.001 \text{ moles adrenaline} \times \dfrac{3 \times 10^4 \text{ moles glucose}}{\text{mole adrenaline}}$
$= 30 \text{ moles glucose}$

$$\frac{30 \text{ moles glucose}}{5 \times 10^3 \text{ ml blood}} \times \frac{180. \text{ g glucose}}{\text{mole glucose}} = \frac{1 \text{ g glucose}}{\text{ml blood}},$$

$$\text{or } \frac{1000 \text{ mg glucose}}{\text{ml blood}}$$

From 60 mg/ml to 1000 mg/ml is an increase of about twentyfold.

23. Papain begins breaking down tough muscle fibers by hydrolyzing their protein.

25. $1 \text{ g glycine} \times \frac{1 \text{ mole glycine}}{75 \text{ g glycine}} \times \frac{2 \text{ moles urea}}{\text{mole glycine}}$

$$\times \frac{60 \text{ g urea}}{\text{mole urea}} = 2 \text{ g urea}$$

27. By repressing urine production and putting water back into the blood, vasopressin allows increased amounts of water to be in the blood. Increased amounts of water cause higher blood pressure.

Appendix A

1. a. 3.49; b. 45.2; c. 67,000.
2. a. 3 (Rules 1 and 3a); b. 4 (Rule 2); c. 2 (Rules 1 and 3); d. 3 (Rule 2).
3.

Calculator Answer	Limiting No. of s.f.	Corrected Answer
a. 12	2	12
b. 60	3	60.0
c. 0.0034	2	0.0034
d. 792	1	800

4. a. 3.981 (uncertain digit in 4th column); b. 54.32 (uncertain digit in 4th column); c. 104 (uncertain digit in 3rd column).
5. This would be true if 4 and 4 are pure numbers. If they were measured numbers containing only one significant figure, the answer would be 20.
6. a. 3.9; b. 11.9; c. −4.0 (answer is negative because negative number was larger than positive number); d. −1.2 (see c).
7. a. $7.9 - 3.3 = 4.6$ c. $-7.7 - 0.2 = -7.9$
   b. $3.3 - 7.9 = -4.6$ d. $-4 - (-2) = -4 + 2$
   $= -2$
8. a. 5.28×10^4; b. 8.97×10^{-6}; c. 2.1×10^4

9. a. Three. $(3.98 \times 10^1)(10^7) = 3.98 \times 10^8$
   b. Three. Number is justified.
   c. Three. $(1.98 \times 10^{-1})(10^{-3}) = 1.98 \times 10^{-4}$

10. a. $7.44 \times 10^{(-5+2)} = 7.44 \times 10^{-3}$
    b. $44.9 \times 10^{(9+10)} = 44.9 \times 10^{19} = 4.49 \times 10^{20}$
11. a. $1.59 \times 10^{(8-2)} = 1.59 \times 10^6$
    b. $0.611 \times 10^{(2-6)} = 0.611 \times 10^{-4}$
    $= (6.11 \times 10^{-1})(10^{-4}) = 6.11 \times 10^{-5}$
12. a. -2.23×10^{-5}
    b. $(3.99 \times 10^{-1})(10^4) = 0.399 \times 10^4$
    $4.68 \ \times 10^4$
    0.399×10^4
    $\overline{5.08 \ \times 10^4}$
    c. $(2.97 \times 10^{-1})(10^{-3}) = 0.297 \times 10^{-3}$
    0.297×10^{-3}
    $\underline{-3.42 \ \times 10^{-3}}$
    $-3.12 \ \times 10^{-3}$
13. a. $(2 \times 10^{-2})(3 \times 10^1) = 6 \times 10^{-1}$
    b. $\frac{6 \times 10^3}{2 \times 10^1} = 3 \times 10^2$
    c. $(2 \times 10^1)(8 \times 10^2)(3 \times 10^2) = 50 \times 10^5$
    d. $\frac{3 \times 9 \times 10^1}{3 \times 10^{-1}} = 9 \times 10^2$
14. a. 20×10^4 (calculator answer correct); b. 1×10^2 (calculator answer incorrect); c. 1×10^1 (calculator answer correct)
15. a. 1.14×10^5; c. 1×10^1; d. 6.2×10^{-24}

Appendix B

1. Kilobuck = 1000 dollars; megabuck = 1 million dollars.

3. a, c, and f

5. b is incorrect. Units would be l^2/qt, not qt. Conversion factor upside down. d is incorrect. Units would be $[(\text{cm}^3)^2 \text{ pt}]/l^2$, not pt. First conversion factor upside down. f is incorrect. Units would be g^2/kg. Last conversion factor upside down.

7. $115 \text{ km} \frac{0.621 \text{ mi}}{\text{km}} = 71.4 \text{ mi}$

9. $\frac{45.0 \text{ franes}}{10.6 \text{ gal}} \times \frac{100 \text{ cents}}{4 \text{ franes}} = 106 \frac{\text{cents}}{\text{gal}}, \text{ or } \frac{\$1.06}{\text{gal}}$

11. $9.3 \times 10^7 \text{ mi} \times \frac{1.61 \text{ km}}{\text{mi}} = 1.5 \times 10^8 \text{ km}$

13. $\frac{3.0 \times 10^{10} \text{ cm}}{\text{sec}} \times \frac{1 \text{ m}}{10^2 \text{ cm}} \times \frac{1 \text{ km}}{10^3 \text{ m}} \times \frac{0.621 \text{ mi}}{\text{km}}$

$$\times \frac{3600 \text{ sec}}{\text{hr}} = 6.7 \times 10^8 \frac{\text{mi}}{\text{hr}}$$

15. $\frac{1 \text{ pt}}{2 \text{ cups}} \times \frac{0.473 \text{ l}}{\text{pt}} \times \frac{10^3 \text{ ml}}{\text{l}} = 237 \frac{\text{ml}}{\text{cup}}$

17. $\frac{0.394 \text{ in}}{\text{cm}} \times \frac{1 \text{ yd}}{36 \text{ in}} = 1.09 \times 10^{-2} \frac{\text{yd}}{\text{cm}}$

19. a. $K = 34.0 \text{ °C} \times \frac{1 \text{ K}}{\text{°C}} + 273.16 \text{ K} = 307.2 \text{ K}$

b. $°F = \dfrac{9\,°F}{5\,°C}(89.6\,°C + 40\,°C) - 40\,°F = 193.3\,°F$

c. $°C = 125\,K \times \dfrac{1\,°C}{K} - 273.16\,°C = -148\,°C$

d. $°C = \dfrac{5\,°C}{9\,°F}(66\,°F + 40\,°F) - 40\,°C = 19\,°C$

e. $K = -90.0\,°C \times \dfrac{1\,K}{°C} + 273.16\,K = 183.2\,K$

f. $°C = \dfrac{5\,°C}{9\,°F}(-21.0\,°F + 40\,°F) - 40\,°C$

$= -29.4\,°C$

g. $°C = 22.0\,K \times \dfrac{1\,°C}{K} - 273.16\,°C = -251.2\,°C;$

$°F = \dfrac{9\,°F}{5\,°C}(-251.2\,°C + 40\,°C) - 40\,°F = 420.1\,°F$

h. $°C = 250\,K \times \dfrac{1\,°C}{K} - 273.16\,°C = -23\,°C$

INDEX
WITH KEY TO DEFINED TERMS

Defined words are in boldface; figures, tables and boxes are in italics